ELVIS UK 2

THE ULTIMATE GUIDE TO ELVIS PRESLEY'S BRITISH RECORD RELEASES 1986 -2002

John Townson and Gordon Minto

First published in the UK 2002 by Elvis UK.

Designed and typeset by
Printflow Graphics,
Worrall Street,
Manchester M5 4TH
Telephone 0161 877 3633

Printed in the UK by
Seddon Printers
Moor Lane,
Bolton BL1 4TH
Telephone 01204 532908

Contents

Contents Continued

Foreword

I don't want to sound like Methuselah, but when I look at my kids and their friends, they have so much we didn't have. It's not that I'm jealous, any more than I believe my parents were jealous that we had more than they did. It's just hard to believe so few years separate us. But at least I had something they didn't: the thrill of going into a record shop and parting with 6 shillings and eight pence for a vinyl single, or thirty two and six for its big brother, the long player. So few interesting records were released back then, it was no stretch to hear them all. The only question was which one would get my carefully saved pocket money.

Thirty or forty years later, I'm glad I can play CDs in the car, and I'm glad that they changed the record business, but neither CDs, nor MTV, nor digital downloads come close to eclipsing the magic of 33 and 45 revolutions per minute. Let's take Elvis: prior to a session, he'd listen to hundreds of songs which would get winnowed down to a handful. He'd go to the studio, eliminate a few more, then spend hours working on the one song which seemed to hold something special. The engineers would tweak it, tighten it, brighten it, and then send a copy to Graceland for approval. And then it would make its way to you. It was very Darwinian: all those songs and all those hours coming down to just two-and-a-half minutes which ended up in my bedroom and in my head.

So now it's 2002, just over one hundred years since Victor Records was launched. RCA had nothing to do with Victor back then, but I had no idea that they were once separate companies until much later. When I started collecting records it was suburban England in the Fifties, and most of the clichés were true. There really was a sense that we'd never had it so good, but of course I had no point of comparison, and my parents could only compare it to the Depression and the War, so the Fifties looked pretty good to all of us. We got one new appliance after another. The TV, the fridge, the Hotpoint, the portable transistor radio ...all of them eclipsed by the record player: in my case, a blue and cream Dansette. Hi-fi didn't come any better, well not for me anyway!

If you described my experience of record collecting to today's teenagers, it would seem like a Druid sacrament in its remoteness and attention to ritual. First a browsing trip down to the local electrical store that also stocked the latest pop tunes. I'd proceed to spend ages standing in isolated listening booth listening to records I couldn't afford, then purchase the one I wanted in the first place. Back home, I'd carefully withdraw the record from the sleeve, and read the warning about the blunted needle. How long has it been since I changed the TC8? Smell the record, another long-lost pleasure. Put the record on the auto-changer, make sure the speed was set at 45, flip the little toggle switch to auto, then wait for the record to fall and crack the deck. When the record had stopped spining, I'd lift it off the turntable and study the wealth of information on the label. The composer, the publisher, the date, the catalogue number. Then there was the other arcane bits of information like the American catalogue number, and "New Orthophonic High Fidelity," whatever that was. Play the B-side. Check the label again. Were the Jordanaires on this one? Play the A-side again. Repeat until bedtime. LPs were another matter entirely. You racked them carefully, maybe alphabetically, admired them from across the room because, unlike CDs, they could be SEEN from across the room. Even more information to be absorbed. Different scents. "Laminated with Clarifoil." That's good.

Elvis was King. Even when the Beatles came along, who could pass up the echoey moodiness of ***Tell Me Why*** or romps like ***Such A Night*** with the little whoop at the end? Then the comeback singles like ***Guitar Man***, ***In The Ghetto***, or ***Suspicious Minds***. Others scoffed, but this was great stuff, and it led me, without even really thinking about it, into the record business. Record labels have personalities, but RCA was special. RCA released records by the one artist who had consistently emptied my pockets. Corny as it sounds, Elvis provided my inspiration to succeed. When I started at RCA in 1973, I can't describe how gobsmacked I was just to be there, and, of course, I had no inkling that I would become so fundamentally involved with Elvis's recorded legacy.

Time passed and, every time RCA reissued an Elvis album, whether I was involved or not, the authors of this book and its companion, ***Elvis UK 1956-1985***, would politely – or was it abusively? - point out every mistake on the labels and record jackets. Some days, I have to admit, I wished they weren't quite so thorough. The sad thing is that record companies aren't always the best custodians of their own history. They've become better lately, but there would often be purges of documentation before moves or after mergers. Logos would be changed, label designs would be changed, and no one would remember why or when. Records are almost always released to impossible deadlines, and the information in the files isn't always sufficient or right. Even today, RCA's global listing notice system is full of factual errors which Ernst Jorgensen and I constantly update and correct.

In 1987, the first volume of ***Elvis UK*** brought memories flooding back. So I wasn't the only person to ascribe mythical significance to some of that information. The enormity of the task slowly dawned on me as I made my way through the book. The detail was astonishing. Truly astonishing. Someone had finally set about documenting the comings-and-goings of the record business in this country, as it related to Elvis Presley. And about time too.

And now there's Volume 2, coming at a point when many predicted that vinyl would be obsolete. Ironically, Elvis's vinyl sales are reviving nicely via Sanctuary Records Group's joint venture with BMG Special Projects. Current releases like ***Sun Singles***, ***The UK No. 1 Singles Collection***, ***Artist Of The Century***, ***"That's The Way It Is"*** boxed set, and Collectors Edition film soundtrack LPs are selling in the UK and all over the world.

So enjoy ***Elvis UK Volume 2*** and immerse yourself in the wondrous detail. And don't bet against Volume 3!

Roger Semon

Note to Reader

Elvis UK 1956-86 was published early in 1987, having spent five or six years in the preparatory stages. This represented a major part of our lives. And, although it was an enormous thrill to see our collective efforts in print, at that time no serious thought was given to another volume. That actually occurred a couple of years later when we determined that a follow-up volume was going to be necessary.

As with the first volume, we are indebted to many people for the help and encouragement they have given us over the years. This spurred us on at times when the task seemed so daunting, and especially when the number of releases - both vinyl and in CD form - seemed never-ending. We faced several critical problems: we both have families; we both have full-time jobs; we both have other interests; we live a couple of hundred miles apart, so the physical task of putting the book together - researching, planning, drafting, re-drafting to incorporate new pieces of information, word-processing, etc. - was always time-consuming and demanding. And, of course, the releases kept on coming, so that just when we would agree a cut-off point, some other major release, or campaign, would be announced. But all of that is really irrelevant, or of little interest to you. What is of interest, we hope, are the contents.

Without doubt the importance of vinyl record releases cannot be overstated. Yes, in marketing terms and perhaps quality of sound, vinyl was superceded inexorably by the emergence of the compact disc. And few would dispute the advantages CDs have over vinyl, but that is not to denigrate vinyl, for it still holds a place in many collectors' hearts. Which is why we compiled this book! Of course, in no way could this be termed the 'golden age' of vinyl, but in many ways it was still an extremely interesting and changeable one - made all the more so by some of the very unusual items released in the post-1986 era. Indeed, it would be foolish to dismiss this era on the grounds that nothing 'new' appeared so, by extension, nothing collectable was released. We would beg to differ and, indeed, assert that the period in question produced some highly collectable items. However, this is a topic we will turn our attention to in more detail in the Rarities Section.

What we have managed to do in this second volume of our work is to chart, almost to the point of its extinction, a format of releasing

Elvis's music which, in his case, lasted almost 50 years. And while vinyl is not yet extinct (there is a small collectors' market catered for by independent companies), it has long ceased to be the predominant medium for marketing recorded music. That now lies almost exclusively with compact discs.

As with *Elvis UK 1956-86*, this book has been compiled and written for fellow collectors. It follows much the same format as its predecessor in that each release in the various sections is dealt with chronologically, thus recording and commenting on changes in the record industry generally, but with specific reference to Elvis releases. By agreement, we opted for a fuller description of each release, though as before, we have tried to steer clear of subjective comment.

Finally, another thank you to all who submitted comments or ideas, and, indeed, offered encouragement to complete this work. We are proud of what we have achieved. We hope you share that view and gain as much pleasure from reading it as we did in writing it. However, we hope it doesn't take you quite as long! Needless to say we welcome any comments, amendments or suggestions.

If anyone has any comments, questions or observations to make about any aspect of this book, then we would welcome them, especially if it concerns items we may not have noted.

You can contact us via our website:
www.elvisuk2.co.uk

You can also email us:
Gordon Minto - gordon@horsleyvale.f9.co.uk
John Townson - john@townsonj.freeserve.co.uk

Or you can write to us:
Gordon Minto
2 Horsley Vale
South Shields
Tyne and Wear
England
NE34 6JF

Acknowledgements

Although the compiling of this particular volume relied less on the direct input of other fans and collectors (by way of label and sleeve differences) - simply because variations became a thing of the past - we readily acknowledge the help and support given by the following people, though it is impossible to quantify their contributions.

However, a few people deserve particular mention. Our friend and unquestionably **the man** when it comes to HMV releases, Alan White from Yorkshire; Dale Hampton in the United States for his invaluable help with US release dates etc; Roger Semon in London, co-producer of Elvis releases; Paul Robinson at BMG in London, and Sam Szczepanski, label manager, Sanctuary, for their unstinting help whenever we telephoned them.

Thank you to Robin Rosaaen of *"All" The King's Things*, San Jose, California, for allowing us to use the wonderful photo of Elvis as featured on the back cover of our book.

We also wish to extend our sincere gratitude to our friend Trevor Cajiao, owner and editor of ***Now Dig This*** and ***Elvis The Man And His Music***, for his help in providing us with the additional photographs used in this book. These photos were taken from the Silver Fox Collection.

Finally, our greatest thanks are reserved for our respective families, in particular our wives, Margaret Minto and Kathy Townson. Unquestionably their love, support and forbearance throughout the mammoth task of researching, writing and producing this book, has been without parallel. We are eternally grateful.

Paul Alner	Richard Harvey	Philip Pastrie
Mark Armitage	Shirley Henderson	Dave Pike
Stephen Ball	Derek Hickman	Doug Price
Gurmeet Bhogal	Rodger Hickman	Alan Raine
Pete Bowen	John Hodges	Pat Robinson
Claire Bromwell	Toby Hughes	Paul Robinson
Alan Brooks	Bob Jones	Joe and Kathleen Rogers
Trevor Bryant	Darell Jones	Bernard Roughton
Dave Bulmer	Phil Jones	Roddy Savage
Trevor Cajiao	Ernst Mikael Jorgensen	Taylor Scott
Manjit Chopra	Mike Kersey	Roger Semon
Mick Clements	Paul Kimberley	Eric Shirley
Howard Cockburn	Bob Kinlen	Martin and Beverley Smith
Michael Curran	Toni Littleford	Charlie Stanford
Mustafa Dervish	John Mallin	Paul Sugars
Richard Dickinson	Phil Mason	Mike Treasure
Tony Dobbs	Peter May	Dave Watson
Norman Dunford	Ronnie Mole	Deke Wheeler
Carrie Fisher	Cliff Moore	Alan White
John and Pauline Fisher	Martin Moritz	Barbara and Tony Wilson
Robert French	Ray Nichol	David Wilson
Jean Marc Gargiulo	Anne E. Nixon	Kevin Wood
Chris Giles	Louise Nixon	Jo and John Woodward
Tracey Guest	Dave Ord	Julie Young
Dale Hampton	Neil O'Sullivan	

Although much has happened on the Elvis scene since August 1977, it is not our intention to revisit the intervening years in any great detail, preferring instead to provide a 'snapshot' of some of the main events, trends and items of interest. Moreover, those events which impinge on, or relate to, the main theme of our book - record releases in the UK, or issues which require further explanation or discussion - will be dealt with in much more depth as, and when, it is appropriate to do so in the text. However if, for instance, you do wish to survey the period between 1977 and 1987 in detail then may we recommend you to Anne E Nixon's excellent *Ten Years After* book.

Of primary interest to our readers, we suppose, is the astounding number of releases there have been in the intervening years. In fact, prior to his death in 1977, there had only been 93 albums released in the UK, mainly by RCA, of course, and many of them re-issues. However, by August 1987 there had been a further 194 issued. But before some of you start panicking, wondering what you might have missed, it is important to add that a great deal of these were re-releases too. Moving on a little further - to August 1992, the fifteenth anniversary of his death - the number had risen to 318 in total, again including re-issues. By early 2002, there were 344 titles listed.

Of course, in the intervening period there were 'new' albums, boxed sets and two EP Collections in 1982, though sadly few previously unissued songs, mainly because so few existed. On the other hand as time went on, the official releases included an increasing number of outtakes - later referred to as unreleased performances - something which marked a distinct policy shift for the company. Many perceived this as being the direct result of the success of bootleg releases over the years. And, indeed, it would be hard to discuss the years since Elvis's death without mentioning the impact of bootlegs.

Of course, they existed before his death, but in relatively small numbers. However, after August 1977, there was a veritable explosion of bootleg releases, comprising the likes of early TV shows, early live appearances, film soundtrack songs, live seventies shows, outtakes from the '68 TV Special, not to mention studio outtakes. And, while the quality of product varied enormously, the prices were uniformly high. Leaving the ethics of the situation aside, the main problem was that no matter how lucrative the trade was for those who manufactured them and the dealers who sold them, they only reached a relatively small number of fans. Many, either because they were not 'in the know', or were unable to afford them, were denied access to this material. And, no doubt, once RCA began to realise that the bootleggers were meeting a demand - albeit an illegal one - some effort was directed in trying to cater for those fans who favoured outtakes and the like. Even so, despite the release of an eight album boxed set in 1980, it was not until late 1982 with the release of the two EP Collections, and later the Essential Elvis series (which started in 1986), followed by the *Collectors Gold* boxed set (1991), that serious and deliberate attempts were made to cater for this element of the market. So, whatever the moral/legal issues were, the company finally - some would say very belatedly - acknowledged that there was a market need to be satisfied. And, while the issues may well have been difficult to resolve, there were real attempts to meet the needs of collectors, as well as balancing that against the needs of the general buyer - alongside such issues as viability and profitability - which no-one should forget underpins all business life, and certainly no less so the record business.

Against this background it is possible to trace the rise in influence of someone like Roger Semon of RCA UK and, later, Ernst Mikael Jorgensen, then of RCA Denmark. A reminder of how changeable and profit-oriented companies are was made when, in early 1992, BMG in the UK made Semon redundant, despite his widely acclaimed efforts. Put simply, his services could not be retained purely on the strength of his excellent efforts with Elvis product. Like it or not, the record industry does not, nor can it ever, survive merely on back-catalogue material - healthy though that is. It requires new product and new artists if it is to go on being profitable. Semon's great strength lay in the fact that he was and still is, of course, a fan. But, more to the point, he was a fan who worked in the highly competitive record industry. Therefore, he was well placed in RCA to offer advice and artistic input on releases, especially on the marketing side of things. His efforts over the years indicate how successful he was. Similarly with Ernst Mikael Jorgensen: his background was also in the record industry but his major contribution to the Elvis scene was his collaborative efforts with Erik Rasmussen and Johnny Mikkelson who jointly researched and produced the various editions of the *Recording Sessions* book. These books established his credentials in terms of his interest in and knowledge of Elvis's session work; indeed this knowledge became invaluable when, in the late 1980s, the serious work of searching through RCA's tape vaults began. Since 1986, of course, Jorgensen's and Semon's names have been closely linked, in that they became largely responsible for all the major Elvis releases throughout the world, though they worked within the parameters of a committee also, which had to agree the release plans formulated by the producers.

On the video front, by 1992 all of Elvis's scripted films were made available on video for the fans to buy. Prior to this fans had also been able to buy copies of some live performances, including for example, *Aloha From Hawaii*, *That's The Way It Is*, *Elvis On Tour*, *This Is Elvis* and material from the NBC TV Special, plus the likes of *One Night With You*, *Elvis '56* and, latterly, *The Lost Performances* (long awaited outtakes from *That's The Way It Is* and *Elvis On Tour*). Alongside those releases were umpteen other video collections purporting to include rare or previously unseen footage. More often than not the material was of poor quality and dubious origin - but still it sold! - as did bootleg copies of live shows from the seventies, some of which were of dreadful quality. Perhaps more than ever what this era began to illustrate was the insatiable nature of some fans who, quite literally, would buy anything from edible knickers bearing Elvis's image, to leaves and bits of grass allegedly from Graceland. Yet, at the same time, once the shock of Elvis's death had subsided somewhat, by the end of the seventies, there was a drop in the number of fans who joined fan clubs, or who bought every release as a matter of course. And, indeed, throughout the early eighties there was a steady decline in the numbers of fans, some who obviously lost interest because of the relative lack of new releases. Record sales fell too; some singles scraped into the charts, while albums comprised mainly unimaginative and repetitive material.

On the other hand, from 1986 there was a steady improvement in the quality of album releases (due largely to the efforts of the Semon/Jorgensen partnership) in the form of releases such as the Essential Elvis releases, *Collectors Gold* boxed set (1991) and the incomparable fifties' boxed set (1992), the sixties' set (1993) and seventies' (1995). When Joan Deary left the US company somewhat summarily in 1984/5 she was succeeded by Greg Geller - remember he initiated the likes of *The Rocker*, *A Valentine Gift For You* and *Reconsider Baby* albums, as well as assuming responsibility for revising the *A Golden Celebration* boxed set. However, his tenure did not last long either, so there was a real gap in the creative and marketing side of things, which was more than adequately filled by Semon and Jorgensen. And naturally, during this time, with the advent of compact discs into the pop market, many of Elvis's back catalogue albums were re-issued in CD format, though not always in vinyl, and not always with the greatest of care.

Of course, one major event in the Elvis calendar was the opening of Graceland in 1982. As with most other things, it generated some controversy regarding whether or not Elvis would have wanted it to happen. The fact was though that had the Estate not decided to open it up then there was a serious risk that it would have had to have been sold, such was the precarious state of finances. By all accounts when Elvis died he was not as rich as people imagined him to be: on the contrary, he had been spending money faster than he was earning it. Addionally, the Estate was earning virtually no revenue from the huge record sales in the wake of Elvis's death. This was as a result of a deal struck by Colonel Parker in 1973, whereby all royalty rights to songs recorded prior to that year were owned by RCA. Consequently for many years the Estate and Elvis's record company were locked in a bitter and extremely acrimonious legal battle regarding issues such as royalty payments. Not surprisingly then, any material held by the Estate would not be made available to RCA for general issue, while RCA, on the other hand, would only issue material recorded prior to 1973 - thus earning all the revenue for themselves. The truth is that everyone suffered, but most of all the ardent and loyal fan who was denied proper releases. Indeed, some would contend that the disarray which the company found themselves in, was a major contributory factor in the diminution of the Elvis market generally throughout the late seventies and early eighties. In short, the company failed to deliver the 'goods', and so many long-term fans simply lost interest, despite the efforts of the bootleggers to meet some of the demand aroused by seemingly insatiable fans. Eventually though, by the mid 1980s, the legal wrangling came to a head in court, and both the Colonel and RCA were castigated for having struck up a deal whereby Elvis (and later his Estate) had been treated unfairly in terms of the financial deal made by Parker in 1973. There were financial adjustments and this led to an improvement in relations between the two major parties involved. And, much later, in a deal involving an undisclosed sum of money, Parker handed over to the Estate a vast store of material he had held over the years, much of it general memorabilia, photographs and so on. And yet, even a number of years on, it is not public knowledge precisely what he handed over, though from time to time snippets of information keep cropping up. But whatever the objections some may have had regarding the opening of Graceland, two things are very clear: it very soon became one of the major tourist attractions in the United States, earning huge revenue for the Estate, and it has given untold joy to millions of fans who have visited Elvis's home.

In fact Elvis's name has rarely been out of the public domain. Book after book has been marketed, many of which have been blatant attempts to cash in on perceived public interest in his private life. Many presented Elvis in an unfavourable light personally; some, like Goldman's *Elvis* (1981) for instance, credited Elvis with no talent at all; others though dealt with proper issues for debate - his session work, his recordings and so on. Then there have been the photo-journals. Many of these were rehashes of previously issued material. Others though, such as Alfred Wertheimer's, Sean Shaver's and Ger Rijff's works, offered fans new and previously unseen photographs. Rijff's, in particular, focused largely on the fifties' era, while Shaver's centred mainly around Elvis's live performances from the 1970s. Also, from time to time, there cropped up the almost perennial 'Is Elvis Alive?' question, 'backed up' or inflamed by literally thousands of alleged sightings of him. What was obvious was that a lot of people were making a lot of money out of such stories. Some, such as the 'writer' Lucy de Barbin, claimed to have borne Elvis a child in the mid 1950s, though not a scrap of evidence was ever produced to support such an audacious claim. But, what made the stories of sightings of him so ludicrous, was the fact that it was frequently claimed that he was dressed as he was on stage in the seventies: wearing a jump suit and sporting long sideburns. Usually he was 'spotted' shopping in a local supermarket. It was simply risible and outrageous, particularly when you think that had Elvis really faked his death, then he would hardly be likely to re-appear in a supermarket dressed as he was in the '70s. Presumably, had he wished to do so, and then 'reappear', he would not do so in this bizarre manner. But, apart from this aspect of things, what we must not forget is the hurt and pain caused to his family by such ludicrous stories. And speaking of his family, in the late eighties Lisa Marie, his

only daughter, married and produced two children. Her mother, Elvis's ex-wife, Priscilla, played a key role in the organisation of the Estate, along with one of Elvis's long-term friends, Jerry Schilling. Priscilla herself tasted stardom in the TV series *Dallas*, and then later in the highly successful film *The Naked Gun* and its sequels. Under her guidance the Estate started marketing Presley product much more positively: *The Great Performances* videos in 1990 and the long awaited outtakes from his two documentary films, *The Lost Performances*, with the promise of more to come. In fact all of this was evidence that, however belatedly, those whose job it was to market Elvis product had started doing so with a level of care and commitment to quality, distinctly lacking in previous years. Thankfully, this in turn, began to re-focus public attention on the things about Elvis which really mattered and were legitimate topics for discussion: his artistic output. In time, the hope is that other issues will be put to one side and treated for what they are: irrelevancies.

And, as the twentieth century drew to a close, Ernst Mikael Jorgensen produced the definitive book on Elvis's recording sessions - *A Life In Music* (1998) (though we ought not to forget Joe Tunzi's earlier efforts in this area too). Also of major interest was the publication of the best researched biography on Elvis, Peter Guralnick's *Last Train To Memphis* (1994) and *Careless Love* (1998).

In the middle of 1999, BMG issued its first release on the newly formed Collector's Label (CD only). This had been discussed for many years previously, but never managed to get beyond the preliminary stage, presumably because of legal wranglings between the Estate and BMG. However, the appearance of the first such release in July 1999 was, however belatedly, an official attempt to stem the flow of the almost constant bootleg releases which, since the advent of compact discs in the 1980s, had become a source of major embarrassment and irritation within the company. Time alone will determine whether or not BMG's initiative came too late to eradicate or seriously diminish bootlegging. Indeed, another concern was whether the project would prove sufficiently viable to be able to continue. Whatever, 1999 saw BMG market Elvis as 'Artist Of The Century', with all product carrying an appropriate sticker to that effect.

Of course, during the Artist Of The Century year (1999), another player emerged in terms of issuing Elvis material on vinyl: Castle Music (which was soon to become a part of the Sanctuary Music Group). Roger Semon, formerly of BMG in the UK, worked for Castle Music and, in his role as co-producer of Elvis product throughout the world, perceived a clear opportunity to cater for those fans who had clamoured for good quality vinyl releases over the years. And as it seemed obvious that BMG had no intention of meeting this market niche, Semon negotiated with BMG to release vinyl product in conjunction with them. This strategy paid off handsomely and the product became very desirable.

The first venture was the hugely successful 5 LP version of *Artist Of The Century* (LP 323) in August 1999 (using the catalogue number ELVIS 100), followed by a picture disc version later in the year. This was quickly followed by a host of other prestigious releases including *Sun Singles* (S 182), *That's The Way It Is* (LP 328) and several other packages. What seemed obvious about this was that the market need, although small by comparison with the CD sector, showed no sign of waning.

Then, early in 2000, yet another company entered the Elvis vinyl scene. Simply Vinyl, a UK company dedicated to the preservation of vinyl LP releases, also negotiated with BMG in London and went on to release a series of Elvis albums, pressed on highest quality vinyl (180gm). In the main these comprised back catalogue titles – usually based on BMG's own revised CD releases - though in late 2000 they released a vinyl version of *The 50 Greatest Hits* (LP 331), a triple vinyl album based on BMG's then current CD release. Once again, the press run was generally low (normally around 2,000 copies) though the company had little problem in marketing them through its various outlets.

Meanwhile, there never seemed to be any lack of activity in the Elvis world. There was an almost never ending stream of official CD releases – the Collector's Label had scheduled no less than five releases a year - though by this time the bootlegs were altogether fewer in number. DVD (Digital Versatile Disc) – a much superior form of video - had arrived in a big way, though for fans in the UK there were very few releases using the Region 2 format. Therefore, fans wanting what Elvis product there was available had to buy modified DVD players (multi-region) that would play discs manufactured in the USA or elsewhere.

And while on the subject of films, the year 2000 also saw the appearance of the revised and much improved *That's The Way It Is* movie, offering better sound and picture quality than ever before. It not only pleased the fans, but garnered critical acclaim too!

Finally, however, to return to our main theme: vinyl releases in the UK. It seems reasonable to conclude that innovative vinyl packages will go on being released as long as there seems to be a demand for them. And while the volume of this market may remain relatively small, there seems no doubt that it is strong, making it fairly lucrative for those meeting that demand.

Introduction

Part 1 : General

General Introduction

While being inextricably linked to **Elvis UK 1956-86**, this book stands independently. And, although it does continue where **Elvis UK 1956-86** left off - indeed we have continued the same numbering system - there has been a clear policy decision not to backtrack, add to previous entries, amend, correct, modify or whatever, at this stage, apart from releases issued in 1986. We, the authors, have long been of the opinion that such a revision was not appropriate at this time.

We are conscious, however, that this book may be being read, or is owned by someone who does not possess, or has not seen, a copy of **Elvis UK 1956-86**. Therefore, it is very apparent that, as in the first book, we must define our terms of reference - what we hope to achieve - and discuss our terminology for the benefit of new readers. Inevitably, therefore, we have to 'graft on' almost to the previous work, while ensuring that this text stands on its own also. We hope that those familiar with the first text will bear with us here, for clearly, there is little point in making reference to items featured in **Elvis UK 1956-86** without clarifying what we mean by them. Hence, we have deemed it necessary to re-state a number of points we included in the general introductory section to **Elvis UK 1956-86** for the sake of completeness and clarity. Similarly, there is a pressing need to explain our numbering and cross-referencing systems, to render the book of maximum interest, ease of use, and enjoyment. There is little point in having a reference book which users find retrieving information from difficult. We would also ask new readers to forgive the number of references to **Elvis UK 1956-86**: it is unavoidable.

Another issue is the one of indexing. Since 1986, the cut-off date for **Elvis UK 1956-86**, there have been a number of 'new' songs released. Consequently the indexing system takes into account the whole vinyl catalogue, while making it clear which songs were featured only in the previous book, and which others are included in this new edition. Incidentally, any release dates given refer, of course, to the UK. If it is otherwise, then we say so expressly.

It seems worth re-stating briefly what **Elvis UK 1956-86** was about, in order to understand what this, its follow-up, hopes to achieve. First of all neither book is merely a discography i.e. simply a list of releases and dates. They are much more than that. What we have tried to do is examine every relevant aspect of Elvis's UK record releases in a thorough, factual and, we hope, interesting way as possible. Please note the word factual. Generally, what this book does not offer are reviews or personal opinions. They are more than adequately covered in other publications. We have written about each record release individually - and that includes records which may only feature one Presley track - and in the context of the whole catalogue, referring to current practices, background material, as well as dealing with all the changes occurring within the industry as they impacted on record buying and collecting. To that end, the book then becomes a detailed history, not only of Elvis's British record releases (our prime interest, of course), but also of the rapid changes within the music industry as a whole - the growth of compact discs for example, which is dealt with later.

Therefore, we cover such things as new releases, re-releases (of which there were many), label changes, variations to labels and sleeves (where they occurred), changes within the company/companies concerned with issuing Presley product, release policies generally - and a host of other factors we regard as being relevant - all with the express intention of providing you, the reader and/or collector, with as wide a view as possible of the situation. As the sub-title of **Elvis UK 1956-86** stated, we set out to offer our readers '**The Ultimate Guide To Elvis Presley's British Record Releases'**. This book shares and adheres to that same guiding ethic.

However, it has to be stressed that while our interest lies in the records rather than in the songs or music itself (for the purposes of this book, of course) we have offered much more detail on contents than we did in **Elvis UK 1956-86**. Nonetheless, like its predecessor, this book is most certainly not in the business of reviewing or assessing the musical merit of particular tracks or releases. As we said earlier, that function is performed perfectly well in other publications. What we are interested in is presenting a factual look at Elvis's UK releases; we strive not to allow personal preference to intrude in the text, other than in a very general way where we may report on how a particular release was greeted by fans or received by the critics. At that point, complete objectivity gives way to what we hope is fair reporting. For example, although we cannot establish this as fact, it seems fair to say that the release of Elvis's first known recording, **My Happiness**, on **The Great Performances**, PL 82227 (**LP 308**), in 1990, was greeted with excitement and enthusiasm by fans, but we believe our readers will allow us that licence from time to time.

A further refinement, or addition to what we normally include in the text of each release, is a clear reference to which version of a song has been included. We believe this to be important and relevant information and a legitimate descriptor of what a particular release comprised. This became necessary with the proliferation of alternative takes, overdubbed or undubbed tracks, as well as significant remixes. What we have tried to establish is which version is included and where and when it first appeared.

While it is true to say that the planning, researching, organising and writing of this book is mainly the work of its two authors, invaluable technical help and background information was offered to us by many individuals. In fact, it is worth noting at this point, that the level of help and co-operation we have received from the various companies and individuals approached on this occasion, was extremely gratifying. To all who have given their time and help we are deeply indebted. And, unless they have requested otherwise, their names have been listed in our acknowledgements.

Finally the chronological release numbering system used in **Elvis UK 1956-86** is continued in this book. Throughout the text, releases discussed in the earlier work are shown in italics e.g. (*S 20*); while releases covered by this current book are in bold print e.g. (**LP 300**).

An Outline Of Contents

As with each entry made in **Elvis UK 1956-86**, there are basic pieces of information given for each release. In the case of albums - by far the biggest of the sections - we have retained more or less the same format as before: album title; track and writers' details; chronological release number; re-issue; previous issue, and so on.

We have, however, tended to expand the text for each release to include more information about the actual material included. Now, we hasten to add, we have still steered clear of qualitative comments, in the main, focusing more on describing the contents in an objective way. Each entry, therefore, particularly the major releases since 1986, has tended to be longer than before. The reasons for this are varied, but, primarily, it is because a) we have simply obtained more information from a wide variety of sources - some extremely well placed; b) we collected information as events unfolded; and, c) because we determined to include more information relating to tracks included on each release, because we felt it was appropriate to do so.

Previously, we tended not to deal with the tracks in any great detail, partly because we were focusing our attention on the records rather than the songs. However, events in recent years persuaded us to take a broader view, in that a fan/collector/casual buyer might see a release listed, and conclude from the track listing that it held no interest for him/her because the tracks had been issued previously. Certainly, a major aspect of releases since 1986 was the inclusion of alternative takes, remixes and so on. Hence, to assist readers in judging the merits of a particular release - not to mention helping them determine whether or not they 'needed' the release in question, because it featured an outtake or rarely used version - we decided to incorporate the information, making clear which version was being used and where it originated.

Arguably, this may have seemed of more interest to buyers/ collectors of CDs, in that certain tracks/versions were unobtainable on CD, although that situation was remedied over the years. But we also recognise that vinyl collectors may find this information equally useful. We hope you agree. The prime examples, of course, concern the likes of *An American Trilogy*, *Always On My Mind*, *If I Can Dream*, and so on. Where appropriate to do so, we have stated which version has been used, particularly if the version used was an unusual one in some way. Another good example of this is Reader's Digest's *The Legend Lives On* (**LP 310**) which, keen listeners noted, included two outtakes (apparently quite accidentally) of *(Such an) Easy Question* and *Anything That's Part Of You*, as well as an outtake of *Wild In The Country* (take 16), which had appeared on *Elvis Aron Presley* (*LP 126*) in 1980. More mundanely, the version used of *She Thinks I Still Care* was the overdubbed version, as featured on the 1981 *Guitar Man* (*LP 146*) album. The net result of this was that many fans would decide they had to have this collection - which it could be argued was not intended for the fan/collector in the first place - because it included some rare items.

As can also be seen, there is more background information for many of the releases than was previously the case. The general reasons for this are not hard to guess at: we improved our network of contacts considerably since working on *Elvis UK 1956-86* and, perhaps more importantly, RCA/BMG took a much more helpful and sympathetic stance when we asked for information, due largely to a shift in the company's policy towards outsiders. Additionally, we were grateful for individual contributions made by the likes of Roger Semon and Ernst Mikael Jorgensen. However, the guiding ethic remained: was what we included of interest to the reader and relevant to the release in question? If the answer was yes, then it was usually included.

At some point in the early 1990s we decided to include CDs in the main text, alongside vinyl releases. However, as time progressed, it became increasingly obvious that it was going to be extremely problematic to write about both mediums with the same degree of accuracy within the same volume. Then, of course, there were other factors to consider: our study of vinyl releases was re-commencing in 1986, while CDs became available in late 1983. Another consideration was the sheer volume of material to include, which would, inevitably, have impacted on the retail price of this latest volume. Mindful of the high retail price of *Elvis UK 1956-86* in 1987 (over which we had no control whatsoever), we determined to concentrate solely on vinyl releases in this book, although references would be made to CD releases in a general way.

The format of this volume is similar to that of *Elvis UK 1956-86*. The book is divided into sections: Introduction, Singles, EPs, LPs, Miscellaneous Releases, Various Artist Compilation LPs, Promotional Records and, finally, an Index.

Following the preface, the introductory section is designed to aid your understanding of what follows. We have separated the Introduction into four sections. The first part provides background material and in this section is a general introduction and a glossary of terms, to which you may wish to refer to clarify any terminology we use.

The second main section of the Introduction deals with such topics as modes, bar codes, release dates, deletions, alternative versions, and so on. The intention here has been to provide some background information to the many aspects that are of interest to fans and collectors. Such topics often demonstrate the importance of selective buying, particularly where a variety of releases containing similar material was concerned. A further benefit of this section is that it provides additional background material to Elvis's UK releases, especially when we deal with items that are included on labels and sleeves.

The third main section of the Introduction concerns pieces of information found on record labels, such as publishers, copyright protection and mechanical rights, matrix numbers and, where relevant, information on errors. These are fully explained and ought to help in your understanding of the descriptions and changes we discuss in the text itself.

The fourth and final section of the Introduction outlines the way in which variations of both labels and sleeves have been treated, and how they are dated and accurately identified. This subject can be complicated and, in order to make this detail quite clear, a more complete analysis is included at the beginning of the sections relating to singles and LP releases.

The three major sections in which we deal with Elvis's UK record releases - singles, EPs and LPs - deal with each release chronologically (as they did in *Elvis UK 1956-86*), that is, in the order of release. The reason for this approach is simple: it enabled us to discuss the development of record releases and the many changes that resulted from this which would not have been possible had we dealt with the records alphabetically. Thus, by adopting a chronological sequence, changes in things such as label design, sleeve changes, and company policy, for example, could be brought to your attention in the correct order, as they occurred. The two sections contain the same basic information: release dates, track information, writers, relevant detail pertaining to that release, label variations, sleeve differences, and so on.

Because we chose to adopt a chronological order, we have included a separate listing of single, EP and LP releases at the beginning of their respective sections and devised a system which enables releases to be cross-referenced. Thus, when we refer to a record release in the script, we use a release number, this being the chronological number of release. For example, release number **S 175** in the Singles' section refers to the single *Mean Woman Blues*. The 'S' indicates single, the 175 shows that it was the 175th UK single. We have maintained the numbering sequence from the previous volume, covering the period 1956-86, in order to demonstrate the total number of releases, and to assist additional cross-referencing.

However, while this system is perfectly adequate for straight forward cross-referencing purposes, it falls down if you wish to read about a particular release, but are unsure when the record was issued. To have to search through the pages until you find the record in question is hardly satisfactory; and so, at the beginning of the Singles' section we have included both chronological and alphabetical listings of A and B sides (including all tracks) for each release, giving the release number, where each one can be found and where it is discussed in detail.

As regards LP releases, we cannot adopt this system in quite the same way, as they are multi-track releases. However, we have still used the basic chronological and alphabetical listings (by use of the title and catalogue number). If, however, you wish to know on which record a particular song is featured, then we would refer you to an index of song titles which is provided at the back of the book. There, alongside the titles, are the release numbers where each song can be found. To further assist, we have retained all references in this index to songs which appeared in the period from 1956-86, to ensure the most comprehensive reference possible. This format is particularly useful when searching for songs which have not appeared on vinyl releases after 1986 - of which there are many. A similar index format has been used for interview material, so that these too can be easily located in the script. This, we hope, covers all possibilities and allows you to find the song(s) and interview(s) you are looking for.

The next section of the book relates to Miscellaneous Elvis releases, a small but important section which, broadly speaking, deals with oddities or unusual releases which did not readily fit into the Singles', EP or LP sections.

The section dealing with Various Artist Compilation LPs contains details of these from the very first one in 1977. Rather than start the section from 1986, we have, in this instance, back-tracked and included those LPs which were released prior to the start of the main sections, to ensure that it was complete. The format is similar to that of the Singles' and LP sections, in that it includes chronological and alphabetical listings, so that a particular LP can be located easily. In addition though, there is a separate alphabetical listing of song titles which have appeared on compilations, so that it is possible to determine whether a particular song has been featured. The header block follows the same pattern as those for singles and LPs, although we have not listed any non-Elvis tracks.

The Promotional Records section includes details of all these releases - singles and LPs. A simple check-list at the beginning of the section will help determine which release had a promotional record issued, as well as providing the catalogue number, and so on.

Finally, the Index section at the back of the book will, as we have discussed earlier, enable you to locate the appearances of any song or interview.

Clarification Of Terms

All release dates quoted in this book refer to UK releases, unless otherwise stated.

When we use the term 'previously unissued' we mean officially. There is no direct cross-referencing to any bootleg releases. Indeed, there are very few references to bootlegs: they are largely irrelevant to the main theme of this book.

Glossary Of Terms

Almost every industry or interest group produces its own sub-language to describe ideas or processes. The motor trade, hi-fi manufacturers and, more recently, the world of computing all have their own specialised (and frequently baffling to outsiders) form of language, commonly referred to as jargon. Not surprisingly the record industry is no exception to this.

In order to aid your understanding (and we hope, enhance your enjoyment) of what we write, we have attempted to produce a layman's guide to many of the terms used in the recording industry, by trying to simplify what they mean. In doing this we are not being patronising; neither, we hope, have we oversimplified and thus risked confusing or misrepresenting the information.

Acetate

An acetate is a disc made for demonstration or other short term purposes - to check the sound, for example - and would not be used for mass production. Acetates are metal discs covered in a soft layer of black vinyl called lacquer, which is why some people refer to them, incorrectly, as lacquers. Acetates can also be made of brittle plastic. See also Lacquer.

Album

The generally accepted understanding of the word, in the context of records, was of an LP (vinyl - either 10 inch or 12 inch). In fact, the word album originally applied to a collection of 78s made up to form an 'album' of a complete classical work and, later, a collection of jazz or 'pop' recordings. Extended Play records (EPs) were originally called extended play albums. However, since the advent of compact discs, it must be understood that a CD carrying more than a few tracks (in which case it is a single) is also an album. In the text we do, therefore, now refer to vinyl albums as well as CD albums to make it clear what we are talking about.

When we use the term album now we may be referring to either a 12 inch album (or LP) or a compact disc album. To avoid confusion we make clear in each case what we mean.

Alternate / Alternative Take

Strictly speaking, as mentioned in *Elvis UK 1956-86*, the term 'alternate take' is not strictly correct for alternate means by turn so that, for instance, in a sequence you could say someone tapped his foot every second drum beat. To be absolutely accurate, grammatically speaking, the word should be 'alternative' meaning of course, any one different from the original. So that in the case of *Hound Dog* the released take (the master take) was take 31. This means that the other 30 takes are alternative. However more recently RCA have taken to referring to 'unreleased performances' as opposed to 'alternate' or 'alternative' takes. We believe this makes much more sense.

This started with *The EP Collection Vol. 2* in October 1982 (although the sleeve of *Elvis - A Legendary Performer Vol. 3* (*LP 106*), released in January 1979, made reference to 'previously unavailable performances') and, it must be said, does make a lot more sense. In fact, in view of the number of live versions of songs now being issued, this is even more sensible because it lets the fans know immediately whether the track(s) in question have been issued previously, especially with well-known songs such as *I Got A Woman, Suspicious Minds* or *An American Trilogy*.

Cut / Cutting

Technically, the process of making a lacquer from the master tape. However, the term was also used as a colloquial term for recording a track e.g. 'He cut three songs..' i.e. he recorded three songs.

Demonstration Records

Demonstration records, 'demos', were usually made before the regular commercial copies sent to retailers. They were, therefore, the earliest pressings of a record and were used as samples for review purposes. Often they were sent to radio stations so that the tracks could be played prior to the regular version being on sale.

Equalising (EQ)

This term refers to balancing the sound level track by track so that the overall level of tracks is consistent. Digitally remastered material implies that EQ has been balanced. But, as *The Great Performances* (**LP 308**) illustrates, this is not always the case. On this album, the sound level (volume) varies noticeably from track to track - an example of poor EQ.

Extended Play Records

Extended play records (EPs) usually contained four tracks and offered twice the playing time of normal 7 inch singles. They were particularly popular during the fifties and sixties, as they were issued in picture sleeves. EPs, then, looked like a smaller version of a long play album (LP).

Flexi Discs

Flexi discs are 7 inch singles pressed on to a very thin plastic, so thin that the disc bends. They had a variety of uses. Record companies often used them for promotional purposes, often for advertising a forthcoming LP. Magazines often included a flexi disc as a free gift.

Interview Discs

The copyright laws in the UK (and in America) allow anyone to produce a record of interview material without fear of prosecution. Copyright on music recordings is much more stringent.

Lacquer

A blank aluminium disc coated with nitro-cellulose, onto which a tape recording would be transferred, and then used in the manufacture of vinyl discs.

Long Play Records (LPs)

The first LPs were issued in America in 1948 by the Columbia record company. Decca issued the first UK LPs in 1950.

Master

Used variously to mean the best take of a song and one which was selected to be the released version. It also means the tape from which the song(s) would be taken in order to be transferred to the disc.

Mastering

The technical process at the production stage, whereby a song, or songs, were finalised for transfer to disc.

In the case of a lot of Elvis's recorded work the final choice was not limited to only one performance of a song. Clearly Elvis tended to do any number of takes (an attempt to perform a complete version of a song satisfactorily) when recording. Normally though one, two or more performances might stand out obviously as the best versions vocally, instrumentally and technically. Therefore the company/a producer/and/or artist will select the take or version which seems to be the best in all respects. This take then becomes known as the 'master' and should, all things being equal, be the take/version used for all subsequent releases. Now at this stage, the artist, producer, company or whoever may well decide to add instrumentation or extra vocals (overdubbing) to a track to make it more artistically/commercially appealing. Normally this would only be done to the master take and, in normal circumstances, the other takes of a song would be filed away and forgotten - sometimes even lost or recorded over - as for many years they were not believed to be of any value or interest to anyone. Occasionally, however, if an artist - Elvis, for instance - could not complete a technically or artistically acceptable version of a song after a reasonable period of time, then all concerned may well have (and often did) decide to use several takes (attempts) at a song and literally cut (with a razor blade) the best bits out of each take and splice (stick) them together. Hence a master take could quite easily be made up of two or more takes. In this case it would be filed as 'no master exists' meaning that a final master had not been approved/achieved. But, when edited and spliced the 'bits' would produce a master.

In fact, when the fast version of **Ain't That Loving You Baby** appeared in 1985, it was not one take at all. Rick Rowe, the engineer who worked on it at RCA New York, actually used 5 takes to produce this 'master' - slowing takes down and speeding others up.

Of course the whole business of master takes regarding Elvis's music is quite strange. This was because Elvis liked to record 'live' with the group (all at the same time) even long after this process was outmoded by technical advances - i.e. the ability to record on more than one, two or three tracks - thus separating the information. This continued throughout his career - a retrograde step in terms of technical advancement - but musically (and now historically) a great advantage for us. In fact, even throughout the sixties it is now known (as the master takes have been found and checked over) that contrary to previous information in most instances Elvis did actually record with the group of musicians and not overdub his vocal track later. Of course subsequently certain overdubs were made but this was also true of material in the fifties e.g. **Shake, Rattle And Roll** - overdubbed later by Elvis, Scotty and Bill. It is now known, however, that he did overdub vocals on **Kissin' Cousins** (strangely and unusually recorded in Nashville) and on a few others too.

Master Tape

Basically a master tape is the tape on which the master take of a song(s) was recorded and sent from the recording studio to the record company involved. The master tape contains the final mix and is, therefore, the production tape.

Mixing

Mixing is a term used to describe the method of changing the presence of different parts of a recording, for example by increasing the level of the vocal, or reducing the guitar part.

Original Version

Quite simply this refers to the first released version of a particular song, usually the most well-known one. For example, if we refer to **Blue Suede Shoes,** unless we say otherwise, it is the original January 1956 version we are talking about, rather than Elvis re-recording of the song during the **G.I. Blues** sessions of April/May 1960. Similarly, references to **If I Can Dream** may be taken as the single version issued in February 1969. Where this is not the case - for instance, if we are referring to the outtake/alternative version of that song - we make this clear to the reader.

Overdubbed

Quite simply this means that extra instruments or vocal accompaniment has been added to a basic track (i.e. the minimum amount of backing plus a vocal version of the song) in order to improve it artistically and/or make it more commercially appealing.

Sometimes, as was evident by some of Elvis's later performances in the 1970s, it was to disguise some vocal imperfections: not being able to reach or hold notes, or, alternatively, because of poor breath control. Having listened to a lot of undubbed material from the 1970s Ernst Mikael Jorgensen did declare early in 1992 that it was obvious why Felton Jarvis (Elvis's producer) had felt the need to overdub tracks: quite simply some of Elvis's vocal performances were not up to his own high standards and needed improving in some way. Hence the amount of overdubbing which took place (also called 'sweetening'). Few of Elvis's 1950s performances were overdubbed though it is known that Elvis, Scotty and Bill overdubbed vocal backing on **Shake, Rattle And Roll** - the only known occasion when the latter musicians sang on any Elvis track. Also, during the recording of the **Jailhouse Rock** soundtrack in April/May 1957, Elvis overdubbed his vocal on **(You're so square) Baby I Don't Care** (this vocal track turned up, surprisingly, in October 1999, when it was included on the **Out In Hollywood** CD, the second release of the Collector's Label.

Promotional Records

There is often some confusion over the term 'promotional'. The term is often used interchangeably with 'demo', yet the two are really quite different. A demo is the same as the commercial release but with a different label design or detail. A promotional record, on the other hand, is specially made for advertising or promotional purposes. Promotional records generally differ to the regular release, they often include additional (or less) tracks.

Session tape

This is the tape(s) used during the actual recording process on to which the entire contents of the session are stored. Theoretically the company then extract the performance(s) they want to use from this tape, cut them out, and use them as the source for the mastering of a record or CD.

Take

This means a complete or partially complete version of a song. Some songs are known to have many takes (famously, 31 for **Hound Dog**). However, it must not be assumed that all takes were complete, because as the release of bootleg and official outtakes reveal, there were many false starts (often only a few seconds of a song) or breakdowns, where half a song or more may have been recorded before the take was aborted. 'False start' and 'breakdown' were examples of session terminology, as they appeared on recording sheets, shows things like 'FS' or 'B/D'.

In the early days of recording, all the musicians and singers would perform a version (take) of a song at the same time. Prior to recording the engineers would set up microphones and establish a sound balance between the musicians and vocalists which gave the best sound quality. However if, for instance, during an attempt (take) of a song, someone made a mistake - played the wrong note, or Elvis forgot the tune, miscued his lyrics or simply turned in a poor or lacklustre performance, then it would have to be abandoned. The group would then compose itself and await the engineer's announcement of the next take and its number. Then, following a count-in, the next take would start. However, even if a take was completed successfully, quite frequently another take would be attempted until an acceptable version was recorded to everyone's satisfaction. Occasionally though, no satisfactory take would be recorded (as in the case of **Doncha' Think It's Time,** recorded on 23 January, 1958 and **My Wish Came True**) in which case the songs would either be abandoned or, as in the case of **My Wish Came True,** re-recorded later at another session. Interestingly, the released version of **My Wish Came True** (take 28, no less) dated from 5 September, 1957. Elvis, however, cannot have been happy about this as he attempted the song a few months later in January and February 1958, though neither occasion produced an acceptable version, it seems. However, if time or patience ran out, and no master take had been produced, the engineers would be called on to 'splice' the best pieces from various takes to make an acceptable take for release.

Test Pressings

A test pressing is just the same as a normal vinyl record (although it may have a white or specially produced label) which the pressing plant uses to check the quality of the pressing.

Undubbed

When used in the context of a song, this means that what you hear on the track is what was recorded by Elvis and his backing musicians in the studio, at the time. Further, it also means that no additional vocal or instrumental tracks have been added to the basic performances. Therefore, the tracks we heard on the two **Our Memories Of Elvis** volumes (*LP 112* and *LP 114*) are as they were recorded in the studio and have, thus, not been tampered with in any way other than by the mixing process. (See also Mixing).

Versions

Serious collectors, and even casual fans, are only too well aware that since Elvis's death in August 1977 very little 'new' i.e. previously unreleased songs have been released. However, there was a major growth in the issuing of outtakes, remixes and over or undubbed material. Therefore, in order to provide readers with further information, we have now specifically included references to which versions of songs have been used. Naturally where no such reference is made, it is reasonable to assume that we are referring to the standard or original version (the best known version in most cases).

Session Information

The main source of any information pertaining to Elvis's recording sessions was Ernst Mikael Jorgensen's 1998 publication *A Life In Music The Complete Recording Sessions.* And, although we did refer to his earlier works, and the books of Joseph Tunzi (*Elvis Sessions 1* and *Elvis Sessions II*), essentially if there was any discrepancy then we opted for what was printed in Jorgensen's most recent work. However, that is not to say that, on occasions, some confusion hasn't occurred. It has - and where we have been uncertain, we have said so.

Part 2 : Background Material

What Is A UK Record?

As the title clearly states, this book is concerned with Elvis's UK record releases, that is records which were officially released in the UK, irrespective of where the record was actually produced. Whilst once we could claim that our main purpose was to deal with records that were made in the UK for home consumption, we can no longer confine ourselves in this way, simply because the record company mainly responsible for Elvis records, RCA, concentrated their manufacturing base in Germany as long ago as 1983, with the majority of product being made there.

This move disappointed a number of Elvis fans, and we know of some fans who had been collecting Elvis records since 1956, who claimed that they simply refused to buy, what they described as 'foreign' releases. This patriotic stance quickly diminished when it became apparent that pursuing such a restrictive policy actually meant not being able to get unissued material on product made in the UK!

Generally, we have not included details of records imported into the UK where there was no official UK release of that record. However, there are notable exceptions to this rule, included not as part of the chronological listings, but noted in the appropriate place in the script. We have done this for records which contain useful parallels to official UK releases, or when important and significant features were to be found on the release in question.

The question of what is, and what is not, an official UK release is not as straightforward as it would first appear, and many collectors have been caught out into believing they have purchased an official album when, in fact, they have not. The reason for this is that official corroboration has not always been possible - the RCA catalogue was largely confined to dealer use only; it was certainly not readily available, as most shops process orders through a computer linked directly to record manufactures' distribution centres, as opposed to conventional paperwork ordering. The RCA catalogue, assuming one could gain access to it, was never entirely reliable in the first place, with imported material being shown alongside UK releases. Another factor was the sheer volume of material available in certain outlets throughout the mid to late eighties.

The price code found on RCA single and LP sleeves was definitely not proof of any kind of official UK status, for there were many examples of where it was shown on an import album, yet a UK price code could be omitted from an official release. This often came about where a sleeve used the same artwork for a re-issue where distribution details were changed, and where the record in question had been deleted in the UK, without an amendment to the sleeve. Our general advice here then is ignore the price code. We have noted in the text for each release where such errors occurred, and consider what we have included in the chronological listings to be the definitive status.

Sometimes the confusion was brought about by dealers themselves who, incorrectly, priced imported material at the lower UK price, misleading buyers into believing that the record was, indeed, a UK issue. Such occurrences, at least those that we are aware of, are noted in the text.

Therefore, we can offer the following guidelines when considering imported records: the price was normally higher than that of an official UK release, and the record should have carried a sticker indicating that the record had been imported. The RCA catalogue should have provided absolute confirmation, but it had to be used carefully.

Modes

Prior to 1960 Elvis records did not indicate recording modes, quite simply because up until that point, all releases had been issued in mono. Indeed, it was not until the mid-eighties when the authors of **Recording Sessions** revealed for the first time that some of Elvis's pre-army material had been recorded in binaural (an early form of stereo). Hopes were dashed, however, when the authors printed a facsimile of a tape box with the word 'Erase' written across it, apparently ruling out the existence of any such recordings. And so, it had always been assumed that his first stereo recordings had not been undertaken until March 1960, when he resumed conventional studio recordings. Imagine then everyone's surprise when certain tapes were found, recorded binaurally, and their contents released on **Stereo '57 (Essential Elvis Volume 2)**, PL 90250 (**LP 298**), in January 1989. Perhaps even more surprising was the fact that these recordings dated from January 1957. It does not require a major leap in logic to believe that subsequent sessions in 1957 and 1958 could have been similarly recorded. However, despite exhaustive tape vault searches, no other such tapes have been located. The strange and confusing release of **Treat Me Nice** (film version) in 'stereo' as part of **The Great Performances**, PL 82227 (**LP 308**), led many to believe that this, too, was some kind of binaural or true stereo recording, and seemed to give increased credibility to the rumour which had circulated for years that **Jailhouse Rock** also existed in a stereo form. The truth of the matter, however, was that the stereo image on **Treat Me Nice** had been created at the film studio by overdubbing a guitar part onto a mono recording! Ironically though, by late 2001, some genuine binaural recordings from **Jailhouse Rock** were released on the CD **Silver Screen Stereo**, a Collectors Label release.

However, backtracking a little, it was not until 1960 that newly recorded albums became available in both mono and stereo (described as 'Living Stereo' on the early labels), and the album covers and label copy showed this where appropriate. In the UK, singles were still issued in mono - even though they may well have been stereo recordings - throughout the sixties. Consequently during that era no recording modes were shown on singles or EPs. In fact the first Elvis single to be issued in stereo in the UK was **I Just Can't Help Believin'**, RCA 2158 (**S 81**), in November 1971. And it was only with the release of the first Maximillion single in July 1971 that any mode - in this case mono - was shown on the label. On the other hand, fans in the USA had had stereo singles since 1960. As regards albums, both mono and stereo versions were available (where appropriate, of course) until 1969. In fact, the last album to be pressed in both modes was **From Elvis In Memphis**, RD/SF 8029 (**LP 38**), released in August 1969. Thereafter, all new album releases were in stereo, unless it stated otherwise. Incidentally, the first electronically reprocessed stereo release was **Rock 'N' Roll (No. 2)**, SF 7528 (**LP 17**), when it was reissued (for the first time on RCA in the UK) in December 1962.

However, it was not until the early 1970s that this process was used extensively on pre-army back catalogue releases. And although apparently exciting at the time, it was not long before fans came to dislike this process. It was not until the early 1980s that steps were taken to restore these recordings to their rightful mode: mono. Subsequently, almost all recordings stated clearly what the recording mode was, even though there were some errors from time to time. The only advice we can offer is to listen carefully to a release and do not take what a label says for granted.

It is worth noting that the only time stereo EPs were available previously was when RCA in the UK issued two sets of extended players in 1982. Since then, the format virtually ceased to exist, although in 2001 Castle Music issued **The International EP Collection** which included some stereo recordings.

We thought it would be useful to define precisely what is meant by the terms used to describe recording modes - mono, stereo, binaural and electronically reprocessed stereo. After all, we use these so frequently, perhaps without fully understanding what the difference is. Obviously, we have no wish to get too involved with the complex technical issues - other than where absolutely necessary - to fully explain the situation.

Mono

Mono, or more correctly monaural, recordings were, up to the late 1950s, what you heard on your record player, radiogram or radio (wireless). The word itself means 'one', so in the context of recordings it meant that no matter how many speakers you listened to, you would hear the same information come from all of them. Of course, the term 'mono' only became significant when stereo came along - prior to this everything was simply 'recorded'. In America, mono was often called 'regular' and stereo 'hi-fi'.

Prior to stereo recordings, where there was a deliberate separation of the recorded information into a left or right channel (or both to produce a central image), all the recorded data - no matter how many or how few musicians played or singers sang - would go on to tape. Of course, even prior to stereo, balancing the sound between musicians and singers (mixing) was still an essential part of the recording process. This was the engineer's and/or producer's job: to ensure that the balance was correct. Therefore, before a recording was committed to tape, the engineer and/or producer would balance the sound between the various instruments and vocals. Fine tuning of the best balance would be done during the actual recording process with the results captured on one or more tape machines.

However, it is worth pointing out that overdubbing additional information had been in use from the late 1940s (onto disc) and Elvis made use of this facility early in his career. A good example of this was **Shake, Rattle And Roll** on which Elvis, Scotty and Bill overdubbed vocals on the chorus of the song. Despite clever processes such as this, the results were still mono recordings as the same information came out of both/all speakers.

Stereo

Stereo is short for stereophonic which, in most dictionaries, is defined something like 'a system for recording, reproducing or broadcasting sound using two or more separate microphones to feed two or more loudspeakers through separate channels in order to give a spatial effect to the sound'. This is reasonably clear, but the record industry did its best to confuse an already baffled public. The following was taken from the inner bag of RCA LPs in the sixties.

'What is stereophonic sound

It is the latest technical development in recording whereby, when reproduced on the proper equipment, the sound of each instrument reaches your ears from the same direction as it would from its position in the concert hall. For example, where in the concert hall the sound of the string section originates from the left side of the orchestra, in your room this sound appears to come from the left. Woodwinds, where originating from the centre of the orchestra, appear to come from the centre of your room. The timpani, where originating from the right of the orchestra, appear to come from the right of your room. The overall effect is to recreate in your room <u>all</u> of the sounds of the "live" orchestra in proper relationship to one another.'

The same notes went on to add:

'NOTE: when held at certain angles the surface of this Stereophonic record <u>looks different</u> than that of a monaural disc... it may even <u>appear</u> to be worn. Of course, this is only an <u>illusion</u> caused by the unusual way in which the grooves of this record are cut.'

So, the next time a dealer tries to sell you a battered and worn stereo album, just remember.. it's only an illusion!

It was interesting that whilst these inner bags referred to stereo as being 'the latest technological development', the truth of the matter is that work in this area had been going since the 1920s. However, the first stereo release was made in the UK in June 1958 by the PYE record company who, initially, charged about 20% more than their normal price for mono records, although this was soon brought down to the same level once other companies issued stereo recordings.

Basically, the word stereophonic was meant to indicate a method of sound reproduction that gave the listener an illusion of spaciousness by separating sound into two channels, one left and one right. To achieve this, information was recorded on a two-track tape machine (not one track, as in mono recordings). Put simply, two microphones would capture two separate pieces of information which would in turn be recorded on to the separate tracks of the tape. But, nothing was recorded in stereo - it had to be mixed to produce the stereo image heard when replaying the recording.

Reprocessed Stereo / Electronic Stereo

The development of stereo recordings actually gave record companies a new problem - in that they had to produce two products - mono and stereo records, with all the extra cost that this involved. Naturally, this was unpopular, and the industry strived to come up with a method of turning original mono recordings into stereo ones. By doing so, one product could be produced which the record companies could legitimately call stereo and, by doing so, turn a marketing ploy into a profit-generating system, as stereo records, initially, cost more money. Of course, it turned out that they used the term 'stereo' loosely, often in conjunction with 're-processed' or 'electronically produced'. The real point about all of this was that this technical advancement eventually became the object of derision once the novelty wore off. Later, when the industry wanted to issue mono recordings, engineers who cared about the end product were presented with another problem, as electronically reprocessed tapes could not be turned back to mono!

Reprocessed stereo first appeared in 1959, and in the sixties many systems were developed by almost all of the leading record companies, all of whom were trying to make old mono recordings acceptable to stereo record purchasers. Reprocessed stereo was the name given to a process whereby the recording was electronically altered to split the frequencies into layers which were then fed into two separate channels - hence the imitation stereo effect. Happily, by the 1980s very few examples of electronically reproduced stereo albums were still available.

Binaural

The dictionary definitions of binaural can be misleading, referring to 'double mono' and 'being capable of giving a stereo sound'. However, binaural was nothing more than a temporary term given to two-track recordings which took the form of placing a voice or single instrument on one channel and everything else on another. Thus, there would be some separation of sound, and this gave the effect of crude stereo. We should point out that, as in all pioneering work, there were no hard and fast rules to follow, and as engineers experimented with different ways of producing sound - by placing microphones in different positions, for example - varying developments were possible. Binaural was only possible because of the availability of two-track recording capability.

We now know that binaural recordings had been made of (at least) some Elvis recordings from 1957 onwards, and despite an order by company executives to erase the tapes some survived. A selection of binaural recordings were released on **Stereo '57 (Essential Elvis Volume 2)** (**LP 298**) in 1989. There are two issues which need to be clarified here: why were binaural recordings made in the first place, given that they were never released at the time; and why was the order given to erase the tapes?

Radio Recorders (where the Elvis recordings in question were made) was, at the time, a very advanced studio with all the latest equipment available. Elvis tended to work in a smaller studio because he had a smaller band and obviously did not require a studio large enough to accommodate an orchestra. However, simply because the studio was smaller did not make it any less advanced. The studio's two-track capability would be used as a back-up, primarily for Elvis's vocal, for the simple reason that if anything went wrong with the mono tapes then it would have been possible to use the vocal from the back-up. Therefore, these binaural recordings were not derived from separate recordings sessions, they are from the same sessions and made at the same time as the mono recordings.

Once a successful master take of a song had been achieved, the mono tape only would be prepared for release in record form. The binaural (back-up) tape would remain untouched and filed away - it was not intended for use. It was, for this reason, that these tapes (which had no commercial value whatsoever at the time) were largely erased. Presumably, the fact that the tapes could be re-used added weight to the decision. Of course, another major factor was that no-one saw any merit in retaining outtakes either, and it would be many years before anyone realised their commercial value.

Tape Machines Used On Sessions

During Elvis's lifetime it was generally accepted that all of his pre-1960 recordings had been recorded in mono, while from 1960 onwards most tracks had been cut in stereo. However, since the mid-1980s, not only has that simplistic division been confounded by RCA locating and releasing binaural recordings from 1957, but the revelation that the soundtrack recordings done for *Love Me Tender* at Twentieth Century Fox in 1956 were recorded in proper stereo sound.

Of course, central to this issue, lies the sort of machines used to record information on over the years. The fact that *Love Me Tender* was recorded in stereo was irrelevant at the time, for the domestic users did not have the equipment necessary to play stereo recordings. It is only now, many years on, that these stereo recordings have been located and issued.

However, out of interest, we have compiled a list of what equipment was used on Elvis's sessions, in particular how many tracks were available to record on (thus allowing for stereo recordings). We are grateful to Ernst Mikael Jorgensen for providing this information.

Sun material (1954-55)	Mono
RCA Nashville (1956-58)	Two track mono
RCA New York (1956)	Two track mono
Radio Recorders - Los Angeles (1956)	Two track mono
(1957-58)	Two track binaural mixed down to mono
RCA Nashville (1960-66)	Three track stereo
RCA Nashville (1967-68)	Four track
NBC Recordings (1968)	Eight track
American Sound, Memphis (1969)	Eight track
Soundtrack recordings (1960-66)	Three track
Soundtrack recordings (1967-68)	Four track
Soundtrack recordings (1968-69)	Eight track

Live Recordings

Las Vegas (1969)	Eight track
General/Las Vegas/Tours (1970-75)	Sixteen track
Tours/Studio (1976-77)	Twenty four track
Tour (Spring 1977)	Eight track

Take Numbers

From the release of **Essential Elvis**, PL 89979 (**LP 280**), in December 1986, BMG began to regularly include extra session information (where known), such as full personnel listings and accurate recording dates. An interesting addition to the Essential Elvis series was the inclusion of take numbers too, some of which had been previously published in, for example, the **Recording Sessions** book. Fans found this information most useful.

With the release of the fifties' set in 1992 virtually all take numbers for those tracks were published. Occasionally though - as in the case of **Danny** from 1958 - this information was still not known. And, as regards the Sun material, it is well-known that Sam Phillips did not keep very accurate session logs (certainly on Presley material), hence any take numbers assigned to Sun records/songs were done so much later on. Indeed, Ernst Mikael Jorgensen expressed the opinion in 1992 that the take numbers given to the Sun outtakes known to exist were assigned by Rick Rowe in the mid-1980s. Prior to this time, take numbers were only given sporadically: for instance in 1982, with the release of the EP collections volumes 1 and 2, the outtakes were not given take numbers on the covers or labels.

Pressing Plants

Fans and collectors have usually been keen to know where a record (or CD) was pressed and, wherever possible, we have endeavoured to include this piece of information when discussing each release. And, while we have been extremely careful in this, we should issue a note of caution at this point. Some releases may have been pressed by more than one company, although this practice became less common as time progressed. It is, therefore, possible that your copy of a particular record was produced elsewhere from what we have stated. This raises the interesting point of how to distinguish product from one company to that of another? Unfortunately, there is no simple answer, as we shall see. Industry specialists can tell almost immediately by checking the profile around the spindle hole; by looking at the edges for the finish; by examining the thickness of the disc; and so on. However, this is, for the layman, an almost impossible task, made much harder since many UK plants closed or, at best, switched to CD-only production following the decline in the demand for vinyl. Vinyl production capabilities are now very limited, not only in the UK but worldwide, and even the largest companies have records produced in other countries which, for the time being, have retained vinyl production. Thus, identifying where a record was made can be virtually impossible.

Nonetheless, sometimes a record company would identify themselves in some way, whether this be in the form of their initials (PR), as in the case of **The Fifties Interviews** (**LP 305**), or by the use of some distinguishing feature, unique to a particular plant. One of the more obvious examples here is BMG who manufactured the bulk of their Elvis output at their own pressing plant - Sonopress - based in Gutteslaw, Germany. We provided a detailed identification procedure in **Elvis UK 1956-86**, but, in simple terms, the presence of a bass clef around the spindle hole indicated that the record was pressed by Sonopress. CDs pressed by Sonopress were even easier to identify as the company's name was engraved around the central section of the disc!

Despite this, quite a few Elvis records were pressed in the UK, particularly those originating locally and for UK issue only, but a variety of pressing plants were used. And, where known, we have given this information.

Alternative Versions

It has to be said at the outset that there is no intention to present a major piece on this subject (deserving as that may be) as, strictly speaking, it is a subject which is on the periphery of our study. Remember, our central interest has always been the records themselves; and yes, while the music itself is the most important factor to all of us as fans, we wish to retain a measure of detachment in our writings.

Necessarily though (and we hope as an aid to our readers), we felt it important to acknowledge the notion of alternative versions, whether that involved the release of an outtake, an undubbed track, an overdubbed track, a re-make, a live version, or a remix. What we have sought to clarify in the text of each release discussed is which version we are referring to. Now, obviously, we have only done so when we believe there was a need to point out differences. A good example of this would be the inclusion of *I've Lost You* on the *Always On My Mind* album (*LP 272*). As we mentioned in the original script, it seems appropriate to indicate that this version was not the studio master, as some had hoped it would be, but a live version as used on the *That's The Way It Is* album (*LP 47*).

Other obvious examples which spring to mind include the various mixes of *Always On My Mind*, the different versions of *An American Trilogy*, and things such as *Guitar Man*, the original studio cut or the overdubbed version from 1980. Any such information given is to assist your choice, or draw a point to your attention: it is purely descriptive, not prescriptive.

The release of the fifties' set in 1992 and subsequent issue (on CD) of the Double Feature film soundtrack sessions, once again raised questions about what was an original version of a song.

To illustrate the point let us consider a couple of examples, and then try to make sense of what is going on.

Tomorrow Night. When this 1954 Sun recording was first issued in 1965 on *Elvis For Everyone* (*LP 26*), it was in an overdubbed form i.e. the original Sun recording had been added to by session musicians earlier in 1965, presumably to fill out what seemed like an otherwise sparse sound. This version lasted for 2 minutes 38 seconds.

Then, later, in May 1985, an undubbed version (purporting to be the complete and original undubbed master, lasting 2 minutes 58 seconds) was issued on RCA PL 85418, *Reconsider Baby* (*LP 271*). However, when the fifties' set was issued in 1992, fans noted differences between the 1985 'version' and the latest issue, even though the song still ran for 2 minutes 58 seconds. For example, not only was the 'bridge' part longer, but the order of the lyrics varied. Evidently, according to the most reliable sources, this was the original take. Apparently, Rick Rowe had edited the 1985 version and re-jigged some of the verses. All versions are the same vocal up to 1 minute 28 seconds, but then differ from that point onwards. The master has a 21 second instrumental break and then goes into the verse, 'Tomorrow night, will it be just another memory', while the 1985 version used the same 'Tomorrow night' but spliced in 'will you remember what you said tonight', taken from another part of the song. More edits follow until 47 seconds from the end of the song when both 'long' versions converge.

Ain't That Loving You Baby. The so-called 'fast' version of this song (recorded in June 1958) first appeared on RCA PL 85418, *Reconsider Baby* (*LP 271*), in May 1985. However, it was not until the release of *Hits Like Never Before (Essential Elvis Vol. 3)* (**LP 306**), in July 1990, that Ernst Mikael Jorgensen revealed that the version previously issued (and thought by almost everyone to be a complete take) had been edited from no less than 5 takes!

Mama. This left-over track from the 1962 movie *Girls! Girls! Girls!* first appeared on INTS 1103 *Let's Be Friends* (*LP 40*) in May 1970, when it featured Elvis and The Amigos. Remember though, Elvis had not sung any of the song in the movie. The version on this album was in mono. However, when the Double Feature soundtrack album CDs were issued in March 1993, the track (in stereo) was much shorter: 0.58 seconds, as opposed to 2 minutes 12 seconds on the *Let's Be Friends* album. Moreover, the introduction was longer and different too. Apparently though, this version was an edited one, featuring extra instrumentation in the middle piece, and a different ending. Elvis's vocal though, was the same on each 'version', being merely repeated on the *Let's Be Friends* album. According to Roger Semon (May 1993), there was no stereo master of this version.

Plantation Rock. This song, yet another left-over from *Girls! Girls! Girls!*, was not released officially until November 1983 on *Elvis - A Legendary Performer Vol. 4* (*LP 204*), though in mono. However, the version used on the Double Feature CD was in stereo, but it sounded different (as well as being shorter), suggesting that this could be an alternative version, especially as the lyrics are different in parts of the song. Incidentally, the recording data claimed that it was released in 1980 when it was, in fact, 1983. The producers of the set could not confirm whether or not the two versions were alternatives; their belief was though that the one used on *Elvis - A Legendary Performer Vol. 4* was edited for release by Joan Deary, but they can not be sure as they did not have the tape copy she was working from.

There are, of course, many other examples of this type of 'alternative version' (not to be confused with original full length recordings which were edited when first released - for example, *King Of The Whole Wide World*, *I Got Lucky*, *A Whistling Tune* and so on). However, the main point is this: the current producers of Presley product have tried, as far as possible, to use what was on the original tape, as a matter of policy, unlike earlier producers who, presumably for equally valid creative reasons, chose to edit and tamper with recordings, for all kinds of reasons. Nonetheless, in recent years, some strange revisions have occurred.

An early example of this was *A Big Hunk O' Love*, which was, in fact, a splice of takes 3 and 4. However, the version on the fifties' set (take 3), appeared as it was originally recorded in June 1958, and a number of subsequent releases have included this version as opposed to the single master. This has caused some consternation among collectors, for they have argued that this is rewriting history, in a sense. Certainly, there seems no problem is using this version, but really it ought to be noted as an alternative recording when used.

A similar situation existed with *Blue River*. Until the release of *For The Asking (The Lost Album)* (*LP 309*), the best known version was the original single cut (*S 52*). However, the version on the previously mentioned album lasted barely a minute and a half. This was the original studio cut; the single version was spliced to include a second guitar solo (identical to the first, of course).

Equally, the versions commonly used for *Follow That Dream* and *Come What May* are, in fact, both outtakes (takes 2 and 7 respectively) simply because, in both cases, the stereo masters could not be located at that time. However, in 2000, the stereo master for the latter track appeared on the Collectors Label CD *Long Lonely Highway Nashville 1960-1968* (74321 76749 2).

All of this suggests that we, the fans, have to be very careful when talking about 'original versions', and be ever mindful to the possibility that a producer or engineer many years ago elected to 'tamper with' what had been recorded. Of course, in some cases it was by necessity - especially when recordings were done in the pre-multi-track recording days - that tracks were spliced. And, the fact that we did not know, ought not really to disturb us. After all, if done properly, then there is no way we should be able to tell. Whatever though, recent disclosures about some early recordings have raised some interesting historical and artistic issues.

Unreleased Performances Issued On Vinyl : 1986 To Date

The term 'unreleased performances' came into usage in January 1989 with the release of *Stereo '57 (Essential Elvis Volume 2)* (**LP 298**).Previously 'unreleased performances' were referred to variously as 'outtakes', 'alternate' or 'alternative takes'. The new term seemed a sensible choice, as it covered things like studio outtakes, and, in the case of live recordings, it was a more apt description.

Now, irrespective of anyone's point of view regarding whether or not RCA/BMG have done a good job in the post 1986 period, what is undeniable is that there were many more unreleased performances made available during this time. As a rule, we have not detailed whether or not they had been bootlegged previously.

What follows then, is a brief note on the number of unreleased performances issued by RCA/BMG in this time. The number shown includes, say, two or more takes of the same song if they are featured as separate tracks. For example, on *Essential Elvis* (**LP 280**), there are three versions of *Loving You* featured, one slow version and two up-tempo versions. However, track nine of the song actually lists two takes, 20 and 21, which for this exercise we regard as one unreleased performance. The film version of *Mean Woman Blues* (track ten) also counts as an unreleased performance in our view. We do not, however, refer to remixes, or include them in the category of unreleased performances.

Clearly, there are complications from time to time, but these are dealt with in detail in the script. On the likes of *Collectors Gold*, (**LP 315**) we do not include the 'snatch' of *Surrender* or *Loving You* as performances in the totals given.

Date	Title	Release Number	Number of Unreleased Performances
Dec 1986	*Essential Elvis*	**LP 280**	11
Feb 1987	*Essential Elvis*	CD	2
Jul 1987	*The Complete Sun Sessions*	**LP 283**	9
May 1988	*The Alternate Aloha*	**LP 294**	17
		CD	1
Jan 1989	*Stereo '57 (Essential Elvis Volume 2)*	**LP 298**	15
Feb 1990	*The Last Temptation Of Elvis*	VA LP 44	1
Jul 1990	*Hits Like Never Before (Essential Elvis Vol. 3)*	**LP 306** CD	14* 3**
	*album cover states 13 ** one an instrumental		
Aug 1990	*The Great Performances*	**LP 308**	2
Feb 1991	*NBC TV Special*	CD	1
Aug 1991	*Collectors Gold*	**LP 315**	48
Jul 1992	*The King Of Rock 'N' Roll The Complete 50's Masters*	**LP 318**	14
Aug 1992	*Don't Be Cruel*	S 179	1
Sep 1993	*From Nashville To Memphis The Essential 60's Masters 1*	**LP 319**	19
Oct 1995	*The Twelfth Of Never*	S 180	1
Apr 1996	*Elvis 56*	**LP 321**	1
May 1996	*Heartbreak Hotel*	S 181	1

It can be clearly seen that, as early as February 1987, additional unreleased performances to those included on the vinyl version were being released on CD. For example, the vinyl album *Essential Elvis*, contained 11 unreleased performances, with two others appearing on the CD version.

For your information, and to make this section as complete as possible, we have included details of the unreleased performances on each vinyl release - single or LP. Where they occurred, we have also added details of their CD equivalent, noting any additional tracks.

LP 280   *Essential Elvis*

Loving You - slow version, take 10

Party - take 7

Loving You - fast version, takes 20 and 21

Mean Woman Blues - film version

Got A Lot O' Livin' To Do! - take 13

Loving You - fast version, take 1

Jailhouse Rock - vocal overdub, take 6

Treat Me Nice - take 10

Young And Beautiful - take 12

Jailhouse Rock - take 5

Love Me Tender - end title version

The CD version, PD 89980, contained two additional unreleased performances not found on the vinyl LP. These were:

Loving You - slow version, take 1
Loving You - fast version, take 8

LP 283   *The Complete Sun Sessions*

I Love You Because - take 3

I Love You Because - take 4

I Love You Because - take 5

I'm Left, You're Right, She's Gone (My Baby's Gone) - take 7

I'm Left, You're Right, She's Gone (My Baby's Gone) - take 8

I'm Left, You're Right, She's Gone (My Baby's Gone) - take 10

I'm Left, You're Right, She's Gone (My Baby's Gone) - take 11

I'm Left, You're Right, She's Gone (My Baby's Gone) - take 12

I'm Left, You're Right, She's Gone (My Baby's Gone) - take 13

The CD version (a single CD) had fewer tracks, and did not include take 4 of *I Love You Because* and takes 8, 10, 11 and 13 of *I'm Left, You're Right, She's Gone (My Baby's Gone)*.

LP 294   *The Alternate Aloha*

See See Rider

Burning Love

Something

You Gave Me A Mountain

My Way

Love Me

It's Over

Blue Suede Shoes

I'm So Lonesome I Could Cry

What Now My Love

Fever

Welcome To My World

Suspicious Minds

I'll Remember You

An American Trilogy

A Big Hunk O' Love

Can't Help Falling In Love

The CD, PD 86985, additionally included **Hound Dog**, another unreleased performance.

LP 298   *Stereo '57 (Essential Elvis Volume 2)*

I Beg Of You - take 1

Is It So Strange - take 1

Have I Told You Lately That I Love You - take 2

It Is No Secret (what God can do) - takes 1, 2 and 3

Blueberry Hill - take 2

Mean Woman Blues - take 14

(There'll be) Peace In The Valley (for me) - takes 2 and 3

Have I Told You Lately That I Love You - take 6

Blueberry Hill - take 7

That's When Your Heartaches Begin - takes 4, 5 and 6

Is It So Strange - takes 7 and 11

I Beg Of You - takes 6 and 8

(There'll be) Peace In The Valley (for me) - take 7

Have I Told You Lately That I Love You - takes 12 and 13

I Beg Of You - take 12

The CD version, PD 90250, contained an additional five tracks, although these had been previously released.

VA LP 44   *The Last Temptation Of Elvis*

King Of The Whole Wide World - takes 1, 2 and 3

LP 306   *Hits Like Never Before (Essential Elvis Vol. 3)*

King Creole - take 18

I Got Stung - take 1

(Now and then there's) A Fool Such As I - take 3

Wear My Ring Around Your Neck - take 22*

Ain't That Loving You Baby - take 1

I Need Your Love Tonight - takes 2 and 10

As Long As I Have You - take 8

King Creole - take 3

Crawfish - take 7

A Big Hunk O' Love - take 1

Ain't That Loving You Baby - takes 5 and 11

I Got Stung - takes 13 and 14

Steadfast, Loyal And True - take 6

I Need Your Love Tonight - take 5

* This is the master take without the 'guitar slapping' overdub, and probably accounts for BMG claiming that the LP only contained 13 unreleased performances. The original version with the overdub is also included.

The CD version, PD 90486, included four additional tracks, three of which were previously unreleased, although one was an instrumental. These were:

I Got Stung - take 12
King Creole - take 8 - instrumental
As Long As I Have You - take 4

LP 308   *The Great Performances*

My Happiness - acetate

Treat Me Nice - overdubbed guitar part

LP 245   *Elvis* (NBC TV Special), NL 83894, was re-distributed in February 1991. Although the LP version contained the same track listing from its original appearance in September 1984, the CD version contained 8 additional tracks, one of which, **Don't Be Cruel**, was previously unreleased.

LP 315   *Collectors Gold*

G.I. Blues - take 1

Pocketful Of Rainbows - takes 22 and 17

Big Boots - take 7

Black Star

Summer Kisses, Winter Tears - takes 1 and 14

I Slipped, I Stumbled, I Fell - take 18

Lonely Man - *take 4*

What A Wonderful Life - takes 2 and 1

A Whistling Tune

Beyond The Bend - take 2

One Broken Heart For Sale - take 1

You're The Boss

Roustabout - take 6

Girl Happy - take 4

So Close, Yet So Far - take 4

Stop, Look And Listen - take 3

Am I Ready - take 1

How Can You Lose What You Never Had - takes 1 and 3

Like A Baby - takes 1 and 2

There's Always Me - take 4

I Want You With Me - take 1

Gently - take 3

Give Me The Right - take 1

I Met Her Today - take 1

Night Rider - takes 1 and 2

Just Tell Her Jim Said Hello - take 1

Ask Me - take 2

Memphis, Tennessee - take 2

Love Me Tonight - take 1

Witchcraft - take 1

Come What May - take 6

Love Letters - takes 3, 4 and 7

Goin' Home - takes 24 and 21

The following are all unreleased live performances from Las Vegas in 1969:

Blue Suede Shoes

I Got A Woman

Heartbreak Hotel

Love Me Tender

Baby, What You Want Me To Do

Runaway

Rubberneckin'

Memories

Jailhouse Rock / Don't Be Cruel

Inherit The Wind

This Is The Story

Mystery Train / Tiger Man

Funny How Time Slips Away

Reconsider Baby

What'd I Say

LP 318   ***The King Of Rock 'N' Roll The Complete 50's Masters***

That's When Your Heartaches Begin - acetate

Fool, Fool, Fool - demo

Shake, Rattle And Roll - demo

Blue Moon - take 2

Reconsider Baby - Million Dollar Quartet

Lawdy, Miss Clawdy - take 3

Shake, Rattle And Roll - take 8

I Want You, I Need You, I Love You - take 16

We're Gonna Move - take 4

Old Shep - *take 5*

Loving You - slow version, take 12

Loving You - fast version, take 13

Young And Beautiful - take 3

I Want To Be Free - take 10

S 179   ***Don't Be Cruel***

I Need Your Love Tonight - take 9

In March 1993, the first batch of Double Feature CDs were issued featuring three unreleased performances. However, no vinyl LPs were issued of these albums. This, indeed, was also true of the second and third batches of Double Feature CDs.

LP 319   ***From Nashville To Memphis The Essential 60's Masters 1***

Beyond The Reef - undubbed master

Come What May - take 7

I'll Remember You - unedited master

Suppose - master

Guitar Man/What'd I Say - unedited master

Hi-Heel Sneakers - unedited master

This Time/I Can't Stop Loving You - informal recording

In The Ghetto - take 4

Suspicious Minds - take 6

Kentucky Rain - take 9

Big Boss Man - take 2

Down In The Alley - take 1

Memphis, Tennessee - take 1

I'm Yours - take 1

(Marie's the name) His Latest Flame - take 4

That's Someone You Never Forget - take 1

Surrender - take 1

It's Now Or Never - undubbed master

Love Me Tender/Witchcraft - Frank Sinatra TV Show

S 180   ***The Twelfth Of Never***

The Twelfth Of Never was from the seventies' 5 CD set *Walk A Mile In My Shoes*. And, although this 5 CD set included a number of other unissued performances, they were not available on a vinyl release.

LP 321   ***Elvis 56***

Heartbreak Hotel - *take 5*

S 181   ***Heartbreak Hotel***

I Was The One - *take 2*

This four track single contained two previously unissued recordings: *Heartbreak Hotel* (take 5) and *I Was The One* (take 2). *Heartbreak Hotel* was also included on the vinyl LP *Elvis 56* (**LP 321**), but the alternative *I Was The One* was not.

Of course, as vinyl releases became so rare, any previously unissued material was released primarily on CD. And, although this is not the right place to enumerate this material, collectors would need to have major collections such as *Walk A Mile In My Shoes* (1995), comprising a spread of seventies material, as well as *Platinum A Life In Music* (1997), a 2 CD retrospective collection spanning all of Elvis's career, and containing no fewer than 77 previously unreleased performances, although not all of these were complete songs.

And, of course, needless to say, other CD releases often contained previously unissued performances/material, most notably on the Follow That Dream Collectors Label which came into being in 1999.

A History Of Bertelsmann

We made no reference to Bertelsmann, or BMG, in *Elvis UK 1956-86* for the simple fact that whilst the company had become linked to RCA in 1985, this was a behind-the-scenes move which had no noticeable impact on any Elvis product. Whilst this was a conscious decision on our part, events after 1985 made it essential to discuss BMG in some detail, as the name crops up now on all Elvis product and it is, therefore, important to understand how Bertelsmann came to own RCA Records and, as a consequence, all of Elvis's RCA recordings.

To provide some background to the company as well as to explain these events, we have included a short history of the Bertelsmann organisation.

To many of us the name Bertelsmann is a new one, brought to our attention only by its appearance on Elvis record sleeves in the mid-late eighties. Whilst this is very recent, the name Bertelsmann, in fact, has a long and noble history. The beginnings of the company go as far back as 1835 when the Royal Prussian Government granted a licence on 1 July to Carl Bertelsmann to start a publishing operation in Gutersloh, a town in what we now call Germany. Prussia was a state in North and Central Germany which was divided between East and West Germany, Poland and the Soviet Union after the Second World War. Later the same year (1835) Bertelsmann published his first books: a schoolbook and a hymn book which proved to be a great success selling over 2 million copies, a major achievement even by today's standards. Bertelsmann concentrated mainly on publication of religious works, which, in those days, was probably an easy option, for at that time there was much censorship and restrictions as to what could, and could not, be published. Government control was tight and it was not until 1848 that newspapers were allowed to report current news items. Despite these restrictions Bertelsmann continued to build up his business.

After the turn of the century the company started to publish works of fiction, again with some success. However, the slow, gradual but nevertheless successful growth was halted during the Second World War when the Nazi Government stopped the publication of any works which they did not authorise and, of course, this was limited largely to material of their own design and primarily for propaganda purposes.

When the war was over the company rebuilt their plant in Gutersloh, but the immediate aftermath of war meant that the population had higher priorities than buying books, although by 1948, surprisingly quickly, enough money had been injected into the German economy to allow the people to once again start buying books. At this time the company commenced a new marketing concept combining book clubs and retail book shops, with the shops helping to recruit members to the book club, and the books themselves being supplied by Bertelsmann publishing companies.

It was in this business area which sealed the success of the company and which allowed them to commence operations outside of Germany itself. There was a continued and rapid development during the 1950s and 1960s, including further expansion into other related business areas, and of particular note is the formation in 1958 of Ariola Schallplatten GmbH, when Bertelsmann entered the music business for the first time. This trend continued during the 1970s culminating in September 1979 when the company entered the American market by buying Arista Records from its owners, Columbia Pictures. The relationship between Bertelsmann and RCA goes back to 1983 when the two companies entered a joint-venture agreement, whereby RCA bought 50% interest in the Bertelsmann company Arista, although, to all intents and purpose, the companies continued to operate as two separate organisations.

The relationship was strengthened (and complicated) in August 1985 when the parent company Bertelsmann and RCA formed a worldwide joint venture for all their music related activities, the new company being called RCA/Ariola Ltd. RCA was then taken over by the giant American conglomerate General Electric who, in December 1986, sold the music business arm of RCA to Bertelsmann. From January 1987, RCA became a wholly owned division of the Bertelsmann group named Bertelsmann Music Group (BMG).

Today, the worldwide Bertelsmann organisation employs over 43,000 people in 200 countries with an annual sales figure of over £4 billion from its many business interests.

The UK operations are centered on the British division of the Bertelsmann Music Group, where, happily, the RCA label continues to thrive.

In the main we still refer to RCA records, and not just for reasons of nostalgia, but from the viewpoint that Elvis releases actually appear on that label, although reference is made to BMG, and, of course, we indicate in chronological sequence the changes in ownership and relate these to details on record labels and sleeves.

US Releases

As the title of the book clearly states, the central theme is UK vinyl releases of course, as it was with our first book *Elvis UK 1956-86*.

However, as with the issue of CDs - which would have been impossible, not to say absurd to ignore, when bearing in mind the veritable explosion in terms of popularity with music buyers over the last few years - we did believe that some reference to American releases was quite legitimate and, we hope, of interest. Readers outside the UK and US will understand, we hope, the need to restrict comparative references to output from these countries. And, whilst not denying the high level of interest of releases from, say, Japan and Australia, the most appropriate point of comparison must be with the USA..

In *Elvis UK 1956-86*, we traced the pattern of releases in the UK and frequently referred to the differences (where they occurred) from US releases. This could be something as simple as one country having a different single release from the other; a release being re-scheduled and issued at a different time or, as frequently occurred early on in Elvis's career (for there used to be quite major changes in album releases), mainly in the tracks used.

However, since the early eighties there was no denying that the UK and European market was pre-eminent in terms of Elvis releases. In fact, other than where stated in the script, most of the major releases originated in the UK and Europe. Hence, we have not devoted time and space to discussing American releases, not just because it is largely irrelevant to our research, but simply because the vinyl market in the USA diminished much sooner than in the UK. However, where there is something to bring to your attention, then we have done so.

The US market still released its own product, some of which was not issued in the UK, for one reason or another, mainly because BMG (in the personage of Roger Semon) decided that the release had nothing of great note to offer UK fans.

And so, although we have not detailed American releases in anything like the depth approaching UK product, we have listed all known US main releases since 1986, and given catalogue numbers and release dates. In the course of the book's narrative - remember it is chronological - we have, where appropriate, made reference to US releases in the text. Further though where, say a UK and US release shared the same title e.g. the Reader's Digest *The Legend Lives On* (**LP 310**) and there were significant track differences, then we have described these as fully as possible, mainly in the form of a postscript to the UK release. In the event of there being a US release not available in the UK for some reason (excluding mail order items), some description of this would appear as a link in the appropriate place, along with any details we thought significant.

One final note: we have chosen to include a reference to *Return Of The Rocker* (which was not released in the UK), at the appropriate point in the script, particularly as UK fans had had *The Rocker* (LP *262*) album, the first in the series. Similarly, we have also made reference to another album entitled *The Rocker Comes Back*, which although scheduled for release in the USA in the autumn of 1987, was never issued.

However, what follows is a list of vinyl releases available in the US from 1986 onwards. It refers solely to standard BMG releases, omitting special product releases which each division marketed from time to time. Items marked * secured no vinyl release in the UK.

Title	Catalogue Number	Release Date
* *Return Of The Rocker*	5600-1-R	Jun 1986
The Memphis Record	6221-1-R	Jun 1987
* *The Number One Hits*	6382-1-R	Jun 1987
* *The Top Ten Hits*	6383-1-R	Jun 1987
The Complete Sun Sessions	6414-1-R	Jun 1987
Essential Elvis: The First Movies	6738-1-R	Jan 1988
The Alternate Aloha	6985-1-R	May 1988*
Elvis In Nashville	8468-1-R	Oct 1988
Stereo '57 (Essential Elvis Volume 2)	9589-1-R	Feb 1989
* *Elvis Gospel 1957-71: Known Only To Him*	9586-1-R	Apr 1989*
The Million Dollar Quartet	2023-1-R	Mar 1990
The Great Performances	2227-1-R	Aug 1990
Collectors Gold	3114-1-R	Mar 1993

Please note: *Collectors Gold* secured only a limited release. Discs were pressed in 1991; the cover made in 1992. However, according to US sources, 10,000 copies were pressed though only 330 were 'released'. All the remaining copies were destroyed by RCA/BMG, thus making the surviving copies extremely rare and collectable.

As with the UK/European division, very few vinyl singles were released in the USA in the period after 1986. And, of those issued, there was very little correlation with the UK/European sector. The US vinyl singles from 1986 onwards were as follows:

Heartbreak Hotel RCA V 8760-7-R November 1988. The B side featured *Heartbreak Hotel* by David Keith & Charlie Schlatter with Zulu Time. Both versions were from the original soundtrack of the film *Heartbreak Hotel*. The single was issued in a picture sleeve.

Don't Be Cruel / Ain't That Loving You Baby 07863-62402-7 November 1992. This single was pressed for juke box dealers only.

Blue Christmas / Love Me Tender 07863-62403-7 November 1992. Also for juke box dealers only.

Heartbreak Hotel / Hound Dog 07863-62449-7 December 1992. For juke box dealers only.

Silver Bells (unreleased version) S*ilver Bells* (LP version) 07863-62411-7 November 1993. For juke box dealers only, but RCA Nashville had issued a cassette version in 1992.

Heartbreak Hotel / I Was The One / Heartbreak Hotel / I Was The One 07863 64476-7 May 1996. Identical to the UK issue (**S 181**).

Global Releases

Just as the early nineties saw a move towards a global cataloguing system, there had been, for a while, a parallel move towards standardising releases throughout the various areas of the world - 'territories' as they are known in the record industry.

And, while there was much to applaud in having a rational and coherent release programme throughout the world, there was, inevitably, a down-side too. For while UK and European fans may have become extremely annoyed that certain albums were available in CD format in other parts of the world - principally Japan and Australia - long before they were widely available locally, the system also had its merits. Now, we do not believe ourselves qualified to comment on the worth, or otherwise, of certain releases peculiar to Japan, Australia, Canada, USA or wherever, but what we can say is that under the 'old system', whereby 'territories' released more or less what they thought appropriate to local interest and demand, UK fans tended to get a better deal than others. For instance, a glance at the UK releases from about 1980 onwards reveals that fans in the UK had a number of albums targeted specifically at the home market - *Elvis Presley Sings Leiber And Stoller* (*LP 125*); *Romantic Elvis* (*LP 192*); *Rockin' Elvis - The Sixties* (*LP 193*); *Jailhouse Rock/Love in Las Vegas* (*LP 196*), and so on; as well as having modified albums (based on US albums), which invariably offered UK fans a better deal in terms of extra tracks. Several examples spring to mind: *The Sound Of Your Cry* (*LP 185*); *It Won't Seem Like Christmas Without You* (*LP 195*); *I Was The One* (*LP 200*); and *I Can Help And Other Great Hits* (*LP 207*) etc. The releases above were almost all the responsibility of Roger Semon at RCA UK.

Sadly though, uniformity does have its drawbacks, for it stifles genuine creativity and could frustrate say, for instance, a CD release of the above mentioned releases, especially as the release programme tended to dictate (based on market forces and what dealers were prepared to stock) that 'extra', locally initiated releases, occurred less and less. Of course, that is not to say they did not happen at all. A scan of the US CD releases over the last few years will reveal that, as was their right, the US division of the company chose to issue certain packages which made little sense to European fans/collectors (not to mention offering poor value for money), but which, in commercial terms, met local needs and made money for the company. And, no-one should overlook that crucial point: record companies need to make a profit. Perhaps this is something which we, as serious collectors, are sometimes in danger of overlooking or choosing to ignore.

Cassette Releases

As we have stated frequently elsewhere in the text, the central concern in the book has been vinyl releases. Inevitably, the increased popularity of CDs has prompted us to make occasional references to them, particularly when vinyl and CD versions differed in some way. To have ignored them would have been impossible - not to say negligent. Indeed, the increasing number of references to them simply reflects the major change in the industry since 1986. But this, we imagine, will be self-evident to the reader.

However, music cassettes, on the other hand, received barely a mention in *Elvis UK 1956-86*, nor in this volume. And, the reason for this is simple; unlike CDs sales which rapidly ascended in the period in question, music cassettes, like vinyl albums, were now thought to be in decline. More though, cassette releases were never seen as a serious challenge to vinyl - as CDs were from the start - rather a complement to them.

Therefore, the only major references to music cassette releases occur as link-pieces in the main album section. And, the only reason we have included them, is because they were unique product, with no vinyl or CD equivalents issued in the UK. The two cassettes in question were: *Greatest Hits - Elvis Presley*, THPA 1234, issued in November 1987, by Telstar, and, *Elvis*, EMC 003, on sale only in the Avon cosmetics catalogue from October 1991.

Full track listings and detailed descriptions of both cassettes can be located in the main album section.

Available Vinyl Releases - January 1986

In the section devoted to deletions, we explain the fairly complicated situation regarding deletion dates and the discrepancy between the 'official' date against the availability of certain items in record shops. The point being that records could still be obtained long after a record company had run out of stocks and deleted the record. In this section it seemed appropriate to establish exactly which records were still available, officially, at the start of 1986. No doubt there were others, held by stores after their deletion by RCA, but below are details of RCA records still available on catalogue at the time.

Throughout the Singles' section we refer to the deletion dates of RCA singles, and, when compared to the number of new issues, this serves to demonstrate how fragile the singles' situation had become, in the sense that their shelf-life was often short, and the number of different singles available at any one time was small.

Putting together a list of singles which were still available at the beginning of 1986 (the effective starting point of this book), proved quite difficult. As shops reduced stock to the point where many simply carried chart singles, locating back catalogue material, including Elvis singles, became all the more difficult, much more so than for back catalogue albums. Some specialist shops still took pride in handling back catalogue material, but by this time the major chain stores had started to move away from stocking this kind of material, leaning towards more profitable markets.

When we compiled the list of available singles we were surprised both by the numbers involved, and, some of the titles which had survived. We have shown the release number, catalogue number, A side title, release date and the date the single was officially deleted in the UK.

S 101	RCA 2695	*Jailhouse Rock*	May 1977	Mar 1989
S 106	RCA 2700	*Wooden Heart*	May 1977	Mar 1989
S 112	RCA 2706	*Return To Sender*	May 1977	Feb 1990
S 114	RCA 2708	*Crying In The Chapel*	May 1977	Mar 1989
S 127	GOLD 500	*I Just Can't Help Believin'*	Jul 1981	Aug 1990

S 128	GOLD 506	***An American Trilogy***	Jul 1981	Mar 1989
S 131	GOLD 534	***Good Rockin' Tonight***	Oct 1981	Mar 1986
S 132	GOLD 541	***If Every Day Was Like Christmas***	Nov 1981	Jun 1986
S 133	RCA 196	***Are You Lonesome Tonight?***	Feb 1982	Nov 1987
S 134	GOLD 544	***Way Down***	May 1982	Mar 1989
S 146	PB 49943	***Always On My Mind***	Jul 1985	Nov 1987
S 147	PT 49944	***Always On My Mind***	Jul 1985	Feb 1987

The point to make about all of these singles was that they were, by 1986, getting towards the end of their run, and were obviously not selling in large quantities. Those that survived until 1989 or 1990 did so because of the numbers pressed on their last, or only, press run. This, therefore, simply reflected the time it took to sell existing stocks. The inevitable conclusion must be that supply outstripped demand - too many were pressed. Nevertheless, the regular RCA singles did well for the company, and, of particular note, were the remaining four singles from the 'Gold 16' batch of 1977: for them to survive for twelve years or so was quite an achievement. ***Are You Lonesome Tonight?***, the 'laughing' version, also deserves a mention both for its chart achievement - it reached number 25, a higher position than almost every subsequent single - and in terms of the numbers sold, which we believe to be around 85,000 copies.

The Golden Grooves series of 'oldies', never matched anything like these numbers, but they served their purpose and did reasonably well, although the long shelf life of ***I Just Can't Help Believin'***, GOLD 500 (*S 127*), said more about lack of sales towards the end of its life than about demand.

The July 1985 release of ***Always On My Mind***, in two formats - 7 inch (***S 146***) and 12 inch (***S 147***) - was more typical of RCA's policy towards singles: smaller press runs, no re-pressings, and final deletion about two years after the initial release, a time span that was further reduced for later singles.

A similar situation existed with Extended Play (EP) releases, by this time almost a defunct medium. RCA released two, 11 EP sets in February and October 1982, both of which were extremely successful, and are still held in high regard by fans. Each set came in a binder package with plastic pockets to hold individual records, and the first set included an EP entitled ***G.I. Blues The Alternate Takes*** (*EP 33*), which, theoretically, could only be purchased with the set, not as an individual item. EP 2 featured two similar EPs, ***G.I. Blues Outtakes Vol. II*** (*EP 43*) and ***Collectors Gold*** (*EP 44*), which, once again, could not be purchased separately - not directly from RCA that is, although many dealers did split the packages. The sets, EP 1 and EP 2, were deleted in April 1984 and December 1984 respectively, but the individual EPs (excluding those referred to above) continued to be available as separate product.

Interestingly, the other EPs which comprised EP 1 were deleted at different times, some of them in 1983, suggesting that the appeal of various titles varied widely, whereas the EPs from the second set were all deleted at the same time - in March 1986.

The individual EPs still available at the beginning of 1986 are listed below, along with their release number, date of release and the date of their eventual deletion. The separate blocks refer to EP 1 and EP 2 respectively.

EP 24	RCX 7189	***Heartbreak Hotel***	Feb 1982	Feb 1987
EP 26	RCX 7191	***Love Me Tender***	Feb 1982	Feb 1987
EP 29	RCX 7194	***King Creole Vol. 1***	Feb 1982	Feb 1987
EP 31	RCX 7196	***Follow That Dream***	Feb 1982	Mar 1986
EP 32	RCX 7197	***Kid Galahad***	Feb 1982	Feb 1987
EP 34	RCX 7198	***Elvis Presley***	Oct 1982	Mar 1986

EP 35	RCX 7199	***Peace In The Valley***	Oct 1982	Mar 1986
EP 36	RCX 7200	***Elvis Presley***	Oct 1982	Mar 1986
EP 37	RCX 7201	***King Creole Vol. II***	Oct 1982	Mar 1986
EP 38	RCX 7202	***A Touch Of Gold Vol. 1***	Oct 1982	Mar 1986
EP 39	RCX 7203	***A Touch Of Gold Vol. II***	Oct 1982	Mar 1986
EP 40	RCX 7204	***A Touch Of Gold Vol. III***	Oct 1982	Mar 1986
EP 41	RCX 7205	***Flaming Star***	Oct 1982	Mar 1986
EP 42	RCX 7206	***Love In Las Vegas***	Oct 1982	Mar 1986

The situation regarding the LPs which were still available at the beginning of 1986 is relatively simple, despite the numbers involved. The fact is, that with very few exceptions, most of the German produced albums were still available. One that had been deleted was PLP 89287, ***I Can Help And Other Great Hits*** (LP 209), the picture disc version of the album. The regular black vinyl version was still on catalogue. The other deleted albums are included in the list below, with appropriate notes.

Clearly, the reason why such large numbers of albums were still available was due to the fact that all of these were relatively new product, with ***The Elvis Presley Sun Collection***, NL 89107 (*LP 201*), being the first one to become available, in October 1983. Those of you familiar with ***Elvis UK 1956-86***, will recall that the bulk of these German albums replaced the fairly extensive International (INTS) series of mid-price releases, issued between 1980 and 1982, and that this was done on a phased basis by attaching a sticker, showing the new European catalogue number (NL) over the existing INTS number. By doing so, RCA were able to introduce the new albums without having to change their catalogue, and enabling them to clear stocks of the older product. Therefore, the deletion date of the INTS albums coincided with the 'release' date of the NL series records - more or less. Sometimes, the dates were precise; sometimes they overlapped, occasionally they fell short, but throughout 1984 this change-over was made. Incidentally, RCA did not consider the move from one series to another to be a case of deletion and re-release. Indeed, their 'release' dates for the NL series are the dates when the INTS albums were deleted, not the date that the NL albums were released. For example, ***His Hand In Mine***, NL 83935 (*LP 214*), is quoted as being issued in August 1981, the date of the INTS 5105 album, not April 1984, when the album was actually released in the UK.

The LP catalogue was, therefore, quite extensive, amounting to over sixty albums in both the mid-price and full-price categories. By and large, the releases that were available represented the bulk of Elvis's original UK album output, although, of course, there were some obvious exceptions. Albums such as ***From Elvis In Memphis***, RD/SF 8029 (*LP 38*), had been deleted for many years prior to this, and was not re-issued until February 1991 (**LP 313**).

The list of available albums is, therefore, quite a lengthy one, but we have noted them all in catalogue number order to ensure that those of you unfamiliar with ***Elvis UK 1956-86***, and the albums produced in Germany. The list follows the same pattern as singles and EPs: release number, catalogue number, title, release date and, finally, the deletion date - a '?' indicates that we have been unable to confirm a precise deletion date. Finally, a '*' refers you to some additional notes regarding the album in question.

LP 259	PL 80504	***The First Year***	Jan 1985	Mar 1986
LP 211	NL 81382	***Elvis***	Apr 1984	Apr 1991
LP 210	NL 81515	***Loving You***	Apr 1984	Mar 1992
LP 232	NL 81707	***Elvis' Golden Records***	Jul 1984	Apr 1984
LP 203	NL 82075	***50,000,000 Elvis Fans Can't Be Wrong***	Nov 1983	*
LP 260	PL 82428	***Moody Blue***	Jan 1985	Jul 1988
LP 222	NL 82558	***Harem Holiday***	Apr 1984	Mar 1986
LP 241	NL 82559	***Frankie And Johnny***	Aug 1984	Mar 1986

LP 255	NL 82560	*California Holiday*	Nov 1984	Mar 1986
LP 244	NL 82564	*Double Trouble*	Sep 1984	Mar 1986
LP 223	NL 82565	*Clambake*	Apr 1984	Mar 1986
LP 247	NL 82568	*It Happened At The World's Fair*	Sep 1984	Mar 1986
LP 273	PL 82587(2)	*Elvis In Concert*	Aug 1985	Aug 1994
LP 237	PL 82642(2)	*Aloha From Hawaii*	Jul 1984	Aug 1990
LP 256	NL 82765	*Elvis' Golden Records Vol. 3*	Nov 1984	Apr 1991
LP 248	NL 83338	*Girl Happy*	Sep 1984	Mar 1986
LP 238	NL 83683	*Blue Hawaii*	Aug 1984	Mar 1992
LP 212	NL 83733	*King Creole*	Apr 1984	Jan 1992
LP 206	NL 83735	*G.I. Blues*	Jan 1984	Mar 1992
LP 235	NL 83758	*How Great Thou Art*	Jul 1984	Apr 1991
LP 245	NL 83894	*Elvis*	Sep 1984	Mar 1992
LP 213	NL 83921	*Elvis' Golden Records Vol. 4*	Apr 1984	Apr 1991
LP 214	NL 83935	*His Hand In Mine*	Apr 1984	Apr 1991
LP 239	NL 83956	*I'm 10,000 Years Old - Elvis Country*	Aug 1984	?
LP 226	BL 84031(?)	*This Is Elvis*	May 1984	Oct 1993
LP 224	NL 84114	*That's The Way It Is*	May 1984	Apr 1991
LP 249	NL 84115	*Kissin' Cousins*	Sep 1984	Mar 1986
LP 243	NL 84116	*Something For Everybody*	Aug 1984	Apr 1991
LP 225	NL 84232	*Elvis For Everyone*	May 1984	Mar 1992
LP 227 (RCALP 3106)	PL 84678	*I Was The One*	May 1984	**
LP 204	PL 84848	*Elvis - A Legendary Performer - Vol. 4*	Nov 1983	Jul 1989
LP 261	PL 84941	*Elvis' Gold Records Volume 5*	Jan 1985	Jul 1989
LP 262	PL 85182	*The Rocker*	Jan 1985	Jul 1989
LP 251	PL 85172	*A Golden Celebration*	Oct 1984	Feb 1992
LP 270	PL 85353	*A Valentine Gift For You*	Jan 1985	Apr 1987
LP 271	PL 85418	*Reconsider Baby*	May 1985	Oct 1988
LP 272	PL 85430	*Always On My Mind*	Jul 1985	May 1991
LP 275	PL 85486	*Elvis' Christmas Album*	Oct 1985	Jul 1989
LP 263	PL 89003	*Rare Elvis*	Jan 1985	May 1991
LP 215	NL 89010	*Paradise, Hawaiian Style*	Apr 1984	Mar 1986
LP 250	NL 89011	*Love Letters From Elvis*	Sep 1984	Mar 1992
LP 228	NL 89012	*Speedway*	May 1984	?
LP 230	NL 89013	*Elvis Is Back!*	Jun 1984	Mar 1992
LP 257	NL 89014	*Fun In Acapulco*	Nov 1984	Mar 1986
LP 216	NL 89024	*20 Greatest Hits Vol. 1*	Apr 1984	Mar 1992
LP 252	NL 89025	*It Won't Seem Like Christmas Without You*	Oct 1984	Jul 1989
LP 267	NL 89046	*Elvis Presley*	Jan 1985	Mar 1992
LP 229	NL 89048	*Girls! Girls! Girls!*	Jun 1984	Mar 1986
LP 240	NL 89049	*Roustabout*	Aug 1984	Mar 1986
LP 264	PL 89051	*Rare Elvis Vol. 3*	Jan 1985	Jul 1989
LP 231	NL 89068(2)	*From Memphis To Vegas From Vegas To Memphis*	Jun 1984	Feb 1992
LP 242	NL 89097	*A Date With Elvis*	Aug 1984	Aug 1989
LP 233	NL 89098	*Pot Luck*	Jul 1984	Mar 1992
LP 217	NL 89099	*Elvis Presley Sings Leiber & Stoller*	Apr 1984	Jul 1989
LP 201	NL 89107	*The Elvis Presley Sun Collection*	Oct 1983	?

LP 218	NL 89116	*Elvis' Christmas Album*	Apr 1984	***
LP 265	PL 89119	*Rare Elvis Vol. 2*	Jan 1985	Jul 1989
LP 220	PL 89124	*Romantic Elvis*	Apr 1984	Apr 1993
LP 236	NL 89125	*Rock 'N' Roll*	Jul 1984	Mar 1992
LP 221	PL 89132	*Rockin' Elvis - The Sixties*	Apr 1984	Apr 1993
LP 219	NL 89168	*20 Greatest Hits Vol. 2*	Apr 1984	Mar 1992
LP 266	PL 89266	*From Elvis Presley Boulevard, Memphis, Tennessee*	Jan 1985	May 1991
LP 207	PL 89287	*I Can Help And Other Great Hits*	Mar 1984	May 1991
LP 234	PG 89387	*The First Live Recordings*	Jul 1984	Apr 1988
LP 253	NL 89429	*Elvis Golden Records Volume 2*	Nov 1984	Apr 1991

Notes:

* NL 89075, **50,000,000 Elvis Fans Can't Be Wrong** (*LP 203*). This album was effectively replaced by a new compilation of fourteen tracks - **Elvis Golden Records Volume 2**, NL 89429 (*LP 253*), in November 1984. As RCA do not show a deletion date for the former title, we can only assume that it was deleted prior to this date, and it was, therefore, not available in 1986.

** PL 84678, **I Was The One** (*LP 227*). This was a real peculiarity in that it was never intended to issue the album in this format in the UK. RCA UK issued their version of **I Was The One**, RCALP 3105 (*LP 200*), in August 1983, just prior to the move towards central European production. Instead of using the original American eleven track album, the UK version included an additional five tracks. Yet, in May 1984, copies of the European version, identical to the American release, surfaced in error in the UK, with a sticker converting the catalogue number back to the UK number, as if they were the same album. No deletion date for PL 84678 has been shown, because, technically the album was never released in the UK.

*** NL 89116, **Elvis' Christmas Album** (*LP 218*). This was another example where a re-issue replaced an earlier release without a deletion date being shown. This particular album was released in April 1984 as a mid-price LP, replacing the earlier International INTS album. In October 1985, a new full-price version was released, PL 85486 (*LP 275*), so, in effect, NL 89116 must have been deleted prior to this date. RCA do not show a deletion date for this album, and obviously considered the PL album a replacement, rather oddly, as there were obvious price differences. NL 89116 was therefore not available as of January 1986.

One final point regarding album availability: thus far we have noted the situation with regard to the German produced albums, but what about those produced in the UK prior to RCA's decision to centralise manufacture? The answer, sadly, is that only two albums survived. A few others had made it until 1985, before being deleted and, of course, in certain cases, no German replacement arrived and the albums remained deleted. The only two UK produced albums to survive, for a short time at least, were:

LP 72	APLI 0606	*Elvis As Recorded Live On Stage In Memphis*	Aug 1974	Mar 1986
LP 183	SDL 004	*Elvis At His Best*	Nov 1981	Jun 1987

Original Vinyl Albums

In some ways the release of Presley material in a vinyl form (alongside CD and music cassette) did not follow the general industry trend too closely. Certainly, since the mid-1980s, when the availability of popular music titles on CD began to increase markedly - alongside the ownership of compact disc machines - vinyl's place in the market had diminished dramatically, although some collectors hung on to it tenaciously.

However, as we discuss elsewhere, the Elvis collectors demonstrated a fondness for vinyl releases long after other collectors had switched loyalty to digital releases. Perversely, for a number of years, a considerable number of Elvis fans probably bought new releases in both vinyl and CD format. Hence, despite loose talk about such and such release being the last vinyl release (heard in the early 1990s), the 3 CD set **Collectors Gold** (1991) was issued in vinyl (**LP 315**), as was the prestigious **The King Of Rock 'N' Roll The Complete 50's Masters** (**LP 318**) in 1992. Indeed 15,000 vinyl copies were produced, and several thousand were shipped to the USA to meet demand there. And, irrespective of market trends and the doom-laden voices of hard-nosed marketing men declaring the end of units selling at approximately £50 each in the UK could not be ignored in terms of earning revenue for the company. Not surprisingly, even in late 1992, with the projected sixties' boxed set at least nine months away, no-one would predict if there would be a vinyl version. More importantly though, no-one would say there definitely would not be one.

Of course, discussion thus far has centred on 'new' releases i.e. old material and/or outtakes being repackaged and re-marketed in the best possible way. We must not forget about conventional back catalogue material, much of which has re-appeared on CD but not all of it re-issued in vinyl form. And it is to this topic that we now turn our attention.

As we have mentioned elsewhere, the advent of CD did spawn a rush of re-releases (often accompanied by a vinyl version), as well as a relatively few CD only releases. Now here we would also direct readers' attention to the list below for vinyl releases. It can be seen that some albums never achieved a re-release, and they are never likely to be issued again in a vinyl form - at least not by a major company such as BMG.

Thus far, the following regular full-priced albums have never been re-issued in vinyl in the UK, although there are several examples (in particular the LPs originally released in the '70s) where German-made imports were available in the UK.

Release Number	Catalogue	Title	Release Date
LP 3	RC 24001	*Loving You* - 10 inch (the original 8 track LP)	Aug 1957
LP 4	DLP 1159	*The Best Of Elvis* - 10 inch	Oct 1957
LP 25	RD 7723	*Flaming Star And Summer Kisses*	Sep 1965
LP 45	LPM 6401	*Worldwide 50 Gold Award Hits Vol.1*	Nov 1970
LP 55	LPM 6402	*Elvis The Other Sides Worldwide Gold Award Hits Vol. 2*	Aug 1971
LP 61	SF 8266	*Elvis Now*	May 1972
LP 62	SF 8275	*He Touched Me*	Jul 1972
LP 63	SF 8296	*Elvis As Recorded At Madison Square Garden*	Jul 1972
LP 68	SF 8378	*Elvis*	Jul 1973
LP 69	APL1 0388	*Raised On Rock/For Ol' Times Sake*	Nov 1973
LP 70	CPL1 0341	*Elvis - A Legendary Performer Vol.1*	Feb 1974
LP 71	APL1 0475	*Good Times*	Mar 1974
LP 72	APL1 0606	*Elvis As Recorded Live On Stage In Memphis*	Aug 1974
LP 74	LPL1 7275	*Hits Of The 70's*	Nov 1974
LP 75	APL1 0873	*Promised Land*	Jan 1975
LP 77	APM1 0818	*Having Fun With Elvis On Stage*	Mar 1975
LP 79	RS 1011	*Today*	Jun 1975
LP 87	CPL1 1349	*Elvis - A Legendary Performer Vol. 2*	Jan 1976
LP 101	PL 12772	*He Walks Beside Me: Favourite Songs Of Faith And Inspiration*	Mar 1978
LP 106	PL 13082	*Elvis - A Legendary Performer Vol. 3*	Jan 1979
LP 112	PL 13279	*Our Memories Of Elvis*	Apr 1979
LP 114	PL 13448	*Our Memories Of Elvis Vol. 2*	Sep 1979
LP 126	CPL8 3699	*Elvis Aron Presley*	Aug 1980
LP 146	RCALP 5010	*Guitar Man*	Feb 1981
LP 185	RCALP 3060	*The Sound Of Your Cry*	Jan 1982
LP 196	RCALPP 9020	*Jailhouse Rock/Love In Las Vegas*	Apr 1983
LP 200	RCALP 3105	*I Was The One*	Aug 1983
LP 204	PL 84848	*Elvis - A Legendary Performer Vol. 4*	Nov 1983
LP 207	PL 89287	*I Can Help And Other Great Hits*	Mar 1984
LP 234	PG 89387	*The First Live Recordings*	Jul 1984
LP 25	PL 85172(6)	*A Golden Celebration*	Oct 1984
LP 261	PL 84941	*Elvis' Gold Records Volume 5*	Jan 1985
LP 262	PL 85182	*The Rocker*	Jan 1985
LP 263	PL 89003	*Rare Elvis*	Jan 1985
LP 264	PL 89051	*Rare Elvis Vol.3*	Jan 1985
LP 265	PL 89119	*Rare Elvis Vol.2*	Jan 1985
LP 270	PL 85353	*A Valentine Gift For You*	Jan 1985
LP 271	PL 85418	*Reconsider Baby*	May 1985
LP 272	PL 85430	*Always On My Mind*	Jul 1985

None of the RCA albums released after this period (i.e. albums included in this book) have been re-issued. In fact, the last full-priced album (and even then it was a buy-one-get-one-free release) was the **Romantic Elvis/Rockin' Elvis - The Sixties** compilation, RCALP 1000/1001 (*LPs 192 and 193*), which was re-issued in April 1984 (*LPs 220 and 221*). Of course, all post-1977 albums had one thing in common - Elvis was no longer around to record any new material, although some of the albums did contain unreleased material of one kind or another. It would be sensible, therefore, to consider that these albums were basically one-offs, compilations of varying quality produced to meet demand. Considered as such, it would be, for most albums, a pointless exercise in producing a re-issue.

What of the albums released prior to Elvis's death? Here too we find opportunist releases which probably never deserved a re-appearance, given that the name of the game was often to re-cycle the same product in different form. Including the 10 inch **Loving You** album (*LP 3*), the first RCA UK release, which has never re-appeared in this format (although a 12 inch album was issued in 1977), a total of 18 albums released in Elvis's lifetime have never been re-issued in vinyl, although a number have been re-issued on CD. Seven of these were mainly 'hits' compilations which, as we have said, were rarely re-issued. Included also are the first two Legendary Performer volumes, which started the trend towards collectors' orientated product.

The remaining albums - original works - mainly from the mid-1970s, when quality studio albums were hard to come by, have never been re-issued, for the simple reason that, even at the time, they were failures in a sales' sense. Many of these albums subsequently achieved cult status with collectors because of their short shelf life and, more significantly, the small quantities pressed in the UK, have made them rare and expensive items. However, there was an undertaking to issue all studio albums in the course of time, as part of restoring the whole catalogue in CD form. Understandably though, some items represented a low priority. Nonetheless, by the mid-90s, this was achieved.

Bar Codes

Readers of **Elvis UK 1956-86** will be aware that we endeavoured to provide as much information as possible on all aspects of Elvis product, whether this was in terms of track details, company policy or whatever. However, one aspect which we did not cover in any depth previously concerns the use of bar codes, which were first introduced by the record industry in the mid-eighties. We realise, of course, that the bar code has no bearing on the quality or otherwise of the final product as far as the buyer is concerned but, nevertheless, we sincerely hope that our layman's guide to their use is of some interest.

In many respects a record is similar to all other kinds of merchandise, in that it has to be ordered from the manufacturer, has to be subjected to some kind of stock control and has to be offered for sale to the customer. This process, greatly simplified in the above explanation, is often quite complicated, and can be both time consuming and expensive, although the size and organisation of a record retailer is clearly an influencing factor.

Always looking for ways of improving the situation, the record manufacturing industry, like many other producers, began considering the use of bar codes to facilitate more efficient methods of getting their product to the customer. Retail outlets, particularly supermarkets and larger chain stores, were introducing modern electronic equipment capable of 'capturing' information quickly in order to speed up the selling process, and the most efficient and successful method of doing this was by using a system known as bar coding.

Guidelines for the bar coding of records and similar products were published in July 1983 by the British Phonographic Industry (BPI), which represents nearly all the record manufacturers. These guidelines were closely related to the earlier standards introduced by the Record Industry Association of America.

So, what are bar codes and how do they work? In basic terms, bar codes are relatively simple codes of black and white bars (lines), and there are several different bar codes in use. The basic system is that a number is represented by a set of black and white bars - the white bars simply being spaces between the black ones. For example, a number could be printed as a narrow bar, wide space, narrow space or wide bar. Thus the number 1 could be represented by a wide bar, while a narrow bar represents 0. The numbers used in a bar code are unique to the particular item and, therefore, can include the catalogue number of the record and a manufacturer's or 'product' number. Today, the use of bar coding is commonplace and everyone involved in the manufacture, distribution and selling of product from the record industry has benefited. Bar codes even provide the basis for assessing sales data to compile the record charts.

The code is read by a hand held wand, 'gun' or scanner, using laser principles, which converts the light reflected from the bars, which is then 'seen' by the equipment as an electronic signal, which is then transferred to a stores receipting equipment. This, then, allows the price to be automatically shown and, if required, the stock of that particular item reduced each time one is sold.

A laser is capable of reading a bar code which is printed in any dark colour except red - some lasers scan with a red light, and therefore they cannot pick up a reflection from red. The background colouring can be any pale or pastel colour, although white is the most common background colour. If you check through the RCA LP sleeves examining the bar code you will notice that the background colour used is often slightly different to that of the sleeve itself, with the majority of bar codes being placed in a white box. It would be interesting to see whether the bar code used on the LP **Always On My Mind,** PL 85430 (*LP 272*), presented any difficulties when being scanned, as it used a red background.

The first Elvis records to include a bar code on the sleeve were those pressed in Germany which were then distributed in the UK with a sticker applied to the sleeve, changing the catalogue number back to a UK-only system. This lasted only for a short time until RCA UK had modified their own systems. These records started to appear in October 1983 and included **His Hand In Mine**, INTS 5105 (NL 83935) and **Elvis Is Back!**, INTS 5141 (NL 89013) (*LPs 156 and 168*).

In practice it is, therefore, not possible to say which was the first Elvis record to include a bar code. The first 'new' release (although it was merely an upgrade of an earlier LP featuring one additonal track) to include a bar code was **The Elvis Presley Sun Collection**, NL 89107 (*LP 201*). This LP was released also in October 1983.

When bar codes first appeared on the cover of Elvis records, RCA used a thirteen digit bar code called the International Article Number (known as the EAN-13) which was used (and still is) throughout Europe. In America, a different system was in widespread use and this was based on a twelve digit system (Uniform Product Code - UPC-A). However, the scanning equipment is capable of reading both systems, so that product made in America could be 'handled' in the UK.

Each country has a bar coding authority - a kind of governing body - to control, administer and provide assistance to member companies; but companies operating on a worldwide basis need only register with one authority in a country of their choice. The bar code authority for the UK is called the Article Number Association (ANA).

Reference to Elvis's LPs from 1984 to 1992 will show that they always commence 0 03562 and singles 5 01239. These numbers were then followed by the catalogue number of the record, which therefore rendered the complete bar code unique to that particular record.

In August 1992, the UK single **Don't Be Cruel** (**S 179**) appeared with a revised bar code system which incorporated further information and took on a dual identity with the catalogue number. This system, now based on twelve digits (the American Uniform Product Code), abandoned the earlier thirteen digit coding and comprised five separate 'codes' combined into one.

Using the bar code from the **Don't Be Cruel** 7 inch vinyl single - 743211107778 - as an example, this could be explained as follows:

The first two digits - 74 - represented the coding authority which issued the number. In this case the German coding authority. Some later BMG Elvis releases commenced 07, the code for America. However, most goods on sale in the UK commence 50, the code issued by the Article Number Association (ANA). If you check the sleeves of the UK Elvis 7 inch singles **Stuck On You**, **Mean Woman Blues** and **Are You Lonesome Tonight?** (**S 162, S 175 and S 177**), you will see that all three bar codes commence 50, indicating they were allocated by ANA.

The next four digits are allocated by the coding authority to the company marketing or manufacturing the product. So the 3211 in our example referred to BMG and so did the 8636, found on the later releases commencing 07. This number, together with the coding authority number, form a unique identification for the company anywhere in the world.

The next four digits - 1077 - identified the release in question and these were allocated by the record company to a particular record. A company may wish to identify its first release by 0001, but is not compelled to do so; they are free to use any four digits they chose but, usually, these form the catalogue number of that particular release.

The next digit, in our example the 7, was referred to as a configuration code. Its purpose was to identify the format (the configuration) of the release in question, thus enabling different versions of the same product, such as CD or cassette, 7 inch or 12 inch, to be readily discriminated. Record companies are not compelled to adopt this principle, and may use different codes for their numbering systems, but the coding authority would seek a consistency of approach. In the UK, and many other countries worldwide, the following configuration codes have been widely adopted:

Digit	Format
1	Vinyl LP
2	5 inch CD (album or single)
3	3 inch CD (album or single)
4	Cassette (album or single)
5	DCC (album or single)
6	12 inch single
7	7 inch single
0	Miscellaneous (picture or shaped discs etc.)

The numbers 8 and 9, which are not generally used, could be if, for some reason, a record company wished to issue an unusual number of different formats. Some companies use the number 1 to represent 12 inch vinyl, whether this was a 12 inch single or LP. BMG has used the number 3 on its Elvis videos.

The number 7 in our example, distinguished the fact that it was a 7 inch single. On the other hand, the CD version (which, incidentally, had a different catalogue number) of the same single has a number 2: the code for a 5 inch CD.

The twelfth and final digit - the 8 - is a computer check digit. This number is used by the scanning equipment to ensure that the preceding digits have been read correctly. The check digit is formed by a mathematical calculation using the previous eleven digits. The number is usually calculated by the company handling the artwork or printing.

Price Codes

Price coding is an extremely simple system used as a means of providing stores with a guide as to how much they should charge for a product. In other words, it provides both the cost to the shop and also the price of the product to the customer - a kind of recommended retail price.

The use of a code is far better than printing the price on whatever is being sold, and you will see the system being used in several different formats, with the best example being found in shops selling greetings cards. Here, the card manufacturers print a code on the back of the card, allowing the shop to display a price list for each code used, dispensing with the need to attach a price label to each card individually. A further advantage of this system comes where a price rise is imposed by the manufacturer, or the shop simply wishes to increase (or reduce!) their charges, because all that is required is for a new price list to be prepared without having to change the codes. In addition, customers do not have the trouble of trying to remove a price sticker without damaging the card.

Price codes worked in exactly the same way for records, with the codes being generated initially by the record company, who advised the record shops of the pricing arrangements. If a new type of format or special release became available, then a new code would be introduced to cater for this. The use of price coding had not been universally adopted in the music industry and many companies made no use of the system, explaining why almost all of the record outlets priced records individually. RCA seemed to have made good use of the system, partly because of their centralised European manufacturing base, from where product was distributed to many countries, allowing a more widespread coding system to be utilised.

Although RCA's use of price codes pre-dated the establishment of their German pressing plant by several years, the system was used sporadically, and it was not until the majority of product was pressed in Germany that the system became fully established.

The use of price codes on Elvis's UK records started in 1974 on LPs, and was, therefore, long established when the first single was issued featuring a code - *Don't Be Cruel*, PB 9265 (*S 118*), in June 1978. The format used was a small box with the words 'price code', with the code itself being AA. Between this release and March 1981, a total of five singles were issued in picture sleeves, all of which used the same price code. However, the November 1979 single *It Won't Seem Like Christmas (without you)*, PB 9464 (*S 120*), was issued in a plain black sleeve only and had no price code shown.

The singles released up to and including March 1981 using the AA price code were:

S 118	RCA PB 9265	*Don't Be Cruel*
S 119	RCA PB 9334	*Old Shep*
S 122	RCA 4	*It's Only Love*
S 124	RCA 16	*Santa Claus Is Back In Town*
S 125	RCA 43	*Guitar Man*
S 126	RCA 48	*Loving Arms*

After these singles came the Golden Grooves series of oldies, which included a total of seven Elvis singles, released between July 1981 and May 1982. Of the seven, five contained the same price code as regular singles (AA), whereas the final two of Elvis's Golden Grooves releases showed no price code - *If Every Day Was Like Christmas*, GOLD 541 (*S 132*), and *Way Down,* GOLD 544 (*S 134*).

The five Golden Grooves singles which incorporated a price code were:

S 127	GOLD 500	*I Just Can't Help Believin'*
S 128	GOLD 506	*An American Trilogy*
S 129	GOLD 510	*The Girl Of My Best Friend*
S 130	GOLD 520	*That's All Right*
S 131	GOLD 534	*Good Rockin' Tonight*

Thereafter, the price coding system seemed to go out of favour for some years, for it was not until July 1985 that the code was again used on a single, despite the issue of mainly picture sleeve singles during the intervening period.

Always On My Mind, PB 49943 (**S 146**), issued in July 1985, displayed the same price code for UK copies - AA - but the format had been expanded to show codes for two other countries - France (F) and Germany (which was shown as a 'D' for Deutschland). This had been possible following the closer working relationship between RCA and Ariola, and even though the record was pressed, and the sleeve printed, in England, it was thought necessary to include these additional details. The system was therefore shown as:

D: AC   F: RC 110   UK: AA

The following two RCA singles, *Ain't That Loving You Baby*, ARON 1 (**S 154**) and *Love Me Tender*, ARON 2 (**S 160**), had no price codes shown, but the same codes re-appeared with the *Stuck On You*, PB 49595 (**S 162**), single released in January 1988. Subsequent releases followed the same pattern, although the French code changed to BM110 on the August 1991 sleeve of *Are You Lonesome Tonight?* (**S 177**).

The UK price code, therefore, remained unchanged since it was introduced in 1978, whereas the code used for 12 inch singles had one minor change since it was introduced. Incidentally, the two 10 inch singles - *I Can Help*, RCAP 369 (*S 141*), and *The Last Farewell*, RCAT 459 (*S 144*), did not display a price code.

The first 12 inch single to use a price code was also the first Elvis UK 12 inch single to be released, *It Won't Seem Like Christmas (without you)*, PC 9464 (*S 121*), issued in December 1979. We mentioned above that the 7 inch format of this single had no code, but this 12 inch used BC. The next 12 inch price code was BB, used on *It's Only Love*, RCAT 4 (*S 123*), in October 1980, and this code remained unchanged. As with the 7 inch version, the 12 inch single of *Always On My Mind*, PT 49944 (*S 147*), included the German and French codes and read:

D: AF	F: RC 120	UK: BB

12 inch singles followed a similar pattern to the 7 inch singles, in that no price codes were used on the ARON catalogue number releases and the French code changed to BM 120 on the 1991 *Are You Lonesome Tonight?* single, PT 49178 (*S 178*).

The first LP to feature a price code was the February 1974 album *Elvis - A Legendary Performer Vol. 1*, CPL1 0341 (*LP 70*), thereby pre-dating the first price coded single by some four years. The early codes were interesting in that they alternated between HH and GG - apparently without reason - for we were not aware of any price change between the albums. This pattern was maintained for over a year, during which time the two RCA Starcall albums, *The Elvis Presley Sun Collection*, HY 1001 (*LP 80*), and *Pictures Of Elvis*, HY 1023 (*LP 83*), were issued in July and November 1975. Other albums were being issued at this time, notably those on the Camden label, none of which used a price code. *Elvis - A Legendary Performer Vol. 2*, CPL1 1349 (*LP 87*), issued in January 1976, used another new code - ZZ.

At this point we thought it would be useful to list all of the RCA albums in chronological sequence, indicating the price code for each of them, as this method would allow the changes to be shown more clearly.

LP 88	RS 1060	*From Elvis Presley Boulevard, Memphis, Tennessee*	HH
LP 90	PL 42003	*Elvis In Demand*	HH
LP 92	PL 12274	*Welcome To My World*	HH
LP 93	PL 12428	*Moody Blue*	HH
LP 94	PL 42354	*Girls! Girls! Girls!*	HH
LP 95	PL 42355	*Kissin' Cousins*	HH
LP 96	PL 42356	*Roustabout*	HH
LP 97	PL 42357	*Fun In Acapulco*	HH
LP 98	PL 42358	*Loving You*	HH
LP 100	PL 02587(2)	*Elvis In Concert*	2xHH
LP 101	PL 12772	*He Walks Beside Me: Favourite Songs Of Faith And Inspiration*	HH
LP 102	PL 42101	*Elvis - The '56 Sessions Vol. 1*	HH
LP 104	PL 42370	*Elvis*	HH
LP 105	PL 42691(2)	*Elvis's 40 Greatest* (Note: on the pink vinyl pressing only)	2xLD
LP 106	PL 13082	*Elvis - A Legendary Performer Vol. 3*	ZZ
LP 107	CPL1 3078	*Elvis - A Legendary Performer Vol. 3* - Picture disc - no code used as the album was made in America.	
LP 108	NL 42757	*The Elvis Presley Sun Collection*	TT
LP 112	PL 13279	*Our Memories Of Elvis*	ZZ
LP 113	PL 42102	*Elvis - The '56 Sessions Vol. 2*	HH
LP 114	PL 13448	*Our Memories Of Elvis Vol. 2*	HH
LP 117	PL 42371	*Elvis Sings The Wonderful World Of Christmas*	DE
LP 119	NL 43054	*Elvis Presley* (Twinpack)	2xCC
LP 126	CPL8 3699	*Elvis Aron Presley*	7xHH

LP 146	RCALP 5010	*Guitar Man*	HH
LP 150	RCALP 5029	*This Is Elvis*	MD

The following albums had no price code shown:

LP 176	RCALP 3018	*Elvis In Demand*
LP 177	RCALP 3020	*Welcome To My World*
LP 178	RCALP 3021	*Moody Blue*
LP 179	RCALP 3025	*Elvis - The '56 Sessions Vol. 1*
LP 180	RCALP 3030	*Elvis - The '56 Sessions Vol. 2*
LP 183	SDL 004	*Elvis At His Best*
LP 185	RCALP 3060	*The Sound Of Your Cry*
LP 192	RCALP 1000	*Romantic Elvis*
LP 193	RCALP 1001	*Rockin' Elvis - The Sixties*
LP 196	RCALPP 9020	*Jailhouse Rock/Love In Las Vegas*
LP 200	RCALP 3105	*I Was The One*

The RCA International series, introduced in March 1980, used a YY price code for all releases up to *Loving You*, INTS 5109 (*LP 160*), released in August 1981, which had no code. The next two albums, *Roustabout*, INTS 5110 (*LP 161*), and *I'm 10,000 Years Old - Elvis Country*, INTS 5111 (*LP 162*), were coded YY. The rest of the series (the last issue being *It Won't Seem Like Christmas Without You*, INTS 5235 (*LP 195*), released in December 1982, had no codes, with one exception - *20 Greatest Hits Vol. 1*, INTS 5115 (*LP 181*), released in October 1981, which also used the YY code.

The transfer of album production to Germany in 1983 introduced the price code box on the sleeve of the first album pressed in Germany to be released in the UK - *The Elvis Presley Sun Collection*, NL 89107 (*LP 201*), released in October 1983. In addition to the UK price code (YY from the old INTS series), the German and French codes were also shown. The codes were:

D: AG	F: RC 330	UK: YY

Listing all of the German produced albums at this stage would seem unnecessary, and, instead, we have summarised these albums into coding categories, noting any exceptions.

This summary takes us to the point where our previous book, *Elvis UK 1956-86*, stopped and this one starts, allowing us to refer to the price code for each record in chronological sequence, so that changes can be more easily identified.

All albums with the catalogue number prefix NL (RCA's mid-price label) used a price code YY, with the following exceptions (in catalogue number order), where no price code was used:

LP 206	NL 83735	*G.I. Blues*
LP 224	NL 84114	*That's The Way It Is*
LP 225	NL 84232	*Elvis For Everyone*
LP 215	NL 89010	*Paradise, Hawaiian Style*
LP 267	NL 89046	*Elvis Presley* (Early copies had no price code; later copies used FF.)
LP 231	NL 89068(2)	*From Memphis To Vegas From Vegas To Memphis*

NL 81707 (*LP 232*), *Elvis' Golden Records*, was very unusual in that it used the full price album code HH; clearly an error as this was also a mid-priced release.

A further album, *The First Live Recordings*, PG 89387 (*LP 234*), also a mid-priced item, used the YY code.

Full-priced RCA albums - generally those with the catalogue number prefix PL - used the price code HH, but there were exceptions. The following albums had no price code:

LP 259	PL 80504	**The First Year**
LP 260	PL 82428	**Moody Blue**
LP 273	PL 82587(2)	**Elvis In Concert**
LP 237	PL 82642(2)	**Aloha From Hawaii Via Satellite**
LP 261	PL 84941	**Elvis' Gold Records Volume 5**
LP 263	PL 89003	**Rare Elvis**
LP 264	PL 89051	**Rare Elvis Vol. 3**
LP 265	PL 89119	**Rare Elvis Vol. 2**
LP 266	PL 89266	**From Elvis Presley Boulevard, Memphis, Tennessee**
LP 209	PLP 89287	**I Can Help And Other Great Hits**

However, the following PL albums used a variety of price codes:

LP 251	PL 85172(6)	**A Golden Celebration**	OO
LP 262	PL 85182	**The Rocker**	FG
LP 271	PL 85418	**Reconsider Baby**	XX
LP 275	PL 85486	**Elvis' Christmas Album**	SS
LP 207	PL 89287	**I Can Help And Other Great Hits**	FG

Only one RCA album appeared with a catalogue number prefix of BL and that was **This Is Elvis**, BL 84031(2) (*LP 226*), and a price code of MD was allocated to this LP.

There is no doubt that the price coding system was far more complicated for albums that it ever was for singles, and the reason behind this was undoubtedly, that albums came in a variety of guises. Obviously, there was a need to distinguish between full priced double albums and full priced single albums, and to achieve this, RCA used a kind of price code prefix by adding 2x, meaning two times the price of a single album. The first **Elvis In Concert**, PL 02587(2) (*LP 100*), released in November 1977, used the code 2x HH, meaning that it was twice the price of a normal HH album. However, it did not follow that the number of records in the set dictated the number by which the full priced single album was multiplied. Take the case of **Elvis Aron Presley**, CPL8 3699 (*LP 126*), issued in August 1980, as an example. The code used was 7x HH, simply because RCA wished to restrict the price of this eight album set, and so they multiplied by seven, not eight (as it was the album cost around £35, full price).

Some codes were only used once: the pink vinyl copies of **Elvis's 40 Greatest**, PL 42691(2) (*LP 105*), released in October 1978, being a good example. It used the code 2x LD, when, to the best of our knowledge, no other UK Elvis album had used the single code LD. It seems reasonable to assume that the code used related directly to the use of pink vinyl. Similarly, the OO code used for **A Golden Celebration**, PL 85172 (*LP 251*), released in October 1984, is unique by virtue of the fact that no other eight album set has been released to date. Other one-off codes are associated with **This Is Elvis**, which used the code MD on both its original release in April 1981, RCALP 5029 (*LP 150*), and on the re-issue in May 1984, NL 84031(2) (*LP 226*). **Elvis Sings The Wonderful World Of Christmas**, PL 42371 (*LP 117*), the re-issue from November 1979, also featured a unique code, DE.

It wasn't surprising to find some errors in the way price codes were allocated, considering that in almost every aspect of record production there was always the possibility of an error being created. The best example here concerned **Elvis' Golden Records**, NL 81707 (*LP 232*), released in July 1984, which used the HH full priced code when it was never the intention to treat this album any differently to the other mid-priced albums, but no doubt at the time some stores legitimately charged the higher price.

Why some of the albums produced in Germany failed to show a price code remains something of a mystery; certainly, logical explanation for this escapes us. Perhaps the intention was that some of these albums were for sale outside the UK only, and we know of some albums that were available in Europe long before a UK release date was granted. Albums such as **Rare Elvis**, PL 89003 (*LP 263*), were in circulation in Europe for months before being released in the UK in January 1985, when a whole series of albums were released as part of Elvis's 50th anniversary celebrations. Whilst this theory (and we stress this word), may have some foundation, albums such as **That's The Way It Is**, NL 84114 (*LP 224*), and **Elvis For Everyone**, NL 84232 (*LP 225*), were UK releases right from the outset. Whatever the truth was behind the omission of price codes on certain products, the fact that a code was not present does not mean that the album was not on release in the UK, as some people once thought. Conversely, the inclusion of a UK price code on the sleeve of albums which were not officially released in the UK, did not suddenly make them UK releases - a point we discuss further in the section dealing with UK and foreign records.

A final point worth noting is that some re-pressings of earlier albums used a price code appropriate to the code in use at the time of the re-pressing, which was not necessarily the same as the original issue.

Chart Entries

Singles

In order to fully explain our reasoning for showing the highest chart position a single reached in the charts, in addition to the chart entry number (that is, a sequential reference to each occasion a release entered the charts), it is necessary to consider some basic facts surrounding the charts, with particular emphasis placed on the significance of chart entries.

We all know that to enter the charts a record had to sell in sufficient quantities, and the more copies sold, the higher the chart placing. At least that is the theory, although in practice it has not always been that straightforward. One problem is that the charts themselves have been compiled to different standards from different sources by different people. The 'charts' have increased in size over the years, expanding from the top ten when the were first introduced, to a 'standard' of seventy five today. It is quite likely that a record released at a time when, say, the charts accounted for the top forty, may have reached the equivalent of number forty one, without this fact being recorded. By definition, this record failed to chart, yet today we would consider its achievement a moderate success.

So, the actual position achieved by any release is relative to the standards in operation at the time. What about the number of records sold? Surely this allows a direct comparison? Well, not really! Over the period that Elvis's records have been released in the UK, there were several quite noticeable changes in market trends, all of which impacted on record sales. In 1956 relatively few people owned equipment to play a record, for these were expensive items at the time and considered a 'luxury' item, which is what they were. Even by 1960, when Elvis's **It's Now Or Never** (*S 30*) sold over a million copies in six and a half weeks, the spread of the portable record player had not reached its peak, making Elvis's achievement all the more remarkable. Even greater sales feats by other artists which came later, were not necessarily because the songs or artists were more popular, but because more people had the opportunity, and cash, to buy. In the 1980s, sales of all records were in decline, a position influenced by the development of cassette tapes and compact discs. The number sold, therefore, was not necessarily a better guide than anything else. For example, the notional record referred to earlier that reached number forty one may well have reached a far higher position in today's chart, and may have outsold today's hit several times over. The reverse is also true of course: a hit today would generally not reach such a high position if it had been in direct competition with say, the records of the mid sixties.

Therefore, the significance of showing the chart entry number, and highest chart position, is that they provide a guide as to how successful a particular record had been, and any comparison to other records had to take into account several economic and social factors, not to mention industry trends. Thus, the chart entry number is the most revealing, in the sense that it demonstrates how consistent Elvis records actually were over a long period of time. Analysis shows that up to the time of his death, a total of 116 singles, spread over a twenty-one year period, were released in the UK (an average of over five per year!). In itself, a remarkable feat. The fact that our analysis shows that in the same period up to August 1977, Elvis had notched up 121 entries in the singles' chart is even more astonishing. Now, you may ask how is it possible to have more chart entries than actual releases? The answer is not too difficult, considering the fact that almost everything Elvis recorded was bought is such quantities that even some LPs and EPs sold well enough to enter the singles' chart. This was true of the **Jailhouse Rock** (*EP 5*), **Strictly Elvis** (*EP 12*) and **Follow That Dream** (*EP 15*) EPs and the 1960 LP **Elvis Is Back!** (*LP 11*). There would probably have been others had the charts been as sophisticated as they are today.

Another significant reason contributing to the higher chart entry figure is the fact that both sides of a single were often credited with reaching the charts, as though they were independent releases. Singles released in the fifties were regularly treated this way, as record shops recorded which title a customer requested, rather than which single they were buying. This strange practice was later abandoned, but this was the reason that songs like **Blue Moon/I Don't Care If The Sun Don't Shine** (*S 5*) both achieved chart status when they were actually the A and B side of the same record. Statisticians will argue that this may also have had a negative result, in that some Elvis singles did not reach a higher chart position because total sales were spread over two songs. There seems little doubt that had the sales figures been combined, then presumably a higher position would have resulted.

It is clear, then, that Elvis has a unique place in chart history, transcending five decades with remarkable consistency. But what of the records that failed to chart? To some extent, these are even more revealing. They remain, of course, the reason why the chart entry numbers are not as high as they could have been. The following is a complete listing of Elvis singles which failed to chart up to the time of his death.

Release Number	Catalogue Number	Titles	Release Date
S 23	RCA 1088	*All Shook Up* *Heartbreak Hotel*	Nov 1958
S 24	RCA 1095	*Hound Dog* *Blue Suede Shoes*	Nov 1958
S 60	RCA 1628	*There's Always Me* *Judy*	Sep 1967
S 61	RCA 1642	*Big Boss Man* *You Don't Know Me*	Nov 1967
S 66	RCA 1768	*A Little Less Conversation* *Almost In Love*	Nov 1968
S 94	RCA 2601	*Blue Moon* *You're A Heartbreaker* *I'm Left, You're Right, She's Gone*	Sep 1975
S 102	RCA 2696	*I Got Stung* *One Night*	May 1977
S 103	RCA 2697	*(Now and then there's)* *A Fool Such As I* *I Need Your Love Tonight*	May 1977
S 107	RCA 2701	*Surrender* *Lonely Man*	May 1977
S 108	RCA 2702	*(Marie's the name) His* *Latest Flame* *Little Sister*	May 1977
S 109	RCA 2703	*Rock-A-Hula Baby* *Can't Help Falling In Love*	May 1977
S 110	RCA 2704	*Good Luck Charm* *Anything That's Part Of You*	May 1977
S 111	RCA 2705	*She's Not You* *Just Tell Her Jim Said Hello*	May 1977
S 113	RCA 2707	*(You're the) Devil In Disguise* *Please Don't Drag That String Around*	May 1977

This made a total of 14 singles that failed to chart, in a career spanning twenty one years! But take another look! Of the 14 only three contained material not previously available on singles: **There's Always Me/Judy**, RCA 1628; **Big Boss Man/You Don't Know Me**, RCA 1642; and **A Little Less Conversation/Almost In Love**, RCA 1768. The first of these, RCA 1628, comprised old material from 1961 - as featured on the album **Something For Everybody** (*LP 14*) -issued in an attempt to halt the chart decline brought about by the two singles issued immediately prior to this release, RCA 1593, **The Love Machine** (*S 58*) and RCA 1616 **Long Legged Girl (with the short dress on)** (*S 59*). Therefore, only RCA 1642 and RCA 1768 were singles which contained new material and failed to chart.

The remaining singles were largely re-issues, the bulk of which were sold as part of the 'Gold 16' number one hit singles, which could have been purchased in a box as a complete package or individually. It is now generally acknowledged that difficulties in accounting for sixteen singles released at the same time proved so complex that a number of record shops simply didn't bother to record actual sales.

Thus, it is highly likely that had the charts reflected the top seventy five when these records were released, then others, if not all, would have achieved chart status.

Of course, after 1977 things became a little more difficult; after all, Elvis wasn't around to make any new recordings; consequently RCA were forced to rely on previously released material, alternative takes and live recordings. This was bound to be reflected in the chart positions; but, having said that, the singles did continue to achieve chart status. From the time of Elvis's death, and up to July 1985, and the starting point of this book, only eight singles failed to reach the charts, out of a total of 23 singles. This total excludes all format variations, which are counted in chart terms as the same release, even though we count them as being separate releases. Seven of these singles were on the Golden Grooves label, a kind of oldies label. And, as we do not really consider Golden Grooves releases as being chart contenders, equally, we cannot regard them as chart failures, for they were never going to have a major impact. Just like the later Old Gold singles, they had a position in the marketplace, but not at the head of it. The only real failure from this period was one of RCA's biggest mistakes of the time, RCA PB 9334, **Old Shep** (*S 119*). It seemed a clear error of judgement to issue such a track as a single.

After 1985 there were few RCA releases. The vast majority of singles (twenty) were released by Old Gold. Of the RCA singles released between July 1985 to date, all managed to reach the charts, though the highest position achieved was number 21 reached by **The Twelfth Of Never**, RCA 74321 32012 7 (**S 180**) in October 1995. This single was available in both vinyl and CD formats, whereas the CD only single, **Always On My Mind**, 74321 48541 2, reached number 13 in 1997. Generally, releases have achieved top fifty or top sixty status for very short periods. And certainly, if the charts comprised only the top forty, then none of these records would have made it.

LPs

A casual glance at the list below will not reveal the true success achieved by many of the Elvis albums released in the period from 1986. By comparison with any previous period, the list itself is relatively small although, of course, the number of 'new' album releases was limited. Besides, chart sucesss is only one factor to take into account when assessing the overall worth of any product, and often their reliability can be questioned. It is widely known, for example, that the Official Elvis Presley Fan Club successfully retailed a considerable quantity of Elvis albums, yet these did not contribute to any chart statistics, and nor did any sales made by retailers outside the chart shops - those who contributed sales' returns to the chart compilers.

Doubtless, the same arguments here could be applied equally to other artists, and we should stress that we are not commenting on the merits or otherwise of the existing system. The point is that before jumping to any conclusions, a number of factors need to be carefully considered. Perhaps the real success of any product is not the position reached in the charts, but of actual numbers sold; yet, this too, did not always allow fair comparison. The numbers pressed, their availability, length of time they were available, competition from other artists and other product by the same artist, price, promotion, and so on, needed to be taken into account. Suffice it to say that success can be measured in many different ways, and being 'popular' - as in chart achievement - is only one method of doing so.

Few fans will be surprised to learn that the most successful album chartwise, both in terms of position achieved and number of weeks spent in the charts, was **Presley - The All Time Greatest Hits** (**LP 287**). The quality, value for money, and the fact that it was advertised on TV, all contributed to its success, but above all of these was its broad appeal to a wider audience. On the other hand, to see albums aimed primarily at the collectors' market reaching the charts was no less of an achievement, irrespective of the number of weeks spent in the charts.

The UK chart positions for Elvis vinyl albums released since the beginning of 1986 is as follows:

LP 287   PL 90100(2)   *Presley - The All Time Greatest Hits*
                          Number 4   22 weeks on chart
LP 298   PL 90250   *Stereo '57 (Essential Elvis Vol. 2)*
                          Number 60   2 weeks on chart
LP 306   PL 90486   *Hits Like Never Before (Essential Elvis Vol. 3)*
                          Number 71   1 week on chart
LP 308   PL 82227   *The Great Performances*
                          Number 62   1 week on chart
LP 315   PL 90574(3)   *Collectors Gold*
                          Number 57   1 week on chart
LP 317   PL 90642   *From The Heart*
                          Number 4   18 weeks on chart
LP 320   74321 22871 1 *The Essential Collection*
                          Number 6   25 weeks on chart
LP 321   07863 66817 1 *Elvis 56*
                          Number 42   3 weeks on chart

Pricing

Pricing has always been another thorny issue when buying records, compact discs or cassettes. Since the abolition of price controls, prices can, and do, vary enormously from dealer to dealer, in spite of what was referred to as RRP (Recommended Retail Price). What further complicated the situation were things such as the incentives offered to dealers to stock certain products in particular quantities (thus earning extra discounts which, in turn, were sometimes passed on to the customer) and the ever-present rivalry among dealers themselves: HMV, Virgin, Our Price and so on. One shop we know of stocked 20 copies of **Collectors Gold** set, PL 90574(3) (**LP 315**), bought it in for £14 per set and sold each of them for £19.99, thus undercutting the likes of HMV by £5 per set. So, it is worth noting that it is not always the big stores which are the cheapest; sometimes smaller independent shops can offer far better deals. This is an ironic twist when you consider events of the early seventies, when major chain shops encroached on the record market in a big way, discounting items which drove many small record dealers out of business and, for the non-chart material buyer, signalled a significant contraction in the number of retailers who were prepared to stock a good range of back catalogue material. The problem for those wanting non-chart

material was to find stockists of the product they were interested in. This was true of new Elvis fans who wanted to buy back catalogue items from the seventies onward.

In recent years, the major retailers have tended to discount certain chart material up to a certain point, but to sell other, less popular items at the full RRP. It's not that major retailers are not offered discounts or incentives from the record companies - they are, and their market position dictates that they receive the best possible deal - the simple truth of the matter is that they often choose not to pass on these benefits to the customer.

From time to time though, some well-managed and aggressive small shops challenged the major outlets and could offer all formats at appreciably lower levels. We know of many shops throughout the country that sold CDs significantly less than major retailers. And, this situation was no different for vinyl singles and albums. Quite frequently, 7 inch vinyl singles could be bought for £0.99, 12 inch singles and CD singles for £1.99, though in general a dealer was looking for a 30% mark up (profit margin on product sold). We should mention that to sell product at these kind of prices, the dealers were offered additional incentives, often in the form of additional copies supplied free of charge, as the cost of an individual copy to the dealer was higher than the prices they were selling them for. To illustrate this, the August 1991 release of **Are You Lonesome Tonight?** Live in Las Vegas (**S 177**), had a dealer price of £1.20 for the 7 inch single and £2.29 for the CD single. However, these could be bought for £0.99 and £1.99 respectively, although the major stores sold the latter at well over £4.

It was reported that the record companies in the UK lost £7.5 million in 1991 on 7 inch singles alone, and much of this was due to keeping the cost of the record to the buyer artificially low. The cost of a 7 inch single to the manufacturer (i.e. the cost of making each record) was £2.19 and yet these were normally sold at £1.99, giving a loss per single of £0.20. To sell records at £0.99 incurred an even greater loss. The thinking behind what appeared to be a sure and very certain road to ruin, was what is known as 'hype' - pushing a record with the intention of making it more attractive to potential buyers because of its low cost, resulting in more records being sold. If more singles were sold, then there was a greater chance of chart success, increasing the probability of more people buying the single at full price. But the real benefit to the record companies was that this 'loss leader' approach would encourage more album sales where the real profit lay. The profit margin to the record industry in 1990 was a massive £273 million for CD sales alone, making the loss on singles look insignificant by comparison.

Nevertheless, when you look at the dealer price for the product around that point in time - full priced compact discs cost them just over £7 and LPs about £4 (provided no special deal was struck between the company and the dealer) - then there was still room for manoeuvre, and the message for the buyer was, and still is, clear and simple: shop around.

Of course, all of the changes in the industry have had implications for the pricing of product. Compact discs had started life in 1983 retailing for around the £12-£13 mark. By 1991, this was still more or less the case, though some pressure groups and consumer agencies maintained that the record companies were exploiting the buyers by keeping the cost of CDs artificially and unnecessarily high. It was claimed high volume production ought to have lowered production costs significantly - which should have been reflected in the cost to the consumer. Needless to say record companies vehemently denied these assertions. However, although production costs can and do vary - influenced by several factors, not least of which is the number of units pressed - there was still a considerable gap between production and retail price.

A relevant factor here was the cost of producing vinyl itself. It is a well-known part of economic theory that the more items which are mass-produced, then so production costs ought to be lowered accordingly. And, while record companies were not overly eager to subscribe to that theory where the cost of CDs were concerned (that high volume does not necessarily mean lower costs), they were rather quicker to point out that the fewer pressing plants there were with the capacity to press vinyl that this would, inevitably, have an impact on the costs of producing vinyl in smaller volumes. In short, those who preferred vinyl were going to have to pay a higher price for the privilege of doing so! In fact, over the period of time between the early eighties and early nineties, it was customary for companies to sell vinyl albums and cassettes at the same price to dealers. By 1992 though, this changed and EMI, for example, charged 15p more on the wholesale price of vinyl albums, compared to the cassette equivalent.

Release Dates

The question of release dates deserves some explanation, we believe. In *Elvis UK 1956-86*, we went to considerable lengths and were able, in the main, to give fairly accurate dates for most releases. Similarly, all the dates we use in this book are, to the best of our knowledge, accurate. However, unlike the hey-day of the sixties when product was announced and then, normally, issued throughout the country on a given day, in recent years dates have varied considerably depending on which area you happened to live in. Truthfully, it is hardly worth trying to explain why this happens when, if anything, distribution ought to be better now than before. Suffice it to say that it probably has much to do with the fact that Elvis product, while still awaited anxiously by the fans, generally has a restricted appeal to the wider buying public. As a result, there is less pressure on the company to ensure a simultaneous release throughout the country. Add to this the ever declining number of retailers who order or stock Presley product, and what you get is an unsatisfactory and very confusing situation regarding releases.

Another topic, closely related to the above, concerns the date(s) given by the company as to when product will be issued. There was a period after Elvis died when it was rare to have precise release dates published in advance of product, either for retailers or the fans. In fact, apart from a few notable exceptions, such as the boxed set releases, release dates were virtually non-existent. Instead the product was prepared, stored, and then released often when there was a gap in the schedule. It has to be recognised that there was a period of time when Elvis product was not a high priority on the part of RCA/BMG, so it was not uncommon for items to be deferred in favour of bigger selling releases. Consequently, any dates given were, at best, provisional. Examples here include the time when HMV's megastore in London's Oxford Street were told, or so they claimed, of the proposed release date in May 1991 of **Collectors Gold**, PL 90574(3) (**LP 315**), that it had been delayed until August because of problems with the artwork.

This, alas, was not an isolated example: there were many similar cases over the years where dates were given, but then releases did not appear until much later. In some specific instances (see the individual releases for details) this went on, quite literally, for months, resulting in inaccurate dates being quoted and, perhaps more importantly, a lot of frustration and ill-feeling among fans, especially when they may have ordered product advertised through the fan club or **Elvis Monthly**, and had to wait an inordinate amount of time for it. It has to be said, in fairness, that this was not the fault of the fan club either. They often advertised forth-coming releases in good faith, acting either on the advice of someone at BMG or anticipating a much-heralded release. Equally though, despite much criticism by fans, what was not understood was that, in the main, delays occurred which, for various reasons, affected certain releases. And, according to Roger Semon, formerly of BMG UK, delays occurred for one or more of the following reasons:

- Sometimes there were delays in completing part of the audio process. In other words, if there were any sound deficiencies, then they would have to be rectified prior to release.

- Alternatively, there may have been a problem with some aspect of the artwork, again requiring rectification.

- Occasionally the company may have had a rush release on a major selling artist. Therefore, in terms of priority, Elvis items were relegated to a later date.

- And, whatever caused the delay, re-scheduling a release date was not as simple as someone saying 'Release it next week instead'. Pressing schedules were normally done on a monthly basis; hence there could be - and often were - significant delays.

Roger Semon also made the point that part of the problem arose because of the relative openness of the company. In other words, a release would be 'announced', either officially or through the Elvis 'grapevine', and tentative dates discussed (albeit in good faith) - only to be passed on a number of occasions. And, whatever anyone thought of BMG corporately or as individuals, it has to be admitted that, galling though delays were/are, it was not in anyone's interest - least of all the company's - to wilfully delay a release for anything other than a good reason. To believe otherwise simply does not make sense. Incompetent the company may have been, but maliciously stupid, they were not.

Moving on to the question of imported records, it was virtually impossible to determine whether an album was intended for UK consumption; buyers had to rely on a retailer charging a higher price or the presence of an import sticker to confirm the fact. This situation occurred because RCA produced little of their product in the UK from 1983, but brought in albums from their German production plant. Consequently, albums just appeared and, even then, may have been import-only material, not UK issues.

It was not uncommon for an avid fan to go into a shop, ask for a new release, only to find that the record/CD in question had been sold - often because the dealer had only one or two copies in the first place. Thus, a casual buyer of Elvis product had little chance, as he/she may not have been aware about any new releases, as so few shops stocked them. Often there was misinformation too: for example, when we were told in one store that three albums had been released on CD only, when in fact one had a vinyl equivalent and could be purchased in the record shop down the road. So, against this background of confusion it was, perhaps, not surprising that many fans ordered direct from the likes of the fan club itself. This may have had other implications of course - such as dealers not stocking product because they thought there was no demand, not to mention the possible impact on chart placing, and so on.

Several smaller companies have produced Elvis product since 1977, and this material is often very hard to place in date order, indeed some of these companies appeared to have haphazard distribution systems and did not seem interested enough to keep accurate details of what product they had been responsible for. It is, perhaps, not surprising to note that many of them ceased to trade, thus adding further difficulties for those wishing to corroborate pieces of information.

The conclusion of all this is simple: while we have tried very hard to establish as clearly as possible when a release did in fact appear in the shops, it has to be said that, on occasions, there are some doubts. Where there is (and this applies in particular to compilation releases and the output of independent companies), then this is indicated in the text.

Deletions

The term deletion was usually a description used when a record was no longer available - in the sense that it could no longer be obtained by a record shop where a specific request was made. A record, was, therefore deleted when it was removed from the list of available product by the record company, and the reason it was removed was because the record company had run out of stocks and had made a decision not to produce any further copies. If stocks had been depleted, but the intention was to press additional copies, then the record would be described as being 'out of stock'. Normally, there was no warning given that a deletion would take place, as the obvious, and understandable, intention of a record company was to sell all remaining stocks. Consequently, record companies did not state that a certain record, or even a batch of records, would be deleted on a given date. The record would, therefore, remain available until the last copy was sold; and as shops made greater use of computer technology, with direct links into record companies' ordering, supply and distribution centres, stock control was simple. Even manual ordering systems were largely conducted over the telephone, enabling shops to have the exact status almost immediately.

When a record was deleted is, therefore, not an exact science, but was instead based on two factors, both related. Firstly, analysis of sales figures over a given period would eventually force a record company to make a decision as to whether a record should be re-pressed - in effect keeping the product on catalogue - or whether sales' levels indicated that the record in question had not been in demand and, therefore, did not warrant the expense of a re-press. This process was a relatively simple one, and it was quite normal for a record company to set a sales target figure which - should a record fail to achieve this total over the period previously agreed - would mean that further pressings would not be made. RCA's policy on this was that when a record sold less than 500 copies in a year, no further copies would be produced. Once that decision had been made, then the record was on an inevitable course to eventual deletion, which may not have been a long drawn-out affair if copies were sold off to wholesalers. The problem was that many people considered that this decision-making process coincided with the date of deletion, when the truth of the matter was that the actual date of deletion occurred, not when the decision was made, but when stocks reached zero level. The effect of all this was that dates quoted when a record was deleted were often unreliable. Further, such dates were not generally widely publicised either.

The second factor to have a bearing on this concerned people's perception of a deleted record. For example, the term deleted seems inappropriate for a record which was officially deleted by the record company, but which could still be purchased in retail outlets which had bought in stock copies. We know from personal experience that records could remain available for months, even years, after reaching the 'official' deleted state. Obviously, it would be unrealistic to consider that a record was not deleted until every last copy was sold, but this point certainly confused many people when they compared availability in one record shop to what they were told in other stores.

Whilst in many ways the fact that a record was deleted was a sad affair (and not just for vinyl format records either, as many compact discs have come and gone), we know that it is often interesting to know how long a record was available. Consequently, although we mention deletion dates throughout the book, we are unable to do so for every release, especially where we have reservations regarding the date, or where we have not been able to corroborate information provided. At best, the dates we have quoted are reasonably reliable, but far less so than release dates, for the reasons we have described.

In 1986, Gregg Geller of RCA America (effectively the man in charge of Elvis product at that time and the man responsible for albums such as *A Golden Celebration*, PL 85172(6) (*LP 251*), *The Rocker*, PL 85182 (*LP 262*), and *Always On My Mind*, PL 85430 (*LP 272*)), was supposedly considering deleting all of the Elvis catalogue for five years with no new issues whatsoever. Geller's reported intention for this was to allow RCA time to sort out the many absurdities in the catalogue, and plan a programme of co-ordinated, chronological releases, including the transfer of material to compact disc. In support of this, it was claimed, there would be a resurgence in demand following the five year 'famine'. At the time fans were horrified at this prospect, but looking more carefully at the proposals suggests that the idea might have had its merits. Certainly, the continued CD release policy that followed would have benefited from a clear strategy at the outset, and five or six years after Geller's idea, this was just starting to take shape.

As regards Elvis product in the UK, there had been a steady decline in the number of albums on catalogue from the peak reached in the eight years following Elvis's death, when the number of re-issues and new compilations reached previously unimaginable levels. The policy was, understandably, to issue and keep on catalogue as much product as possible, in an attempt to satisfy the seemingly endless public demand for both 'new' and back catalogue material, to the point where albums, previously considered 'spent', were re-instated. Clearly, the interest and overwhelming desire to obtain this material could not last forever and, gradually - initially at least - certain product failed to sustain sales and, when allied to the move towards central European production and, later, the availability of compact discs, wholesale deletions began to take place. Not surprisingly, among the first to go were the film soundtrack albums from the sixties, which had long been considered the weak link in the chain, having less appeal to a broader audience.

In fact, many of the film soundtrack albums had been close to deletion in the UK prior to their subsequent re-issue during 1984, following RCA's move to European, instead of local, production. As it turned out, many were only available for two years or so before being deleted. Consequently, these albums and the songs they contained were, in the main, unobtainable from 1986, although because of the anomalies created by central production, it remained possible to buy some of the albums as imported records in certain outlets for some time afterwards. Among these were albums such as *Roustabout*, *Fun In Acapulco*, *Harem Holiday*, and so on. Some film soundtrack albums survived, of course, but these were few in number and had always featured in the best selling album stakes. Examples here included *G.I. Blues*, *Blue Hawaii* and *King Creole*.

Even 'new' albums were not immune from deletion, nor were original, non-soundtrack LPs, such as *I'm 10,000 Years Old - Elvis Country*, which also lasted less than two years, following its release on the German black label in August 1984. By 1989, BMG had become much more conscious of sales performance figures, and a tremendous amount of material was deleted, including *Elvis' Gold Records Volume 5* the three *Rare Elvis* volumes, *Elvis Presley Sings Leiber & Stoller* and so on. Many of these were quality albums, but this was of little consequence if the product did not sell.

By 1994, a revised stock control policy meant that, as stocks dwindled, or simply ran out, then product was deleted. Singles, however, were a little easier to deal with as regards policy, in that once a single had had its run - whether it charted or not - it was deleted immediately, often within three months of issue. A direct result of this policy, and the limited output from 1985 onwards, effectively meant that no RCA Elvis singles were available for long periods.

Re-Issues

In *Elvis UK 1956-86* we discussed what actually constituted a re-issue or, to use another term, re-release. We argued that a re-issue was a record that had been given a new catalogue number and treated as a new product, but which contained identical tracks to an original release. The key thing being the catalogue number, for without a new catalogue number being allocated, then the record remained simply a variation of the original release.

Where a record was released with additional or fewer tracks, or where tracks had been substituted (even in the case of only one track), then this could not be considered a re-issue. Nor, for that matter, would any re-packaging in the form of a new sleeve or label design.

Having said that, we have to confess that, strictly speaking, we broke our own rule in *Elvis UK 1956-86* when we included details of the RCA single *Jailhouse Rock*, RCA 1028 (*S 136*), released in January 1983, which used the same B side, *Treat Me Nice*, as the 1958 original single release (*S 18*). It would have been remiss of us to consider this important release as anything other that a new issue. To classify the release as a variation of the original would have been foolish. After all, the original single had been deleted since the early seventies, effectively replaced by the maxi single RCA 2153 (*S 80*). Our insistence that this was a re-issue was really based on the circumstances surrounding its re-appearance, given that RCA's intention was to market a new product in celebration of the twenty fifth anniversary of the original release. Obviously using a copy of the original label, and RCA's desire to give the record a 'period' feel to it by producing a copy of the original sleeve, was all about nostalgia and the recognition of the original record's achievement: being the first record to enter the charts in the number one position. And so too was the use of the original catalogue number.

In this current book we are faced with a similar example which deviates from our 'old catalogue number therefore not a re-issue' rule. The release in question does not have the same pedigree as the *Jailhouse Rock* single and made no major impact on the charts, or for that matter fans and collectors. However, after much consideration, we finally decided to show *The Elvis Tapes*, RED 1 (**LP 281**), first released in April 1977 (*LP 91*) and then re-released in April 1987 as a new product (though it still had the old catalogue number). Our reasoning this time was influenced by the fact that the record did not achieve the status it perhaps deserved, as many fans simply did not bother to buy the original when it first appeared. Another factor was that Bob Jones re-mastered the record the second time around, and we wished to include this information also.

We have devised a cross-referencing system which indicates when a record has been classed as a re-issue, and, if appropriate, any previous re-issues of the same record are also noted. Under each release, we have indicated where the original release can be found, any subsequent re-issues, along with release dates for all appearances.

For example:

> ***Girls! Girls! Girls!*** Camden CDS 1221 (**LP 278**)
>
> Original Issue February 1963. RCA RD/SF 7534 (*LP 18*)
> Previous Re-issue October 1977. RCA PL 42354 (*LP 94*)
> Previous Re-issue August 1981. RCA INTS 5107 (*LP 158*)
> Previous Re-issue June 1984. RCA NL 89048 (*LP 229*)

It can be seen here that this version on the Camden label was the fifth time that the album had been issued. The first was the 1963 original, followed by three re-issues. The number in brackets refers to the chronological release order, which will enable you to find details more quickly. Clearly, some of the cross referencing refers to records included in *Elvis UK 1956-86*, and not in this volume. We refer to them simply to present a clearer and more complete analysis of the number of occasions a record has been re-issued.

As a point of interest, where some track alterations took place - in that additional or fewer tracks were included - details of these are always included under the release date of the record in question.

Licensing Deals

In many ways the wheel regarding licensing of Elvis product has just about come full circle, and it seems timely to recap the situation from March 1956 when Elvis records were first made available in the UK.

The original company responsible for issuing RCA's catalogue in the UK was EMI. They released Presley product on the HMV label between March 1956 up until September 1958, when the arrangement ended. In that time they issued 13 singles, plus one additional single which, although obtainable in the UK, was intended for export only (***Mystery Train/I Forgot To Remember To Forget***, 7MC 42 (*S 8*). They also released 2 EPs and 3 albums (two 12 inch albums and one 10 inch: ***Rock 'N' Roll, Rock 'N' Roll (No. 2)*** and ***The Best Of Elvis*** - *LPs 1, 2* and *4*).

From July 1957 though, the Decca Record company assumed the main responsibility of issuing RCA's catalogue in the UK. And, for a while, this led to the absurd situation whereby two major record companies were issuing Presley product without any reference to one another in respect of what was released and when. This meant that, on occasions, there were a number of releases launched on to the market simultaneously. It seemed a recipe for disaster. However, Decca held the rights to issue new material, whereas HMV had to rely entirely on back catalogue recordings, all of which had been made prior to the deal with Decca. The sole rights to handle Presley product in the UK were held by Decca from September 1958 up until 1968 (although Decca pressed records for RCA using their orange label design for a good while after this point).

With the opening of RCA's own pressing plant in Washington, Tyne and Wear, in 1969, it was obvious that Decca's place in handling Presley product was coming to an end. However, it was not as simple as it seemed. The last single to bear the old RCA Victor black label design, ***A Little Less Conversation***, RCA 1768 (*S 66*), was pressed by Decca, but so too was ***If I Can Dream***, RCA 1795 (*S 67*), despite the appearance of RCA's new orange label. In fact, evidence of Decca's hand in producing records for RCA - albeit using RCA's orange labels - persisted until 1971. It was not until 1975 that the Washington plant would, as a matter of course, press all RCA 7 inch releases, although from time to time (as is still the case today) other companies would press material when the main company in question neither had time nor the capacity to do so itself.

On the other hand, the situation regarding EPs was slightly different, in that EMI had issued two: ***Love Me Tender*** and ***Good Rockin' Tonight*** (*EP 1* and *EP 3*), both highly sought after now, and Decca, using various RCA/RCA Victor logos, released twenty between 1957 and 1967. In fact, no new EP releases were made on the orange label format, although a number of back catalogue items were repressed up until 1971. EPs were no longer fashionable in the late sixties and early seventies. They did, however, experience a resurgence of public interest in the early 1980s with the release of two EP Collections (in February and October 1982 respectively). More recently though Castle Music issued ***The International EP Collection*** (**EP 45**) and, additionally, the five Collectors Edition soundtrack albums (**LPs 337, 338, 342, 343** and **344**) also included an EP as a bonus.

As of April 1969, with the release of ***Elvis***, (the NBC TV Special), RD 8011 (*LP 36*), RCA albums appeared using the orange label, even though Decca continued to press certain back catalogue albums for a couple of years. Please note, that not all original black label RCA albums appeared on the orange label.

Of course, all of this was happening under the control of RCA, who were using EMI and Decca as contractors for production of their product, and were doing so simply because RCA had no manufacturing or distribution arrangements of their own in the UK. The licencing arrangement was, therefore, not one of leasing Presley material from RCA, even though the EMI arrangement meant that releases appeared on EMI's HMV label, but deals struck to provide the mechanism to release Presley material, and that of others artists, without the need for a manufacturing base.

Meanwhile, a new phenomenon was occurring in the industry: artists were recording for labels other than their own - either anonymously or with their company's permission - and companies were issuing compilation releases featuring various artists from their stable. Even more significant was the advent of inter-company co-operation, to the extent of allowing other companies' artists to appear on a different company's compilation album. For a long time - and contrary to popular trends - RCA stood their ground and refused to lease any Presley tracks to other companies. This, however, ended in quite a block-busting way in 1974, with the release on Arcade of ***Elvis's 40 Greatest*** (*LP 73*), a double album which benefited from TV promotion (Elvis's first in the UK) and promptly outsold every other Presley album a couple of years either side of it. A strange irony.

Since then, of course, a host of other companies have leased Presley material, which obviously contributed to a flood of Presley product on the market, though in the main it was all previously issued material. Indeed, this development prompted us to produce a section of the book entirely devoted to various artists' records featuring Elvis material produced from 1977 onwards. However, as a lead up to this, we thought it would be useful to identify earlier releases which have appeared as a result of a licencing deal between RCA and the various companies responsible for the product. It is worth noting that not all of the releases which contained Presley material have been subject to these kinds of arrangements, and we are thinking here of all the releases which contained interview material only, which apparently does not require the permission or co-operation of RCA, as no copyright exists on this kind of material.

The relationship between RCA and Pickwick was different to that of other companies in that, initially, RCA put their own logo on the sleeves of any product that was issued, although this was later dropped. Remember the name Camden was an RCA label name, and right up to August 1981, all Camden releases had 'Manufactured by RCA and distributed by Pickwick' printed on the sleeve. Later albums simply showed that they were licensed from RCA. For the sake of completeness, we have listed all the Camden albums. Reference to the list will show that the first three releases pre-date the Arcade release discussed above, although, as regards the first true licence arrangement release, that honour belongs to Arcade. Having said that, perhaps the first occasion when licensing took place was as far back as March 1957, when the **Weekend Mail** magazine offered **The Truth About Me**, a talking only release! Incidentally, we have not listed the two mail order-only Camden albums available at the end of 1975, as these comprised existing albums re-packaged to form two, 3 record sets. If you require further details of these, please refer to *LPs 85* and *86*.

Below is a list of all the companies (in alphabetical order) which have officially released Elvis material in conjunction with RCA up to 1985. Titles marked with an asterisk (*) are various artist releases. Similar releases beyond this date are extensively discussed in the album and Various Artist Compilation Albums Sections of this book.

Arcade

ADE P12	LP 73	Elvis's 40 Greatest	Oct 1974

Cambra

CR 061	LP 194	Images	Nov 1982

Everest

CBR 1014	LP 191	Elvis In Hollywood	Jul 1982
EPC 1000	LP 205	Blue Rhythms	Dec 1983

Harrods

PL 42146	VA LP 2	A Century Of Sound*	?May 1977

Imperial

DR 1124	LP 151	American Trilogy	May 1981

K-tel

NE 1062	LP 116	Love Songs	Oct 1979
NE 1101	LP 139	Inspirations	Nov 1980
NE 1141	LP 182	The Ultimate Performance	Oct 1981
NE 1170	LP 190	Rock 'N Roll Rebel	May 1982

Lever Brothers

LB 1	Other	The Wonder Of You	1981

Marks & Spencer

IMP 113	LP 137	Elvis Presley	Oct 1980
IMPD 204	LP 138	The Wonderful World Of Elvis Presley	Oct 1980

News Of The World/Sunday Magazine

SUNDAY 1	LP 258	The Golden Album	Jan 1985

Orbis (The History Of Rock)

HRL 001	LP 184	The History Of Rock Volume One	Nov 1981

Pickwick

CDM 1008	LP 48	You'll Never Walk Alone	Mar 1971
CDS 1110	LP 64	Elvis Sings Hits From His Movies	Oct 1972
CDS 1118	LP 67	Separate Ways	May 1973
CDS 1146	LP 76	Easy Come Easy Go	Feb 1975
CDS 1150	LP 78	The U.S. Male	Jun 1975
CDS 1155	LP 81	Elvis' Christmas Album	Oct 1975
CDS 1154	LP 84	I Got Lucky	Nov 1975
PDA 009	LP 89	The Elvis Presley Collection	Aug 1976
PDA 042	LP 103	The Elvis Presley Collection Vol. 2	Jun 1978
CDS 1175	LP 109	Please Don't Stop Loving Me	Apr 1979
CDS 1185	LP 110	Flaming Star	Apr 1979
PDA 054	LP 111	The Elvis Presley Collection Vol. 3	Apr 1979
CDS 1182	LP 120	Double Dynamite Vol. 1	Jan 1980
CDS 1188	LP 121	Double Dynamite Vol. 2	Jan 1980
PDA 057	LP 122	Double Dynamite	Jan 1980
CDS 1190	LP 123	The King...Elvis	Jan 1980
CDS 1200	LP 141	Return To Sender	Jan 1981
CDS 1201	LP 142	Elvis Presley	Feb 1981
PDA 073	LP 143	The Wonderful World Of Elvis	Feb 1981
CDS 1203	LP 163	It's Now Or Never	Aug 1981
CDS 1204	LP 164	Heartbreak Hotel	Aug 1981
CDS 1206	LP 188	Suspicious Minds	Apr 1982
CDS 1207	LP 189	Are You Lonesome Tonight?	Apr 1982
CDS 1210	LP 197	Can't Help Falling In Love & Other Great Movie Hits	May 1983
CDS 1211	LP 199	Love Songs	Aug 1983
CDS 1212	LP 202	The Legend	Oct 1983
CDS 1213	LP 246	The First Ten Years	Sep 1984

Premier

CBR 1014	LP 268	Elvis In Hollywood	Jan 1985
PPD 2001	LP 269	Blue Rhythms	Jan 1985

Reader's Digest

GELV-6A	LP 82	Elvis Presley's Greatest Hits	Oct 1975

Telstar

STAR 2264	LP 274	Ballads	Oct 1985

World Records

SW 9869	VA LP 3	The Great Transatlantic Hits*	? 1978

A total of fifteen companies were, therefore, in one kind of licensing deal or another with RCA, or perhaps it would be more accurate to say that Elvis songs appeared on thirteen different labels in addition to RCA, for two of the companies listed above, Everest and Premiere, were actually one and the same company run by the same people. Indeed, each label issued the same material with the same titles. Imperial and K tel were also run by a single company. But what of the companies issuing Presley product, whether singing or otherwise, without approval or involvement of RCA? We haven't listed any of the many flexi-discs produced for the **Elvis Monthly Collectors Special**.

It would, perhaps, be appropriate to call these companies opportunists and leave it at that; after all most were legitimate organisations and released this material without breaking the law.

On the other hand, some of the releases did seem a little dubious at the time, and undoubtedly met with little approval from RCA. However, our brief here is not to argue the merits or otherwise of such releases, simply to list them. The content of these records is mainly interview material, although some contained recordings made before Elvis joined RCA and, in the case of **The Million Dollar Quartet**, a 'jam' session from December 1956.

Ace
NS 71	Others	*Deke Rivers*	?	1977

Archive
ARCH 001	Others	*The Elvis Interviews Vol. 1*	Mar 1985
ARCH 002	Others	*The Elvis Interviews Vol. 2*	Mar 1985
ARCH 003	Others	*The Elvis Interviews Vol. 3*	Mar 1985

Audiofidelity
AFESD1032	*LP 186*	*Personally Elvis*	Mar 1982
PD 1032	*LP 208*	*A Historical Documentary*	Mar 1984

Buttons
BUT 2	*LP 145*	*Elvis Answers Back*	Feb 1981

Charly
SUN 100	*LP 99*	*The Sun Years*	Oct 1977
SUN 1006	*LP 152*	*The Million Dollar Quartet*	Jul 1981
SUN 1007	*LP 198*	*The First Year*	May 1983

Golden First Editions
KING 1	*LP 118*	*The First Year*	Nov 1979

Hammer
HMR 9005	*LP 115*	*The King Speaks*	Oct 1979
HMS 6002	*LP 147*	*The King Speaks*	Mar 1981

Magnum Force
MFLP 015	Others	*The King Is Dead*	Sep 1977

Redwood
RED 1	*LP 91*	*The Elvis Tapes*	Apr 1977

Tiger
EPL 269	Others	*Elvis Presley Remembers Vol. 1*	? 1983
EPL 270	Others	*Elvis Presley Remembers Vol. 2*	?
EPL 271	Others	*Elvis Presley Remembers Vol. 3*	?

Topline
TOP 106	*LP 254*	*In The Beginning*	Nov 1984

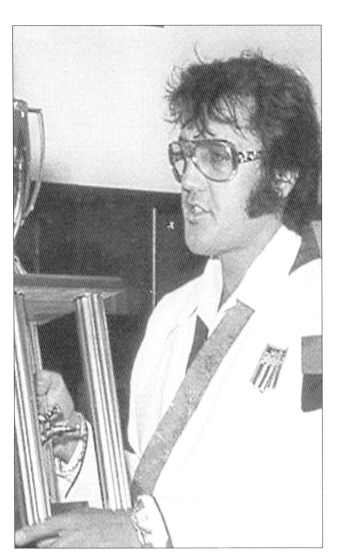

Part 3 : Label Features

The label illustrated below of ***Always On My Mind***, PL 85430 (*LP 272*), released in July 1985, was typical of the layout and design of the German black label album releases of the period. We have reproduced the label here for two reasons: firstly, as an introduction to our discussions on label features and the information they contain; and, secondly, to provide a starting point for noting any changes in design and layout. Later, in the album section itself, we have printed a photograph of the final RCA album to be included in ***Elvis UK 1956-86***, ***Elvis' Christmas Album***, PL 85486 (*LP 275*), for comparison purposes.

On the label below we have indicated what each piece of information means although, admittedly, many of these are self-explanatory. Then, on the pages that follow, we have expanded on certain pieces of information to further aid your understanding, and to provide some relevant background to the topics concerned. Some of the design features, in particular the logo and printed format of the Mechanical Rights' Societies, are important elements in determining label variations, and are referred to in more detail in the section dealing with these subjects.

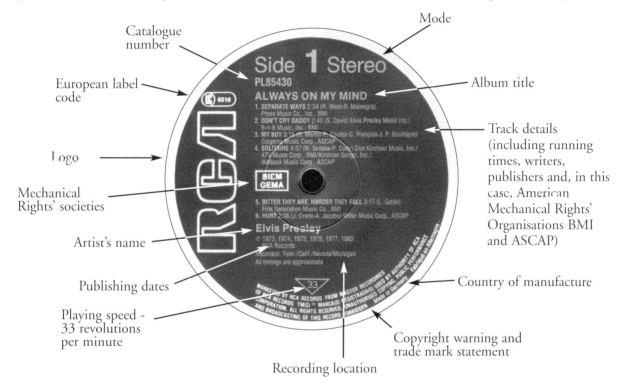

Stereo	This is the recording mode of the songs featured on the record.
PL 85430	The catalogue number. Minor printing variations appeared on different records. Often the prefix was separated from the number itself, so that, using this record as an example, it would read PL 85430. On other records, a space appears in the middle of the number, reading 85 430. Whatever format has been used, we always show catalogue numbers as follows - PL 85430.
ALWAYS ON MY MIND	The album title.
LC 0316	This refers to RCA/BMG's Label Code In Europe, which was basically a registration number for the company. Label codes were allocated by a central source in Hamburg, Germany, to companies with European distribution/production systems. Other companies obviously have different codes - Reprise Records use LC 0322, Epic LC 0199, for example.
RCA	The record label name.
Separate Ways etc.	The track listing. These include the running time of each song (with a note at the bottom of the label informing us that these are approximate); the song's writers; the publishers and, finally, the American Mechanical Copyright Protection Organisations - BMI (Broadcast Music Incorporated) and ASCAP (American Society of Composers Authors and Publishers).
BIEM GEMA	These are the European Mechanical Rights' organisations. See the section dealing with publishers, Copyright Protection and Mechanical Rights, for their full names and further details.
Elvis Presley	The artist.
P 1973, 1974, 1975 RCA Records	These are the dates the songs were first published. Unfortunately the dates shown do not relate directly to the sequence of songs shown on the label.
Recorded: Tenn./Calif/Nevada/Michigan	These are the American States where the songs were recorded. As with the publishing dates, they do not directly relate to where any individual song was actually recorded.
33	The playing speed of the record - 33 1/3 revolutions per minute (RPM).
Marketed by RCA Records etc.	This was a basic copyright and trade mark statement by RCA. Also included was a reference to where the record was made.

Interestingly, some of the items referred to above were mentioned early in 1981, when an organisation entitled The International Association Of Sound Archives, produced a document which recommended that record packaging should display what they considered to be important information regarding the recording. Admittedly, they were primarily concerned with classical recordings, or so it seems, but some of their recommendations seemed to have filtered into the mainstream. Among other things, they recommended the following be included:

- The date of recording(s)

- The duration of songs

- The location where the recording took place, and an indication of whether it was a live recording

- The names of the producer, engineer and editor.

Some of their recommendations were adopted, but information relating to where the recordings were made, for example, was rarely seen on labels. Much of the information, however, did form the basis for general recording data made available to collectors on later releases, often in accompanying booklets and/or liner notes.

Catalogue Numbers

Over the years there have been several different catalogue numbers used by RCA/BMG, some of which have been very simple, some much more complicated. There seems little point in describing all of them in any detail here, particularly as many of the earlier systems were covered in detail in *Elvis UK 1956-86*, and had ceased to exist by the end of this period. However, fans and collectors will recall with some affection the simple numbering system for RCA singles, whereby a sequential number was added to the RCA prefix, and SF for albums (once these were released in stereo only). By the mid-seventies, the RCA prefix had been replaced by a more sophisticated, though unwieldy, system where the prefix - APBO for singles, CPL1 (with variations) - took on additional purposes like indicating the origin, format and recording mode. This system proved unpopular and was later shortened to PB for singles and PL for albums, although some 'meaning' was retained - the 'P' supposedly stood for 'Popular', the 'L' for label.

Different series of releases from the main company product of both singles and albums, warranted their own system - the Golden Grooves singles used GOLD as a prefix, and the International albums used INTS, for example. Later, some Elvis singles were allocated ARON as a prefix, a move which pleased many fans.

In 1986, then, the RCA/BMG catalogue numbering system was made up of a prefix and sequential number. Different prefixes were allocated to different formats so that:

PB = 7 inch single

PT = 12 inch single

NL = Mid-price album

PL = Full-price album

ND = Mid-price compact disc (from 1987 onwards)

PD = Full-price compact disc (compact disc singles used the same prefix as CD albums)

NK = Mid-price cassette

PK = Full-price cassette (cassette singles used the same prefix as cassette albums)

Originally some of the codes had a meaning: 'D' stood for 'Disc', the 'K' for Cassette (perhaps another company had used 'C'). We have never worked out if there was any meaning to 'N' although it was suggested that it was a letter mid-way through the alphabet (mid-price!). Additional prefixes were introduced, even prior to 1986, where there was a need to distinguish a release in some way from the

normal pattern, so that 'BL' (*This Is Elvis*, LP 150) and 'CL' (*Special Edition*, LP 297), for example, were one-offs.

The number following the prefix comprised five digits and served, not just as a sequential release number, but identified the original of the record (USA and non-USA); the format (for example, 4 for singles, 8 for albums), and to RCA label licensees (which were not relevant for our purposes, of course). The first two digits, then, represented the originator and format.

The final three digits were just a sequential number so that, when added to the first two digits, the catalogue number itself was formed. However, it did not follow that a record released in, say, March would have a number higher than a record released in January. The record industry was never that simple. RCA singles followed a decreasing sequence, rather than an incremental one, so that a later release had a lower number than the previous one. Further details on this can be found in the Singles' Section.

There were other reasons why a record was released apparently out of the numbering sequence. Firstly, when a record was released in the UK much later than in Europe, it created an apparent anomaly, as it appeared with a number out of sequence with other albums released around the same time. A good example of this was *Elvis Sings The Wonderful World Of Christmas*, NL 81936 (**LP 311**), first released in the UK in November 1990, it had been released years earlier in Europe. A similar situation occurred when a proposed release date was delayed for some reason, again placing the allocated catalogue number out of sequence. An example here would be *Stereo '57 (Essential Elvis Volume 2)*, PL 90250 (**LP 298**).

In situations where a double, or multi-album, was released, the total number of albums in the set were added (in brackets) to the catalogue number. The addition of a (2) indicated a double album, (6) a six-album boxed set, and so on.

This, then, was the basis for RCA's catalogue numbering system. The problem was that, however it was modified, it was nothing more than a reference number for ordering purposes - retailers would order copies from the number provided, just as they had always done. RCA/BMG were no different from other major companies, in that they needed to take advantage of improvements, and savings, offered by computer technology. Certainly, the record industry as a whole saw benefits in having a system which would allow the requirements of all the interested parties to be combined to provide for stock control, product and format identification and, of course, straightforward ordering. If this information could be incorporated into a bar code, then the catalogue number and bar code could be combined, instead of being separate pieces of information. So evolved the concept of having a series of numbers which could be scanned in retail outlets to display the artist, title, format, price etc., and which, when linked to their computer systems, could provide stock control. When linked to the record companies' systems, this information could then be shared.

Another major development took place in 1992, and first appeared on an Elvis single in August of that year when *Don't Be Cruel* (S 179) was issued. BMG (along with other companies) adopted a worldwide numbering system which incorporated much more detail into the catalogue number, including the country of origin, company number, format of the product, as well as the catalogue number itself. This number was also incorporated into the bar code (dispensing with the earlier system), so that it could be captured at the point of sale and used for pricing and stock control purposes. This development also allowed BMG (and others) to stop using a price code (AA for 7 inch singles, HH for full priced LPs, and so on) which had to be used to determine the retail price of the product concerned.

The catalogue number from this point onwards comprised 11 digits. Using the single *Don't Be Cruel* as an example, the catalogue number quoted was 74321 11077 7.

The first five digits 74321 identified the country of origin and the company issuing the product. In this case the 74321 referred to BMG Europe (the UK being classed as part of that territory).

Later, 07863 was used, although it only appeared on one LP - **Elvis 56** (**LP 321**) and never on a single. This code - 07863 - indicated that it originated at BMG America and had been in use there since the summer of 1991. This did not mean the record was made in America, rather the term refers to who commissioned the work. All subsequent releases on CD have either used 74321 (indicating that the product originated in Europe, and more often that not, in the UK), or 07863, indicating America.

The next five digits - 11077 in our example - form the catalogue number itself, and from that the actual product: artist, title and price. This sequential number worked in exactly the same way as the earlier systems and was used by all those involved to identify, manufacture, and sell the product. To do so, the number had to be unique to an individual item.

The final digit - 7 - indicated the format of the product. The record industry utilised a range of codes for this purpose. For example:

> 1 = vinyl LP
> 2 = 5 inch CD
> 3 = 3 inch CD
> 4 = cassette
> 5 = DCC albums
> 6 = 12 inch singles
> 7 = 7 inch singles
> 0 = miscellaneous, shaped discs etc.

Following the catalogue number, an additional number appears at the end of the bar code, but this is not part of the catalogue number. This is called a check digit, and is derived mathematically from the preceding numbers and is included to ensure that the other numbers in the code are correctly scanned.

Throughout the book we have shown the full catalogue numbering system, excluding any check digits.

Matrix Numbers

Matrix numbers are to be found between the run-out grooves and label on almost all records. They can be stamped by machines or etched by hand. Whatever, they have fascinated fans and collectors alike for many years and have been the subject of much argument and analysis as to their meaning and purpose. In **Elvis UK 1956-86**, we explained the purpose and use of matrix numbers, and how, essentially, they provided a great deal of information relating to where a particular recording was made, the year it took place and so on. Of course, all of this related to the matrix numbers found on all of Elvis's record output from the first releases from 1956, to the mid-seventies, when RCA ceased to use this system in favour of a much simpler approach, whereby the catalogue number doubled-up as the matrix number. The effect of this was that the matrix number no longer enabled the reader to glean additional information from that already provided. Irrespective of which system was used, one of the functions provided by the matrix number was that of a filing reference. So, for example, if a record was numbered 5566, then the stamper used to manufacture the record could also be numbered 5566 and filed accordingly. This would, therefore, enable the record company to retrieve the appropriate stamper should the need arise for a re-pressing of that record.

The matrix numbers used by BMG became, in fact, merely job numbers, assigned by the production factory. They consisted usually of a four-digit number (the 'filing' number which identifies the

appropriate record), and several other letter and number codes. The four-digit number bore no relationship to the catalogue number: they were entirely independent of each other, except in the sense that they both related to the same end product, although consecutive releases in catalogue number terms, for example, **For LP Fans Only**, NL 90359 (**LP 303**), and **A Date With Elvis**, NL 90360 (**LP 304**), had job numbers which suggested that they were mastered and - in this case - produced around the same time. Equally, a job number could be used without the record ever being released.

The job number for a vinyl record was usually sequentially close to that of the compact disc format of the same product, as they tended to be produced at the same time. Vinyl copies of **Hits Like Never Before (Essential Elvis Vol. 3)** (**LP 306**) were numbered 5171, with the CD format numbered 5172, but again, not all releases followed this principle.

The two sides of a record - side 1 (or A side) and side 2 (B side) - generally used the same job number, but clearly there was a need to be able to distinguish between the two, otherwise there would result much confusion, and many more collectable items would find their way on to collectors' shelves! The most common method of identifying the sides was to add an 'A' and a 'B' to the job number.

On some RCA albums a date also accompanied the job number, but it should be noted that this was not the date the record in question was manufactured, rather the date of mastering i.e. when it was finalised prior to production. Obviously, when a record was re-pressed, and providing the stampers were undamaged and could be re-used, the new pressings would show the original date, in effect giving misleading information to those who believed it to be the date the record was made. A good example here was the album **Elvis Sings The Wonderful World Of Christmas**, NL 81936 (**LP 311**), which was issued in the UK in November 1990. The album was not old stock, having being held in a warehouse pending the Christmas season, as it featured the latest RCA label design. Yet next to the job number were the dates of January and February 1984 (sides 1 and 2 respectively). The fact was, then, that this album was re-pressed in 1990 using stampers originally produced in 1984. Mastering and production dates could, of course, agree, or, at least, be closely related, particularly as far as new records were concerned, where there was a need to release product as quickly as possible. **The Alternate Aloha**, PL 86985 (**LP 294**), was mastered, according to the date shown, in May 1988, and was on general release in the UK during the same month. If this was correct, then we can also conclude that the entire production process from pressing through to delivery to the shops was achieved well within the space of thirty days.

When a stamper was damaged or could not be re-used for some other reason, a new one was prepared and, from time to time, it was possible to glean some extra information from this. For example, the original pressings of **Presley - The All Time Greatest Hits**, PL 90100(2) (**LP 287**), had job numbers of 9023 (for record 1) and 9024 (for record 2) and also featured Bob Jones's 'Ten Years After' inscription. This record, although mastered in the UK by Bob Jones, was manufactured in Germany. However, on a later re-pressing, we noticed that for record one (which had now dispensed with Bob's message), a July 1989 date had been added to the previous job number, which had been retained. This suggests that a new stamper was prepared in July 1989 in order to replace the earlier ones. It was, however, interesting that record two re-used the original stampers, or, at least, it did on copies we have seen. This, however, does not mean that a record produced from 1989 stampers does not exist. It simply means that we have not seen one.

On the other hand, several of Elvis's records did not use the job code system, especially the singles which were produced in the UK, which tended to use the catalogue number only as the matrix reference - but the principle was much the same in that the stamper was stored in the (albeit unlikely) event that further copies were required.

In addition to the job number, and the A or B to identify each side of the record, an additional number was used to uniquely identify the stamper. The first stamper prepared would be numbered '1', the second '2' and so on. Many collectors once believed that a record bearing the number 1 must have been the original pressing, and a record containing a later number resulted from a later pressing. This is not - and never was - the case. In the 'golden days' of Elvis's records, several stampers may have been prepared at the same time, so that the production process could have been speeded up to meet demand, and in this way several pressing machines would have been utilised to press records at the same time. Thus, a record carrying a number of, say, 5 may have been produced at the same time as a record featuring a 1. It was also possible that no records with a 1 were ever produced if that stamper was damaged in any way. Similarly, a re-pressing may have used the 1, if it was not possible to re-use the 5. In short, the stamper number offered few additional clues as to the date or precise origins of each record.

We do not generally show the matrix numbers for the records featured in the book, but occasionally we may refer to them, usually those indicating a date, as this was useful information in assessing production-to-release timescales. Our intention, therefore, has been to use the numbers to provide additional detail to the records we discuss, and believe that you may find more enjoyment in checking out the matrix numbers for yourselves, should you be interested in this topic.

Publishers, Copyright Protection And Mechanical Rights

Two further pieces of information included on record labels and sleeves (although not necessarily on both), concerned the publishers of the songs and the company(ies) responsible for safeguarding the publishers', songwriters', and artists' interests in the recordings. Again, this is a topic we discussed in *Elvis UK 1956-86*, but one which we need to further clarify.

The songs' publishers were simply the company which owned the publishing rights to the material and who, therefore, received a percentage of the profits from the work. The actual name of the company concerned with a particular song frequently changes due to company mergers, take-overs and so on, and reference to a song like *Heartbreak Hotel*, for example, demonstrates this clearly.

The other piece of information related to organisations such as BIEM and GEMA, which were companies that act on behalf of the publishers. They were concerned with what is known as 'mechanical rights', which is a term used to cover reproduction of a song on a record, CD, tape, video or whatever. The mechanical rights' organisations receive a percentage of the retail price of a record which, in turn, they distribute to the appropriate publishers.

The two mechanical rights organisations found regularly on Elvis's RCA records were, as we have said, BIEM, an acronym for Bureau International Des Sociétés Gérant Le Droit D'en Regisatrement Et De Reproduction Mechanique, a French organisation with a very long name! They are an international body to which most of the world's mechanical rights' societies subscribe, and are basically a negotiating body for the world's mechanical rights societies. The other organisation, GEMA, which stands for Gesellschaft Für Musikalische Auffürhrungs Und Mechanische Vervielfältigungsrechte, was a German mechanical rights' protection society.

Publishing Dates

As in *Elvis UK 1956-86*, the benchmark we have used is simple and, we hope, logical. If nothing else, we have tried to achieve consistency, and seek to clarify what was often a confusing and sometimes misleading piece of information. However, some re-capping may be necessary here in order to provide new readers some background to the topic.

The term 'Recording First Published' first appeared on a UK Elvis single in July 1958 when *Hard Headed Woman*, RCA 1070 (*S 21*), was released. We have always believed that originally RCA intended the information to show when a song or an album was first available - published - in America. This may not have been a conscious decision, but as most Elvis material first appeared in his home country, the inclusion of a published date presented little difficulty. However, over the years, many discrepancies became apparent, brought about, generally speaking, for two reasons. Firstly, in situations where, say, a song was first published in America during one calendar year, and in the UK the next or subsequent year, there appeared to have been confusion over which date should have been used - the date of the American release, or the later UK date. The single *Are You Lonesome Tonight?* (*S 31*), was issued in America in November 1960. But when it was released in the UK in January 1961, it showed a recording first published date of 1960, the date of the American release. On the other hand, *If I Can Dream* (*S 67*), released on a American single in October 1968, and in the UK in February 1969, had a publishing date of 1969 on the UK label.

The second area to create discrepancies was brought about because RCA's American Division (due largely to the creative efforts of the UK Division), ceased to be the driving force in terms of Elvis product it once was, and, since the early eighties, a high proportion of new material was instigated and first released in the UK. Some of this material was released in America, often much later than the UK release date, but these cases clearly prevented the inclusion of the American first published date.

As far as the first published date for a song is concerned, the most logical, and, sensible, definition which could be applied is to provide the date when the song was first released, irrespective of country. Our belief is, therefore, that the date ought to relate closely to when a song was issued, not to when it was recorded - though in lots of cases the years do correspond. For example, the song *Crying In The Chapel*. It was recorded in November 1960 at the *His Hand In Mine* sessions, but not issued until 1965, when it appeared on a single in both America and in the UK (RCA 1455, *S 50*). We believe that the publishing date should, therefore, read 1965 on that and all subsequent releases.

Perhaps more problematical has been the question of outtakes, especially as, since 1986, we have seen a lot more issued officially, Once again, our position is simple. *Ain't That Loving You Baby* (*S 47*), the original slow single version, was recorded in June 1958, but not released until 1964, and should, therefore, have a published date of 1964. On the other hand, the 'fast' version of the song did not appear until 1985 on the album *Reconsider Baby*, PL 85418 (*LP 271*), and should, therefore, read first published 1985. Further, the additional, alternative fast versions, as included on *Hits Like Never Before (Essential Elvis Vol. 3)*, PL 90486 (*LP 306*), should have read 1990. Obviously this principle can only apply to different versions of songs, not re-mixes or mono/stereo versions; similarly a live version ought to show the date it, and not the original recording, was released.

So far we have considered the published date for individual songs, a topic which, although not entirely straightforward, was relatively simple when compared to the more complicated issue of album publishing dates. Basically, we need to consider two publishing dates: that of the record itself, and the publishing dates of the songs it contained. Using an example from *Elvis UK 1956-86*: the original issue of *Elvis' Golden Records Vol. 2*, RD 27159 (*LP 10*), was issued in America in 1959, but not released in the UK until 1960. Yet the label information gave a published date of 1959, even though the tracks were released in 1957, 1958 and 1959. The date shown - 1959 - related to when the record was first released in this form, not to when individual tracks were published, which were not identified separately.

By the time the third gold record compilation was released, *Elvis' Golden Records Vol. 3*, RD/SF 7630 (*LP 21*), in April 1964, the practice of identifying the publishing dates for individual tracks was being used. Needless to say there were some discrepancies to UK dates, as the album originated in America and obviously followed the dates when songs were first issued in that country. However, no publishing date for the album was shown on the label, although the sleeve did point out that the compilation was copyright 1964. Despite the discrepancies, individual identification was the ideal solution, as it provided all the information relevant to the record, but at the same time it presented RCA with the problem of maintaining consistency, and, inevitably, errors appeared frequently. They should not have, of course, for had the principle of providing the date of original publication dates been adopted early enough, maintaining accurate files would have been relatively simple.

A variety of other systems were used also, with one refinement showing the published dates as a list i.e. 1973, 1974, 1975 etc., without identifying which song(s) were first published during each of the years quoted. The more common approach of stating 'This Compilation P 19..' was also used, but this was actually the earlier system of identifying the publishing date for the record only.

In later years, there was a significant improvement in the accuracy of this information, but inconsistencies still persist. Albums like *From The Heart*, PL 90642 (**LP 317**), demonstrated the way it should have been done with each song being separately dated, along with the publishing date for the compilation.

In the text we have noted instances where we believe an error has occurred, and, in support of our guidelines, we have tried to supply all the necessary correct dates. Having said that, this issue was very difficult to fully document and was (to quote from *Elvis UK 1956-86)*, 'bedevilled with pitfalls'.

Running Times

Until the advent of compact discs, few record collectors were very bothered about song timings - apart from those which varied by a matter of minutes, of course! Few people would be likely to cross-check such information closely for two main reasons: most would not possess the kind of accurate equipment necessary to carry out such checks and, secondly, often all but the very best record player decks were subject to speed variations, thus making accurate checking difficult.

On the other hand, digital equipment on CD players has allowed users to monitor and check the song timings in a variety of ways: the length of a song or, alternatively, a running-up time (from zero upwards) or diminishing time i.e. from, say 3 minutes down to zero, as well as giving total playing times of discs. Consequently, collectors are not only more alert to discrepancies in timings, but, more pertinently, they can check them more easily. And while there can still be slight speed variations, they are far less extreme than was once the case with record player decks. So one 'sport' favoured by fans/collectors now is to compare the running times of the same songs featured on different releases, checking the running times - in the hope of discovering something unusual. And, while some may scorn such practices, claiming they are a waste of time, the results can be quite interesting at times, a matter which is dealt with later in more detail with examples given. However, there is still the question of the 'grey' area to consider: when the clock should stop on the fade out of a song. Presumably this ought to be when there is no information to be read, or when you can no longer hear any of the recording. But this is not always the case and can account for a number of discrepancies, as will be seen later.

Now the practice of regularly noting song timings on UK albums dates back a number of years, in fact to late 1983, when UK albums started to be pressed in Germany. However, as this was a transitional period, there was not always complete consistency. For example, the UK inspired *The Elvis Presley Sun Collection*, NL 89107 (*LP 201*), which was the first German produced UK album to be issued,

contained no reference to running times on labels or sleeves. In fact, quite a few other albums re-pressed around that time also failed to show these details. However, the first album on the German black label to include the information on the label was *Elvis' Golden Records Vol. 2 (50,000,000 Elvis Fans Can't Be Wrong)*, NL 82075 (*LP 203*), released in November 1983, while *G.I. Blues*, NL 83735 (*LP 206*), released in January 1984, was the first to include the details on both label and sleeve. We should point out that while these albums were indeed pressed in Germany, using the catalogue numbers shown above, the initial batch had a sticker applied to the sleeve which converted the catalogue number to the UK system - INTS - until such time as the UK catalogues were amended to fit in with the European system. Technically then, these were International INTS releases, not NL releases.

While the transition to German produced albums (late 1983) seems to have been the signal to include running times on a regular basis - albeit sporadically in the initial stages - the first UK album to include references to timings dated back to 1974 when *Elvis - A Legendary Performer Vol. 1*, RCA CPL1 0341 (*LP 70*), was issued. Admittedly, the timings were shown not on the record label, but on the inner card sleeve, which was printed in America where, right from the early days, it had been common practice to include running times on the sleeves. It was not until the release of the UK International INTS series in the early eighties that these details were again shown; but, once again, it was almost by default, as these releases used the artwork from original American releases - which, of course, included the running times.

As regards singles, the situation was quite different. In the USA, even in the fifties, many RCA singles displayed running times, though the Sun singles did not. On the other hand, in the UK, the first recorded instance of timings appearing on Elvis singles dated back to 1967 with the release of *The Love Machine*, RCA 1593 (*S 58*). On one variation (see variation number 3) the time shown boldly was 2.47 for the A side and 2.16 for the B side, *You Gotta Stop*. However, in fairness, this was an exception rather than a rule, as few other RCA black label singles included these references. It was not until the release of *In The Ghetto*, RCA 1831 (*S 68*), released in June 1969, that running times became a regular feature on singles' labels, although there were some notable exceptions.

Of course, even prior to the issue of compact discs, it was possible to detect differences on different records, not only in the times quoted, but regarding how long a record actually lasted. Take *(Now and then there's) A Fool Such As I*, as an example. On *Elvis - A Legendary Performer Vol. 1*, RCA CPL1 0341 (*LP 70*) a running time of 2.30 was given, whereas on *Elvis' Golden Records Vol. 2 (50,000,000 Elvis Fan's Can't Be Wrong)*, NL 82075 (LP 203), the same song was quoted as 2.36.

Staying with the same song (although it was not actually included on the vinyl version), its inclusion of the February 1992 CD release of *From The Heart*, PD 90642, highlighted an odd thing. This time its running time was shown as 2.38, but when compared to 'other versions' released over the years, it was discovered that some collections featured marginally shortened versions of the track, but fading it out on the refrain. However, on *From The Heart*, the song was reinstated to its full length, including the four refrains, as it had been on the original 1959 single release. This is a small point, perhaps, but one of interest to zealous collectors.

A similar situation exists with *Always On My Mind*, as included on *The Great Performances*, PL 82227 (**LP 308**). This clocked in at 3.46, a few seconds longer than earlier releases. The significant point here though, was that rather than just hearing the repetition of the closing lines, on this version it is possible to hear Elvis actually singing, 'That's enough'. In the majority of cases though it would seem that there are no real differences in the versions, rather a difference in how the timings are calculated and shown. Occasionally, however, some of the discrepancies between what is quoted on a sleeve or label, and what is actually registered on the digital read-out on a CD player, are significant and, we would suggest, unnecessary. A couple of examples from *Presley - The All Time Greatest Hits*, PL 90100(2) (LP 287), serves to illustrate the point. *Always On My Mind* is listed at 3.01, but shows 3.27 on the clock; *An American Trilogy* is listed as 4.31 but clocks up 4.22; *My Boy* is listed as 3.18 but plays for 3.10, while *Suspicion* is listed as 2.45, yet runs for 2.32.

This is all very interesting as BMG claimed to use a central source (in Hamburg) for information relating to song timings. Clearly though, there is some room for manoeuvre, particularly on the part of the person responsible for mastering, and it is obvious from the examples given, that the fade out will create discrepancies in timings if applied differently. Therefore, it seems unlikely that timings are checked to a central master log; it is much more likely that they are provided at the time of mastering. How else could different times be shown?

So, although running times are now a regular feature of all BMG releases - and quite rightly so - in truth they provide nothing more than an approximate guide as to how long a song or version lasts. Seen in that light, they should not be taken too seriously, but we would argue that they could - indeed ought to be - more accurate and consistent.

Label And Sleeve Errors

One key part of our work for *Elvis UK 1956-86* was to include in the text for each release any label or sleeve error relating to song titles, writers' names, and the date when the song was first published. We know, from your letters and reviews in various magazines, that many of you found this to be of great interest, completing as it did the 'picture' of each release. On the other hand, some people thought we had gone too far, arguing that whether or not a comma or full stop should be included was irrelevant. Some viewed these things as pedantry or unnecessary nit-picking; and whilst we acknowledge this point of view, we would disagree, arguing that these errors ought not to occur and that, for the sake of completeness and accuracy, we wish to highlight these mistakes and omissions. Our reasoning was that it would have been difficult to draw your attention to some errors and not others and that this would require a decision of what was, or was not, important. As this was subjective, our intention was to include all the errors we noticed, and let you decide what was important, rather than risk being accused of negligence. We felt then, as now, that this was an important aspect of what we were doing because, apart from anything else, these things were descriptors and helped discriminate between variations. We should point out that we prefer to present a comprehensive analysis of all releases, and consider that label and sleeve errors are of extreme importance.

Therefore, at the end of each piece of text devoted to a particular release, we refer to what we call 'label and sleeve errors'.

We readily acknowledge that we have made mistakes in the past, and we have taken steps to remedy the situation, with any amendments clearly indicated. Similarly, we are acutely aware that some of you may have specialist knowledge of some Elvis song titles recorded by other artists where different spellings, words or writers' names are used, and wonder why we persist in using the 'wrong' title or name. Our basis is that we are dealing with Elvis's recordings and, if the title of a song was changed by Elvis, his recording company or whoever, then that is a point worth noting (as we have tried to do), but it is largely irrelevant to our purpose. Take *Milkcow Blues Boogie* as an example. Most people would agree that this Sun recording was based on an earlier blues standard *Milk Cow Blues*, which was written by James Arnold in 1935. Very few other artists (although there are some) have used the same title as Elvis's version of the song, but the fact that the song's title was changed for an Elvis release does not matter, and is therefore not an error. However, if the song appeared on an Elvis record and was called *Milk Cow Boogie*, or even *Milk Cow Blues*, then these would be errors.

In *Elvis UK 1956-86* we highlighted a couple of examples which we recognised as being inaccuracies, but which cannot truly be regarded as errors. These are worth repeating here, as they illustrate perfectly the kind of background dealings so common in the recording industry. The first concerns those occasions where it is known that the writer of a song allowed Elvis's name to be added in return for Elvis recording the song, thus allowing Elvis to receive some composer royalties. This kind of arrangement was not untypical at the time, and most songwriters would have been happy to receive a share of a song recorded by Elvis. Writing credits for songs like *Paralyzed* and *All Shook Up* show Blackwell, the actual writer, and Presley, who probably had little to do with the actual composition. And, although this practice may be inaccurate, the fact remains that Elvis was credited as being co-author which is the reason we have retained his name and do not regard this as being an error.

A similar situation exists regarding the songs used in the film *Love Me Tender* - the title track, *Let Me*, *Poor Boy* and *We're Gonna Move*. Whilst it is generally accepted that all of these songs were written by Ken Darby, the Musical Director of the film, Vera Matson (Darby's wife) and Elvis were given writing credits, supposedly for copyright reasons. Again, while not strictly true, it is not an error.

Another point worth re-visiting, concerns those instances where Elvis was shown as arranging or adapting a song, in particular, the religious items found on albums such as *His Hand In Mine*, for example. References to 'arranging' and 'adapting' generally mean that the writer was not known and the song is considered 'traditional'. We do not consider this to be an error either, because it is known that Elvis did indeed contribute in such a way, not only on religious recordings, but on most other types also. Unfortunately, there are examples where Elvis was given similar credits, when the actual writer was known. In these cases, we have shown the writer of the song, and consider the omission of the name as an error. A good example of this is *I'll Take You Home Again Kathleen*, where Elvis is credited for the adaptation without reference to the actual writer, Thomas Westendorf.

In the case of singles and LPs, we have listed the correct song titles and what we believe to be the correct writers. The question of the recording first published dates is dealt with under a separate heading. In addition, the song index at the back of the book also quotes the correct song title, in alphabetical order. This will enable any queries you may have to be easily checked.

Since the late eighties, early nineties, there have been fewer mistakes appearing and some long standing, and often very annoying errors, have been removed, which we are pleased to see. Indeed, we understand that this occurred partly because of our modest efforts in *Elvis UK 1956-86*. The simple explanation for the improvement is that, finally, BMG - mainly in personage of Roger Semon, Ernst Mikael Jorgenson et al - exerted efforts to achieve some consistency in what title was used and so on. In fact, this very topic was a subject debated at length at one of the Committee's meetings in late 1991. Ultimately, it was decided that the correct title, for instance, would be taken from the original American label copy when the song first appeared. This standard was first applied across the board during mid-1992, when the boxed set, *The King Of Rock 'N' Roll The Complete 50's Masters* (LP 318), was issued. However, the question of publishers' names can vary for very good reasons: firms are sold, and sometimes when someone dies the ownership of that song may be changed. Consequently, with each release, it is necessary for the Copyright Department to re-check the information before it is printed. However, that is not to say that errors will not be made; they will, but, it is hoped, there will be fewer of them.

Of course, this policy decision had some impact on our work, as the question of what was right or wrong was something we made much of. We have, therefore, had to re-think our approach to this, in light of BMG's decision. And our conclusion is simply this. For the sake of continuity and consistency, we are adhering to our previous 'standards', set in *Elvis UK 1956-86*, unless convinced otherwise to change. We hope that our beliefs as to what is 'right' coincide with those of BMG; where they do not, we will explain why.

Song Titles

The errors in song titles found on both labels and sleeves can be categorised, and we have attempted to do this so that the kind of thing we have been looking for can be more clearly illustrated.

1. Brackets

A common error is where the words in brackets are omitted from the title, creating a 'new' title. And, whilst we acknowledge that it is common practice to refer to the song by its main, or abbreviated title, the actual title does include the words in brackets. You may be surprised to learn that well over thirty of Elvis's song titles contain the use of brackets.

Brackets can be found at the beginning or end of the main title, sometimes both, and include such classics as:

> *(Now and then there's) A Fool Such As I*
>
> *(You're the) Devil In Disguise*
>
> *(Let me be your) Teddy Bear*
>
> *(There'll be) Peace In The Valley (for me)*
>
> *Santa Bring My Baby Back (to me)*

Sometimes the brackets themselves are omitted, leaving titles like:

> *You're The Devil In Disguise*
>
> *It's A Long Lonely Highway*
>
> *There'll Be Peace In The Valley For Me*

We should point out that for all song, film, and album titles, we use a capital letter for each word in the title, but this is not to suggest that a label or sleeve not using this format is in error - it is simply a style point we decided to use. When a song title uses words in brackets, we use lower case for the initial letter in each word except for the first word and, of course, where a capital letter should be used as in the case of proper nouns. We would not consider an error to have been made if words in brackets deviate from our format.

Finally, another point worth noting about the use of brackets concerns songs which were based on foreign language recordings where, on many early Elvis records, the tune or song on which they were based, was usually mentioned. Examples here include:

> *Surrender (Torna A Surriento)*
>
> *It's Now Or Never (O Sole Mio)*
>
> *Ask Me (Io)*

Later releases generally failed to mention the original source, but we do not consider this to be an error, as the version recorded by Elvis was only based on that original, and the presence of the original source was often only shown for copyright reasons, considered necessary at the time.

2. Words

Another common error involves a situation where words are added or removed from song titles, which we find inexcusable. Examples of song titles where a word, words, or even entire lines, have been frequently added are:

> *(Marie's the name of) His Latest Flame* - 'of' added
>
> *One Night (with you)* - 'with you' added
>
> *Don't Be Cruel (to a heart that's true)* - 'to a heart that's true' added

Example of song titles where a word is omitted include:

> *A Big Hunk O' Love* - 'A' omitted
>
> *An American Trilogy* - 'An' omitted

A further type of error which fits into this classification, concerns the separation of certain words to make two different words, creating something which is grammatically incorrect and giving a different meaning to the title.

> *Anyplace Is Paradise* - shown as *Any Place Is Paradise*

The reverse of this situation is also true:

> *Any Way You Want Me (that's how I will be)* - shown as *Anyway You Want Me (that's how I will be)*

3. Punctuation

We recognise that this is the most difficult area on which to establish firm rules (also it is the most controversial!). There are many songs recorded by Elvis which make use of punctuation marks, some used accurately, others less so. Some titles, particulary those which ask a question, have no question mark, when perhaps they ought to have. Examples here include:

> *Where Do You Come From*
>
> *Who Needs Money*

Our view here is that, providing a title is consistent with how it was shown on the original release in the UK, then no error occurs.

To illustrate examples of song titles incorporating the use of punctuation marks, we have listed some titles where errors involve the omission of the appropriate punctuation mark.

> *Are You Lonesome Tonight?* - question mark
>
> *Got A Lot O' Livin' To Do!* - apostrophes and exclamation mark
>
> *Dirty, Dirty Feeling* - comma
>
> *Rock-A-Hula Baby* - hyphens

Occasionally an apostrophe is replaced by a letter (and vice versa), and whilst this seems perfectly sensible, it is not how the title was intended. Therefore, we see titles written as such (the correct title shown first in all cases):

> *Good Rockin' Tonight*   *Good Rocking Tonight*
>
> *Playin' For Keeps*   *Playing For Keeps*
>
> *Trying To Get To You*   *Tryin' To Get To You*

4. Spelling

There are a few examples of where a song has had an alteration to the way in which it is spelt. However, it would be unfair to consider the spelling of **Harbour Lights** (where a 'u' was added to the American way of spelling) as an error. On the other hand, changing a 'z' to an 's' in the case of **Paralyzed** is considered unnecessary as both forms are acceptable in English. We do, of course, recognise that the Americans still use a 'z' in words such as realize etc.

Writers

Turning our attention now to writers' names, the question of errors is an interesting one. Frequently, 'errors' concern normal conventions, whereby the name of the lyric writer is normally shown first, followed by the music writer. Similarly, it is usual to retain a certain order for writing 'teams', so that Lennon and McCartney, Pomus and Shuman, Leiber and Stoller remain in this format, irrespective of who wrote what part. Sometimes the order in which the writers' names are shown has changed, inexplicably, from the order shown on the original release. Therefore, we refer to the writers being in the wrong order when these kinds of errors occur, and usually indicate how they are shown.

Where a song is taken from, or based on, a foreign language song or tune, for example, *Surrender*, *It's Now Or Never*, *You Don't Have*

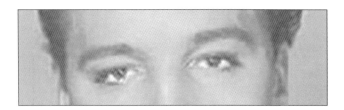

To Say You Love Me, it is normal practice to show the original writers' names first i.e. De Curtis, Di Capua and so on. However, sometimes not all of the original writers of a foreign language recording are credited when the song was 'converted' to English. A good example of this concerns the song **It's Now Or Never** on the album **Elvis In Concert**, where Elvis sang the English version of the song whilst Sherrill Nielson sang the song on which it was based - **O Sole Mio** - which was credited to Di Capua and Capurro. Only Di Capua's name was retained for the English language version, so presumably he had something to do with the music, whereas Capurro wrote the words.

Another common practice was for writers to use a pseudonym despite it being common knowledge who the writer was. Jerry Reed sometimes appeared as 'Hubbard', but again, we do not consider this to be an error, as his full name is Jerry Reed Hubbard.

Frequently, writers' names are often mis-spelt. We referred to Claude DeMetrius many times in **Elvis UK 1956-86**, as his name seemed to be mis-spelt most often.

Finally, there was often inconsistency in the way names were shown, even on the same sleeve or label. Sometimes full names were used, but more often than not only the surname appeared, a strange practice, and we are unclear why this should be the case. Perhaps we should also mention that US albums tended to give the full names of writers, a practice not widely adopted for UK/European releases, where a variety was used. We tend only to use surnames, and do not consider errors to occur where a mixture of full names, or surnames, only appear on UK releases, even when inconsistencies occur.

Backing Vocalists

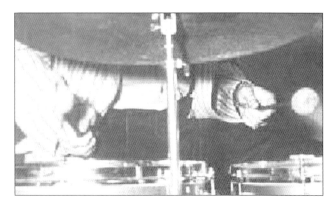

Sometimes false or incorrect information regarding vocal backing groups were to be found on labels and sleeves. For example, **Are You Lonesome Tonight?**, (the 'laughing' version recorded in Las Vegas in 1969) frequently gave credit to J. D. Sumner and The Stamps and Kathy Westmoreland when, in fact, they did not join Elvis until 1971. Where errors such as these occur, these are noted, and the correct backing vocalists are listed.

Published Dates

We have covered this topic in detail in a separate section and, as part of the text for each release, we indicate where an incorrect recording first published date is shown.

We sincerely hope that you will find all of this interesting. Our hope is that the identification of any error has been made easier by our explanation. As we said previously, our intention is to highlight the inconsistencies, not to be overly critical.

Part 4 : Variations

Introduction

Variations in label and sleeve design and details, are what make one record different from another and, as those of you who have had access to *Elvis UK 1956-86* will testify, this can be an extremely complicated yet, at the same time, a wonderfully enjoyable aspect of record collecting. Certainly, the amount of effort we put into identifying, analysing, collating and presenting our findings, represented the major part of our work, but, in many respects, it also gave us the greatest sense of satisfaction. Identifying variations gave anyone interested enough the scope for an apparently unlimited number of records to seek out - not that we have ever suggested that this was the purpose of our work. This gave everyone a chance to examine the records they already had, and establish in their own mind whether or not to continue in the same vein or branch out into another aspect of collecting. The number of variations we showed took collecting to the limit, and we know that many of you appreciated our efforts. However, we ought to make it clear that it is almost impossible for any one person to own every variation of every UK Elvis record. This is beyond the reach of most collectors - ourselves included.

However, we were particularly pleased to have answered many of the questions which had troubled so many fans for so long: what did the first label look like? Was there an orange label version? And it was answers to questions like these that enabled us to clear issues that had troubled collectors for so long. Using *Elvis UK 1956-86* as a guide to collecting, saved money too: dealers should now know better than to boast 'an original', when the copy offered was produced years later. Sadly though they still try.

What we tried to do was to present as complete a picture as possible. And, whilst we were confident that we had tracked down and included the majority of variations, we were aware that others were still likely to turn up. The problem was very much the unknown factor - did certain variations exist? We knew that there was a likelihood that some records would be there, somewhere, but following our own strict rules of not including details of a record until we actually saw the hard evidence for ourselves, prevented us from being certain. Speculation did not constitute proof. Until a new variation turned up, we never really knew that it existed. Fortunately many did appear, and they still do, but only at a trickle, and we have continued to keep our files up to date, so that one day we shall be able to present our findings. We owe a debt to all those people who took the trouble to contact us regarding new variations. Many new variations became available, particularly the records made in Germany issued during the final years covered by *Elvis UK 1956-86*.

We mentioned earlier that this part of our work formed the major part of *Elvis UK 1956-86*, and indeed it did, both in terms of the mass of information we unearthed, and the amount of time it took to compile. In total, we spent four years working on this and it was with some trepidation that we approached the subject this time. However, the task has been so much easier this time for three basic reasons. Firstly, fewer records were produced on the first press run, meaning that it was far easier to concentrate the effort required to complete the process.

Secondly - and this is linked to the first reason - record companies were able to achieve a far greater consistency in their product because fewer different people were involved in the manufacturing. This was best illustrated with the problem which manifested itself in the sixties, in particular, where several different people produced the label layout in different ways from the same basic information. Similarly, there were not many significant changes to layout and label colour over the last few years of vinyl releases. Finally, there were fewer re-pressings on any product. The tendency was to produce a given quantity - and, once supplies were sold, then no more were made. Obviously, there were some exceptions, indeed any record that underwent a re-pressing did extremely well, and it was on these re-pressings that variations commonly occurred. Also, the longer a record remained on catalogue, the more likely it would be that a new label design or colour was introduced.

Happily, variations still exist; not many it's true, but some; and throughout these pages we have been able to present all those we have located. This begs the question: what do we mean by variations? And, perhaps more importantly, how can we tell when we have found a variation, and how can we tell the difference between variations? We classify variations as being differences in both label and sleeves, no matter how small the difference might be. For example, it will be perfectly obvious to all if the same record is produced with a black and blue label, or with a gatefold and a single pocket sleeve, that one is a variation of the other. But if, say, two records both have a black label we may have to pick up some other detail to highlight the difference. Once again, the use of the chronological format has enabled us to discuss changes in both label and sleeve design as, and when, the changes occurred.

To categorise label variations we utilise three indicators throughout the book to determine the base details for each record. These are:

1. Label colour
2. Type of centre
3. Type of logo

Using these three areas it will be immediately apparent if a variation exists. If necessary, other, less obvious, details are noted in the text which then uniquely identify the record in question.

Because there were fewer variations we have been able to make greater use of photographs, with the added benefit of providing greater clarity and reduced printed details which, in some cases, was open to interpretation. We think this will greatly assist in identifying where a variation is not included - and here we are back to the unknown factor again - as you will be able to determine the fact quickly.

For each record, the label variations are listed in the following way:

1   1987 PRESSING

The figure '1' represents the sequential number allocated to each variation, so that the number of label variations (and sleeve variations) for each release can quickly be determined. All variations are listed in a chronological sequence, i.e. the date in which they first appeared. And so, in this example above, variation 1 was pressed in 1987. Please note: whilst the pressing date was normally the same as the release date, it was possible that a record pressed in December of one year could be released in January of the next. Where this has occurred, we have made a note of the fact in the text.

For each LP release we have also specified the audio mode for each variation, but please note, this is the actual mode, not necessarily the mode quoted on the record label or sleeve, as this can be inaccurate. The mode for each single is shown in the header block.

Also included are details which describe the variation itself. By reference to this information, the photographs provided, and by examining the record label itself, it should be possible to identify each record variation. We must point out that it has not been possible for us to reproduce exactly what is featured on certain record labels, other than by the use of photographs. The style of print, its size, and the spacing of words are, quite often, the only discriminating factors. So, although we have referred to them, we have not been able to replicate them precisely. However, we have developed certain conventions which are maintained throughout the book. We always show the detail in the same way as on the record label itself. For example, if the track details took up three lines, then we use three lines too, and all label features are printed in a different typeface to the details used to describe them.

All of this may sound very complicated, but reference to the variations themselves will confirm that it is far harder to try and describe what can be gleaned simply by looking.

Label Details

The photographs of the record labels below show details common to most of the RCA records issued during the period covered by this book. There was much more consistency in label features - the details printed on the label - than there used to be, and there are two fairly basic reasons for this. Firstly, there are far fewer variations, as there were far fewer re-pressings and, secondly, the detail included had been reduced to a bare minimum. These details gave only the essential information pertinent to the songs and basic label information.

Most of the label details are self-explanatory, but we have made a note on each and elaborated our explanations where we felt this was necessary and beneficial.

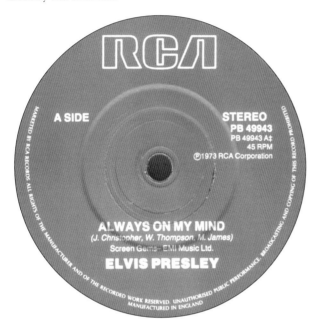

Logo

The logo is the company identifier. It is the record label on which the artist appears. We refer to the RCA logo here as being in the 'computer' style - RCA's original stylisation of the print.

Mode

The label usually showed the mode mono or stereo (depending on the mode in which the recording was made), although the label should not necessarily be relied upon to show the correct mode.

Sometimes the omission of the word stereo signified that the mode was mono. Therefore, we always quote the correct mode in the text, highlighting erroneous claims.

Catalogue Number #1

This is the UK catalogue number. Each label quotes the record's catalogue number, being a unique identifier of the record in question. The format of the catalogue number changed over the years, including the period covered here, and these changes are fully described in the text.

Catalogue Number #2

In addition to the catalogue number itself, this also shows the A or B side of the record. This was really a throwback to the days when the American catalogue number was shown in addition to the UK number. Later, a separate number, different again to the UK pattern, was developed for European releases, and it is this number that was now used for releases.

Playing Speed

This is the playing speed of the record - either 45 or 33 1/3 revolutions per minute. These are standard to most 7 inch singles and long play (LP) records and we do not generally indicate the playing speed for this reason. Rarely, there is an exception, and where this occurs, we have noted this in the text.

Published Date

This is the date when the recording was first published. This is a complex area and is the subject of further analysis in a separate section.

Song Titles - Song Writers

Both of these are self explanatory, but we refer to these where errors are apparent and both features are examined in greater detail in separate sections.

Song Publisher(s)

These are the companies which publish the songs (or own the publishing rights). The names can, and do, change frequently. Again, we have given this subject further airing in a separate section.

Artist

Self-explanatory.

Copyright

Copyright warnings are generally displayed on labels and concern the unauthorised copying and playing the record in public.

A Side - Side 1

Again self explanatory.

The items above form the bulk of label details included, but where a record label contains some unusual, or additional, details your attention will be drawn to this in the text.

Label Combinations

We use the term label combination to describe where one label design appeared on one side of a record, with a different design on the second side. A record with different designs on both sides, however small the difference, was therefore a hybrid, a label combination. When we refer to label variations we always use at least one feature which is common to both sides of each variation, a practice which should enable a combination of labels to be identified, if we are not aware that such a combination exists. Perhaps we should remind you that we do not include details of any record that we have not actually seen or have documentary proof of its existence, and this is equally true of label combinations.

In all honesty, label combinations became extremely rare, as computer technology allowed for exact copies to be made, without the need to typeset additional print 'masters'. Another reason was, undoubedly, the fact that records were not always re-pressed after the initial press run, but when records were produced in large quantities, particularly in the sixties, label combinations were relatively common. One reason for their existence was because different people would have been responsible for producing label layouts from the same basic details, referred to as label copy, and, providing the contents were accurate, minor variations would occur. As long as the label accurately reflected the contents of the record, in that the key song, writer, and track details etc., were correct, then no attempt would have been made to marry up minor, less important, design features.

Constant re-pressings of certain titles would also have resulted in label combinations, where the production of labels would have been an almost constant process. Many label combinations produced in this way were often barely recognisable as such, but the most noticeable type of label combinations occurred where a completely new label design was being introduced at the same time as stocks of the old design were being used up. Obviously, some attempt would have been made in this case to ensure that the same design was used. For example, we know of no label combination which comprised an original RCA Victor black label design and an RCA orange label, which could have appeared when RCA moved to this label colour in 1969. Presumably at the time of this important change, RCA would have placed great emphasis on producing records with the correct labels to accurately represent their new company identity. Such combinations were, therefore, much less common than those brought about by the procedures described earlier.

Clearly, the factors that generated the majority of label combinations in the past were no longer pertinent: there are few, if any, re-pressings; all label copy appears to come from the same source; press runs were small in comparison; and changes in design and basic layout were few. Consequently, the bulk of all records produced, contain the correct labels. Having said that though, label combinations do exist, despite ongoing visual checks, and, in view of these contributory factors, they are even rarer than any of their predecessors.

Unfortunately, it is impossible to accurately estimate the numbers of label combinations in existence, either for records produced in the sixties, for example, or more recently. We do, however, believe the figure to be a very small percentage of the total produced, and the likelihood was that this percentage had probably remained relatively constant over the years. Having said that, we have to agree that the contents of the record are of greater importance than label designs and, admittedly, this particular area does not appeal to everyone, but we do know that label combinations are held in high regard. Conversely, we know that some people had even returned examples of label combinations to stores, believing them to be unacceptable or inferior in some way. This was understandable perhaps if the variation involved, say, the blue Elvis label, which must have had more obvious appeal. Nevertheless, whatever your viewpoint on all of this, where we have located a label combination, we have included details.

Errors In Production

Errors in record production were once relatively commonplace, despite the quality control measures put in place by record companies, simply because of the sheer volume of records being made, and, of course, by human error. In fairness to record companies, most of these errors were detected by both audio and visual checks, and corrected before a record went into production or before despatch to the distributor. Therefore, the record buying public rarely had a chance to buy records containing production errors.

Yet, despite the considerable efforts made by the record companies, production errors did find their way to the shops and became rare items by virtue of the fact that so few existed. Even so, the customer could view a production error in one of two ways: for example, if a label was missing or the wrong label was included, a record could be considered unacceptable, in which case some people would return the record, or refuse to buy it in the first place. On the other hand, this kind of error was much sought after by some collectors and can now command a fairly high price. Where you stand on this is all a matter of opinion. We should make it clear that records which contain an obvious sound fault - in that they jump, or are warped, are also production errors, but we would not consider these to be rare, collectable or even worth further consideration. For our purposes, we are interested in those errors which, in some way, rendered the record a unique, and, therefore, collectable item.

As an example, we have located a copy of the LP **Harem Holiday**, NL 82558 (*LP 222*), which was pressed, we believe, in 1991, which had an incorrect label on side 2 - it was actually for a Deep Purple album **Slaves And Masters**, PL 90535 - although the record itself was the correct one. Details of this error are not to be found in **Elvis UK** simply because **Harem Holiday** had been deleted in the UK by this time, although copies were still available (as imports), generally at a higher price than other mid-price RCA releases. This example simply serves to illustrate the fact that production errors could still exist.

In **Elvis UK 1956-86**, we stated that most production errors concerned the label, and we were able to highlight the four main areas of error which affected labels and which are still applicable, although examples of some of these have not been observed for any record covered by this book. We have listed the areas in question again, as it is conceivable that such errors do exist:

- The same label used on both sides of a record
- Printing errors
- No printing on a label
- No label at all

There is no question that any record found with this kind of production error is now quite rare, although, as we have already seen, they do exist, and where we have been able to locate examples, details have been included.

Production errors involving audio faults were extremely rare, so that it was unlikely that many records exist where the same song was featured on both sides, or where Elvis was on one side and a different artist appeared on the other.

Where we have located a record containing a production error, we have included this in the list of variations for each record release.

Sleeve Variations

There can be little doubt that variations in label colour and design form the main source of interest for collectors. And, while this may be true, there are, nevertheless, many people who enjoy seeking out different sleeve variations.

Throughout the period covered by this book, the number of discernible variations in sleeves decreased, just as it did with variations in labels. And, it is easy to see why this occurred. As the number of pressings decreased - to the point where often there was only a single pressing - so too did the main source of variations of any kind. Only where a record achieved good sales figures did a re-pressing occur, and, sometimes, a variation of some kind would become available.

Most sleeve variations can be found on Old Gold, who adopted a policy of producing new sleeves for their singles every 18 months, or so. There were few RCA sleeve variations from 1986 onwards.

In the Singles' and LP Sections we have provided details of sleeve variations and, in the case of singles, identified when a particular variation was produced. This should prove useful in determining the number of variations available and, if you have bought items second-hand, to match the appropriate sleeve with the correct label variation.

Where a sleeve variation exists we have always provided sufficient detail to identify it correctly.

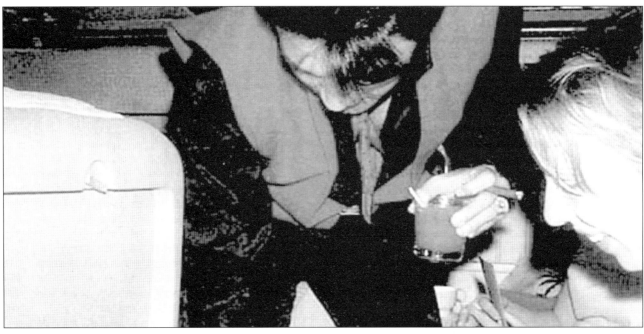

Singles

Introduction

In the years following Elvis's death in 1977 the situation regarding singles' releases was less than exciting. In particular, there was a lack of imagination and coherence behind many of the tracks issued. Not surprisingly then, chart success was neither frequent nor impressive. In fact it was virtually non-existent!

RCA releases came in fits and starts - as a quick glance at the singles' release schedule will testify - and often long gaps ensued between releases, with no-one apparently interested enough to devise and implement a policy about singles. And although there were some attempts from time to time to give advance notice about releases (in itself something rare), what happened was that titles would be announced but then changed at the last minute, all of which upset and frustrated fans. It is probably no exaggeration to say that the relationship between Elvis fans and those responsible for release policy (for all product) - never really good, it must be said - descended to an all time low in the mid-eighties.

For the purposes of this book, the narrative regarding single releases begins in July 1985 with the release of *Always On My Mind*, RCA PB 49943 (**S 146**), issued in July 1985. This was to be the last RCA single release until *Ain't That Loving You Baby*, RCA ARON 1 (**S 154**), in March 1987, a gap of twenty months. For the first time ever there was a year - 1986 - in which no Elvis single was released on RCA in the UK (a point we discuss further in the singles' section itself). In fact the only movement regarding singles came from the company Old Gold who, in 1986, issued six Elvis singles under a licensing deal with RCA/Ariola, as BMG were then known. The implication was clear: RCA/Ariola were, in effect, relinquishing some of their back catalogue material and allowing a much smaller company to promote the artist who had once been their major seller. And without being at all disparaging to Old Gold, some viewed this as a sad move, even though Old Gold, were only allowed to issue previously released product. Nonetheless, it has to be said that the behind-the-scenes squabbles and machinations between the Presley Estate and RCA in the USA did not help the situation either. A consequence of this, of course, was that yet more fans lost interest and the number buying new product - when it did appear - diminished even further. This was due, in part, to the mistrust many fans held towards RCA - particularly their oft repeated statements about the lack of material to issue, not to mention the generally poor marketing of what was released.

Single releases were given a low priority, a situation evidenced by the fact that between August 1985 and the end of the eighties there were only four RCA releases, none of which produced any major chart action. Even the artificially extended *Bossa Nova Baby* (**S 161**) and oddly edited version of *Mean Woman Blues* (**S 176**) created only a minor ripple in the charts. Moreover, the other choices had been released before, typifying a dependence on material which had already been released - with varying degrees of success - as singles before. Not surprisingly, in this unimaginative context, there were no Elvis singles released between February 1989 and August 1991. RCA chose not to issue any singles from the major albums *Hits Like Never Before (Essential Elvis Vol. 3)* (**LP 306**) or *The Great Performances* (**LP 308**).

Of course, alongside this depressing and confused state of affairs, we must also consider that there had been a general trend away from vinyl single releases for all artists - certainly in terms of volume sales, it seems. Quite simply, singles ceased to be pre-eminent in the record industry from the mid-eighties onwards, especially with the phenomenal growth of CD albums, CD singles, and so on. And against this general back-drop of singles falling out of favour with the record buying public, had to be added the 'Elvis' factors: the apparent lack of previously unissued product; a sizeable reduction in the

number of fans who would buy 'new' releases as a matter of course - arguably because they had felt cheated over the years and so had lost interest; the vexed situation regarding who, precisely, could action a single release - popularly perceived as a struggle between those who had the interest and will to act, and those who 'called the shots' and made decisions, not on artistic grounds, but in economic terms; and, finally, the perennial problem of what to issue from the back catalogue, a problem epitomised by the strong belief that if ten fans were asked for their choice of songs there would be ten different answers.

However, ironically, if sales were falling, and releases were only appearing sporadically, then the design and quality of the singles' sleeves was improving markedly. Unlike the early days of picture covers for UK singles' sleeves in the late sixties and early seventies (when one picture was used for no less than six releases!), there was much effort to make picture covers as attractive as possible, largely because this was now the industry norm. Indeed, RCA had not used a plain paper sleeve for any Elvis single since the release of the *Guitar Man*, RCA 43 (*S 125*), in February 1981, which appeared with, and without, a picture cover. And, however belated the use of picture sleeves as standard was, it was to be welcomed.

Of course, the fluctuating, but ever-diminishing Elvis market had an effect on two other key areas of interest to fans and collectors: the question of variations (a major part of our work in *Elvis UK 1956-86*) and deletions. Clearly major label and sleeve variations for Elvis releases became firmly a thing of the past, because few, if any items, warranted a second pressing or print run. Furthermore, as pressings were kept to a minimum (even allowing for companies to be magnanimous in the deals they offered to some retailers - some of which was reflected in startling variations in prices charged for the same product), this meant that some items were deleted very quickly - not untypically, within a few months of release. If you found a shop with stocks of singles then it was a fairly safe bet that it was old stock. Now it must be said that, as with many other points we have made here, it was often no different for other artists either.

Nevertheless, having asserted that the role of the single was changing, there were occasional contradictions which proved that if the imagination of the general record buying public was stimulated, then sales above normal expectations could be achieved. It is interesting to note that the very long chart run of songs like *(Everything I do) I Do It For You*, by Bryan Adams, was based on sales figures which compare with records from the sixties which failed to make such major impact on the charts. Similarly in 1992, Whitney Houston's version of Dolly Parton's song *I Will Always Love You*, became the highest selling single by a female artist in the UK because it was featured in a major film (*The Bodyguard*). It stayed at number one for many weeks. And while this was highly creditable, it is worth remembering the days when Elvis would enter the charts at number one with advance orders of 500,000 copies - and then still go on to sell more!

Not any more though, for Elvis or anyone else for that matter. A single can chart, go to number one and enjoy a reasonable run of success on relatively low sales. It seems clear, therefore, that despite what many fans wanted, the days of Elvis single releases were numbered. If there was to be any serious chart action with an Elvis release then it would require a whole lot more effort and support than the company had thus far given Elvis releases in recent years. Perhaps they (the company) would have liked the thought of an Elvis single in the charts, but what was obvious was that no-one seemed to possess the will or imagination to create the circumstances whereby this could happen. Undeniably, no such release would achieve any success without a massive promotional campaign on the part of the company who would have to secure the co-operation of so many different parties: the likes of the Presley Estate, for example - not to mention the support of non-Elvis fans to buy the product.

Even when the prestigious '50s boxed set was issued in July 1992, there were missed opportunities to successfully market and promote vigorously the accompanying single, *Don't Be Cruel/All Shook Up* etc (**S 179**). There was a promotional video produced in the USA, featuring some Elvis stage footage interspersed with shots of an actor playing Elvis. And because of the fast cuts and skilful editing there would be those who thought that it was Elvis throughout the video. Sadly though, the video, for whatever reason, was not seen much on the terrestrial channels. Ironically Billy Joel's cover version of *All Shook Up*, as featured in the film *Honeymoon In Vegas*, achieved more air-play and a higher chart position than the Elvis release.

It was to be just over three years before the next Elvis single appeared, in October 1995, this time the previously unreleased rehearsal of *The Twelfth of Never* (**S 180**), which was used to promote the seventies' boxed set. Remember though, no single had been issued to help support the sixties' boxed set in 1993. Ironically, however, in May 1996, slightly over 40 years after HMV released the first ever UK Elvis single - *Heartbreak Hotel* - RCA released what was thought to be the final 7 inch vinyl single in the UK. And, although probably not planned as such, it was, in fact, a re-issue of *Heartbreak Hotel* coupled with its original B side, *I Was The One*. Additionally though, the release also contained previously unreleased versions of both titles. It is worth noting that of the singles released between August 1985 and May 1996, only one new, previously unissued song, *The Twelfth Of Never* (**S 180**), was featured as an A side release. Other releases, of course, had included previously unissued performances.

Then in March 2000, came another surprise for vinyl collectors. Castle Music, who had licensed the *Artist Of The Century* material from BMG (**LP 323** and **324**) in August and December 1999, and issued limited edition vinyl versions of the sets, released facsimiles of the original five Sun singles, plus a four track EP in what was another limited edition vinyl set. RCA/BMG's only direct involvement in this was that they agreed to license the material.

Of course, we shall be returning to some of the points raised above in much more detail as we progress through the chronological listings, picking up on issues in their correct sequence. What does seem clear is that however unlikely it may seem to be, no-one can rule out the possibility of future releases on vinyl, although in all likelihood they would be limited editions.

UK Singles Listed Chronologically

This section lists the UK singles' releases from July 1985 onwards and, in order to allow the number of such releases to be put in perspective, we have decided to maintain the chronological numbering sequence from the previous book, *Elvis UK 1956-86*. To allow some extra details to be incorporated, including photographs, we have included both the 7 and 12 inch versions of *Always On My Mind* (**S 146** and **S 147** respectively) from *Elvis UK 1956-86*.

Unlike the record companies and compilers of chart statistics, we do not consider format variants as being the same record. For example, a normal 7 inch, 45 rpm single, would generally comprise two songs - an A and B side. However, a very common practice was to issue a 12 inch variant which often had additional material and a modified catalogue number. Other variants may also have existed: picture discs, shaped discs, and so on, each with its own unique identifier, but all with the same basic purpose: to bolster sales and increase the chances of the record entering the charts. Having said that, special variants of Elvis singles were no longer produced by RCA, a topic we discuss elsewhere.

Our view is that each variant was actually a different release and that this is, obviously, reflected in the chronological listing number because, as far back as 1979, RCA promoted the single *It Won't Seem Like Christmas (without you)/Merry Christmas Baby* (*S 120* and *S 121*) in both 7 inch and 12 inch formats, with the latter containing the long version of the B side track. The catalogue numbers were PB 9464 and PC 9464 respectively. Please note that at the time these singles were released, a different number was not used to identify formats however, both were the same in this case (9464). It was the prefix (PB and PC) that indicated the format. Later, each format was given a separate number in addition to a variable prefix.

Where a single was released containing material identical to a previous release (even when the A and B sides were reversed), we consider that the single had been re-issued, and we indicate this fact next to the track titles.

This section should, therefore, enable you to determine, for each release, its release number; label and catalogue number; all of the songs featured; whether it was a re-issue of an earlier single, and the date of release. If a single is not listed here, then it was released prior to July 1985 and can be found in *Elvis UK 1956-86*.

In addition to the basic chronological listing, we have provided further analysis of Elvis's singles - 7 and 12 inch picture sleeve singles and picture discs - to enable you to determine, at a glance, the numbers involved and where these are discussed in detail. Again, these listings follow on from the previous book, and therefore show a 'total to date' figure, maintaining a full count and placing releases from the period covered here into context. The release number is, therefore, the number of occasions that such a format has been used.

Finally, to further assist readers, we have also indicated where a song is an alternative version - either an outtake or live version - from the one normally released. This information will help readers discriminate, for instance, between the 'original' version of, say, *Ain't That Loving You Baby* (as issued in October 1964 - *S 47*, and the faster version issued in July 1985 - *S 147*).

If no additional reference appears after the song title(s), then it is safe to assume that this is the 'original' or standard version of the song.

This additional information does not appear in the chronological listings or the alphabetical listings, but is included in the header block for each release. And where this information requires further explanation, then it will be discussed in the script.

This, as readers of *Elvis UK 1956-86* will be aware, is a refinement of details given before. The reason for offering such detail is in order to make clear distinctions between the increasing number of live or alternative versions offered for release by the likes of BMG and, to a lesser extent, Old Gold.

Release Number	Catalogue Number	Titles	Release Date
S 146	RCA PB 49943	*Always On My Mind* *Tomorrow Night*	Jul 1985
S 147	RCA PT 49944	*Always On My Mind* *Tomorrow Night* *Ain't That Loving You Baby* *Dark Moon*	Jul 1985
S 148	Old Gold OG 9616	*In The Ghetto* *Suspicious Minds*	Oct 1986
S 149	Old Gold OG 9618	*Party* *Got A Lot O' Livin' To Do!* (re-issue)	Oct 1986
S 150	Old Gold OG 9620	*Blue Moon* *I Don't Care If The Sun Don't Shine* (re-issue)	Oct 1986
S 151	Old Gold OG 9622	*(Marie's the name) His Latest Flame* *The Girl Of My Best Friend*	Oct 1986
S 152	Old Gold OG 9624	*An American Trilogy* *Until It's Time For You To Go*	Oct 1986
S 153	Old Gold OG 9626	*Love Me Tender* *(Let me be your) Teddy Bear*	Oct 1986

S 154	RCA ARON 1	*Ain't That Loving You Baby* *Bossa Nova Baby*	Mar 1987
S 155	RCA ARONT 1	*Ain't That Loving You Baby* *I'm Comin' Home* *Bossa Nova Baby* *Rock-A-Hula Baby*	Mar 1987
S 156	Old Gold OG 9700	*Hound Dog* *Don't Be Cruel* (re-issue)	Apr 1987
S 157	Old Gold OG 9702	*Are You Lonesome Tonight?* *Wooden Heart*	Apr 1987
S 158	Old Gold OG 9704	*Heartbreak Hotel* *All Shook Up* (re-issue)	Apr 1987
S 159	Old Gold OG 9706	*Wild In The Country* *I Feel So Bad* (re-issue)	Apr 1987
S 160	RCA ARON 2	*Love Me Tender* *If I Can Dream*	Aug 1987
S 161	RCA ARONT 2	*Love Me Tender* *If I Can Dream* *Bossa Nova Baby*	Aug 1987
S 162	RCA PB 49595	*Stuck On You* *Any Way You Want Me (that's how I will be)*	Jan 1988
S 163	RCA PT 49596	*Stuck On You* *Always On My Mind* *Any Way You Want Me (that's how I will be)* *Are You Lonesome Tonight?*	Jan 1988
S 164	Old Gold OG 9740	*Jailhouse Rock* *Treat Me Nice* (re-issue)	Jan 1988
S 165	Old Gold OG 9742	*It's Now Or Never* *Surrender*	Jan 1988
S 166	Old Gold OG 9744	*Always On My Mind* *Burning Love*	Jan 1988
S 167	Old Gold OG 9746	*Loving You* *Paralyzed*	Jan 1988
S 168	Old Gold OG 9750	*King Creole* *Hard Headed Woman*	Jan 1988
S 169	Old Gold OG 9752	*Don't* *Wear My Ring Around Your Neck*	Jan 1988
S 170	Old Gold OG 9754	*Can't Help Falling In Love* *Rock-A-Hula Baby* (re-issue)	Jan 1988
S 171	Old Gold OG 9756	*My Boy* *My Way*	Jan 1988
S 172	Old Gold OG 9758	*Way Down* *Moody Blue* (re-issue)	Jan 1988
S 173	Old Gold OG 9761	*The Wonder Of You* *If I Can Dream*	Jan 1988
S 174	Baktabak BAKPAK 1008	*Interview Picture Disc Collection*	Apr 1988
S 175	RCA PB 49473	*Mean Woman Blues* *I Beg Of You*	Jan 1989
S 176	RCA PT 49474	*Mean Woman Blues* *I Beg Of You* *Party* *Mean Woman Blues*	Jan 1989
S 177	RCA PB 49177	*Are You Lonesome Tonight?* *Reconsider Baby*	Aug 1991
S 178	RCA PT 49178	*Are You Lonesome Tonight?* *Runaway* *Baby, What You Want Me To Do* *Reconsider Baby*	Aug 1991
S 179	RCA 74321 11077 7	*Don't Be Cruel* *All Shook Up* *Jailhouse Rock* *I Need Your Love Tonight*	Aug 1992
S 180	RCA 74321 32012 7	*The Twelfth Of Never* *Walk A Mile In My Shoes* *Burning Love*	Oct 1995
S 181	RCA 74321 33686 7	*Heartbreak Hotel* *I Was The One* *Heartbreak Hotel* *I Was The One*	May 1996
S 182	Sun Castle Music ELVIS 101	*Sun Singles*	Mar 2000
		That's All Right *Blue Moon Of Kentucky*	
		Good Rockin' Tonight *I Don't Care If The Sun Don't Shine*	
		Milkcow Blues Boogie *You're A Heartbreaker*	
		I'm Left, You're Right, She's Gone *Baby Let's Play House*	
		Mystery Train *I Forgot To Remember To Forget*	
		That's All Right *Harbour Lights* *Tomorrow Night* *Trying To get To You*	
S 183	RCA Castle Music ELVIS 103	*The UK No.1 Singles Collection*	Aug 2000
		All Shook Up *That's When Your Heartaches Begin*	
		Jailhouse Rock *Treat Me Nice*	
		One Night *I Got Stung*	
		(Now and then there's) A Fool Such As I *I Need Your Love Tonight*	
		It's Now Or Never *Make Me Know It*	
		Are You Lonesome Tonight? *I Gotta Know*	
		Wooden Heart *Tonight Is So Right For Love*	
		Surrender *Lonely Man*	
		(Marie's the name) His Latest Flame *Little Sister*	
		Rock-A-Hula Baby *Can't Help Falling In Love*	
		Good Luck Charm *Anything That's Part Of You*	
		She's Not You *Just Tell Her Jim Said Hello*	
		Return To Sender *Where Do You Come From*	
		(You're the) Devil In Disguise *Please Don't Drag That String Around*	
		Crying In The Chapel *I Believe In The Man In The Sky*	
		The Wonder Of You *Mama Liked The Roses*	
		Way Down *Pledging My Love*	

Picture Sleeves

Picture Sleeve Number	Release Number	Catalogue Number	Titles	Picture Sleeve Release Date
36	S 146	RCA PB 49943	*Always On My Mind* *Tomorrow Night*	Jul 1985
37	S 154	RCA ARON 1	*Ain't That Loving You Baby* *Bossa Nova Baby*	Mar 1987
38	S 160	RCA ARON 2	*Love Me Tender* *If I Can Dream*	Aug 1987
39	S 162	RCA PB 49595	*Stuck On You* *Any Way You Want Me (that's how I will be)*	Jan 1988
40	S 175	RCA PB 49473	*Mean Woman Blues* *I Beg Of You*	Jan 1989
41	S 148	Old Gold OG 9616	*In The Ghetto* *Suspicious Minds*	Jan 1989*
42	S 152	Old Gold OG 9624	*An American Trilogy* *Until It's Time For You To Go*	Jan 1989*
43	S 166	Old Gold OG 9744	*Always On My Mind* *Burning Love*	Jan 1989*
44	S 164	Old Gold OG 9740	*Jailhouse Rock* *Treat Me Nice*	Sep 1989*
45	S 153	Old Gold OG 9626	*Love Me Tender* *(Let me be your) Teddy Bear*	Apr 1990*
46	S 156	Old Gold OG 9700	*Hound Dog* *Don't Be Cruel*	Jun 1990*
47	S 173	Old Gold OG 9761	*The Wonder Of You* *If I Can Dream*	Jun 1990*
48	S 177	RCA PB 49177	*Are You Lonesome Tonight?* *Reconsider Baby*	Aug 1991
49	S 179	RCA 74321 11077 7	*Don't Be Cruel* *All Shook Up* *Jailhouse Rock* *I Need Your Love Tonight*	Aug 1992
50	S 180	RCA 74321 32012 7	*The Twelfth Of Never* *Walk A Mile In My Shoes* *Burning Love*	Oct 1995
51	S 181	RCA 74321 33686 7	*Heartbreak Hotel* *I Was The One* *Heartbreak Hotel* *I Was The One*	May 1996

*Please note:

The Old Gold singles were produced in picture sleeves long after their original release date, but to maintain a chronological sequence these singles are listed in the order in which they appeared using a picture sleeve.

The date when the singles were first released can be obtained from the full chronological listing.

12 Inch Singles

12 Inch Number	Release Number	Catalogue Number	Titles	Release Date
3	S 147	RCA PT 49944	*Always On My Mind* *Tomorrow Night* *Ain't That Loving You Baby* *Dark Moon*	Jul 1985
4	S 155	RCA ARONT 1	*Ain't That Loving You Baby* *I'm Comin' Home* *Bossa Nova Baby* *Rock-A-Hula Baby*	Mar 1987

5	S 161	RCA ARONT 2	*Love Me Tender* *If I Can Dream* *Bossa Nova Baby*	Aug 1987
6	S 163	RCA PT 49596	*Stuck On You* *Always On My Mind* *Any Way You Want Me (that's how I will be)* *Are You Lonesome Tonight?*	Jan 1988
7	S 176	RCA PT 49474	*Mean Woman Blues* *I Beg Of You* *Party* *Mean Woman Blues*	Jan 1989
8	S 178	RCA PT 49178	*Are You Lonesome Tonight?* *Runaway* *Baby, What You Want Me To Do* *Reconsider Baby*	Jan 1991

Picture Discs

Picture Disc Number	Release Number	Catalogue Number	Titles	Release Date
5	S 174	Baktabak BAKPAK 1008	*Interview Picture Disc Collection*	Apr 1988

UK Singles Listed Alphabetically

The Singles' section of this book shows all the details of Elvis's singles in chronological order, rather than alphabetically, to enable you to follow the developments and changes that resulted. If, however, you do not know when a particular single was released and you are unable to find it in the chronological section, then you can use this listing to determine its location in the chronological section, and turn to the page in question where the record is discussed in detail.

Where a song was used more than once on a single in the period covered by this book, the listings place the song's release in a chronological sequence, but reference to the catalogue number will clearly distinguish between the two.

Also for the purpose of this section, any words found in parenthesis in titles on record labels and sleeves, while still being shown, have been ignored when placing the songs in alphabetical order. For example, *(Let me be your) Teddy Bear* is listed under 'T' for ***Teddy Bear***.

Further, we have provided listings of A and B sides in alphabetical order; and where a single contains more than the usual two songs, all of the songs have been listed, enabling a single to be clearly identified and located from whichever song is used as the access point. Please note: when considering singles with more than two tracks we only regard one song as the lead track (and therefore the A side). Thus in the alphabetical listings of B sides, the lead (A side) track is always listed last.

A Sides

Titles	Catalogue Number	Release Number
(Now and then there's) A Fool Such As I *I Need Your Love Tonight*	RCA/Castle Music ELVIS 103	S 183
Ain't That Loving You Baby *Bossa Nova Baby*	RCA ARON 1	S 154
Ain't That Loving You Baby *I'm Comin' Home* *Bossa Nova Baby* *Rock-A-Hula Baby*	RCA ARONT 1	S 155

All Shook Up *That's When Your Heartaches Begin*	RCA/Castle Music ELVIS 103	S 183
Always On My Mind *Tomorrow Night*	RCA PB 49943	S 146
Always On My Mind *Tomorrow Night* *Ain't That Loving You Baby* *Dark Moon*	RCA PT 49944	S 147
Always On My Mind *Burning Love*	Old Gold OG 9744	S 166
An American Trilogy *Until It's Time For You To Go*	Old Gold OG 9624	S 152
Are You Lonesome Tonight? *Wooden Heart*	Old Gold OG 9702	S 157
Are You Lonesome Tonight? *Reconsider Baby*	RCA PB 49177	S 177
Are You Lonesome Tonight? *Runaway* *Baby, What You Want Me To Do* *Reconsider Baby*	RCA PT 49178	S 178
Are You Lonesome Tonight? *I Gotta Know*	RCA/Castle Music ELVIS 103	S 183
Blue Moon *I Don't Care If The Sun Don't Shine*	Old Gold OG 9620	S 150
Can't Help Falling In Love *Rock-A-Hula Baby*	Old Gold OG 9754	S 170
Crying In The Chapel *I Believe In the Man In The Sky*	RCA/Castle Music ELVIS 103	S 183
(You're the) Devil In Disguise *Please Don't Drag That String Around*	RCA/Castle Music ELVIS 103	S 183
Don't *Wear My Ring Around Your Neck*	Old Gold OG 9752	S 169
Don't Be Cruel *All Shook Up* *Jailhouse Rock* *I Need Your Love Tonight*	RCA 74321 11077 7	S 179
Good Luck Charm *Anything That's Part Of You*	RCA/Castle Music ELVIS 103	S 183
Good Rockin' Tonight *I Don't Care If The Sun Don't Shine*	Sun/Castle Music ELVIS 101	S 182
Heartbreak Hotel *All Shook Up*	Old Gold OG 9704	S 158
Heartbreak Hotel *I Was The One* *Heartbreak Hotel* *I Was The One*	RCA 74321 33686 7	S 181
(Marie's the name) His Latest Flame *The Girl Of My Best Friend*	Old Gold OG 9622	S 151
(Marie's the name) His Latest Flame *Little Sister*	RCA/Castle Music ELVIS 103	S 183
Hound Dog *Don't Be Cruel*	Old Gold OG 9700	S 156
I'm Left, You're Right, She's Gone *Baby Let's Play House*	Sun/Castle Music ELVIS 101	S 182
In The Ghetto *Suspicious Minds*	Old Gold OG 9616	S 148
Interview Picture Disc *Collection*	Baktabak BAKPAK 1008	S 174
It's Now Or Never *Surrender*	Old Gold OG 9742	S 165
It's Now Or Never *Make Me Know It*	RCA/Castle Music ELVIS 103	S 183
Jailhouse Rock *Treat Me Nice*	Old Gold OG 9740	S 164
Jailhouse Rock *Treat Me Nice*	RCA/Castle Music ELVIS 103	S 183
King Creole *Hard Headed Woman*	Old Gold OG 9750	S 168
Love Me Tender *(Let me be your) Teddy Bear*	Old Gold OG 9626	S 153
Love Me Tender *If I Can Dream*	RCA ARON 2	S 160
Love Me Tender *If I Can Dream* *Bossa Nova Baby*	RCA ARONT 2	S 161
Loving You *Paralyzed*	Old Gold OG 9746	S 167
Mean Woman Blues *I Beg Of You*	RCA PB 49473	S 175
Mean Woman Blues *I Beg Of You* *Party* *Mean Woman Blues*	RCA PT 49474	S 176
Milkcow Blues Boogie *You're A Heartbreaker*	Sun/Castle Music ELVIS 101	S 182
My Boy *My Way*	Old Gold OG 9756	S 171
Mystery Train *I Forgot To Remember To Forget*	Sun/Castle Music ELVIS 101	S 182
One Night *I Got Stung*	Sun/Castle Music ELVIS 103	S 183
Party *Got A Lot O' Livin' To Do!*	Old Gold OG 9618	S 149
Return To Sender *Where Do You Come From*	RCA/Castle Music ELVIS 103	S 183
Rock-A-Hula Baby *Can't Help Falling In Love*	RCA/Castle Music ELVIS 103	S 183
She's Not You *Just Tell Her Jim Said Hello*	RCA/Castle Music ELVIS 103	S 183
Stuck On You *Any Way You Want Me (that's how I will be)*	RCA PB 49595	S 162
Stuck On You *Always On My Mind* *Any Way You Want Me (that's how I will be)* *Are You Lonesome Tonight?*	RCA PT 49596	S 163
Surrender *Lonely Man*	RCA/Castle Music ELVIS 103	S 183
That's All Right *Blue Moon Of Kentucky*	Sun/Castle Music ELVIS 101	S 182
That's All Right *Harbour Lights* *Tomorrow Night* *Trying To Get To You*	Sun/Castle Music ELVIS 101	S 182
The Twelfth Of Never *Walk A Mile In My Shoes* *Burning Love*	RCA 74321 32012 7	S 180
The Wonder Of You *If I Can Dream*	Old Gold OG 9761	S 173
The Wonder Of You *Mama Liked The Roses*	RCA/Castle Music ELVIS 103	S 183
Way Down *Moody Blue*	Old Gold OG 9758	S 172
Way Down *Pledging My Love*	RCA/Castle Music ELVIS 103	S 183

Wild In The Country *I Feel So Bad*	Old Gold OG 9706	S 159
Wooden Heart *Tonight Is So Right For Love*	RCA/Castle Music ELVIS 103	S 183

B Sides

Titles	Catalogue Number	Release Number

Ain't That Loving You Baby
  Tomorrow Night
  Dark Moon
  Always On My Mind
	RCA
	PT 49944
		S 147

All Shook Up *Heartbreak Hotel*	Old Gold OG 9704	S 158

All Shook Up
  Jailhouse Rock
  I Need Your Love Tonight
  Don't Be Cruel
	RCA
	74321 11077 7
		S 179

Always On My Mind
  Any Way You Want Me
  (that's how I will be)
  Are You Lonesome Tonight?
  Stuck On You
	RCA
	PT 49596
		S 163

Any Way You Want Me
  (that's how I will be)
  Stuck On You
	RCA
	PB 49595
		S 162

Any Way You Want Me
  (that's how I will be)
  Always On My Mind
  Are You Lonesome Tonight?
  Stuck On You
	RCA
	PT 49596
		S 163

Anything That's Part Of You *Good Luck Charm*	RCA/Castle Music ELVIS 103	S 183

Are You Lonesome Tonight?
  Always On My Mind
  Any Way You Want Me
  (that's how I will be)
  Stuck On You
	RCA
	PT 49596
		S 163

Baby Let's Play House *I'm Left, You're Right, She's Gone*	Sun/Castle Music ELVIS 101	S 182

Baby, What You Want Me To Do
  Runaway
  Reconsider Baby
  Are You Lonesome Tonight?
	RCA
	PT 49178
		S 178

Blue Moon Of Kentucky *That's All Right*	Sun/Castle Music ELVIS 101	S 182
Bossa Nova Baby *Ain't That Loving You Baby*	RCA ARON 1	S 154

Bossa Nova Baby
  I'm Comin' Home
  Rock-A-Hula Baby
  Ain't That Loving You Baby
	RCA
	ARONT 1
		S 155

Bossa Nova Baby
  If I Can Dream
  Love Me Tender
	RCA
	ARONT 2
		S 161

Burning Love *Always On My Mind*	Old Gold OG 9744	S 166

Burning Love
  Walk A Mile In My Shoes
  The Twelfth Of Never
	RCA
	74321 32012 7
		S 180

Can't Help Falling In Love *Rock-A-Hula Baby*	RCA/Castle Music ELVIS 103	S 183

Dark Moon
  Tomorrow Night
  Ain't That Loving You Baby
  Always On My Mind
	RCA
	PT 49944
		S 147

Don't Be Cruel *Hound Dog*	Old Gold OG 9700	S 156
Got A Lot O' Livin' To Do! *Party*	Old Gold OG 9618	S 149

Harbour Lights
  Tomorrow Night
  Trying To Get To You
  That's All Right
	Sun/Castle Music
	ELVIS 101
		S 182

Hard Headed Woman *King Creole*	Old Gold OG 9750	S 168

Heartbreak Hotel
  I Was The One
  I Was The One
  Heartbreak Hotel
	RCA
	74321 33686 7
		S 181

I Beg Of You *Mean Woman Blues*	RCA PB 49473	S 175

I Beg Of You
  Party
  Mean Woman Blues
  Mean Woman Blues
	RCA
	PT 49474
		S 176

I Believe In The Man In The Sky *Crying In The Chapel*	RCA/Castle Music ELVIS 103	S 183
I Don't Care If The Sun Don't Shine *Blue Moon*	Old Gold OG 9620	S 150
I Don't Care If The Sun Don't Shine *Good Rockin' Tonight*	Sun/Castle Music ELVIS 101	S 182
I Feel So Bad *Wild In The Country*	Old Gold OG 9706	S 159
I Forgot To Remember To Forget *Mystery Train*	Sun/Castle Music ELVIS 101	S 182
I Got Stung *One Night*	RCA/Castle Music ELVIS 103	S 183
I Gotta Know *Are You Lonesome Tonight?*	RCA/Castle Music ELVIS 103	S 183

I Need Your Love Tonight
  All Shook Up
  Jailhouse Rock
  Don't Be Cruel
	RCA
	74321 11077 7
		S 179

I Need Your Love Tonight
  (Now and then there's) A
  Fool Such As I
	RCA/Castle Music
	ELVIS 103
		S 183

I Was The One
  Heartbreak Hotel
  I Was The One
  Heartbreak Hotel
	RCA
	74321 33686 7
		S 181

If I Can Dream *Love Me Tender*	RCA ARON 2	S 160

If I Can Dream
  Bossa Nova Baby
  Love Me Tender
	RCA
	ARONT 2
		S 161

If I Can Dream *The Wonder Of You*	Old Gold OG 9761	S 173

I'm Comin' Home
  Bossa Nova Baby
  Rock-A-Hula Baby
  Ain't That Loving You Baby
	RCA
	ARONT 1
		S 155

Jailhouse Rock
  All Shook Up
  I Need Your Love Tonight
  Don't Be Cruel
	RCA
	74321 11077 7
		S 179

Just Tell Her Jim Said Hello *She's Not You*	RCA/Castle Music ELVIS 103	**S 183**
Little Sister *(Marie's the name) His Latest Flame*	RCA/Castle Music ELVIS 103	**S 183**
Lonely Man *Surrender*	RCA/Castle Music ELVIS 103	**S 183**
Make Me Know It *It's Now Or Never*	RCA/Castle Music ELVIS 103	**S 183**
Mama Liked The Roses *The Wonder Of You*	RCA/Castle Music ELVIS 103	**S 183**
Mean Woman Blues *I Beg Of You* *Party* *Mean Woman Blues*	RCA PT 49474	**S 176**
Moody Blue *Way Down*	Old Gold OG 9758	**S 172**
My Way *My Boy*	Old Gold OG 9756	**S 171**
Paralyzed *Loving You*	Old Gold OG 9746	**S 167**
Party *I Beg Of You* *Mean Woman Blues* *Mean Woman Blues*	RCA P1 49474	**S 176**
Please Don't Drag That *String Around* *(You're the) Devil In Disguise*	RCA/Castle Music ELVIS 103	**S 183**
Pledging My Love *Way Down*	RCA/Castle Music ELVIS 103	**S 183**
Reconsider Baby *Are You Lonesome Tonight?*	RCA PB 49177	**S 177**
Reconsider Baby *Runaway* *Baby, What You Want Me To Do* *Are You Lonesome Tonight?*	RCA PT 49178	**S 178**
Rock-A-Hula Baby *I'm Comin' Home* *Bossa Nova Baby* *Ain't That Loving You Baby*	RCA ARONT 1	**S 155**
Rock-A-Hula Baby *Can't Help Falling In Love*	Old Gold OG 9754	**S 170**
Runaway *Baby, What You Want Me To Do* *Reconsider Baby* *Are You Lonesome Tonight?*	RCA PT 49178	**S 178**
Surrender *It's Now Or Never*	Old Gold OG 9742	**S 165**
Suspicious Minds *In The Ghetto*	Old Gold OG 9616	**S 148**
(Let me be your) Teddy Bear *Love Me Tender*	Old Gold OG 9626	**S 153**
That's When Your Heartaches Begin *All Shook Up*	RCA/Castle Music ELVIS 103	**S 183**
The Girl Of My Best Friend *(Marie's the name) His Latest Flame*	Old Gold OG 9622	**S 151**
Tomorrow Night *Always On My Mind*	RCA PB 49943	**S 146**
Tomorrow Night *Ain't That Loving You Baby* *Dark Moon* *Always On My Mind*	RCA PT 49944	**S 147**

Tomorrow Night *Harbour Lights* *Trying To Get To You* *That's All Right*	Sun/Castle Music ELVIS 101	**S 182**
Tonight Is So Right For Love *Wooden Heart*	RCA/Castle Music ELVIS 103	**S 183**
Treat Me Nice *Jailhouse Rock*	Old Gold OG 9740	**S 164**
Treat Me Nice *Jailhouse Rock*	RCA/Castle Music ELVIS 103	**S 183**
Trying To Get To You *Harbour Lights* *Tomorrow Night* *That's All Right*	Sun/Castle Music ELVIS 101	**S 182**
Until It's Time For You To Go *An American Trilogy*	Old Gold OG 9624	**S 152**
Walk A Mile In My Shoes *Burning Love* *The Twelfth Of Never*	RCA 74321 32012 7	**S 180**
Wear My Ring Around Your Neck *Don't*	Old Gold OG 9752	**S 169**
Where Do You Come From *Return To Sender*	RCA/Castle Music ELVIS 103	**S 183**
Wooden Heart *Are You Lonesome Tonight?*	Old Gold OG 9702	**S 157**
You're A Heartbreaker *Milkcow Blues Boogie*	Sun/Castle Music ELVIS 101	**S 182**

Sample Of Detail Included

As in *Elvis UK 1956-86*, by choosing to discuss Elvis's UK singles in chronological order (rather than alphabetically) we have been able to discuss any changes in label and sleeve design, along with the information they contain as, and when, they occurred. In addition, comparisons between consecutive releases are brought to your attention easily and in a more meaningful manner.

For each single we have included the following information.

S 146
The chronological number of release. This maintains the numbering sequence from *Elvis UK 1956-86* for the sake of continuity. This number immediately tells you how many Elvis singles have been released in the UK, but please see the chronological listing for further details.

RCA
The record label on which the single was released.

PB 49943
The single's UK catalogue number.

Always On My Mind   Tomorrow Night
The full and correct song titles, including where appropriate the words in brackets, as they ought to appear. From time to time, the labels (and sleeves) incorrectly title a song. Where this occurs the nature of the error is drawn to your attention in the text.

Alternative Version   Live Version   Extended Version
We have indicated where a song is different from the version normally released by adding the appropriate version details. If no additional reference appears, the standard version is being used.

{U}

Previously unreleased performance. This indicates the first appearance of a song, or alternative version, as indicated by the record company. Please note though that the same version may also have been shown as an unreleased performance when it appeared on an album issued around the same time as the single.

{S} or {M}

The mode of each song. {S} indicates stereo, {M} mono. Please note: this is the actual mode which is not necessarily the same as claims made on labels and sleeves.

Writers

The song's composers. Over the years, these have been the subject of many label errors. The correct writers are shown, irrespective of what appears on the labels. And, as with song titles, errors are noted in the text.

Release Date

The month and year that each record was released in the UK.

Original Issue

Where a single is a re-issue of an earlier release, the month and year of the original issue is noted. Remember, a re-issue is defined as a single that has the same A and B side of a previous release, even if the sides are reversed.

Chart Entry Number

This is a running total of songs entering the UK chart and is further discussed in the introductory section. Obviously, unless a record made an appearance in the top 75 then no chart entry position is shown.

Highest Chart Position

The highest chart position reached by each record in the charts produced for the BBC - amongst others - and acknowledged by the music industry as being the most reliable source.

Following the title block (comprising the above features) each record is discussed in detail with any important or interesting information listed, including any errors in titles or writers' names.

For each record we have given details of the known variations in label design, colour and layout, the type of centre, logo changes, etc. Where these variations occur we have placed them in the order in which they appeared.

To further assist identification we have shown the year in which each variation appeared. Additionally, we have given details of the sleeve variations for each release.

For further information on label and sleeve variations, see the notes below. However, these refer to RCA singles only. Releases by other companies, notably Old Gold, are dealt with in a separate section.

1 Label Colour

(A)   New Black

We used the term 'new black' in **Elvis UK 1956-86** to distinguish between the earlier RCA black labels (1957-68) and later versions, which were first used in the UK in 1980 on re-pressings of singles and on new singles from 1984 onwards.

(B)   Silver

The first silver label single was released in 1984, **The Last Farewell**, RCA 459 (*S 143*), but this label colour was not used again until 1991.

(C)   Cream

A white/pale cream coloured label had been used for the promotional single, (**Now and then there's) A Fool Such As I/Danny**, TCB 001, in 1990. This colouring was used only once on a regular issue 45 when a variation of **The Twelfth Of Never** (**S 180**) appeared.

2 Type of Centre

There is not much consistency in the terms people use to describe the type of centre used for single releases, and in **Elvis UK 1956-86** we adopted the following terms, which we continue to use in this edition.

(A)   Knockout

Sometimes called a round centre. This was once the most common type of centre, but it now seems out of favour and few releases use this format. Indeed, from 1985, we know of no UK Elvis single release which used this type of centre. The last new release (as opposed to re-issue) to appear with a knockout centre was **Green, Green Grass Of Home** (*S 142*) in May 1984.

Released prior to the period covered by this book, this was the last known knockout centre Elvis single in the UK.

(B)   Solid

This is the type of centre found on all later singles.

(C)   Spider

Sometimes referred to as 'die-cut', a 'spider' is a removable plastic insert which was used to form the centre of the record. Occasionally a record was manufactured with no centre and a 'spider' had to be used before the record could be played. However, do not get confused with ex-juke box records which have had the centre mechanically removed. We know of no RCA single produced during this period that was sold originally with a 'spider' centre.

3 Type of Logo

(A)   Used on new black label singles.

(B)   Used on silver and cream label singles.

(C)   Used on a black label single.

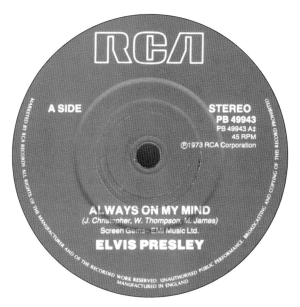

New black label/solid centre/RCA logo

Silver label/solid centre/round RCA logo

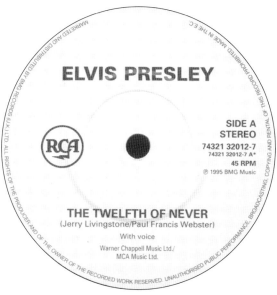

Cream label/round RCA logo

Black label/solid centre/RCA Victor logo

Sleeves

Sleeve variations for singles became almost a thing of the past in this era, as so few exist. Nevertheless, where a variation exists we have noted sufficient detail for you to identify the copy or copies you own.

A reference to the first single included in this book, *Always On My Mind*, RCA PB 49943 (**S 146**), released in July 1985, will enable you to follow the above detail if you are unfamiliar with the format we have adopted. Reference to the photographs and text will, we believe, quickly clarify any query you may have.

In order to maintain continuity from the previous book, and for the benefit of new readers, the label design used for *Always On My Mind* had first been introduced in 1980. Initially it was used for re-pressings of earlier singles. However, the first new release to use the design came in May 1984 when the single *Green, Green Grass Of Home*, RCA 405 (*S 142*) was issued. This design, standard for the day, therefore becomes the starting point for this book, and the basis of all the future changes we go on to describe.

The new black label design was relatively simple and contained fewer details than some of its predecessors. We mentioned earlier that we opted to use the term 'new black' to distinguish it from the first RCA black labels which were issued between 1957 and 1968. Only two new 7 inch singles had used the 'new black' design up to the release of *Always On My Mind*, and only minor amendments had been made. For example, the previous single, *The Elvis Medley*, RCA 476 (*S 145*), released in January 1985, had contained an additional point of detail included with the copyright warning to say that the record was published in 1985 by RCA Records.

The 12 inch format version of *Always On My Mind*, RCA PT 49944 (**S 147**), also used the same 'new black' label design, but with minor layout amendments; specifically, the mode was moved from the right to the left hand side of the label.

RCA used the standard logo and, in keeping with all 12 inch releases, the record had a solid centre.

Catalogue Numbers

For their singles RCA had used a catalogue numbering system which included their company name as a prefix, followed by a four digit catalogue number. By the mid-seventies RCA singles started to use an American inspired system commencing APBO and, later, a shortened version, PB. The catalogue number itself was either four or five digits.

By 1985 the RCA prefix disappeared completely and was replaced with the PB (or PT for 12 inch format singles) and the special prefix ARON. Worthy of special note is the interesting way in which catalogue numbers for RCA singles did not follow the normal incremental pattern, whereby successive singles were allocated a higher number, as was once the case. Instead, as of release number **S 146,** a decreasing sequence was used, so that a later single used a lower catalogue number than an earlier release.

This can clearly be illustrated by looking at the catalogue numbers for the singles included in this book. The first of these, *Always On My Mind* (**S 146**), released in July 1985, had a catalogue number PB 49943, whereas the next RCA single to use a catalogue number commencing with the prefix PB, *Stuck On You* (**S 162**), released in January 1988, was numbered PB 49595. Two intervening singles, *Ain't That Loving You Baby* (**S 154**) and *Love Me Tender* (**S 160**), released in March and August 1987 respectively, used the ARON catalogue numbering system. However, in the case of *Ain't That Loving You Baby*, etched in the vinyl between the run-out grooves was PB 49745 - the catalogue number which would have been used had the ARON not been substituted. It can be seen, therefore, that this number fits between the two examples shown above, thus maintaining the decreasing catalogue number sequence.

Following the two ARON singles, RCA returned to using PB for their next single, released in January 1989. *Mean Woman Blues* (**S 175**) used PB 49473, again retaining the now established pattern. Incidentally, the 12 inch equivalents of these singles used the next highest number e.g. 49944, 49596 and so on.

This system was then abandoned in favour of the industry standard catalogue number/bar code identifier, first used on *Don't Be Cruel* (**S 179**) in August 1992. This incorporated a number to identify the company itself, the product medium - vinyl, CD or cassette - as well as a conventional catalogue number to identify the product. Unfortunately, not only did this produce a very long 'catalogue' number, but a complicated explanation. Further details can be found in the introductory section on catalogue numbers.

RCA Picture Sleeves

In *Elvis UK 1956-86* we were able to categorise variations in the paper sleeves used for singles, and, as the period we covered was so lengthy, there were a considerable number of different designs and variations in use. Fortunately for the period covered by this book, our task has been that much easier, as all of the singles issued by RCA appeared in picture sleeves.

The trend away from paper sleeves actually goes back as far as 1981 when the last black (the standard for the time) paper sleeve was used on copies of the *Guitar Man* single, RCA 43 (*S 125*), and even then these were only used to supplement the picture sleeve versions which were used for the bulk of this particular single. Obviously the use of picture sleeves was far more desirable to the general public and fans alike, but this move restricted us to discussing the details featured on each sleeve and noting new or distinguishing characteristics. Not that this matters, for the real benefit - if that's the right word - of paper sleeves as far as we are concerned, was that any change in design helped to identify when a re-pressing of an earlier record was made. As records were not normally re-pressed and were removed from the catalogue within months of their initial release, this identification process was not normally required.

As a starting point then, we ought to mention that the quality of picture sleeves produced by RCA was second to none, and a vast improvement over what was once held as standard. When the first picture sleeves became available (the first being for the November 1969 single *Suspicious Minds*, RCA 1900 - *S 70*), the quality of the paper was no different to that of the regular paper sleeves. Also it didn't seem to matter too much at the time that all the subsequent releases in picture sleeves used the same photograph for several years! See releases *S 70, S 71, S 72, S 76, S 77* and *S 82.*

However by 1985, the standard had improved with the first batch of each new single using a high quality, glossy, thick card sleeve. Admittedly, later re-pressings often used a paper, matt finish sleeve (usually with a different shape to the cut-out), but nevertheless the quality was still good. Later still, the practice of re-pressing singles was abandoned, leaving only the gloss card sleeves, although initial pressings of *Heartbreak Hotel* (**S 181**), the last Elvis 7 inch vinyl single, appeared in a thin paper sleeve only. To all intents and purposes the sleeve quality was like that of the old EP sleeves, making the single an attractive proposition. Of course, it was more expensive for the manufacturers to make records with this type of sleeve, but falling sales figures encouraged new ideas, and by 1985 picture sleeves were standard, even for Elvis releases.

Almost all of the sleeves opened at the top, but there were two exceptions: *Don't Be Cruel* (**S 179**) and *The Twelfth Of Never* (**S 180**), both of which had openings at the side of the sleeve.

Standard features were the inclusion of a bar and price code, along with distribution and manufacturing details, so that the sleeve itself was more like that of an LP sleeve. It seemed quite obvious to all concerned that RCA put a great deal of effort into producing their singles in the most attractive and imaginative design possible, and reference to the variety of sleeves for records included in this book will clearly demonstrate how successful they were.

Bar Codes

A bar code appeared for the first time on a UK Elvis picture sleeve when *Always On My Mind* (**S 146**) was issued by RCA in July 1985. The bar code, a 13-digit number, was printed in the top right hand corner on the back of the sleeve. Its purpose was to allow electronic scanning of the information it contained, at the place where it was sold, so that the retailer could use this to update stock records and, more importantly, display the price of the product without having to label each item.

The bar code on the 7 inch version was different from that of the 12 inch version, because they had different catalogue numbers. For more detailed information on this see the introductory section.

Price Codes

Price codes had been a regular feature on RCA albums since February 1974, but their use on single releases had not occurred until June 1978 when *Don't Be Cruel*, PB 9265 (*S 118*) was issued. Furthermore, their use had been sporadic and, although the price code was included on the RCA single, *Always On My Mind* (**S 146**), no codes were printed on a number of the singles that followed.

In addition to the UK price code - the standard AA - those for Germany (shown as a 'D', for Deutschland) and France ('F') were included. The price code on the 12 inch versions was BB. Further background information on price codes can be found in the introductory section.

Track Descriptions

In the general introductory section of this book we have outlined what is meant by the terms 'Alternative Version', 'Unreleased Performance', 'Alternate Take', and so on. These terms have become much more commonplace and relevant as time has passed and were regular features on most Elvis LPs and CDs. However, these descriptions were not used on singles until *Always On My Mind* (**S 146**) was issued in July 1985.

The back of the sleeve made reference to *Always On My Mind* being an 'Alternative Version' and *Tomorrow Night* being the 'Original Sun Version', explaining to prospective buyers that these tracks were different from the regular versions. The 12 inch version of the single added 'Alternative Version' to *Ain't That Loving You Baby*. However, no mention of the unusual nature of the songs was made on the labels.

Unfortunately, not all subsequent releases showed this information, despite the need for additional identification. This was surprising given that they provided an excellent marketing opportunity which could have been exploited more fully with collectors.

A Complete Listing Of The UK Singles From 1985

A significant feature of the releases from this period was the number of releases by Old Gold who contributed a total of twenty singles, some of them straight re-issues of original couplings, with others being composite releases of various A sides. We realise that this can be very confusing, complicated by the fact that RCA, whose release pattern was erratic, tended to release a mixture of original material amidst alternative versions and live recordings. Therefore, to separate a re-issue from 'new' versions, we have adopted the same approach as for LPs and included details of the original issue and any previous re-issues, enabling a quick and easy cross-reference. Obviously the original issue and many of the re-issue references are detailed in *Elvis UK 1956-86*, but, if nothing else, this system will allow the number of re-issues to be noted more easily.

With one exception (the October 1995 release of *The Twelfth Of Never* - **S 180**) all of the releases in the singles' section, 7 inch and 12 inch, play at 45 revolutions per minute (rpm), which has enabled us to drop the reference to the playing speed throughout this section. *The Twelfth Of Never* plays at 45 rpm on the A side, but 33 1/3 RPM on the B side - the only UK Elvis single ever to do so.

To provide a greater sense of continuity we have re-presented details of the last two singles included in *Elvis UK 1956-86*, PB 49943 (**S 146**) and PT 49944 (**S 147**), both featuring *Always On My Mind* in different release formats. We felt this was necessary because of the large gap between RCA releases (July 1985 - when the above were issued - to March 1987). Also we wished to correct the omission of label and sleeve photographs, and at the same time we have been able to add a few extra details not included in the original book.

S 146	RCA	PB 49943

Always On My Mind {S} (James, Carson, Christopher)
Tomorrow Night {Undubbed} {M} (Coslow, Grosz)

Released July 1985   **Chart Entry Number 139**
                               Highest Chart Position 59

Always On My Mind had, of course, been issued as a single in December 1972, coupled with *Separate Ways* (*S 85*). This was the version which featured an electric guitar. However, a remixed version of the song was included in the 1981 film *This Is Elvis*, and the album of the same name (*LP 150*). This time there was no lead guitar evident in the mix and, thus, this 'version' was tagged the 'acoustic' version. Finally though, in July 1985, came this latest version of the song, which featured a heavy string and horn accompaniment.

Although there has always been some division of opinion as regards how many versions there have been of this track, all evidence points to the fact that the three 'versions' referred to above were simply remixes of the same recording, as cut on 29 March 1972 at RCA's Studio C in Hollywood. To date the only genuine alternative version of the song (take 2) was included on the CD *Platinum A Life In Music* released in July 1997.

The B side of this release was an undubbed version of *Tomorrow Night*, as featured on the album *Reconsider Baby* (*LP 271*), issued in 1985, not the overdubbed version released in 1965 on *Elvis For Everyone* (*LP 26*). A further complication occurred in 1992 with the release of what was said to be the original Sun recording of this track on the fifties' boxed set. The implication was obvious: both the 1965 and 1985 'versions' had been subject to editing and splicing.

The publishing date given for the A side was 1973 when, in fact, it was originally issued in 1972. The fact that this was a remix does not alter the publishing date. However, the B side is different. This 'original', undubbed version was not published in 1965, but in 1985. Needless to say the reference that the track was stereo, as the label claimed, was nonsense.

The release came in a very attractive picture sleeve, showing a side shot of Elvis, in colour, from the very early 1970s. The back of the sleeve had the song titles, a reference to what versions they were, their writers (incorrectly shown as Christopher, Thompson, James for *Always On My Mind* - an error repeated on the label), and which albums they were taken from. No vocal accompaniment credits were shown on the label or sleeve.

For the first time the cover of a single carried the bar code and European price codes, even though it was a UK inspired release. In the bottom left hand corner was the LC 0316 number - also making its first appearance on a single sleeve.

The single was deleted in November 1987.

Label Variations

NEW BLACK LABEL/SOLID CENTRE
1   **1985 PRESSING**

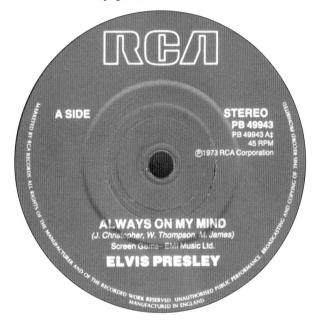

Sleeve Variations

1   Gloss
2   Matt

RCA Special Singles

The use of special edition format singles had become a very common method of promoting and increasing sales for many years by the time the first of Elvis's 'special' singles was released in December 1979 - *It Won't Seem Like Christmas (without you)*, RCA PC 9464 (*S 121*). On that occasion the special format was a 12 inch format single with a coloured cardboard sleeve and large labels, including a picture of Elvis on the A side. Whilst the special format contained the same songs, the 12 inch version of the B side, **Merry Christmas Baby**, was the full song, not an edited version, making the 12 inch version more attractive to buyers. At that time, the method of denoting that this was a special format was to prefix the catalogue number PC, instead of the PB used for the regular 7 inch single, PB 9464. The important thing was that both used the same catalogue number, a vital consideration for RCA when the main purpose of the 12 inch version was to increase overall sales. If the special format had been numbered differently, there might have been a possibility of the two records being treated as two separate products, thus damaging chart success for both. The industry was, however, rather tolerant of such tactics and this practice of special editions became quite acceptable.

However, for our purposes we have always considered the 7 and 12 inch version of the above to be two separate records; our reasoning being that they have different catalogue numbers and the material they used was also different, albeit in the length of one song. The 7 inch single was released in November 1979, and the 12 inch version in December 1979, demonstrating that the latter was released as a sales stimulant.

RCA's next single, **It's Only Love**, RCA 4 (*S 122*), was less attractive in its 12 inch format. Issued in a black 12 inch sleeve with a blue label, it was really just a larger version of the 7 inch single, although it did contain the artificially extended version of the A side. It was given the catalogue number RCAT 4, the 'T' denoting twelve inch, and we allocated it the release number *S 123* to show that we considered it a separate release.

In June 1982 RCA issued the song **The Sound Of Your Cry** (*S 135*) on a single and allocated the catalogue number RCA 232. A picture disc version was also available at the same time, and this special release was given the prefix RCAP (for picture disc), although it used the same catalogue number (232). The overriding consideration for our purposes was that both singles contained the same material, the A side and *I'll Never Know* on the B side. We, therefore, considered that this was the same single and allocated the same release number *S 135*, believing that the special, picture disc format was merely a variation of the regular, 7 inch single. After this, RCA used a 'P' in the catalogue number prefix to indicate a picture disc; and much later the 'T' (used to indicate a twelve inch single in the past) was also used when a ten inch single was released in November 1984 - **The Last Farewell** (*S 144*). However, when a picture disc was also released in the ten inch format, only a 'P' was used, as in the case of *S 141*, **I Can Help**.

We thought it would be useful to list all of the special Elvis singles released prior to the starting point of this book, along with their 7 inch equivalents, to allow for comparisons to be made.

Release Number	Catalogue Number	Titles	Release Date
S 120	RCA PB 9464 7 Inch	**It Won't Seem Like Christmas (without you)** *Merry Christmas Baby*	Nov 1979
S 121	RCA PC 9464 12 Inch	**It Won't Seem Like Christmas (without you)** *Merry Christmas Baby*	Dec 1979

The 12 inch single contained what was thought to be the full studio recording of **Merry Christmas Baby**.

Release Number	Catalogue Number	Titles	Release Date
S 122	RCA 4 7 Inch	**It's Only Love** *Beyond The Reef*	Aug 1980
S 123	RCAT 4 12 Inch	**It's Only Love** *Beyond The Reef*	Oct 1980

The 12 Inch single contained an artificially extended version of **It's Only Love**.

Release Number	Catalogue Number	Titles	Release Date
S 135	RCA 232 7 Inch	**The Sound Of Your Cry** *I'll Never Know*	Jun 1982
S 135	RCA 232 Picture Disc	**The Sound Of Your Cry** *I'll Never Know*	Jun 1982

Both formats contained identical material.

Release Number	Catalogue Number	Titles	Release Date
S 136	RCA 1028 7 Inch	**Jailhouse Rock** *Treat Me Nice*	Jan 1983
S 137	RCAP 1028 Picture Disc	**Jailhouse Rock** *The Elvis Medley*	Jan 1983

The picture disc contained a different B side.

Release Number	Catalogue Number	Titles	Release Date
S 138	RCA 332 7 Inch	**(You're so square) Baby I Don't Care** *True Love*	Apr 1983
S 139	RCAP 332 Picture Disc	**(You're so square) Baby I Don't Care** *One-Sided Love Affair* *Tutti Frutti*	Apr 1983

The picture disc featured a different B side and used two songs, not one.

S 140	RCA 369 7 Inch	*I Can Help* *The Lady Loves Me*	Nov 1983
S 141	RCAP 369 10 Inch Picture Disc	*I Can Help* *If Every Day Was Like Christmas* *The Lady Loves Me*	Dec 1983

The 10 inch picture disc contained an additional track.

S 143	RCA 459 7 Inch	*The Last Farewell* *It's Easy For You*	Oct 1984
S 144	RCAT 459 10 Inch	*The Last Farewell* *It's Easy For You* *Shake, Rattle And Roll* *Flip, Flop And Fly* *That's All Right* *My Heart Cries For You*	Nov 1984

The 10 inch single placed the B side from the 7 inch on the A side, with several tracks added - overdubbed live versions of **Shake, Rattle And Roll** and **Flip, Flop And Fly**, and an alternative version of **That's All Right** (previously issued).

The special releases up to 1985 had one thing in common: they all used an identical catalogue number, although the prefix, as we have seen, changed to identify the special release format. The 12 inch single release of **Always On My Mind** (**S 147**) in July 1985, deviated from this pattern. The single used the prefix PT, to denote 'Popular Twelve Inch' which, in itself was new, but it followed the European number conventions adopted by RCA UK. However, the catalogue number itself was now five digits (as was the 7 inch version), again from the European numbering system. More importantly, the 12 inch version was numbered differently to the 7 inch version - 49944 and 49943 respectively - the first time this had occurred. Subsequent special releases followed the same pattern.

S 147   **RCA   PT 49944**

Always On My Mind {S} (James, Carson, Christopher)
Tomorrow Night {Undubbed} {M} (Coslow, Grosz)
Ain't That Loving You Baby {Fast version} {M} (Otis, Hunter)
Dark Moon {M} (Miller)

Released July 1985

Released simultaneously with the 7 inch version of **Always On My Mind**, this was the 12 inch extended play edition featuring four songs: the two on the 7 inch release, along with the alternative fast version of **Ain't That Loving You Baby** and **Dark Moon**. **Dark Moon** was a 'home' recording, first released on the album **A Golden Celebration**, PL 85172(6), in October 1984 (*LP 251*). Originally it was thought that this single release would be a 10 inch record, and it was advertised as such in **Elvis Monthly**.

The sleeve featured the same photograph of Elvis as the one shown on the 7 inch version, but this time Lisa and Priscilla were also included. Note that some touching up had been done on the 7 inch cover as Lisa's hair could not be seen at all on that sleeve.

The reverse of the cover was very similar to the 7 inch cover but, of course, carried slightly different details. The bar code and price codes were different, and the record had been given a different catalogue number, unlike other 'special' or extended versions. Unlike the 7 inch cover, the 12 inch sleeve credited J.D. Sumner and The Stamps on **Always On My Mind**, but the label did not. Another difference was the addition of a note that the title track was included on the video release of **This Is Elvis**. This 12 inch picture sleeve was, and still is, unique in that it had a side opening to take out and insert the record, exactly as LPs do. All subsequent 12 inch sleeves opened at the top.

The two extra tracks were featured on side two and they, along with **Tomorrow Night**, were asterisked to show that they were in mono. The label, however, showed all tracks to be stereo. The back of the sleeve quoted an incorrect catalogue number for **Reconsider Baby** - *LP 271* - (shown as PL 851418 instead of 85418) and the typeface for the writer of **Dark Moon** was inconsistent to that of other writers. As with the 7 inch release, the publishing date given on side two i.e. 1958, was ludicrously wrong; the alternative version of **Ain't That Loving You Baby** was published in 1985 and **Dark Moon** in 1984. The writers of **Always On My Mind** were incorrect, and ought to have read James, Carson, Christopher. Finally, **Ain't That Loving You Baby** was shown on both label and sleeve as **Ain't That Lovin' You Baby**.

This 12 inch single was deleted in February 1987, eight months before the 7 inch format.

Label Variations

NEW BLACK LABEL/SOLID CENTRE
    1   1985 PRESSING

Sleeve Variations

    1   Gloss

To the dismay of many fans no single, re-issue or otherwise, was released by RCA in the UK during 1986, the first time this had happened since the initial (HMV) release in 1956 - a thirty year period.

RCA had come close to this on a couple of occasions, 1979, for example, when *It Won't Seem Like Christmas (without you)* (S 120) made a late appearance. Fortunately 1986 was not completely void of a single release because Old Gold happily stepped in and released six singles issued simultaneously in October. Nevertheless, the lack of a new RCA single was both disappointing and upsetting to many fans, who saw the lack of activity as being a result of total apathy at senior level within RCA.

The other unusual thing about 1986 was that, as far as RCA were concerned, there was no mention anywhere, to the best of our knowledge at least, of a single even being considered or planned. In itself this was strange, as it was quite commonplace for rumours to circulate amongst fans about a forthcoming release, even though these often proved misleading, with proposed tracks being changed or cancelled completely.

If anything, this symbolised the sad state of affairs at RCA, whose release policy was, even at the best of times, confused. Having said that, the industry as a whole was beginning to feel the wind of change more in favour of compact discs, as the general decline in the sale of vinyl continued, particularly of 7 inch singles. The trend of stocking only chart material spread to many of the larger chain stores, effectively bringing to an end the long established tradition of shops carrying a wide range of product from which potential customers were able to select.

Viewed in hindsight then, the lack of an RCA Elvis single in 1986 was symptomatic of the times, but what fans found hard to understand was that RCA had found the time, and the willingness, to enter a licencing deal with Old Gold, who then proceeded to release six singles under their own banner. Old Gold's policy was to issue old hits and, in their way, they were extremely successful at doing so. For many fans this move was welcomed, but there was a feeling that RCA had 'sold out' (having 'milked' whatever they could from these tracks) and worse still, that they had failed to capitalise on a marketing opportunity which was then left to others to grasp, and reap whatever rewards were available. Admittedly the potential for the high profits once associated with singles had long passed, as had the desire for retaining singles on catalogue, particularly with the relentless in-roads made by compact discs which, to the record companies, made far better economic sense.

Nevertheless, if Old Gold could do it, why not RCA? Of course we are in no position to judge the business value of such a decision to RCA, a decision that they alone could have made. Our concern is that a sensible policy, based on a planned series of imaginative releases, was not evident.

Of course, there has never been universal agreement among fans as to which songs would make good singles, with all possible suggestions being greeted with scorn and derision in certain quarters and unbounded enthusiasm elsewhere; and, clearly, there seems little point in discussing here what should have been done with certain songs. If we look back over the ten year period from Elvis's death (1977 to 1987) and analyse the singles that were released, we find that they fall broadly into two catagories. There were opportunist releases like RCA 476, *The Elvis Medley* (S 145), and album promotional releases like RCA 369, *I Can Help* (S 140). An idea not fully exploited was the release of singles to tie in with anniversaries, such as the one used in January 1983 when *Jailhouse Rock*, RCA 1028 (S 136), was issued to commemorate the twenty fifth anniversary of its original release in the UK. It would have been pleasing to see this extended to other notable events - what about *It's Now Or Never* in 1985? This kind of release, suitably handled, could

have done well; not top ten material perhaps, but sufficient to stimulate enough interest in complementary releases of 'new' singles or albums.

In conclusion, and for your general information, we thought it would be useful to include at this point a list of the singles released following Elvis's death until 1985 and the first single included in this book. They are referenced in the same way as those in the full chronological listings.

Release Number	Catalogue Number	Titles	Release Date
S 117	RCA PB 1165	*My Way* / *America, The Beautiful*	Nov 1977
S 118	RCA PB 9265	*Don't Be Cruel* / *Hound Dog*	Jun 1978
S 119	RCA PB 9334	*Old Shep* / *Paralyzed*	Nov 1978
S 120	RCA PB 9464	*It Won't Seem Like Christmas (without you)* / *Merry Christmas Baby*	Nov 1979
S 121	RCA PC 9464	*It Won't Seem Like Christmas (without you)* / *Merry Christmas Baby*	Dec 1979
S 122	RCA RCA 4	*It's Only Love* / *Beyond The Reef*	Aug 1980
S 123	RCA RCAT 4	*It's Only Love* / *Beyond The Reef*	Oct 1980
S 124	RCA RCA 16I	*Santa Claus Is Back In Town* / *I Believe*	Nov 1980
S 125	RCA RCA 43	*Guitar Man* / *Faded Love*	Feb 1981
S 126	RCA RCA 48	*Loving Arms* / *You Asked Me To*	Mar 1981
S 127	RCA GOLD 500	*I Just Can't Help Believin'* / *Bridge Over Troubled Water*	Jul 1981
S 128	RCA GOLD 506	*An American Trilogy* / *Suspicious Minds*	Jul 1981
S 129	RCA GOLD 510	*The Girl Of My Best Friend* / *Suspicion*	Jul 1981
S 130	RCA GOLD 520	*That's All Right* / *Harbour Lights*	Aug 1981
S 131	RCA GOLD 534	*Good Rockin' Tonight* / *Mystery Train*	Oct 1981
S 132	RCA GOLD 541	*If Every Day Was Like Christmas* / *Blue Christmas*	Nov 1981
S 133	RCA RCA 196	*Are You Lonesome Tonight?* / *From A Jack To A King*	Feb 1982
S 134	RCA GOLD 544	*Way Down* / *Moody Blue*	May 1982
S 135	RCA RCA 232	*The Sound Of Your Cry* / *I'll Never Know*	Jun 1982
S 135	RCA RCA 232	*The Sound Of Your Cry* / *I'll Never Know* (Picture Disc)	Jun 1982
S 136	RCA RCA 1028	*Jailhouse Rock* / *Treat Me Nice*	Jan 1983

S 137	RCA	*Jailhouse Rock*	Jan 1983
	RCAP 1028	*The Elvis Medley* (Picture Disc)	
S 138	RCA	*(You're so square) Baby*	Apr 1983
	RCA 332	*I Don't Care*	
		True Love	
S 139	RCA	*(You're so square) Baby*	Apr 1983
	RCAP 332	*I Don't Care*	
		One-Sided Love Affair	
		True Love (Picture Disc)	
S 140	RCA	*I Can Help*	Nov 1983
	RCA 369	*The Lady Loves Me*	
S 141	RCA	*I Can Help*	Dec 1983
	RCAP 369	*If Every Day Was Like Christmas*	
		The Lady Loves Me (Picture Disc)	
S 142	RCA	*Green, Green Grass Of Home*	May 1984
	RCA 405	*Release Me (and let me love again)*	
		Solitaire	
S 143	RCA	*The Last Farewell*	Oct 1984
	RCA 459	*It's Easy For You*	
S 144	RCA	*The Last Farewell*	Nov 1984
	RCAT 459	*It's Easy For You*	
		Shake, Rattle And Roll	
		Flip, Flop And Fly	
		That's All Right	
		My Heart Cries For You	
S 145	RCA	*The Elvis Medley*	Jan 1985
	RCA 476	*Blue Suede Shoes*	

Please note: We allocated the same release number to both the regular 7 inch and picture disc singles of **The Sound Of Your Cry**, as both used the same catalogue number, unlike other 12 inch or special releases.

Single Deletion - March 1986

On 1 March 1986 RCA deleted one of the Elvis 'Golden Grooves' releases, **Good Rockin' Tonight/Mystery Train**, GOLD 534 (*S 131*). This single had been originally released in October 1981.

Single Deletion - June 1986

Another one of the seven Golden Grooves releases featuring Elvis, **If Every Day Was Like Christmas/Blue Christmas**, GOLD 541 (*S 132*), first released in November 1981, was deleted on 20 June 1986.

Old Gold

Eight years after the formation of the company, Old Gold issued their first Elvis records in October 1986. Old Gold had been launched in January 1978, and quickly established itself as being the premier supplier of "Golden Oldies" - original hit recordings - often with vastly improved sound quality when compared to the original. Old Gold's claim that they probably had the largest selection of such material went unchallenged. Initially Old Gold concentrated on 7 inch singles (on which their reputation was developed), producing good quality product and making available otherwise difficult to locate material at affordable prices.

The man behind Old Gold was Keith Yershon, who once worked for record distributors Lightning Records during the mid-seventies. It was during this time that Yershon became aware of the constant demand from retailers and juke box operators for deleted 7 inch singles, which they were unable to obtain from record companies. This was the prompt for Yershon to start Old Gold (journalist Roger St. Pierre thought up the name), although still within the Lightning Records organisation. Old Gold's brief was to license the requested songs from the owners, the record companies, and issue them in 7 inch singles' format on their own label. The first single to be released was **Wild Thing** by the Troggs.

Over the next four years, the Old Gold catalogue grew steadily and, by 1982, had developed to include 120 singles. Yershon bought Old Gold from Lightning Records and devoted considerable time and effort into further expansion, to the point where he was able to launch a further 120 singles simultaneously - the biggest ever number of singles issued at any one time by any one record company.

In 1985, the first 19 Old Gold albums were released in the Revival series. These were followed by the first 12 inch singles series and, by June 1988, the first Old Gold CDs appeared. This expansion into so many different formats, including plans for videos, allied to high sales figures, attracted the attention of the giant Pickwick group who were responsible, via another licensing arrangement, for many Elvis albums which appeared on the Camden label. In July 1988 Yershon and his partner, Brian Gibbon, sold Old Gold to Pickwick. Gibbon headed Old Gold's sister label Start, the company which issued **The Songs Of Bob Dylan**, a various artist compilation, which included Elvis's **Tomorrow Is A Long Time**. (See the section on various artist compilation LPs, **VA LP 39**.)

However, to backtrack, Old Gold released their first Elvis material in October 1986 when six singles were issued simultaneously. They were:

OG 9616 **In The Ghetto/Suspicious Minds**

OG 9618 **Party/Got A Lot O' Livin' To Do!**

OG 9620 **Blue Moon/I Don't Care If The Sun Don't Shine**

OG 9622 **(Marie's the name) His Latest Flame /The Girl of My Best Friend**

OG 9624 **An American Trilogy/Until It's Time For You To Go**

OG 9626 **Love Me Tender/(Let me be your) Teddy Bear**

It can clearly be seen how these releases fell into two categories: those where two original A sides had been combined to produce a unique coupling and, secondly, those which were straight re-issues of the original release. The overall result was an extremely varied and pleasing collection of firm favourites and material long since deleted in singles' format.

It has to be noted that many of the songs appeared in stereo for the first time on a single, and there seems little doubt that we have to thank mastering engineer Bob Jones for this. At least it was Bob who supplied the tapes. Yet the first batch was cut by 'Bilbo', whose real name, incidentally, is Denis Blackham and who used to be a staff engineer at RCA. Denis etched into the vinyl 'Bilbo tape one' or 'DB tape one' when someone else did the cutting.

Old Gold had, in fact, acquired the rights to a further eight Elvis songs, but because some legal clearances were delayed, the additional four singles planned to accompany those listed above, had their release date put back until April 1987.

The first six releases were all pressed in September 1986 with a press run of 2,000 copies. This figure represents the number of copies ordered by Old Gold, but the actual quantity produced could be lower or greater than this figure, depending on faults or errors in the production process. Old Gold, in keeping with many companies, used a variety of major and independent record companies to press records on their behalf. However, all of the first six singles were pressed by Polygram at their factory in Walthamstow, North London. Later pressings of these singles - and many of the later releases - were pressed elsewhere after the Polygram plant closed down.

However, irrespective of where the records were pressed, Old Gold singles always used the solid centre format throughout the time they were available. Any spider centre copies were prepared for jukebox use, after they left Old Gold.

Label Colour

As with all other record companies' product, the colour of the label varied considerably, even within the same print run. Old Gold's chosen colour, however, did seem to suffer more than most in this respect, with some wide fluctuations in shade. However, in keeping with Old Gold's intentions, we have described the colour as 'Gold', and , with one exception, have made no further attempt to create other categories. Little would be gained by doing so, for it would necessitate impossible descriptions on our part and, you would need to own several copies of the same record to make any comparison meaningful.

Label colours are, therefore, described as Gold with the exception of an unusual variation which can only be described as 'Mottled Gold', being darker than the normal label colouring, with a marble effect.

Bar Codes

One feature, possibly unique to Old Gold, and certainly for UK Elvis records, was the inclusion of a bar code printed on the record label. Its purpose, described in more detail in the introductory section, was to enable stores to scan electronically the information contained in the stripes, reducing, if not eliminating, the need for sales' assistants to manually key the price details into the till.

Normally the bar code would have been located on the record sleeve only, as it was on Camden and RCA releases, for example. Later, when Old Gold issued picture sleeve singles, the bar code was printed on the sleeves, but was retained on the record label. Of course, it was never possible to print the bar code on the normal Old Gold paper sleeve, simply because each bar code was unique for each record release, and only where the sleeve was different to other releases could it be included.

Label Detail

The first batch of six Old Gold releases showed that they had negotiated with RCA/Ariola in obtaining the licence for the twelve songs released on Old Gold in October 1986. This was made quite clear, as each label quoted:

Licensed from RCA/Ariola Ltd.

However, this detail only appeared on the first six Old Gold releases, as it was changed with the subsequent batches, reflecting the changing 'ownership' of RCA. Normally detail such as this was extremely useful in helping to date when a particular record was pressed and/or released, but in the case of Old Gold releases, this was not as helpful as it might have been.

The reason for this was due to the fact that Old Gold did not update their label details when any re-pressings were made, making later pressings identical to the original pressing. This makes dating a record from the label details virtually impossible. Thankfully though, regular changes in Old Gold sleeves meant that we can refer to the sleeve design to identify the period in question.

In summary: the first six releases retained the detail shown above, despite being re-pressed, even though later releases showed the licencing information appropriate at the time of their release.

Sleeve Types

Packaging has always been a vital part of marketing, of helping the product sell, and the sleeves used by record companies was often changed to re-stimulate interest in the product. Old Gold were no exception to this, and regularly modified their sleeve design whilst the record label design remained unchanged. Consequently knowing when a particular sleeve design was introduced goes some way to identifying when a record was pressed, although this is not a foolproof guarantee if the record was bought second-hand.

We have separated the various Old Gold sleeves into types and described how these can be identified.

Type 1 October 1986 - March 1987

At the time when the first six Elvis singles were released, Old Gold were using what they referred to as a 'house bag' for all their singles. What this meant was that they had a standard sleeve which was used for any record they released, thus keeping production costs to a minimum. These sleeves were yellow and chocolate brown and featured some of the songs available as singles printed on the sleeve - a highly effective method of advertising.

The back of the sleeve retained the same design, although at the sides were foldovers, and at the bottom details of how to obtain an Old Gold catalogue were added.

Type 2 April 1987 - April 1989

From time to time Old Gold updated their sleeve design, and by the time the second batch of Elvis singles were released in April 1987, a change in the 'house bag' had taken place. The basic design itself remained unchanged from type 1 sleeves, but the colours had been reversed so that brown now became the predominant colour.

The song titles had also been amended and updated with many new titles being added, reflecting the ever changing additions and deletions to the Old Gold catalogue. Careful observers will note that no fewer than three Elvis tracks available on Old Gold at that time had been included - *(Marie's the name) His Latest Flame* (minus the words in brackets), *In The Ghetto* and *Love Me Tender*.

Type 3 May 1989 - Mid 1991

The intention was for type 2 sleeves to remain in use for at least one year to eighteen months before a new design was produced. As it turned out though, this was slightly longer.

Type 3 sleeves dispensed with the layout used so successfully from 1986, and used a completely new design, retaining only the Old Gold logo. The same colours of yellow and chocolate brown were used, although these were given greater contrast by virtue of the diagonal yellow band running down the sleeve. Incidentally, this meant that the design on each side was identical, whereas the previous sleeves were not.

Type 4 Late 1990 - Mid 1991

This was almost identical in design to the type 3 sleeves. These sleeves appeared with the same mottled yellow marble-like effect that had been used on some labels. The yellow appeared as a much darker image and was easily distinguished from the more common type 3 sleeves.

Type 1

Type 2

Type 3

Type 4

Picture Sleeves

Old Gold used two quite distinct designs for their picture sleeves. The first design featured a rectangular title box superimposed over a pattern of blue shapes. The design was first used from January 1989 and subsequently a total of five Elvis singles appeared using this design. The singles in question were:

OG 9616   *In The Ghetto/Suspicious Minds*
OG 9624   *An American Trilogy/Until It's Time For You To Go*
OG 9626   *Love Me Tender/(Let me be your) Teddy Bear*
OG 9740   *Jailhouse Rock/Treat Me Nice*
OG 9744   *Always On My Mind/Burning Love*

The second design featured a diamond shaped title block over a montage of photographs showing famous recording artists. First used from June 1990, only two Elvis singles were released in this type of sleeve. These were:

OG 9700   *Hound Dog/Don't Be Cruel*
OG 9761   *The Wonder Of You/If I Can Dream*

Old Gold's picture sleeves were really an extension of the 'house bag' idea, where one design could be used for all releases. The difference with picture sleeves being that because they had to contain a picture of the artist in question along with the song titles, it was necessary to overprint the variable features onto a standard background, and that is what Old Gold had to do with their picture sleeves. Of course, this 'extra' process could lead to errors, and we have seen examples of Old Gold picture sleeves without the titles or picture, although this did not happen for any Elvis single, as far as we are aware.

The actual dates when each single became available in a picture sleeve is provided in the chronological listing of 7 inch picture sleeve releases.

S 148 | Old Gold OG 9616

In The Ghetto {S} (Davis)
Suspicious Minds {S} (James)

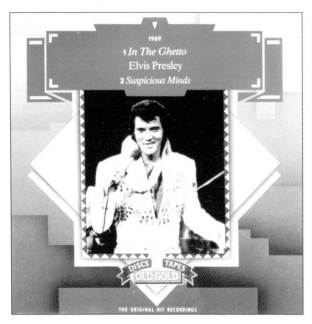

Released October 1986

This was the first (by virtue of it having the lowest catalogue number) of the first batch of Old Gold singles receiving simultaneous release in October 1986. The most surprising feature of the release appeared on the record label on which *In The Ghetto* was subtitled *(Vicious Circle)*. You may recall that, according to the booklet accompanying the LP *Elvis - A Legendary Performer Vol. 3,* RCA PL 13082 *(LP 106)*, that the song was originally copyrighted with its full title *In The Ghetto (The Vicious Circle)*, but RCA had requested, and was granted, permission to release the song without the subtitle. Note that this Old Gold single omitted the word *The* in the subtitle on the label, and that the subtitle was not mentioned at all on the picture sleeve, produced later.

Although we cannot be absolutely certain, this appears to be the only occasion where this subtitle was used on any release. Certainly it had never been used in the UK previously. It does seem unlikely that the original arrangement referred to earlier had expired, necessitating use of the subtitle, as it was not used on the RCA LP release *The Memphis Record*, RCA PL 86221(2) (**LP 284**), released in August 1987. Probably the only reason for it being used here, was that someone at RCA just sent out the wrong information, although it is possible that the previous arrangement covered RCA releases only.

As regards the material, both songs were recorded two days apart at the same session in January 1969, but they were not released as consecutive UK A sides because RCA 1869, *Clean Up Your Own Backyard* (*S 69*) separated them. This Old Gold release represented the third appearance of *Suspicious Minds* on a single, once as the A side - in November 1969, RCA 1900 (*S 70*), and then on the B side of *An American Trilogy*, RCA GOLD 506, in July 1981 (*S 128*) - and perhaps this was why *In The Ghetto* received the honours this time around, as its June 1969 appearance was its only other outing on a single (*S 68*). The version of *Suspicious Minds* featured here was the full length, original single version, complete with the extended ending. However, for the first time on a UK single, both songs were in stereo.

This single was re-pressed in January 1989 with a press run of 5000 copies, and issued in a picture sleeve, featuring a shot from *Aloha From Hawaii*. Two other Old Gold singles, *An American Trilogy*, OG 9624, and *Always On My Mind*, OG 9744, (see **S 152** and **S 166** respectively) were also re-pressed at the same time, and were

also issued in picture sleeves. *In The Ghetto*, thus, became the forty-first UK picture sleeve. Later, in October 1989, a further 3,000 copies were produced, although Old Gold used the same picture sleeve design as the earlier batch.

Other than the use of the subtitle referred to above, there were no label errors, and perhaps the use of the subtitle was more a quirk of the system rather than an error. The picture sleeve used for later pressings did have some rather interesting points, however. Firstly the photograph of Elvis was from *Aloha From Hawaii* in 1973 and was, therefore, not really 'representative of the period', as was Old Gold's intention. Secondly, and more seriously, the sleeve notes referred to *Suspicious Minds* as being 'cunningly spliced from two separate takes'. Our understanding of this is that the ending from the same take was spliced on again at the end to increase the length of the song. Finally, *In The Ghetto* was quoted as having reached the number one position in the UK charts, when it actually peaked at number two.

Label Variations

GOLD LABEL/SOLID CENTRE
1   **1986 PRESSING**

Sleeve Variations

1	Type 1
2	Type 2
3	Picture sleeve - first design

S 149 | Old Gold   OG 9618

Party {M} (Robinson)
Got A Lot O' Livin' To Do! {M} (Schroeder, Weisman)

Released October 1986
Original Issue October 1957 (*S 14*)

This release retained the original coupling of the second RCA release in the UK (*S 14*), although it was the fourteenth consecutive release overall when considering HMV releases too. It was issued twenty-nine years to the month after the original single was released.

However, neither of these songs had been available on a single since the original RCA single was deleted in the mid-1960s, making this release, therefore, a welcome change to some of the more familiar material which continued to be re-issued. This single, however, did not sell very well and went on to suffer the fate of being one of the earliest deletions from Old Gold's catalogue.

As with all the other film soundtrack material re-released by Old Gold, no reference was made to the fact that both songs were featured in the film *Loving You*. This was not really surprising when considering that the idea of including this detail originally was to encourage people to visit the cinema in the hope that they would then buy LPs and more singles. Clearly the cinema reference was no longer relevant.

The only label errors concerned *Got A Lot O' Livin' To Do!* which included the word *of* instead of *O'* and, predictably, no exclamation mark appeared at the end of the title.

Label Variations

GOLD LABEL/SOLID CENTRE
1   1986 PRESSING

Sleeve Variations

1   Type 1
2   Type 2
3   Type 3

S 150	Old Gold	OG 9620

Blue Moon {M} (Rodgers, Hart)
I Don't Care If The Sun Don't Shine {M} (David)

Released October 1986
Original Issue November 1956 (*S 5*)

This was Elvis's one hundred and fiftieth UK single release and, along with the previous single (**S 149**), became the only re-issues in the first batch of Old Gold releases. Despite its humble origins, this was the third time that **Blue Moon** had appeared on the A side of a UK single and the second time with its original B side.

Considering the extremely high quality of the material released by Old Gold (of the twenty Elvis singles for which they were responsible, all forty songs had reached the number eleven position or better), this single, albeit a top ten entry in its day, stood out as being unusual and almost insignificant when compared to more well known Elvis material.

This was the earliest Elvis material issued by Old Gold which, in itself, was quite fitting as the original single, the fifth to be issued in the UK, was the first single to contain Sun material.

All four types of the Old Gold sleeves were used for this single over a period of four years; yet, as with all the Old Gold singles, there were no changes evident in label design.

Label Variations

GOLD LABEL/SOLID CENTRE
1   1986 PRESSING
2   PRODUCTION ERROR 1990 PRESSING
         (Type 4 sleeve) - No label A side

Sleeve Variations

1   Type 1
2   Type 2
3   Type 3
4   Type 4

S 151	Old Gold	OG 9622

(Marie's the name) His Latest Flame {S} (Pomus, Shuman)
The Girl of My Best Friend {S} (Ross, Bobrick)

Released October 1986

This single combined two popular and well known A sides, although officially when *The Girl Of My Best Friend* was first released in the UK it was as the B side of *A Mess Of Blues* (*S 29*). This was the third time that both of these songs had appeared on singles, but the first time together. *(Marie's the name) His Latest Flame* had originally appeared as an A side in October 1961 (*S 35*).

Both songs appeared here in stereo. Of course both had appeared in this mode on LPs, but only occasionally on a single. *The Girl Of My Best Friend* was in stereo when it appeared on Golden Grooves, GOLD 510 (*S 129*) in July 1981, while *(Marie's the name) His Latest Flame* only appeared in stereo on an RCA single when it was re-pressed on the blue label (RCA 2702) in 1982 - even though the label had stated mono. The reason for this was that Bob Jones had re-mastered this song (and a number of others, it seems) in stereo, apparently without RCA's knowledge. It can only be assumed that at the time no-one at RCA would have been interested in what modes were being used!

Incredibly, the co-author of *(Marie's the name) His Latest Flame* was still shown as Schuman, exactly as it always had been on singles right from the first release. If nothing else, it demonstrated a certain consistency in RCA's copyright department. But what we find difficult to understand is why this spelling only appeared on singles. The albums which feature the song do so with the correct spelling and this seems to suggest that details such as writers' names are taken from a file marked for single use and a separate one for album format. How else could this kind of unnecessary error occur? In all probability details must have come from the previous single release, thus perpetuating the error. Over the years there was a tendency to change the title of the song by including the word '*Of*', so that it read *(Marie's the name of) His Latest Flame*. Now, whilst we can agree that this is more grammatically correct, it is not how the title was originally shown, and we, therefore, consider it an error. Once again, most albums correctly display the title. Incidentally, Doc Pomus died in March 1991, and Mort Shuman in November 1991.

Label Variations

GOLD LABEL/SOLID CENTRE
1   1986 PRESSING

Sleeve Variations

1   Type 1
2   Type 2
3   Type 3

| S 152 | Old Gold | OG 9624 |

An American Trilogy {S} (Arr. Newbury)
Until It's Time For You To Go {S} (Sainte-Marie)

Released October 1986

This was the best selling of the Old Gold Elvis singles, as the number of sleeve variations demonstrated - each variation representing a further pressing of the record. Sales of the record were consistent enough to warrant regular press runs throughout the late eighties and early nineties, and, as Old Gold changed the design of their singles' sleeves (including a move to picture sleeves for more popular releases), this record became available in many sleeve variants.

The songs included here were consecutive UK A sides, both top ten hits in 1972, although, surprisingly, *Until It's Time For You To Go* (*S 82*) achieved a higher chart position, reaching number five. This was the first Old Gold release to include material from the seventies, and both songs were in stereo.

In January 1989 *In The Ghetto*, OG 9616 (**S 148**), *Always On My Mind*, OG 9744 (**S 166**), and this single had sold enough copies to warrant picture sleeves, the first Elvis Old Gold singles to achieve this distinction. The first copies of the picture sleeve for *An American Trilogy* featured a live performance shot of Elvis from the correct period (1972) and had a green background to the title block at the top of the sleeve. On later pressings (which appeared in 1990) a bright red background was used with the final batch, produced, we believe, in early 1991, using a much darker red (Old Gold called it maroon). The later pressings continued to use the first picture sleeve design, after a new design was introduced.

The notes on the picture sleeve erroneously suggested that *An American Trilogy* was used as the finale to Elvis's live appearances. And, whilst we would agree that the song was an undoubted tour de force for most of its concert life, it was never used to end a concert - a place reserved almost exclusively for *Can't Help Falling In Love* for the period in question. (Incidentally the latter song was also released by Old Gold, but was never issued in a picture sleeve.)

The label failed to refer to the full and correct title *An American Trilogy*, omitting the *An*, although this was rectified on the sleeve. Another frequent error concerned the 'writer' of the song. This was regularly shown as Mickey Newbury, who in fact, only adapted and arranged the song. We discussed the correct writers in some detail in the notes for *S 83*.

Label Variations

GOLD LABEL/SOLID CENTRE

    1   **1986 PRESSING STEREO**

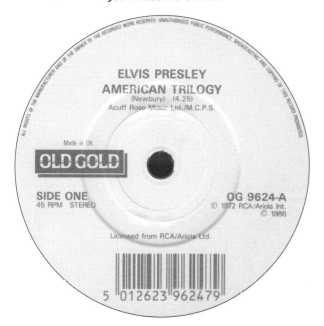

Sleeve Variations

1	Type 1
2	Type 2
3	Picture sleeve - green
4	Picture sleeve - red
5	Picture sleeve - maroon

Production Error

You will recall that in the introductory notes preceding **S 148** we referred to the fact that Old Gold usually ordered an initial run of 2,000 copies of each single, but that the number of the finished product actually delivered could be slightly lower or greater than this figure, depending on whether any problems were encountered during the production process. Often the final number was less than the order and to illustrate this, only 1,818 copies of the next Old Gold single, *Love Me Tender*, OG 9626 (**S 153**), were delivered to Old Gold.

Normally this would have presented no major problem, but, on this occasion, an error appeared on the record label which had remained unobserved throughout production until the entire batch was received. In this case the error was that the catalogue number had been printed as OG 9611 which, unlike the majority of errors we normally discuss, prevented the record from reaching the shops. This was because the Old Gold catalogue had already been printed showing the 9626 number, and it would, therefore, have been impossible for Old Gold and record stores to co-ordinate ordering and filing. Imagine the confusion it would have created. So, rather than take that kind of risk, Old Gold had the record re-pressed with the correct catalogue number.

In normal circumstances the incorrect batch would have been destroyed and put down as an expensive mistake, but on this occasion 1,000 copies were sold to a record dealer with a small number being distributed privately, leaving just over 800 which were eventually destroyed.

This was the kind of production error that record companies try so hard to prevent, and, usually they succeed. As a result of what we have said, we believe this record is unique. Certainly we have never heard of an entire batch that completed the production process with such a glaring error which then had to be disposed of.

S 153   *Old Gold*   *OG 9626*

Love Me Tender {M} (Presley, Matson)
(Let me be your) Teddy Bear {M} (Mann, Lowe)

Released October 1986

This was the last in the first batch of six Old Gold singles and combined two A sides from the fifties - **Love Me Tender**, first released in 1956 (*S 6*), and **(Let me be your) Teddy Bear** from 1957 (*S 12*). Interestingly the original B side of the latter, **Loving You**, was also released by Old Gold as an A side in January 1988 (**S 167**). This single, therefore, combined a song, **Love Me Tender**, which, at this time, had previously only appeared in the UK on an HMV single with Elvis's first RCA UK A side, **(Let me be your) Teddy Bear**.

The release of **Love Me Tender** by Old Gold went some way to demonstrate that, having licensed a song to another company, the 'owners' were not prevented from releasing the song in their own right. Which is precisely what RCA did in August 1987, when they issued the song in both 7 and 12 inch formats, even though the Old Gold version was still available and selling steadily. And, of course, both of the songs featured here had appeared on the **Essential Elvis** LP, PL 89979 (**LP 280**), which had been released in December 1986.

Despite the early difficulties (see the previous note on Production Error) the single did fairly well, and by April 1990 merited a picture sleeve, with 3,500 copies being printed initially. Unfortunately though, the photograph shown was from a much later period (1962) - a publicity shot from the film **It Happened At The World's Fair**. The picture sleeve version of the record claimed that **(Let me be your) Teddy Bear** (minus the words in brackets) had reached number three in the charts. We believe this to be an error for, according to **Music Week**, it reached the number two position.

Whilst this record had a certain appeal in itself, there was no doubt that the copy to watch out for was the one which carried the incorrect catalogue number of OG 9611 instead of the correct OG 9626 number. Please see the notes preceding this release for further details.

Label Variations

GOLD LABEL/SOLID CENTRE

1   **1986 PRESSING**
         Catalogue number OG 9611

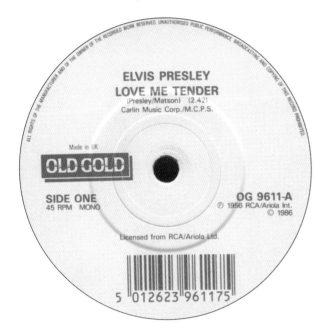

2   **1986 PRESSING**
         Catalogue number OG 9626

Sleeve Variations

1   Type 1
2   Type 2
3   Picture sleeve - first design

Bertelsmann

In January 1987 the Bertelsmann Music Group (BMG) was formed after the sale of RCA's music division by General Electric in December 1986. This important and historical change went unheralded on the next RCA single, *Ain't That Loving You Baby* (**S 154**), released in March 1987.

Single Deletion - February 1987

The 12 inch single comprising four tracks - *Always On My Mind*, *Tomorrow Night*, *Ain't That Loving You Baby*, and *Dark Moon* - first issued in July 1985, RCA PT 49944 (**S 147**), was deleted on 27 February 1987. The 7 inch version containing the first two tracks only (**S 146**), survived until November 1987, before it too was deleted from the catalogue.

RCA Catalogue Numbering System

RCA's previous experiments with their catalogue numbering system had never proved particularly successful. Indeed their APBO system, first introduced in 1974, turned out to be a complete failure and was quickly shortened to PB, mainly at the insistence of record shops who found the four character code cumbersome and difficult to manage. The PB system was never popular with fans, many of whom preferred the simple logic of the traditional, straightforward RCA prefix. RCA UK seemed to prefer this also as they began to use this code for the second time in 1980, when they started the numbering sequence from number 1, with Elvis's *It's Only Love*, RCA 4 (*S 122*), making an early appearance.

In March 1987 RCA issued *Ain't That Loving You Baby* (**S 154**) and with it introduced a new system with a catalogue referencing system based upon Elvis's middle name - ARON. Now, we know the spelling of Elvis's name was later changed to Aaron, but nonetheless this was a popular move which was appreciated by many.

In fairness this kind of 'artist identity' had become commonplace with almost all record companies, and RCA themselves had adopted this practice for other artists in their stable, using BOW on releases by David Bowie, for example.

Unfortunately the ARON system did not last long, only running for two releases during 1987. The reason for this, was that both of these releases were UK inspired and not widely distributed elsewhere. It seems worth remembering that it was RCA UK who instigated the ARON system, demonstrating once again that at they at least put a certain amount of care and attention into their product, even down to minor details such as this.

RCA Label Detail Change

First indications regarding the takeover of RCA by the German company Bertelsmann had come, as far as Elvis records were concerned, in the form of a note on the label of the six Old Gold singles released in October 1986, which read 'Licensed from RCA/Ariola Ltd.' Although there was no direct reference to Bertelsmann (not yet known as BMG), the Ariola label was owned by the company, and this was a reference to the joint venture undertaken by Bertelsmann and RCA. Two months later, when *Essential Elvis*, PL 89979 (**LP 280**), was issued in the UK, there was a reference to RCA/Ariola International on both label and sleeve, the first Elvis release to carry such information. The next single release, RCA ARON 1, *Ain't That Loving You Baby* (**S 154**), released in March 1987, contained the same detail.

Ironically though, the reference to RCA/Ariola was out of date because in January 1987 RCA had become part of the giant German company Bertelsmann, though the label failed to make this clear. The introductory section at the beginning of this book contains a short history of Bertelsmann, and further details surrounding the relationship between the two companies are to be found there.

As we mentioned earlier though, this kind of detail no longer provided an accurate indicator as to when a particular record was produced, especially re-pressings. When there was a regular stream of Elvis releases it was a simple matter of recording the information printed on the record label, checking the style and the detail contained, and being able to pinpoint with some accuracy when a record had been manufactured. Details such as those referred to above would have been vital when trying to determine if a re-pressing of another record had been made during this period.

However, the rather obvious reason why the significance of minor changes such as these had, by this period, little or no value, was that records were simply not being re-pressed. Singles, in particular, were normally a one-time pressing, and where chart success was limited then opportunities for increased production were unlikely. Nevertheless, we continue to show changes to both label and sleeve detail as a reference point, allowing events - small and large - to be placed in their correct sequence.

RCA Sleeve Change

A number of changes and omissions were apparent on the sleeve of **Ain't That Loving You Baby**, ARON 1 (**S 154**), when compared to the previous RCA single, **Always On My Mind** (**S 146**). First of all there was no bar code, price code or LC 0316 feature, all of which had been introduced on the **Always On My Mind** single. Secondly, reference was now made to the RCA/Ariola merger, the first single sleeve to do so - a fact also printed on the label.

Finally, there was no reference to side one or side two printed on the sleeve (again a feature that was normally present), although this information was shown in different ways.

S 154 | RCA   ARON 1

Ain't That Loving You Baby {Fast version} {M} (Otis, Hunter)
Bossa Nova Baby {S} (Leiber, Stoller)

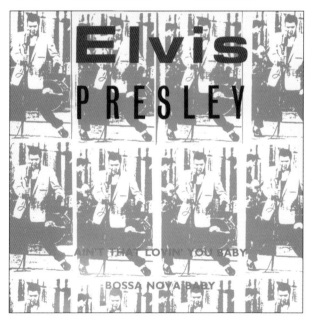

| Released March 1987 | Chart Entry Number 140 |
| | Highest Chart Position 47 |

This was the first RCA Elvis single release in twenty months, the previous one being **Always On My Mind**, RCA PB 49943 (7 inch) and RCA PT 49944 (12 inch) in July 1985 (**S 146** and **S 147**). This exceeded the previous longest gap between releases of twelve months created between **Old Shep**, RCA PB 9334 (*S 119*), released in November 1978, and **It Won't Seem Like Christmas (without you)**, RCA PB 9464 (*S 120*), released in November 1979.

In terms of chart success, although **Ain't That Loving You Baby** managed to achieve a highest chart placing of 47 (which at one time would have been considered a total failure!), it did represent the highest chart placing since **I Can Help**, RCA 369, (*S 140*) which made number 30 in 1983. Having said that, many of the thirteen releases in the intervening period were 12 inch companion records (i.e. the same single with additional tracks), and a further six were largely re-issues on Old

Gold which were never going to be serious chart contenders anyway.

The most unusual thing about this release was that the A side, **Ain't That Loving You Baby**, had been one of the tracks on the 12 inch format of the previous RCA single **Always On My Mind**! The song itself proved popular with fans when it was first released in 1985 on the **Reconsider Baby** album, RCA PL 85418 (*LP 271*); and, when coupled with **Bossa Nova Baby**, a song which had achieved almost cult status with younger fans (so we are told!), it made a strong single. **Bossa Nova Baby** had, of course, been an A side, RCA 1374, in October 1963 (*S 42*).

The sleeve featured a most appealing multi-image grey picture on the front, with a different picture on the back, again presented as a multi-image. Elvis's name and the song titles were boldly printed in red and green, producing a very effective overall design.

As mentioned earlier, this was the first single to show, on both the label and sleeve, the new ownership details - RCA/Ariola International - which had first appeared on **Essential Elvis** (**LP 280**) in December 1986.

Mastered by Bob Jones and made in England, the record featured the standard RCA black label, but the sleeve carried more detail than normal, for it included recording information such as the musicians, date and recording location - a wonderful idea that could so easily and inexpensively have been included on all releases. No recording mode was shown for the A side, which was in mono, but **Bossa Nova Baby** was correctly identified as being in stereo. Despite the fact that this single used ARON 1 for a catalogue number, the European PB number wasn't far away, for engraved in the vinyl between the run-out grooves was PB 49745. Neither the bar code, nor the European price codes, were shown on the sleeve of this single, or for that matter its 12 inch companion, making these records all the more unusual and somehow more British!

Both the label and sleeve had the same error regarding **Ain't That Loving You Baby** which appeared as **Ain't That Lovin' You Baby**, as it had on the previous RCA single. That aside, there were no other errors, and how refreshing it was to report that the date of publication was correctly shown on the sleeve as 1985, when this version of the song was first released.

The single was deleted in March 1989, exactly two years after it was issued.

Label Variations

NEW BLACK LABEL/SOLID CENTRE
1   1987 PRESSING

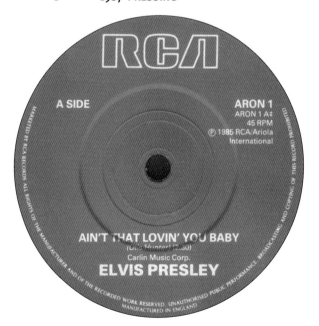

Sleeve Variations

| 1 | Picture sleeve - gloss |
| 2 | Picture sleeve - matt |

Ain't That Loving You Baby {Fast version} {M} (Otis, Hunter)
I'm Comin' Home {S} (Rich)
Bossa Nova Baby {S} (Leiber, Stoller)
Rock-A-Hula Baby {S} (Wise, Weisman, Fuller)

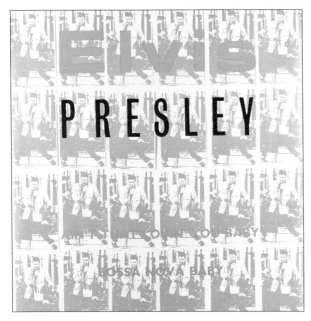

Released March 1987

Released simultaneously with the 7 inch version, this 12 inch 45 rpm single added two further tracks and was sold for around £3.30.

Using the same design as the 7 inch single, and retaining the two song titles on the front of the cover, without reference to the additional tracks, the design became even more attractive in the larger format. A notable first was the inclusion on the cover of the recording details - musicians, dates and locations - which were included on a UK single for the first time. This information was included on the 7 inch record, but the details for **Rock-A-Hula Baby** were incomplete, omitting the date and location. For the sake of completeness, the song was recorded on 23 March 1961 at the Radio Recorders studios in Hollywood. Including such detail was a welcome move, making the sleeve more informative, and providing some background to the songs in question, easily and inexpensively. This kind of improvement suggested more care was being taken with single releases and it was a great pity that the provision of such detail had failed to become standard practice.

Clearly the T added to the ARON catalogue number prefix represented twelve inch and, like the 7 inch single, the European number was also etched in the vinyl, reading PT. Incidentally, the sleeve showed the prefix incorrectly - ARON T1, whereas the label correctly displayed ARONT 1.

Capitalising on the then current dance club craze for Latin American rhythms, this record was popular, but the inevitable question raised was: how did **I'm Comin' Home** find its way on to the collection? Did someone at RCA like the song better than other 'Baby' songs? Didn't it occur to someone at RCA that it didn't fit the pattern? Incidentally, **I'm Comin' Home** was taken from the 1961 **Something For Everybody** album (*LP 14*), and was making its debut on a single in the UK twenty six years after it was recorded.

Note that no LC 0316 number appeared on either the 7 or 12 inch format sleeves, presumably because this was a UK inspired release and this detail was considered unimportant.

Happily, the recording modes were correctly identified for all of the tracks, but no hyphens were shown in **Rock-A-Hula Baby** on the label, whereas they were present on the sleeve. As with the 7 inch single, the G was replaced by an apostrophe in **Ain't That Loving You Baby**.

Like the 7 inch version, this single was deleted in March 1989.

Label Variations

NEW BLACK LABEL/SOLID CENTRE
1   1987 PRESSING

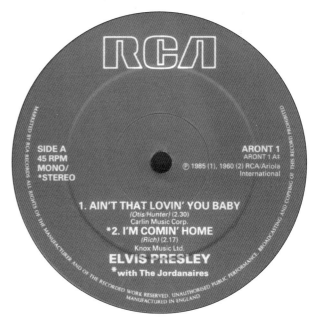

Sleeve Variations

1   Gloss

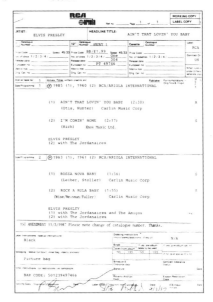

ARONT 1 Label copy

Bossa Nova Baby

Ordinarily we would not include details of any record we had not seen personally. However, we have it on good authority that the extended version of **Bossa Nova Baby**, issued by BMG in August 1987 (**S 161**), became available on a 12 inch single - catalogue number ARONT R1 - around the same time as the regular version was issued as part of the **Ain't That Loving You Baby** single releases (**S 154** and **S 155**).

It is known that the extended mix had been in circulation for some time prior to its appearance on **S 161**, having been used in clubs and even on Capital Radio. Quite possibly the record in question could have been a special DJ pressing, but we cannot say for certain. What is clear though is that the matrix number engraved between the run-out grooves of ARONT 2 (**S 161**) reads 'ARONT 1R'.

Old Gold

The Old Gold catalogue for summer 1987, which was printed in April, quoted a further four Elvis singles as being new releases, joining the previous six existing releases. And, as we mentioned earlier, the original intention was to issue all ten in October 1986, but one or two legal clearance problems caused a delay. The new titles were:

OG 9700	*Hound Dog/Don't Be Cruel*
OG 9702	*Are You Lonesome Tonight?/Wooden Heart*
OG 9704	*Heartbreak Hotel/All Shook Up*
OG 9706	*Wild In The Country/I Feel So Bad*

As you can see only two of the couplings were the original ones - *Hound Dog/Don't Be Cruel* (*S 4*) and *Wild In The Country/I Feel So Bad* (*S 34*).

Strangely, in many stores, (WH Smith being particularly prominent) along with Old Gold display cards for the above, was a further card advertising an additional release - *Way Down* coupled with *Moody Blue*. However, in all cases, this turned out to be the black label RCA GOLD 544 release (*S 134*), which was not an Old Gold release, despite the similarity in title. One explanation offered by the shops concerned was that Old Gold had bought out existing stocks of the record for issue under their own banner, until such time as stocks had been used up, after which the records would be re-pressed using their own label.

However, this was simply untrue. Old Gold only licensed material from the record companies for issue on their own label and did not carry stocks of any other companies' finished product. The confusion was caused by retailers themselves using Old Gold advertising material for display of 'oldies' generally. This would obviously apply to other companies' repertoire, as well as RCA's, and doubtless, other Elvis records would have been treated in a similar manner.

We mention the above simply to show how misleading such information can be, particularly when considering the date of release of records. What made this case so intriguing was that the single *Way Down/Moody Blue* (**S 172**) was later released by Old Gold in January 1988!

Old Gold Label Detail Change

When the delayed batch of four Old Gold singles was finally released in April 1987, six months after originally planned, the licensing information included on the label had changed. The previous six singles had referred to RCA/Ariola Ltd., whereas the latest four quoted:

Licensed from RCA/Ariola Ltd. & RCA Records

The detail under the catalogue number had also changed, showing RCA/Ariola International, instead of the abbreviated Int.

It is unlikely that these details had anything to do with the delay in releasing these singles: RCA probably just wanted this information included at that particular time. Having said that, it would have made more sense to have included details of the Bertelsmann takeover of RCA which came into effect in January 1987. But as these singles were delayed (the process from initial negotiation to final product is both long and complicated in the case of licensing deals), the wording must have been agreed upon well before their actual release.

As with the earlier releases, all pressings of these four singles retained the above detail, even though later releases contained updated information. However, the six singles released in October 1986 were never updated to show the April 1987 details, despite being re-pressed during this time.

| **S 156** | **Old Gold** | **OG 9700** |

Hound Dog {M} (Leiber, Stoller)
Don't Be Cruel {M} (Blackwell, Presley)

Released April 1987
Original Issue September 1956. HMV POP 249 (*S 4*)
Previous Re-issue June 1978. RCA PB 9265 (*S 118*)

This was the first of the four delayed singles (originally planned for release in October 1986) to be issued.

Surprisingly, this particular coupling had only been released as a single on two previous occasions (see above) over a thirty-one year period. The truth of the matter was that this Old Gold release was only the third time that these songs had appeared together in their original coupling, but they were often separated, with *Hound Dog* being coupled with *Blue Suede Shoes* for single release in November 1958 on RCA 1095 (*S 24*). There was also an RCA maxi single (a kind of EP minus the picture sleeve) which was issued in July 1971 with a third track, *Heartbreak Hotel* (*S 78*), added. And note, *Hound Dog* was not always classed as the A side, because the sides were reversed for the June 1978 re-issue.

In June 1990 the Old Gold single was issued in a picture sleeve, with an initial press run of 2,200 copies. The sleeve featured a photograph from the film *Loving You*, but this would have been better placed on the picture sleeve for OG 9626, *Love Me Tender* (*S 153*), which had *(Let me be your) Teddy Bear* on the B side, a song actually featured in the film *Loving You*.

There were some errors in the sleeve notes, where it was claimed that it took 33 takes before Elvis was satisfied with *Hound Dog*. All sources, including the most authoritative one to date: Ernst Jorgensen's *A Life In Music The Complete Recording Sessions* (1998), insist that the actual number was 31 takes. The sleeve notes also referred to Otis Blackwell as the writer of *Fever*, which some people may have regarded as an error. Ironically though, despite usually being credited to Davenport and Cooley, in this instance the former name was a pseudonym used by Blackwell when he wrote the song in 1958.

There were no label errors.

Label Variations

GOLD LABEL/SOLID CENTRE
1   1987 PRESSING

Sleeve Variations

1   Type 2
2   Type 3
3   Picture sleeve - second design

S 157	*Old Gold*	**OG 9702**

Are You Lonesome Tonight? {M} (Turk, Handman)
Wooden Heart {M} (Wise, Weisman, Twomey, Kaempfert)

Released April 1987

This single combined two consecutive UK A sides from 1961, both number one hits (*S 31* and *S 32*). This was the first such double A sided coupling of this batch of four Old Gold releases and also the first time that two UK numbers ones had been placed back-to-back. Incidentally, both of these songs were featured on the Old Gold LP *Number Ones 60's Volume 1 - Pop* (**VA LP 16**) released in May 1988, and, as on the LP itself, both songs were in mono, which seemed unnecessary for they had been recorded in stereo, and both had appeared in stereo on blue label singles during the 1982/83 period, when they had been re-mastered by Bob Jones (*S 105* and *S 106*).

The information supplied to Old Gold by RCA regarding the 'Recording First Published' date seems to have been derived from the date both songs were released on singles in the UK. Certainly the date 1961 shown for *Are You Lonesome Tonight?* is correct, as the song's first appearance in the UK was on the single released in January of that year, but 1961 was incorrect for *Wooden Heart*, which was first released on the album *G.I. Blues* (*LP 12*) in November 1960, although not released on a single until February 1961.

No picture sleeve was made for this single, suggesting that sales were insufficient to warrant such a move, but it is hard to determine the precise reason for this. Certainly these songs had lost much of their appeal, having been regular inclusions on many albums released by RCA and others over the years, but then again so had most of the other number one hits Elvis achieved. One could point at releases like the previous Old Gold release *Hound Dog/Don't Be Cruel* (**S 156**) which, whilst never achieving the number one position, was a very popular single over a long period of time and contained two tracks which featured on virtually every compilation album, or so it seemed. Yet, the *Hound Dog/Don't Be Cruel* coupling did sell well enough to justify a picture sleeve, indicating that people still found the purchase an attractive one. Perhaps there were still enough collectors around buying copies of singles though; if so, we would have thought that they would have been interested in a unique coupling which this release offered. Furthermore, it seems reasonable to assume that all of the Old Gold singles would have sold in similar quantities. If not, then the casual record buyer must have made the difference, though it is difficult to understand why *Hound Dog/Don't Be Cruel* seemed to have fared better than *Are You Lonesome Tonight?/Wooden Heart*, when the latter seemed much more orientated to that market.

A rare production error exists in the form of the labels being reversed, in that the A side label is attached to the B side; the B side label to the A side.

There were two label errors, both relatively common for these songs. The first was the omission of the question mark after *Are You Lonesome Tonight?* and the second being that the writers of *Wooden Heart* were shown in the wrong order, reading Kaempfert, Twomey, Wise, Weisman. The correct order is shown above.

Label Variations

GOLD LABEL/SOLID CENTRE
1   1987 PRESSING
2   1987 PRESSING
         Production error. A side label on B side;
         B side label on A side

Sleeve Variations

1   Type 2
2   Type 3

S 158 | Old Gold OG 9704

Heartbreak Hotel {M} (Axton, Durden, Presley)
All Shook Up {M} (Blackwell, Presley)

Released April 1987
Original Issue November 1958. RCA 1088 (*S 23*)
Previous Re-issue May 1977. RCA 2694 (*S 100*)

Although this single combined two original A sides from 1956 and 1957 respectively, this release was also a re-issue as these songs had been issued together previously in 1958, and again in 1977, when RCA released them as part of the Gold 16 set. The two songs had originally been coupled in 1958 when RCA had run short of material whilst Elvis was in the Army (*S 23*), although an added benefit at the time was to restore the two songs to the catalogue following their deletion on HMV.

All Shook Up was included on the Old Gold LP **Number Ones 50's Volume 2 - Pop** (**VA LP 15**), released in May 1988. Both songs were given their correct 'Recording First Published' date and there were no label errors. There was no picture sleeve version either.

Label Variations

GOLD LABEL/SOLID CENTRE
    1   1987 PRESSING

Sleeve Variations

    1   Type 2
    2   Type 3

S 159 | Old Gold OG 9706

Wild In The Country {M} (Peretti, Creatore, Weiss)
I Feel So Bad {S} (Willis)

Released April 1987
Original Issue August 1961. RCA (*S 34*)

This was the last of the batch of four singles released by Old Gold in April 1987, and was a straight re-issue of Elvis's number two hit from 1961 (*S 34*). This was one of only eight straight re-issues on Old Gold, the remainder combining two A sides. Remember, we define a re-issue as a straight copy of the original coupling, despite a new catalogue number or even, as in this case, product of a different company.

Although the original single of **Wild In The Country** reached number 2 in the charts, it fared less well than all the other single releases in the early sixties, and this was the first time that the song had appeared on a single since the original was deleted in the late sixties. The same was true for **I Feel So Bad**, a much under-rated song which had actually been the A side when the single was first released in America. The UK A side was the title song from Elvis's 7th film release. In total Old Gold released five songs which were the title/lead songs in Elvis films.

Inexplicably **Wild In The Country** was in mono, whilst **I Feel So Bad** was in stereo.

For the second Old Gold single in succession there were no label errors.

Label Variations

GOLD LABEL/SOLID CENTRE
    1   1987 PRESSING

Sleeve Variations

    1   Type 2
    2   Type 3

RCA Label Detail Change

Whilst the basic layout of RCA singles remained unchanged, a minor amendment took place when the next single, ARON 2, **Love Me Tender** (**S 160**), was released in August 1987. The ownership details were changed to read BMG Music instead of RCA/Ariola International. The Ariola name was not used again other than for the record distribution details for some of the other European countries, a detail included on the back of record sleeves.

RCA Sleeve Change

As with the label information, copyright details on the sleeve referred to BMG; and because the release of **Love Me Tender** was initiated by the UK division, the sleeve stated BMG Records (UK) Ltd.

One feature worthy of special note was the inclusion of the round RCA logo which once graced all of the company's output, until it was replaced by the 'computer' style logo first introduced in 1969. The UK inspired singles *Jailhouse Rock* (*S 136*) and *(You're so square) Baby I Don't Care* (*S 138*), both released in 1983, featured the round RCA logo as part of the 'authentic' label design - remember both these singles were issued 25 years after their original release. Later this logo would become standard, and it did seem that an idea originating in the UK gained acceptance throughout Europe.

Once again there were no bar or price codes printed on the sleeve, but the LC 0316 did re-appear, on the back of the sleeve.

S 160 — RCA ARON 2

Love Me Tender {M} (Presley, Matson)
If I Can Dream {S} (Brown)

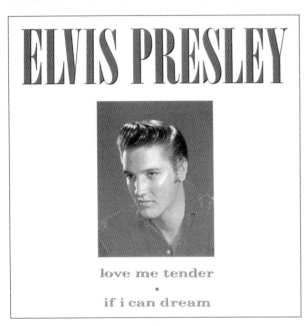

Released August 1987

Chart Entry Number 141
Highest Chart Position 56

This was the second ARON catalogue number series release, and also the second RCA single of 1987 - this release tying in with the tenth anniversary of Elvis's death. Again this was a UK inspired release which was issued to promote the superb album *Presley - The All Time Greatest Hits*, PL 90100(2) (*LP 287*), also released in August. Both tracks were taken from the album and the photograph of Elvis on both the 7 and 12 inch picture sleeves was the same as that used on the album. Once again, the sleeve was extremely well designed and confirmed the move to improved quality of product, often lacking with many previous RCA releases. There was no doubt that a good degree of care and imagination had been applied, and the overall result was well received.

However, while the sleeve design may well have been popular, the choice of *Love Me Tender* surprised many when it appeared as the A side, as it was considered a fairly weak choice. But careful observers will note that *If I Can Dream*, far from being considered as the B side, was being promoted as the AA side! This was the first time this designation had appeared on Elvis's UK releases, although, in essence, this was merely a 1980s update of the old double A side system, used to such good effect in the 1950s.

Another unusual fact about *Love Me Tender* was that the song had been released less than a year earlier, in October 1986, on the Old Gold label (*S 153*), which at the time was considered as a sign that RCA had already got all the mileage it could out of the song as a

single and had 'put it out to grass' via a licensing arrangement to another company.

The version of *If I Can Dream* used here was the original single version from the TV Special, whereas the version used by Old Gold later, in January 1988 (*S 173*), was, unusually, an alternative version - as had first been issued on *He Walks Beside Me: Favourite Songs Of Faith And Inspiration*, RCA PL 12771 (*LP 101*), in March 1978. This was the only time a genuine alternative version - as opposed to a remix - appeared on Old Gold.

The label was again the standard RCA logo, with minor modifications to reflect changes in RCA's ownership. Unlike the revious RCA single, the LC 0316 number was shown at the bottom of the sleeve, which also included the round RCA logo, destined to become a regular feature on sleeves and labels of later releases. The sleeve did not have the bar code or European price codes included.

Both songs were mastered by Bob Jones who added his 'Ten years after...' inscription to the vinyl in the run out groove.

Unfortunately, the label claimed that *Love Me Tender* was in stereo - it was not. The song was in mono, and this was clearly stated on the 12 inch version. That aside, the only other error was the one on the label which placed Presley, Matson in the wrong order. Incidentally a stereo version of *Love Me Tender* did appear later in the 1990s and was included on the CD *Jailhouse Rock*.

Label Variations

NEW BLACK LABEL/SOLID CENTRE
1   1987 PRESSING

Sleeve Variations

1   Picture sleeve - gloss
2   Picture sleeve - matt

S 161 | RCA ARONT 2

Love Me Tender {M} (Presley, Matson)
If I Can Dream {S} (Brown)
Bossa Nova Baby {Extended mix} {S} (Leiber, Stoller)

Released August 1987

This 12 inch single contained only three tracks, as the whole of side two was taken up with the extended mix of *Bossa Nova Baby*, which had been produced by Simon Harris, a DJ in London. The extended mix had proved very popular with club-goers and fans generally, and had been played extensively on London's Capital Radio. And, although RCA did not commission Harris to do this work, they had to pay royalties in order to issue his mix, even though RCA themselves owned the recording!

The front of the sleeve carried a sticker proclaiming the record a 'Collectors Edition' and announcing the inclusion of the extended *Bossa Nova Baby*, allowing the artwork to remain unaltered from the 7 inch version of the single. Therefore, no reference was made to the song on the front of the sleeve, other than the sticker.

Unlike the first ARON 12 inch single, the label and sleeve both showed the catalogue number in the same format - ARONT 2. Etched into the vinyl of the B side of the record was the unusual ARONT 1R matrix number, denoting the extended mix.

It had been suggested (in *Elvis Monthly*, for example) that RCA's original plan was to produce a 12 inch cut-out picture disc for this release. Further, there was also talk of a regular 12 inch picture disc. However, neither appeared, and we can confirm that there were no plans whatsoever to issue them. The topic had not even been raised. As we have noted elsewhere, the use of these special pressings made little economic sense - they simply cost too much and did not justify (in financial terms) the additional production costs. These suggestions were, therefore, just the usual round of speculation - or mis-information - that surrounded most Elvis product.

The error, suggesting that *Love Me Tender* was in stereo, found on the 7 inch version, was corrected here, but the claim that *Bossa Nova Baby* was first published in 1963 was misleading, given that the extended mix was new. However, because the song was originally published in that year, and the mix contained no new material then the claim seemed justified. It is also worth pointing out that there were no publishers shown for *Bossa Nova Baby*, and instead the term 'Copyright Control' was used. This was normally used where there was any uncertainty as to who owned the rights to the song, and presumably this was the case here. Carlin Music were shown as the

publishers on ARON 1, when the song appeared as the B side of *Ain't That Loving You Baby*, in March 1987 (**S 154**), suggesting that the confusion was probably caused by the extended mix. The single was pressed in the UK by Damont.

As with the 7 inch version, the error of showing Presley, Matson in the wrong order was repeated here. This single, too, was deleted in March 1989.

Label Variations

NEW BLACK LABEL/SOLID CENTRE
1   1987 PRESSING

Sleeve Variations

1   Gloss

Singles' Deletions - November 1987

In November 1987 RCA deleted two more singles from their catalogue. The single *Are You Lonesome Tonight?/From A Jack To A King*, RCA 196 (*S 133*), was first released in February 1982. And, although the single was a only a moderate chart success (it reached number 25), sales over the five or so years it was available had amounted to well over 84,000 by the time it was deleted - a respectable performance.

The single *Always On My Mind/Tomorrow Night*, RCA PB 49943 (**S 146**), first released in July 1985, was deleted by RCA on 6 November 1987. Its 12 inch equivalent, containing the additional tracks *Ain't That Loving You Baby* and *Dark Moon*, RCA PT 49944 (**S 147**), had been deleted in February 1987.

Label Detail Change

An interesting change in label detail occurred with the next RCA single release, PB 49595, *Stuck On You* (**S 162**), in that the sides were identified as Side A and Side B, whereas up to this point the norm had been to show this detail as A Side and B Side. We can think of no specific reason why this was thought necessary, but whatever the reason, this was how sides were identified from this point onwards.

RCA Sleeve Change

After a break of two singles, both the bar code and price code were once again printed on the back of the sleeve.

S 162 | RCA PB 49595

Stuck On You {S} (Schroeder, McFarland)
Any Way You Want Me (that's how I will be)
{M} (Schroeder, Owens)

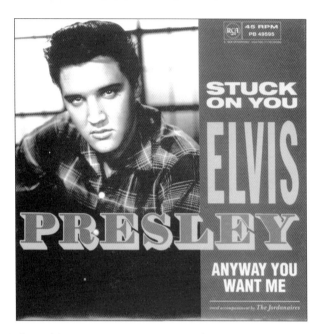

Released January 1988   **Chart Entry Number 141**
Highest Chart Position 58

The use of Elvis's 1960 recording of **Stuck On You** by Evostick, for their advertisements on TV, provided RCA with an opportunity not to be missed, and rumours regarding the use of the song as a possible single spread rapidly in early November 1987. The Evostick campaign had been running for some time, yet by the time the single was eventually released (to tie in with what would have been Elvis's 53rd birthday), much impetus had been lost. Not to be denied however, RCA had another opportunity come their way when the 1987 Christmas TV campaign by the electrical giants Sony chose to use **Any Way You Want Me (that's how I will be)** - a recording from 1956 - to promote their product. This particular campaign did not mention Elvis specifically by name, but with the song and the tag line 'there is only one set fit for a king' what other conclusion could be drawn? The advert was used extensively and proved very popular, especially with RCA who, in a blaze of free publicity, opted to release this as the B side of the new single.

Both songs were taken from the album **Presley - The All Time Greatest Hits**, PL 90100(2) (**LP 287**), released in August 1987, making this the second single to be taken from the album. Regrettably, the single dropped the ARON catalogue numbering system in favour of the European PB system, which many considered a poor decision by RCA.

What is not generally known is that **Stuck On You** was also remixed as an extended version by Simon Harris, who had been responsible for the extended **Bossa Nova Baby** found on ARONT 2 (**S 161**). However, RCA felt that the song did not lend itself to this kind of treatment, and the proposed release was cancelled.

Please notice that the sleeve used the round RCA logo on both the front and back, and the old 'A "New Orthophonic" High Fidelity Recording' slogan was once again featured. No reference was made to the recording mode of either song on the sleeve, but **Stuck On You** was correctly identified as being in stereo on the label. Presumably the absence of a mode on the B side was sufficient to signify a mono mode.

The words in brackets were not shown on either the sleeve or label for **Any Way You Want Me (that's how I will be)**, and **Any Way** was shown, incorrectly, as one word.

Strangely, the co-writer of **Stuck On You**, Leslie McFarland, was correctly identified on the label, but not on the sleeve, where the name Wyche appeared. The team Schroeder, Wyche were responsible for **A Big Hunk O' Love**, a song which just happens to be the track immediately preceding **Stuck On You** on the album **Presley - The All Time Greatest Hits**, where the writers of both songs were correctly identified. We don't know if this has anything to do with the error, but it is a possible explanation.

Label Variations

NEW BLACK LABEL/SOLID CENTRE
1   **1987 PRESSING**

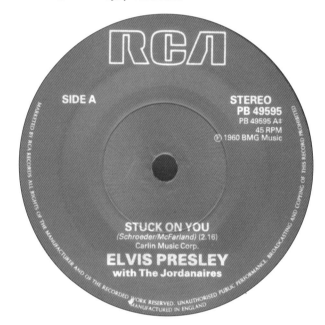

Sleeve Variations

1   Picture sleeve - gloss
2   Picture sleeve - matt

S 163   RCA   PT 49596

Stuck On You {S} (Schroeder, McFarland)
Always On My Mind
{Alternative version} {S} (James, Carson, Christopher)
Any Way You Want Me (that's how I will be)
{M} (Schroeder, Owens)
Are You Lonesome Tonight?
{Live version} {S} (Turk, Handman)

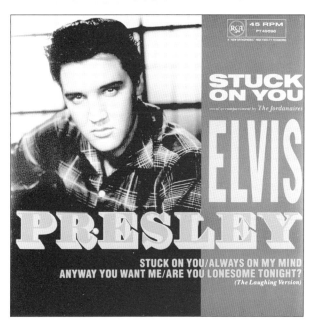

Released January 1988

This 12 inch release, besides containing the two songs that made up the 7 inch version of the single, contained two old favourites appearing on a single for the second time around. The so-called 'Laughing Version' of **Are You Lonesome Tonight?** (recorded live in Las Vegas in August 1969) had appeared on a 7 inch single in February 1982 (*S 133*), whereas this version of **Always On My Mind** had been used for both 7 and 12 inch releases in July 1985 (**S 146** and **S 147**). The original version of the song had, of course, also been issued on a single previously (*S 85*), reaching the charts in December 1972.

The 12 inch sleeve was a modified version of the 7 inch release, in that all the titles had been added and reference to the Jordanaires re-located, although the photograph and basic design remained unchanged. As was usual Bob Jones had an inscription in the run-out grooves of the vinyl, which read 'Stuck On Elvis'! The record was pressed by Damont.

The publishing date shown on the label for **Always On My Mind** was rather confusing, reading 1973. The first version of the song, which, as we have already mentioned, reached the charts in December 1972; whilst this 'version' was not released until 1981 when it appeared on the album **This Is Elvis**, RCALP 5029 (*LP 150*).

No recording mode was shown on side 2, and the errors regarding **Any Way You Want Me (that's how I will be)** and **Stuck On You**, found on the 7 inch version, were continued here. Additionally, both label and sleeve incorrectly showed the writers of **Always On My Mind** as Christopher, Thompson, James.

As regards the vocal accompaniment, the reference on **Are You Lonesome Tonight?** to J.D. Sumner & The Stamps, the Sweet Inspirations and Kathy Westmoreland was inaccurate as, of those mentioned, only the Sweet Inspirations were with Elvis in 1969, when the song was recorded. This particular error can be traced back to the January 1982 album **The Sound Of Your Cry**, RCALP 3060 (*LP 185*).

Label Variations

NEW BLACK LABEL/SOLID CENTRE
1   1987 PRESSING

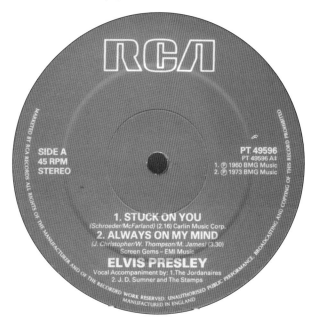

Sleeve Variations

1   Gloss

CD Singles

In addition to the three established formats - cassette and both 7 inch and 12 inch vinyl, a CD version was released in the UK for the first time in January 1988, when **Stuck On You** (PD 49596) was released. However, it did not feature exactly the same tracks as the 12 inch version, for **Always On My Mind** was replaced by **Fame And Fortune**, the original B side of **Stuck On You** (*S 28*).

From this point onwards, all of Elvis's RCA UK singles were released on CD as well. However, specific information relating to CD releases is not included in this volume of **Elvis UK**.

Stuck On You - Extended Mix

For many years the problem of rumours circulating as to what RCA/BMG were intending to release on albums and singles had beset fans. Basically the 'Chinese Whispers' syndrome (not peculiar to Elvis fans alone) operated, whereby somebody would hear something, then pass it on to someone else, who would change, add to or subtract from, as the case may be, who in turn would tell someone else about what, allegedly, the company were going to do! And so on. The net result of this was (and still is to some extent) confusion and disappointment.

Now throughout Elvis's career and since his death, there were a number of examples of tracks supposedly about to be issued by RCA. A couple of famous examples from the sixties spring to mind. In 1965, RCA were rumoured to be releasing **Tennessee Saturday Night** on the **Elvis For Everyone** (*LP 26*) album. Of course, it never materialised then, nor has it since. Later, in 1968, Elvis was thought to have re-recorded some of his early songs - **Baby Let's Play House**, for example, as well as there being a version of Elvis doing Jerry Reed's **Tupelo Mississippi Flash**. Again, neither materialised, though it is easy to offer an explanation as to why such stories existed. Elvis had been re-recording some of his early songs, but as part of the informal 'sit down' and 'stand up' shows, as well as the production numbers for the NBC Special, taped in June 1968. To the best of anyone's knowledge though, **Baby Let's Play House** was not amongst them. Similarly with **Tupelo Mississippi Flash**. In fact, Jerry Reed did provide guitar accompaniment for Elvis on several tracks cut in Nashville in September 1967 and January 1968 - principally two of Jerry's songs: **Guitar Man** and **U.S. Male**. **Tupelo Mississippi Flash** was a song which gently poked fun at the Elvis story.

Therefore, the phenomenon of rumours circulating - some based on sound information/plans which were later changed or abandoned or, alternatively based on erroneous, unfounded speculation - has dogged Elvis fans throughout the years. However, from time to time, stories do circulate, and anticipation rises only to be squashed when things change. A good example of this was the artificially extended version of **Stuck On You**, a version which, unlike the two examples above, did exist but was not, nor is it ever likely to be, released.

Following on from the success of **Bossa Nova Baby** (and presumably inspired by the television advert for Evostik, which used **Stuck On You**), Simon Harris (the DJ) spliced and mixed an extended version (lasting over five minutes) of the song and submitted it to Roger Semon at BMG for consideration. In turn, Bob Jones was asked to listen to and comment on it. The net result of this was that the version was never issued. You must draw your own conclusions as to why this was the case.

Old Gold 1988

The plan for the simultaneous release of the Old Gold singles issued in January 1988 had been in the pipeline for many months. The process involved lengthy negotiations between Old Gold and RCA before permission was granted and a contract drawn up. Once finalised, RCA supplied all the detailed information that was usually found on a record label: the song title, the writer(s), publishers, time, publication date, and so on, and from this Old Gold prepared label copy for their printers. This was normal procedure and explains why label errors were often identical to those found on releases for which RCA were directly responsible; they were simply carried forward to another company who copied what they had been told. Of course, the reverse was also true where RCA supplied the correct detail, but the licensee made the error. This was true for OG 9754, **Can't Help Falling In Love** (**S 170**), where RCA furnished details of the B side, **Rock-A-Hula Baby**, complete with hyphens which failed to appear on the record label.

Back in October 1987, Old Gold had formulated plans to issue their next batch of singles in picture sleeves, and were looking for suitable photographs appropriate to the period of the tracks on each single. Old Gold asked the authors of this book for permission to use extracts from **Elvis UK 1956-86** as accompanying sleeve notes. Although we were more than happy to agree to this, we felt it more appropriate to write new notes more in keeping with the spirit of Old Gold releases, but although we prepared these, they were never used. Todd Slaughter, President of the Official Elvis Presley Fan Club, eventually supplied the photographs. The artwork for the picture sleeves had to be in production by 21 December 1987 in order to meet the proposed January release date, a good indication of how quickly the final stages leading up to a release could be effected.

At the same time (and to further demonstrate the level of confidence Old Gold had in their Elvis repertoire), consideration was being given to putting the first ten Old Gold Elvis singles, first released in October 1986 and April 1987, into picture sleeves for a limited edition run, issued in a box with an accompanying booklet. To some extent this release depended on how well received the individual picture sleeve of the second batch of releases proved to be.

In addition, Old Gold were also exploring the possibility of issuing a selection of EPs in a similar format to those of the excellent RCA collections, released in 1982.

However, for a variety of reasons, none of these plans came to fruition in the way they had first been conceived. The likelihood is that a combination of factors caused this, rather than one overriding problem.

Undoubtedly contributing to this was the fact that Old Gold themselves had other projects on the stocks, expanding their interests which, in strict business terms, clearly proved to be more beneficial, but prevented a concentrated effort to get collectors' items to the Elvis market.

However, some of the ideas were adopted later, with a gradual move to picture sleeves being made on a 'sales' basis by which a batch of singles - usually 50 - had a picture sleeve produced as stocks of the record became low. This typically came before stocks were depleted entirely, but when sales were buoyant enough to ensure continued sales. In simple terms, a picture sleeve would not be issued when sales did not justify this. The policy adopted was that the top 50, in sales terms, would move to picture sleeves, followed by the next 50, and so on. Later still, when Old Gold were looking again at the possibility of issuing collectors' material, RCA had begun to have doubts about licensing Elvis material to other companies, effectively stopping outside organisations being able to use this kind of material.

Old Gold Label Detail Change

The third and final batch of ten Old Gold releases, whilst still retaining the same basic layout as the previous releases, now included new detail regarding the licensing arrangements. The detail just above the bar code read:

Licensed from BMG Records (UK) Ltd./BMG Music

Similarly, BMG Music was quoted next to the publication date, below the catalogue number. The labels thus reflected the fact that RCA had become a division of the Bertelsmann Music Group (BMG), a year after this had actually occurred.

However, as mentioned previously, re-pressings of earlier singles did not use the above detail; instead they continued to use identical information to that printed on their original labels.

S 164　　Old Gold　　OG 9740

Jailhouse Rock {M} (Leiber, Stoller)
Treat Me Nice {M} (Leiber, Stoller)

Released January 1988
Original Issue January 1958. RCA 1028 (S 18)
Previous Re-issue May 1977. RCA 2695 (S 101)
Previous Re-issue January 1983. RCA 1028 (S 136)

No Elvis era would seem complete without the release of this classic coupling of the original single from 1958. Used three times previously by RCA (the last time being in 1983 when the single was re-issued to mark the twenty-fifth anniversary of its original release), this Old Gold release became the fourth time that the single had been released. By coincidence, rather than by design, the release date of January 1988 just happened to be the single's thirtieth anniversary, a fact which went by seemingly unnoticed by the industry or fans.

Jailhouse Rock was also featured on an Old Gold LP - *Number Ones 50's Volume 2 - Pop* (**VA LP 15**), released a few months after this single in May 1988. Both songs quoted a publication date of 1957 on the label, although neither were released in the UK at that time, although they were in America. In keeping with all the Old Gold singles there was no reference to the film which featured both songs, presumably because it was no longer thought to be relevant.

By September 1989, the single had sold in sufficient quantities to justify a further press run, this time using a picture sleeve. A total of 3,200 copies were produced. Unfortunately, the sleeve notes contained some inaccurate statements concerning the recording information for *Jailhouse Rock*. The song was recorded at the famous Radio Recorders Studio on 30 April 1957, and not on 2 May 1957 at the MGM Studios, Culver City; furthermore, the claim that Elvis played piano was really strange. To our knowledge there is no documentary evidence that Elvis played piano on the song *Jailhouse Rock*, although he is thought to have done so on some of the other tracks recorded at the session. For example, it is known that Elvis played bass guitar on *(You're so square) Baby I Don't Care*.

Label Variations

GOLD LABEL/SOLID CENTRE
1   1987 PRESSING

Sleeve Variations

1	Type 2
2	Type 3
3	Picture sleeve - first design

S 165   Old Gold   OG 9742

It's Now Or Never {S} (DiCapua, Schroeder, Gold)
Surrender {S} (DeCurtis, Pomus, Shuman)

Released January 1988

It's Now Or Never remains Elvis's biggest selling UK single, a fact which is unlikely to change, but it is interesting to note that this unique Old Gold coupling of two A sides from 1960 and 1961 respectively (*S 30* and *S 33*), did not achieve the distinction of being issued in a picture sleeve. This suggested that sales of the single did not keep pace with some of the other Old Gold releases and, therefore, did not justify such a move being made. Of course, this might not be the case, for it is possible that it was simply a matter of timing that prevented a picture sleeve being issued. Old Gold's policy of introducing a picture sleeve was indeed based on sales, and as many as fifty releases at a time were involved. *It's Now Or Never* obviously never entered Old Gold's 'top fifty' in sales terms for the first batch or, indeed, the second or third batches, but it is likely that RCA's decision to restrict licensing arrangements had more to do with the non-appearance of a picture sleeve than poor sales figures.

It is interesting to note that both of these songs were number one hit records in the UK and America, and that both were based on Italian melodies. Importantly, both songs appeared in stereo.

Incidentally, this release meant that Old Gold had made available five consecutive RCA single A sides from the period 1960-1961, starting with *It's Now Or Never* (*S 30*), and ending with *Wild In The Country* (*S 34*), which Old Gold released in April 1987.

There were no label errors.

Label Variations

GOLD LABEL/SOLID CENTRE
1   1987 PRESSING

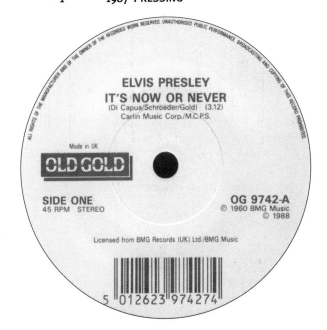

Sleeve Variations

1	Type 2
2	Type 3

S 166   Old Gold   OG 9744

Always On My Mind {S} (James, Carson, Christopher)
Burning Love {S} (Linde)

Released January 1988

This was the second Old Gold single to feature consecutive A side singles combining **Burning Love** (*S 84*), from September 1972, and **Always On My Mind** (*S 85*), from December 1972. Both songs were recorded in RCA's Hollywood studios in late March 1972.

The version of **Always On My Mind** was the original single version, complete with electric guitar break. Strangely enough though, **Always On My Mind**, despite having been released twice previously by RCA (*S 85* and **S 146**), did rather well sales-wise, and a year after its initial release had sold enough copies for it to justify a re-pressing with a picture sleeve. The picture on the sleeve was from the NBC TV Special in 1968 - thus predating by four years the time these tracks were recorded.

There were no label errors and both songs were featured in stereo.

Label Variations

GOLD LABEL/SOLID CENTRE
1   1987 PRESSING

Sleeve Variations

1   Type 2
2   Picture sleeve - first design

S 167 | *Old Gold   OG 9746*

Loving You {M} (Leiber, Stoller)
Paralyzed {M} (Blackwell, Presley)

Released January 1988

Loving You was originally released in 1957 as the B side of *(Let me be your) Teddy Bear* (*S 12*), a song which Old Gold themselves also released in October 1986, but as the B side of *Love Me Tender* (*S 153*).

Paralyzed has been spelt differently since it first appeared in April 1957 on Elvis's second UK album, *Rock 'N' Roll (No. 2)*, HMV CLP 1105, where a 'z' was used, as it was on the HMV single released in August 1957. This, of course, was the American spelling of the word. Later, when RCA issued the song on the EP *Strictly Elvis*, RCX 175 (*EP 12*), initially following the line adopted by HMV, the 'z' changed to an 's' on later issues. And, by the time the song was used as the B side to *Old Shep*, RCA PB 9334 (*S 119*), in November 1978, the 'z' had long disappeared.

Whether, after all this time, it is still relevant to consider the use of the 's' a label error may seem pointless, but as we wish to remain consistent, we merely indicate that the original spelling is shown in the title block and we continue to use this throughout.

Label Variations

GOLD LABEL/SOLID CENTRE
1   1987 PRESSING

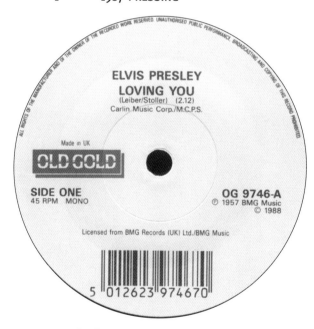

Sleeve Variations

1   Type 2
2   Type 3

Old Gold Catalogue Numbers

Reference to the catalogue numbers used by Old Gold for the final batch of ten Elvis singles, issued simultaneously in January 1988, will show that there was a gap in the sequence following OG 9746, *Loving You/Paralyzed*, and OG 9750, *King Creole/Hard Headed Woman*, in that no Elvis single with the catalogue number OG 9748 was ever issued. Indeed, no Old Gold single appears to have been released bearing that number, but a Marvin Gaye single, *(Sexual) Healing*, did appear with a catalogue number OG 9749.

On the other hand, Old Gold did not stick to a consistent formula of using even number catalogue numbers, as the final Elvis single, OG 9761, *The Wonder Of You*, clearly demonstrated. There was no obvious rationale for this; Old Gold simply allocated the next batch of singles a range of numbers (see **S 173** for further details).

S 168 | *Old Gold   OG 9750*

King Creole {M} (Leiber, Stoller)
Hard Headed Woman {M} (DeMetrius)

Released January 1988

This Old Gold single comprised two consecutive A sides from 1958, although *Hard Headed Woman* was the first to be issued in July, on RCA 1070 (*S 21*). *King Creole*, RCA 1081, (*S 22*), was issued in September 1958 - which was closer to the August release date of the film of the same name. With the release of *King Creole*, this meant that all four title tracks of his pre-army films had been issued on Old Gold.

Neither of these songs had been used on a UK single since their original issue, despite their obvious qualities.

There were no label errors. Nor was there a picture sleeve available.

Label Variations

GOLD LABEL/SOLID CENTRE
1   1987 PRESSING

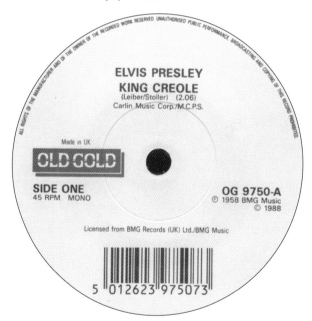

Sleeve Variations

1   Type 2
2   Type 3

S 169 | *Old Gold* OG 9752

Don't {M} (Leiber, Stoller)
Wear My Ring Around Your Neck {M} (Carroll, Moody)

Released January 1988

Neither of these two songs had been used on singles since they first appeared as consecutive A sides in 1958 (*S 19* and *S 20*), making this release particularly attractive.

However, although a steady seller, sales were never high enough to warrant a picture sleeve being used.

The version of **Wear My Ring Around Your Neck** was the compressed, original single version, not the one featured on the album *Presley - The All Time Greatest Hits* (**LP 287**), which was uncompressed.

There were no label errors.

Label Variations

GOLD LABEL/SOLID CENTRE
1   1987 PRESSING

Sleeve Variations

1   Type 2
2   Type 3

S 170 | *Old Gold* OG 9754

Can't Help Falling In Love {M} (Peretti, Creatore, Weiss)
Rock-A-Hula Baby {S} (Wise, Weisman, Fuller)

Released January 1988
Original Issue January 1962. RCA 1270 (*S 36*)
Previous Re-issue May 1977. RCA 2703 (*S 109*)

This single was a straight re-issue of an old favourite which last appeared in May 1977. There has always been some confusion over which of the songs should have been classed as the A side on the original single, as both did well in the charts.

There was no reference on the label that both songs had been featured in the film *Blue Hawaii*, but, as we mentioned earlier, there seemed to be no need to do so twenty six years after the film was released.

Inexplicably, however, **Can't Help Falling In Love** was featured in mono, whilst **Rock-A-Hula Baby** was in stereo. The former track appeared on the Old Gold album *Number Ones Sixties Volume 3 - Ballad*s (**VA LP 17**), again in mono - yet it had been issued innumerable times in stereo, including blue label copies of the RCA single 2703, issued in 1982 (*S 109*). Old Gold were only supplied with a mono tape.

The licenced tracks and copyright information prepared by RCA and passed on to Old Gold clearly showed the hyphens in the song **Rock-A-Hula Baby**, but these were omitted on the record label.

Label Variations

GOLD LABEL/SOLID CENTRE
1   1987 PRESSING

Sleeve Variations

1   Type 2
2   Type 3

S 171   Old Gold   OG 9756

My Boy {S} (Francois, Bourtayre, Martin, Coulter)
My Way {S} (Thibault, Francois, Revaux, Anka)

Released January 1988

Three years separated the original A side release dates of these songs, the longest gap in the whole Old Gold series. *My Boy* was released as an A side single in October 1974 (*S 91*), and *My Way* in November 1977 (*S 117*). Note that this was the original single version of *My Way* taken from *Elvis In Concert* (*LP 100*), and recorded in June 1977.

In the introductory section we discussed the advantage of showing a song's running time on both label and, where possible, on the sleeve. Our view is that this was an essential piece of information which often highlighted discrepancies between releases, and frequently pointed to those occasions where songs had been 'compressed' (shortened) or 'opened up' (made longer). The problem, of course, is knowing which time (or speed) is correct, but displaying the running time is one way of establishing a standard and, happily, most Elvis releases these days do include this detail. Earlier releases did not, and comparisons with, say, the original issue of a particular song is sometimes difficult without having to undergo the dubious delights of hand-timing! When it is possible to do so, and the case of *My Boy* is a good example, there are some startling differences.

The time shown on this Old Gold single was 2:54, which fell far short of the 3:18 quoted on the original (the American grey label release, also available in the UK) or *Presley - The All Time Greatest Hits*, PL 90100(2) (*LP 287*), which also used 3:18. Of course, playing the records in question is the only way to determine where the difference lies, as the quoted time may not be accurate in the first instance. The difference here turned out to be that the Old Gold single had a much faster fade out than the original, giving a shorter running time.

Both of the songs featured on this single were composed by French writers and were subsequently adapted for the English language so that new lyrics were applied to the existing music. Inevitably this presents problems in determining who the actual composers were. Should the writer who supplied the French lyrics be ignored in favour of the English lyricist, or should both names be included? Which ought to be the correct order - French first or last?

We have stuck with our view that the writers shown above are correct. The addition of the Dessca to *My Boy* was interesting, as it was not referred to on the licenced track and copyright information supplied by RCA to Old Gold. Also, it does seem rather unfair to show Paul Anka's name first as co-writer of *My Way*, when he merely supplied the English lyrics to the original.

Label Variations

GOLD LABEL/SOLID CENTRE

1   1987 PRESSING

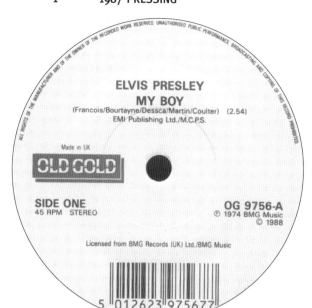

Sleeve Variations

1	Type 2
2	Type 3
3	Type 4

91

S 172   Old Gold   OG 9758

Way Down {S} (Martine Jr.)
Moody Blue {S} (James)

Released January 1988
Original Issue May 1982. RCA Golden Grooves Gold 544 (*S 134*)

This release was a coupling of the two A sides issued in 1977, prior to Elvis's death, **Moody Blue** (*S 99*), and **Way Down** (*S 116*). Indeed these were consecutive 'new' singles - at the time - the large gap between release numbers being brought about by the release of the Gold 16 singles issued simultaneously in May 1977. To date **Way Down** was Elvis's last number one hit in the UK, and had been issued with **Moody Blue** on a previous occasion, when the songs appeared together in May 1982 on RCA's Golden Grooves label (*S 134*). This was the seventh and final straight re-issue produced by Old Gold; all of their other singles were new couplings.

In the notes preceding single **S 156**, we mentioned that some shops were advertising this coupling as an Old Gold release in April 1987. However, in truth, they were selling the Golden Grooves single, using Old Gold advertising material. Old Gold had no rights to the songs at that time. **Way Down** was incorrectly credited to Martin, Kennedy.

Label Variations

GOLD LABEL/SOLID CENTRE
     1   1987 PRESSING

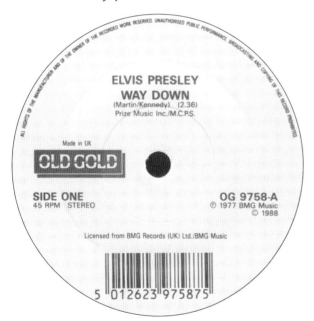

Sleeve Variations

   1   Type 2
   2   Type 3
   3   Type 4

S 173   Old Gold   OG 9761

The Wonder Of You {M} (Knight)
If I Can Dream {Alternative version} {S} (Brown)

Released January 1988

This was the twentieth and final Old Gold single, and it is interesting to note that this one deviated from the pattern set by all other Elvis singles released by the company, in that its catalogue number was an odd number and was, therefore, not an increment of two over the previous release. Had the normal pattern been observed, the number would have been 9760. Reference to Old Gold's catalogue offered no clues as to why, as other singles were issued with an odd, rather than even catalogue number, but a non-Elvis single with 9760 as a catalogue number was never issued. The reason for this was simply that Old Gold gave a batch of planned releases a range of numbers and allocated each single a catalogue number within that range, irrespective of whether it was an odd or even number. Clearly this single could have used 9760, but all the paperwork went ahead using 9761, and that was the number that appeared on the single. The single was not, therefore, an afterthought or a 'extra' single, as some have suggested, merely a blip in a basic system. Interestingly, no Elvis single was issued with a catalogue number 9748, proving that Old Gold lacked a certain consistency in this area (see the notes preceding release number **S 168** for further details).

Another unique feature concerned the B side, **If I Can Dream**, because, despite Old Gold's claim that their records featured 'the original hit recordings', the version of the song contained here was far from being the 'original'. This was not the version which appeared on RCA's original single, RCA 1795, in February 1969 (*S 67*), but the version, an alternative take, which appeared on the LP **He Walks Beside Me: Favourite Songs of Faith And Inspiration**, RCA PL 12772 (*LP 101*), released in March 1978. Obviously this was something quite unusual, as different versions were not used that often and presumably this was unplanned, for RCA themselves used the original version of the song as the B side of **Love Me Tender**, ARON 2, in August 1987 (**S 160**).

The Wonder Of You was one of the tracks used by Old Gold on their LP **Number Ones 70's Volume 2 - Ballads** (**VA LP 18**), released in May 1988, and as on the LP, the song was a mono recording. The mix used by Old Gold was the one originally used on the **On Stage February 1970** album (*LP 41*) in July 1970 and the version used on the RCA single released the same month (*S 73*), not the slightly re-mixed version which was featured on the 1987 album **Presley - The All Time Greatest Hits** (**LP 287**). Incidentally, **The Wonder Of You** was used to advertise Bovril on TV in late 1991.

This single did well for Old Gold, with steady sales over the two years following its release, and in June 1990, the single was issued in a picture sleeve with an initial press run of 2,100 copies. However, the picture on the front of the sleeve was taken from the NBC TV Special. The sleeve notes suggested that the Joe Guercio Orchestra accompanied Elvis during his performances at the International Hotel where the recording of *The Wonder Of You* was recorded. We believe that this was not the case, for although Guercio appeared with Elvis from the August 1970 season onwards, it was the Bobby Morris Orchestra who accompanied Elvis during the February 1970 engagement when *The Wonder Of You* was recorded.

Label Variations

GOLD LABEL/SOLID CENTRE
1   1987 PRESSING

Sleeve Variations

1   Type 2
2   Type 3
3   Picture sleeve - second design

Interview Picture Disc Collection
1 WMPS, Memphis, with Bob Neal, 31 August 1955
2 San Antonio, Texas, with Charlie Walker, 15 April 1956
3 Warwick Hotel, New York,
with Robert Carlton Brown, 24 March 1956

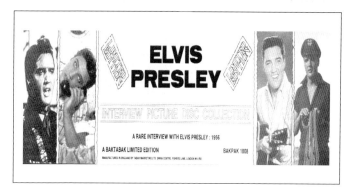

Released April 1988

This set was undoubtedly a UK Elvis first, comprising four singles of interview material presented in a plastic foldover wallet which, when opened, could be hung up to display the four picture discs. The concept was new and only a handful of other artists were given similar releases. Above the four plastic pockets housing the records was a card header sheet with Elvis's name, the title, and four small black and white photographs of Elvis covering the period 1956 to 1968.

These photographs also formed the front of each picture disc, although the picture on the back was the same for all the records. Of course, many of the photographs were inappropriate to the period of the interviews - 1955 and 1956 - and many dated from around the time of *It Happened At The World's Fair* (1962), while there was also one from the NBC TV Special in 1968. A nice little touch was the use of both black and white print which changed when the background colour altered, so that the print was always readable, even for single characters.

The interview material was nothing unusual, indeed the interview picture disc album put out by Baktabak at the same time (**LP 293**) contained the same material with the exception that the Peter Noone 'interview' (from August 1965) was, happily, omitted. The same material could also be found on Baktabak's Interview Picture Disc CD, CBAK 4007, although the CD version included short instrumental links of Elvis songs and introductions by Len Leonards.

The main criticism of this kind of release was that there were no details of which interviews were included, either on the title card or on the discs themselves. The only clue - a rather misleading 'A rare interview with Elvis Presley: 1956' - was wholly inaccurate. There were three interviews and these were far from being rare. The first two interviews were included on the first of the four singles; the third interview being continued over the remaining three records. Nonetheless, this sort of release became very collectable - largely because relatively few were produced and, moreover, because few fans knew about its existence.

Label Variations

BLACK/WHITE PICTURE DISC
1   1988 PRESSING

Sleeve Variations

1   Clear plastic sleeve

RCA Sleeve Detail Change

The next RCA release, **Mean Woman Blues**, PB 49473 (**S 175**), featured a new logo - BMG - in addition to the circular RCA logo in the bottom left hand corner on the back of the sleeve, thus making its first appearance on a single. A new statement that 'All trademarks and logos are protected' was also added.

RCA Sleeves

The previous RCA 7 inch single, **Stuck On You**, PB 49595 (**S 162**), released in January 1988, was the final RCA single to have both a gloss and matt finish sleeve. The next single, **Mean Woman Blues**, PB 49473 (**S 175**), appeared in a gloss sleeve only, and from this point onwards virtually all of RCA's 7 inch singles used this format.

Gloss sleeves had been used on singles for the initial press run from 1984 onwards, with the first single being **The Last Farewell**, RCA 459 (*S 143*). Later re-pressings had used the matt sleeve format, but with diminishing sales, additional copies were not made after the initial batch was sold.

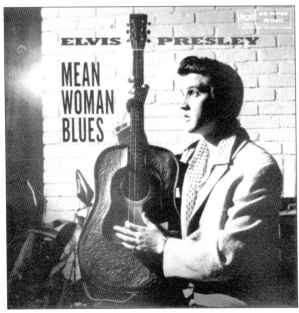

S 175	**RCA PB 49473**

Mean Woman Blues {S} (DeMetrius)
I Beg Of You {S} (McCoy, Owens)

Released January 1989   **Chart Entry Number 142**
Highest Chart Position 63

Twelve months had passed since the previous RCA single, **Stuck On You** (**S 162**), and the songs on this single were taken from the album

Stereo '57 (Essential Elvis Volume 2) (**LP 298**), also released in January. Indeed the rear of the single sleeve showed a picture of the album, and used the same photograph of Elvis in the recording studio in July 1956. These songs were in binaural which had been mastered by Bob Jones, and it was a proud moment when a label could accurately state stereo for recordings made in January 1957.

This was the first time that **Mean Woman Blues** had been used on a single, but **I Beg Of You** had been the B side of **Don't** when it was released in February 1958 (*S 19*). On that occasion though, the version used was obviously the more familiar one, whereas this version was an entirely different treatment of the song, heard by many fans for the first time, though some had heard a poor quality version of this on the **Jailhouse Rock Sessions** bootleg in the mid-eighties. It was, in fact, take 6.

The round RCA logo was to be found on both front and back of the sleeve, which also featured the new BMG logo. The legend 'A "New Orthophonic" High Fidelity Recording' appeared on the front, giving the single an authentic 'period feel', as this detail was to be found on most labels during the fifties and sixties.

The single cost £1.99 and, unlike all of the regular RCA 7 inch singles going back to **The Last Farewell**, RCA 459 (*S 143*), in October 1984, was produced in a gloss sleeve only. What happened was that after the initial press run, matt sleeves were then produced, thus creating a sleeve variation. From **Mean Woman Blues** onwards, a gloss-only finish was used on sleeves, until **Heartbreak Hotel** was released in May 1996 (**S 181**).

Not surprisingly, the label made no reference to the fact that **Mean Woman Blues** had been featured in the film **Loving You**.

Despite the obvious qualities of the single, chart success was limited to a peak of number 63, and by October 1989, the single had been deleted from RCA's catalogue - clear indication of the company's policy of removing product from the catalogue once sales fell. There were no re-pressings.

Label Variations

NEW BLACK LABEL/SOLID CENTRE
1   1988 PRESSING

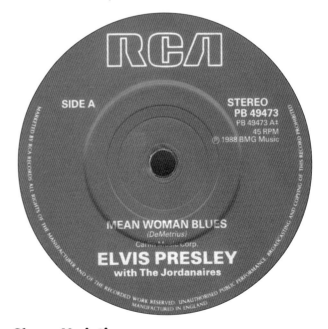

Sleeve Variations

1   Gloss

S 176 RCA PT 49474

Mean Woman Blues {S} (DeMetrius)
I Beg Of You {Alternative version} {S} (McCoy, Owens)
Party {Alternative version} {M} (Robinson)
Mean Woman Blues {Alternative mix} {S} (DeMetrius)

Released January 1989

This 12 inch single cost £3.49 when it was released and, in addition to the two songs used on the 7 inch version, two other tracks had been added to make a four-track release. The final track, the 'dub' version of **Mean Woman Blues**, was edited by Bob Jones, at the request of Roger Semon, whereby Elvis's voice was omitted on certain passages, thus creating almost a semi-instrumental version of the song. Whilst this did create an unusual effect - and no-one can doubt the obvious technical skills required to achieve this - opinion regarding how desirable or successful this was remained openly divided.

Strangely, the sleeve drew attention to the fact that the title tracks and **Party** were songs featured in the film **Loving You**, an accurate reference, though oddly out of place. The rear of the sleeve also added a note suggesting that all the tracks were taken from the LP **Stereo '57 (Essential Elvis Volume 2)** (**LP 298**), when, in fact, only the first two were from the album. **Party** (take 7) was, in fact, taken from the album **Essential Elvis**, (**LP 280**). A second studio photograph had been added to the back of the sleeve when compared to the 7 inch version.

As with the 7 inch single, the record was printed and pressed in England, probably by CBS.

There were no label errors, though the alternative version of **Party** was in mono, whereas the label suggested that it was in stereo.

This 12 inch version was not deleted until February 1990, thereby outliving its 7 inch counterpart by four months.

Label Variations

NEW BLACK LABEL/SOLID CENTRE
1   1988 PRESSING

Sleeve Variations

1   Gloss

Old Gold Picture Sleeves

In January 1989 three Old Gold singles had sold in sufficient quantities to warrant a re-pressing using picture sleeves, the first of Elvis's Old Gold releases to achieve this status. The three singles were:

S 148 OG 9616   *In The Ghetto/Suspicious Minds*

S 152 OG 9624   *An American Trilogy/Until It's Time*
                     For You To Go

S 166 OG 9744   *Always On My Mind/Burning Love*

The first two originated from the original batch released in October 1986, while **Always On My Mind** was first released only a year previously, in January 1988, suggesting that sales of this single had been particularly good.

Singles' Deletion - March 1989

A number of singles, including some regular RCA label releases, dating back to 1977, and Golden Grooves' releases from the early 1980s, were deleted on 3 March 1989. They were as follows:

	Catalogue Number	Title	Release Date
S 101	RCA 2695	*Jailhouse Rock* *Treat Me Nice*	May 1977
S 106	RCA 2700	*Wooden Heart* *Tonight Is So Right For Love*	May 1977
S 114	RCA 2708	*Crying In The Chapel* *I Believe In The Man In The Sky*	May 1977
S 126	GOLD 506	*An American Trilogy* *Suspicious Minds*	Jul 1981

S 134	GOLD 544	*Way Down* *Moody Blue*	May 1981
S 154	ARON 1	*Ain't That Loving You Baby* *Bossa Nova Baby*	Mar 1987
S 155	ARONT 1	*Ain't That Loving You Baby* *I'm Comin' Home* *Bossa Nova Baby* *Rock-A-Hula Baby*	Mar 1987
S 160	ARON 2	*Love Me Tender* *If I Can Dream*	Aug 1987
S 161	ARONT 2	*Love Me Tender* *If I Can Dream* *Bossa Nova Baby*	Aug 1987

Old Gold Type 3 Sleeves

Despite the fact that Old Gold had started to use picture sleeves for some singles, it was felt necessary to introduce a new sleeve design for non-picture sleeve singles. The new design, which we have called type 3, became available from May 1989 onwards, and several of Elvis's Old Gold singles (notably re-pressings of earlier releases) used this type of sleeve. For further information, please refer to the notes on Old Gold picture sleeves preceeding **S 148.**

Old Gold Picture Sleeves

In September 1989, the fourth Old Gold single to attain picture sleeve status was re-pressed. *Jailhouse Rock*, OG 9740 (**S 164**), first released in January 1988, therefore demonstrated its rightful claim to be one of the most popular songs Elvis ever recorded.

Single Deletion - October 1989

On 16 October 1989, RCA deleted the single *Mean Woman Blues/I Beg Of You*, RCA PB 49473 (**S 175**), first issued in January 1989. Its short run on catalogue of just 10 months was overshadowed by its 12 inch counterpart, PT 49474 (**S 176**), containing additional tracks, which was not deleted until February 1990.

Singles' Deletion - February 1990

The last of the 'Gold 16' singles from May 1977 was finally deleted on 9 February 1990, thirteen years after it was first released. *Return To Sender/Where Do You Come From*, RCA 2706 (*S 112*) had outlasted them all!

Also on 9 February 1990, RCA deleted the 12 inch single comprising *Mean Woman Blues/I Beg Of You/Party/Mean Woman Blues*, RCA PT 49474 (**S 176**). Surprisingly, the 7 inch version, PB 49473 (**S 175**), comprising the first two tracks only, had been deleted earlier, in October 1989.

Old Gold Picture Sleeves

In April 1990 *Love Me Tender*, OG 9626 (**S 153**), from the original batch released in October 1986, was re-pressed using a picture sleeve. This was followed, in June 1990, by a further two singles, the last ones to achieve this status, and making seven in total. These singles, from April 1987 and January 1988 respectively, were *Hound Dog*, OG 9700 (**S 156**), and *The Wonder Of You*, OG 9761 (**S 173**).

Strangely, the Old Gold catalogue for 1990 did not include information on either of the last two singles, even though the catalogue itself was prepared in December 1989, suggesting that sales of these singles accelerated during the first half of 1990.

Single Deletion - August 1990

In July 1981, RCA had released the first of their 'Golden Grooves' singles, an Elvis record featuring *I Just Can't Help Believin'* and **Bridge Over Troubled Water** (*S 127*). This was the last of the seven Golden Grooves Elvis releases to be deleted (on 30 August 1990). Indeed, it was the last pre-1986 single to suffer that fate.

Old Gold

By October 1990, five Elvis singles had been dropped by Old Gold from their repertoire, a fact revealed when the company's 1991 catalogue was issued. The singles in question were:

S 149	OG 9618	*Party/Got A Lot O' Livin' To Do!*
S 150	OG 9620	*Blue Moon/I Don't Care If The Sun Don't Shine*
S 157	OG 9702	*Are You Lonesome Tonight?/Wooden Heart*
S 158	OG 9704	*Heartbreak Hotel/All Shook Up*
S 159	OG 9706	*Wild In The Country/I Feel So Bad*

If we had to predict which singles would have been first to suffer this fate, then it would seem probable that most of the above would have been likely candidates, for despite their obvious qualities, they could be considered as weaker items, particularly when many of Old Gold's customers were chance or casual buyers. On the other hand, the coupling of **Are You Lonesome Tonight?** and **Wooden Heart** would appear to have a timeless feel about it and ought to have survived longer. There was a possibility, of course, that the live - the so-called 'laughing' - version of **Are You Lonesome Tonight?** had become more of a favourite in recent years, having achieved some considerable air-play and attained moderate chart success - not to mention its popularity with the folks at BMG in the UK!

Of course, the deletion of these records was not just about reduced sales figures, but more about timing, in the sense that the instruction issued by RCA that licensing arrangements had to be terminated, following difficulties encountered between all parties involved in Elvis product. The instruction issued to Old Gold was that no further releases would be granted and, that further pressings of existing catalogue were not to be undertaken. Despite this, no instruction was placed on the company to cease selling Elvis singles by a certain date; but the decision effectively meant that when stocks of each record became low then deletion was inevitable. So it was, in effect, a phased sort of deletion programme.

However, the deletion of five singles left fifteen still on catalogue, though the deleted items were still available in fairly large numbers well into 1991. The term deleted on this occasion referred to the fact that the company had no stocks. To illustrate this point, the Virgin Megastore in London ran a campaign in April 1991 offering a free Old Gold single with every two purchased. The campaign claimed that stocks were a 'special purchase' which suggested that Virgin had bought up stocks of deleted singles. Incidentally, Virgin charged £2.49 for each single, whereas the usual price elsewhere was £1.99!

The Singles' Market

Between April 1989 (remember that RCA issued a special four-track CD single in March 1989) and August 1991, no Elvis single of any description was released in the UK. This meant, that for the first time ever a whole year - 1990 - was without an Elvis single on any label. By this time we had come to realise that RCA did not issue singles as a matter of course; those that were issued immediately prior to this period had been to promote albums or were opportunist releases, often capitalising on TV advertisement campaigns which had used an Elvis track. From the mid-eighties onwards few RCA Elvis singles were issued - one, or possibly two, each year - but none were issued during 1986, although another company, Old Gold, released six singles in October of that year.

As with albums, the singles that RCA did issue were concentrated on the two 'peak' Elvis periods - January and August - the anniversaries of his birth and death. It is difficult to see why 1990 should have been treated differently. Certainly there were two albums issued around the thirteenth anniversary of his death. In July 1990, **Hits Like Never Before (Essential Elvis Vol. 3)**, PL 90486 (**LP 306**), was issued, followed in August by **The Great Performances**, PL 82227 (**LP 308**). Both of these releases contained some strong material and perhaps a single of **My Happiness**, released for the first time on **The Great Performances**, would have been a worthwhile 'collectors' issue, especially if it had preceded the album. We do know that the people responsible for Elvis product share the general belief that not enough was made of this important recording, but presumably a single release was thought inappropriate. A promo-only single was issued in America in August 1990.

RCA, by this time, had accepted the fact that without additional - and possibly unintentional - promotion, (for example, the use of an Elvis song in a popular film) that major chart action would never again be seen. This view though, not shared by all, was understandable. After all, the collectors' market alone could not generate sufficient sales to provide chart success, and the possibilities of issuing a song which would capture the interest of the casual buyer seemed ever more unlikely.

RCA Singles

Another long gap had passed since the previous RCA single, **Mean Woman Blues**, PB 49473 (**S 175**), released in January 1989. This meant that no Elvis single had been released on any label (remember previous RCA lapses had been filled by Old Gold) in the UK for thirty-two months, despite what would appear to have been the occasional opportunity for a single. The release of **For The Asking (The Lost Album)**, NL 90513 (**LP 309**), in November 1990, perhaps offered the greatest potential for a single, as it used material from a period not featured on any recent RCA single and contained a number of popular songs which could have appealed to a wider audience. In addition, further selections not included on the album, could have been brought in to give a single a track(s) not readily available elsewhere. Whatever the reason was (and we accept that this form of record does not make money), no single was released during the calendar year 1990, and the gap between releases was the longest ever.

RCA Label Change

The next RCA 7 inch single, **Are You Lonesome Tonight?**, PB 49177 (**S 177**), released in August 1991, appeared with a silver coloured label, instead of the more usual black label. This was only the second time that such a label colour had been used by the company, the first occasion being in October 1984, when **The Last Farewell**, RCA 459 (*S 143*), was issued.

The silver label featured the original, circular RCA logo, present on all the releases during the fifties and sixties, until the label colour changed to orange in 1969, although here the logo was very small and located at the top of the label. This circular logo had replaced the 'computer' style logo, and had appeared on several albums prior to this. The actual logo had first appeared on the sleeve of the previous RCA single, **Mean Woman Blues**, PB 49473 (**S 175**), released in January 1989.

However, the 12 inch format of **Are You Lonesome Tonight?** used the normal black label, although this too featured the round RCA logo in its full size, and located on the left of the centre hole, in keeping with LP labels.

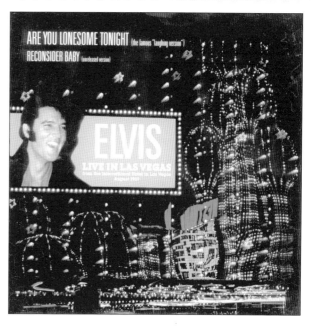

| S 177 | RCA | PB 49177 |

Are You Lonesome Tonight? {Live version} {S} (Turk, Handman)
Reconsider Baby {Live version} {S} (Fulson)

Released August 1991

Chart Entry Number 143
Highest Chart Position 68

Clearly the release of an album with the credentials of **Collectors Gold**, PL 90574(3) (**LP 315**), had to generate a single release, but there was a mixture of dismay and derision amongst fans to learn that the A side was to be the 'laughing version' of **Are You Lonesome Tonight?**, considered by many to be well past its play-by date. Still, here it was making its second UK A side appearance, the first being in February 1982 on RCA 196 (*S 133*), and its third on a single. Remember it had also been used on the January 1988 12 inch **Stuck On You** single, PT 49596 (**S 163**), the last but one RCA single. Undeniably the song had its merits, and it was probably used because of its wider appeal, but with previous appearances on singles and albums, its re-issue left many feeling disappointed.

We should point out that **Are You Lonesome Tonight?** was an edited version from that featured on **Collectors Gold**. There was no opening chord and no 'chat' at the end of the song. The track ran for 2.40 minutes, compared to the 2.50 on the **Stuck On You** single (**S 163**). However, although mastered by Bob Jones, the track had been pre-edited by someone at BMG.

The single itself used a silver label, for the second time only. The only previous appearance of this label colour was in October 1984 on the single **The Last Farewell**, RCA 459 (*S 143*). Another notable feature was the return of the round RCA logo, now company standard, which was displayed at the top of the label, albeit in a very small format. Perhaps the most interesting thing about the label was that it gave the record a title - **Live In Las Vegas** - the first time such a feature had appeared on a single, although, of course, all albums and EPs followed this practice.

The sleeve design was splendidly different, featuring a splash of lights in a firework-like display, and observers could make out the reverse image words 'Westward Ho'? The small colour shot of Elvis used on the sleeve was from the opening night press conference on 31 July 1969. Another first, this time incorporated into the back of the sleeve, was the 'Elvis in the 90's' logo, usually found in the form of a sticker on album covers. Not only did the back cover show a colour advert for the forthcoming **Collectors Gold** set, but it also featured an advert inviting people to join the Elvis Presley Fan Club (of Great Britain). Perhaps we should also point out that the sleeve had foldovers on the back, a feature of production not seen for many years on a picture sleeve. As referred to earlier, the single was mastered by Bob Jones and had been pressed in England by EMI.

The single was widely distributed, with shops taking larger than average stocks, and so it was no surprise that many of them offered the single at the heavily discounted price of 99p, even though the dealer price was actually £1.20.

Claims that *Are You Lonesome Tonight?* had first been published in 1980 were accurate, as it had first appeared on the *Elvis Aron Presley*, CPL8 3699 (*LP 126*), boxed set, released in August of that year. And, as this version of the B side, *Reconsider Baby*, had not been released previously, the publishing date of 1991 was also accurate. It was sad, therefore, to find that the question mark had been omitted from *Are You Lonesome Tonight?*, on both label and sleeve. Worse still was the label's assertion that *Reconsider Baby* was written by Lowell and Fulsom, when, if fact it was one person - Lowell Fulson.

Label Variations

SILVER LABEL/SOLID CENTRE

1   1991 PRESSING

Sleeve Variations

1   Gloss

PB 49177 label copy.

| S 178 | RCA | PT 49178 |

Are You Lonesome Tonight? {Live version} {S} (Turk, Handman)
Runaway {Live version} {S} (Crook, Shannon)
Baby, What You Want Me To Do {Live version} {S} (Reed)
Reconsider Baby {Live version} {S} (Fulson)

Released August 1991

The sleeve for this 12 inch release used the same design as the 7 inch format single, with the additional tracks listed and included one or two other minor amendments.

Unlike the 7 inch version, this record used the standard RCA new black label, and it featured the round RCA logo on the left hand side, in the same manner as albums. Once again, Bob Jones had done the mastering and gave the magazine *Elvis - The Man And His Music* a nice little plug, with a mention in the run-out grooves - 'Read E-TMAHM'.

As with the 7 inch single, dealers discounted the cost of the single and reduced it to £1.99, although the full price was £3.49. However, we even saw copies on sale at £3.99!

All four tracks were from August 1969, recorded live in Las Vegas. It was the first live stage appearance of *Baby, What You Want Me To Do*, apart from its inclusion on the NBC TV Special album; and *Runaway* was an alternative recording to that featured on *On Stage February, 1970* (*LP 41*). And, with the release of the fifties' set in 1992, a number of different recordings of *Reconsider Baby* were now available: a studio jam version from 1956; the studio version on *Elvis Is Back!* (*LP 11*) in 1960; another live recording from 1961; this live version from 1969, and then again, as a live version in 1972 and included on *Elvis Aron Presley* (*LP 126*) in 1980.

Once again the publishing dates given were correct, but the errors regarding *Are You Lonesome Tonight?* and *Reconsider Baby* remained the same as the 7 inch version. As regards the writers of *Runaway*, we have always listed them as being Crook, Shannon, not the other way around, although we cannot remember why, unless it had something to do with how it appeared on Del Shannon's original single. Perhaps then we should not consider this an error! However, one thing that most certainly is an error, is the claim that vocal accompaniment was by J.D. Sumner and The Stamps, The Sweet Inspirations and Kathy Westmoreland, as the side A label suggested. Reference to the booklet included with the *Collectors Gold* set correctly identified The Imperials, The Sweet Inspirations and Mildred (Millie) Kirkham. J.D. Sumner, The Stamps and Kathy Westmoreland did not join Elvis until 1971, so where this particular reference came from was unclear.

Label Variations

NEW BLACK LABEL/SOLID CENTRE

1   1991 PRESSING

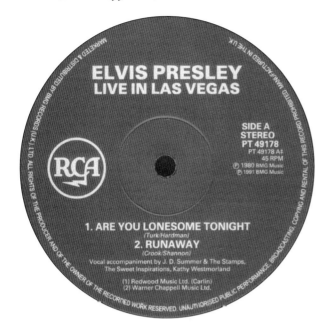

Sleeve Variations

1   Gloss

7 Inch Singles

Another long standing tradition effectively came to an end with the release of RCA PB 49177, *Are You Lonesome Tonight?/Reconsider Baby* (**S 177**), as it was the last 7 inch single to feature two tracks only. Admittedly there were few vinyl singles issued after this, but the need to generate sales in a diminishing market demanded better 'value for money' concepts, and singles were issued featuring both three and four tracks.

12 Inch Singles

With the advent of CD singles (there had been three UK Elvis CD singles up to this point), the industry moved away from producing special 12 inch (and 10 inch) versions, as restrictions on the number of different formats allowed for chart purposes, was set at three. The 'standard' thus became 7 inch, CD and cassette versions, although before long many singles were only issued in one format - CD.

The four track, 12 inch version of *Are You Lonesome Tonight?*, PT 49178 (**S 178**), was the last Elvis 12 inch vinyl single to be released in the UK.

Old Gold - 1992

The Old Gold catalogue for 1992, which had been prepared for publication in November 1991, listed only eight of the original twenty Elvis singles which the company had issued, demonstrating clearly the phased deletion policy forced on them by BMG. The remaining twelve singles had been deleted, although it was still possible to find odd copies in certain stores. Even the singles listed in the catalogue as being available, remained so only 'while stocks last'.

The eight remaining singles were:

OG 9618   *Party/Got A Lot O' Livin' To Do!*

OG 9620   *Blue Moon/I Don't Care If The Sun Don't Shine*

OG 9624   *An American Trilogy/Until It's Time For You To Go*

OG 9742   *It's Now Or Never/Surrender*

OG 9746   *Loving You/Paralyzed*

OG 9750   *King Creole/Hard Headed Woman*

OG 9752   *Don't/Wear My Ring Around Your Neck*

OG 9758   *Way Down/Moody Blue*

OG 9624 was the only single still available in a picture sleeve.

Reference to the Old Gold catalogue of 1991 will reveal that the first two singles listed here - OG 9618 and OG 9620 - were not listed as being available; strange then that both were shown in the catalogue for 1992. We can only assume that one of the catalogues contained an error, for Old Gold were not allowed to press further copies of any Elvis material following RCA's decision to terminate the licencing arrangement.

Catalogue Numbers

The August 1992 release of the four track single ***Don't Be Cruel*** (**S 179**), marked the UK debut of BMG's worldwide catalogue numbering system (see the introductory section for a more detailed description). This new system indicated the country of origin, company number, and product type, as well as the catalogue number itself. The overall number (made up of 11 digits) corresponded with the bar code, so that all of this information could be gathered at the point of sale, making pricing, ordering, stock control etc., simpler and more reliable. This allowed BMG to dispense with the price code (AA for singles).

Despite adopting an agreed format, BMG showed the digits incorrectly on both the label and sleeve of ***Don't Be Cruel***. Later releases followed the correct pattern, but on this occasion the number was shown as 7432-111 0777, instead of 74321 11077 7. In order to maintain consistency, we have shown the correct format on all listings.

The CD single version showed the correct numbering sequence: 74321 11061 2, although it is worth noting that, unlike 7 and 12 inch versions of the same release - which usually shared the same number, perhaps with a different prefix - CD singles were given a different catalogue number - 11061 compared to 11077 for the vinyl format.

S 179 | RCA 7432I II077 7

Don't Be Cruel {M} (Blackwell, Presley)
All Shook Up {M} (Blackwell, Presley)
Jailhouse Rock {M} (Leiber, Stoller)
I Need Your Love Tonight {Alternative version} {M} (Wayne, Reichner)

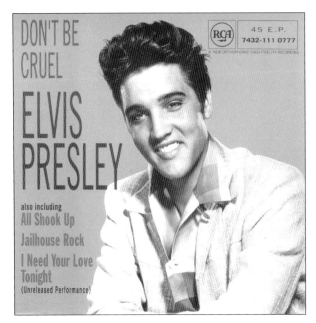

Released August 1992   **Chart Entry Number 144**
Highest Chart Position 42

Thirty six years after Elvis's first UK single was released (in March 1956) came this single, and, after all that time, it seemed incredible that there were still some unique features to describe for any single release.

Perhaps the most important feature of this release was that four tracks were included on a 7 inch single. And note, it was a 7 inch single, despite the fact that the sleeve showed E.P., standing for Extended Play, on the front. Extended Play releases, you will remember, once commonplace in the fifties and sixties, had gone out of fashion in the mid sixties, only to make a sensational re-appearance in 1982, when RCA issued two Elvis EP collections before it, once again, became a defunct medium. And without wanting to labour the point, the old EPs were thought of as being extended play (as opposed to long play) albums, whereas this new release was an extended play single. Perhaps this rather flimsy distinction is of no consequence as, to all intents and purposes, the end result remained the same: both featured more than the standard two tracks, and both came in a card sleeve (which, unusually, opened at the side, not at the top). Whatever, BMG issued this as a single and, as such, it was classed as a single for chart purposes. It seems worth noting that other companies had issued similar product, and it had become rather fashionable to use the letters EP and talk about extended singles. So, as well as being a piece of clever marketing, it was actually right up to date!

Of course, this was not the first Elvis UK single to feature four tracks, and nor was the inclusion of well-known songs to produce a kind of mini 'greatest hits' package, a new idea either. In the early seventies, Maxi-singles were popular - the term being used to describe a 'more-than-two-track' single. These were really EPs without the card sleeve, although the three Elvis Maxi-singles were issued in specially produced sleeves. In July 1971, RCA introduced Elvis to their Maximillion series of singles, with the release of RCA 2104 (*S 78*) (note that the normal catalogue numbering system was retained), which included **Heartbreak Hotel**, **Hound Dog** and **Don't Be Cruel**.

But a second unusual feature of this new release was that, for the first time in eight years, the 7 inch single was not supported by either a

12 (or 10) inch single release. These usually contained an additional track(s) not found on the 7 inch version - in a fairly blatant attempt to generate further sales, it has to be said. Obviously - and aside from the fact that neither vinyl format was selling particularly well - with four tracks on the 7 inch format, there was really no need to produce the larger format. Predictably, a CD single containing identical tracks was, however, issued. And, for collectors, in addition to the more commonplace silver finish, there was also a black label version. It is worth noting that this wasn't just a UK issue, it appeared in a number of territories as a 'trailer' for the '50s set, even though the '50s set was available at this point.

This was also the first Elvis single to bear the new BMG catalogue number, which was discussed in more detail in the notes preceding this release. These features aside, there was one more aspect that we have so far not mentioned, and that was that the single included a hitherto unreleased performance, which was not available on any other release. Not since November 1977 had a single been issued in the UK with a performance not previously released. On that occasion the performance was, admittedly, a new song - **America, The Beautiful** - released as the B side of **My Way**, PB 1165, (*S 117*). Nevertheless, the release of an alternative version in this way was significant; and probably its inclusion here was the deciding factor in not producing a 12 inch version, which had often been the medium to release the less well-known or unusual tracks as bonus items. The inclusion of a previously unreleased version of **I Need Your Love Tonight** (take 9) was a welcome addition.

Yet, despite the fact that the single comprised items previously well-featured on previous single releases, these were not random choices but were carefully selected to support, or benefit from, other projects: **Don't Be Cruel** was chosen primarily to promote the boxed set **The King Of Rock 'N' Roll The Complete 50's Masters** (**LP 318**), although two of the other tracks in their original form were also included in the set. **All Shook Up** was included to benefit from Billy Joel's then current single - which received lots of airplay; while **Jailhouse Rock** was used to promote the issue of **The Lost Performances/Jailhouse Rock** double video collection which, incidentally, reached number 11 in the video charts. The inclusion of **I Need Your Love Tonight** (take 9) was directed squarely at the collectors' market, as it was an unreleased performance not available elsewhere.

Of course, all of these songs had been major UK chart numbers, although this was the first time they had appeared together. The previous release numbers were as follows:

Don't Be Cruel *S 4, S 78, S 118* and **S 156**

All Shook Up *S 11, S 23, S 100* and **S 158**

Jailhouse Rock *S 18, S 80, S 101, S 136, S 137* and **S 164**

I Need Your Love Tonight (the master take) had appeared on *S 26* and *S 103*

Additionally, both **Don't Be Cruel** and **Jailhouse Rock** had appeared as part of **The Elvis Medley** on singles, (*S 137* and *S 145*).

Unusually, the single was released (on August 17th) after the boxed set it was partly intended to promote, but this was a planned move designed to add further impetus to sales. Moreover, a video promotional clip accompanied the release; sadly though, this was given little air time on terrestrial channels, and many fans complained that they had been unable to see it; and those that did claimed that it was, for a variety of reasons, unsatisfactory, featuring only glimpses of the 'real' Elvis - the majority of it a performance by the actor, Michael Gerard, who had played Elvis in the television series **Good Rockin' Tonight**. The video was produced in America.

Further, some fans expressed a degree of unhappiness with the choice of **Don't Be Cruel** as the lead track, often supporting this argument with their own preferred choice. But all of this was, of course, pointless, for this single's main purpose was to promote and support other work - although if sales were good and a reasonable chart position resulted, then so much the better. However, as it turned out, the single only managed to reach a modest number 42 in the charts, though this was the highest position any single had reached since *I Can Help* made it to number 30 in late 1983.

The label design was the old style RCA black label, copied from the 1950s, similar to that last used on the *Jailhouse Rock* and *You're so square) Baby I Don't Care* singles in 1983 (*S 136* and *S 138*). And, as mentioned previously, the label proudly boasted 'Extended Play', gave detailed accurate original publishing dates for individual songs, but correctly added a 1992 compilation date. Happily, there were no label errors either. And for those interested in such matters, they would note that etched in the run-out grooves was a personal greeting from Miles at Copymasters to Bob Jones - which read 'Hello Bob'!

Unusually, the sleeve - again error free! - listed the recording locations and dates. These small pieces of information, along with the details found on the label, were worthy additions to any record and, as such, ought to have been standard practice in our view. And so, despite some gripes here and there, this was generally regarded as a quality UK record, testimony to the thought and care behind it.

Label Variations

BLACK LABEL/SOLID CENTRE

1   1992 PRESSING

Sleeve Variations

1   Gloss card
2   Matt paper

Price Codes

Don't Be Cruel, RCA 74321 11077 7 (**S 179**), was the last RCA single to feature a UK price code on the sleeve. Most, but not all, of RCA's UK singles since *Always On My Mind*, issued in July 1985 (**S 146**), had used an AA code to indicate to retailers how much to charge. From this point onwards, the use of UK price coding was abandoned, although the French code BM 110, continued to appear on UK sleeves, unnecessarily.

Blue Christmas

In September 1994 there were plans afoot to release a single to tie in with the release of the definitive Christmas collection CD *If Every Day Was Like Christmas*, 07863 66482 2, issued in late October. However, it was to have been in CD form only.

A couple of options were considered:

1)   A reissue of the original Christmas EP (*EP 8*) from 1957; or,

2)   A three or four track CD of which the 'lead' track would have been a live version of *Blue Christmas*, from the sit-down portion of the NBC TV Special in June 1968. The other tracks were to have been *White Christmas* (1957), *It Won't Seem Like Christmas (without you) (1971)* and, possibly, *If Every Day Was Like Christmas* (1966). The latter choice was the preferred one of the UK Division.

Sadly, the proposal was eventually abandoned in mid-November as the company had wanted to use the appropriate live footage from the NBC TV Special to support the release, but was unable to secure the rights to do so.

Now while this may seem an absurd situation for BMG to be in - their not being able to use appropriate film footage to support a release by their own artist - it must be understood that it was far from a simple matter to do so. There were conflicting copyright difficulties which, in effect, scuppered this release.

Nonetheless, as sales figures showed, the CD *If Every Day Was Like Christmas*, did extremely well, despite not having a 'single' to support it. By the end of December 1994, the album had, for example, sold more than 25,000 copies. It remains open to debate as to how much a single release to tie in with it, would have increased sales even further.

The Twelfth Of Never

The release of *The Twelfth Of Never* single in three formats: 7 inch vinyl, CD and cassette in October 1995, meant it was the first Elvis single to be issued since August 1992, when BMG issued the four track album *Don't Be Cruel* (**S 179**), to tie in with the release of the fifties boxed set. *The Twelfth Of Never* was a UK only release; no other territories issued it.

There had been no single release to support the release of the sixties' boxed set when it was issued in September 1993; nor was there one for either *Amazing Grace His Greatest Sacred Performances*, 07863 66421 2 or *If Every Day Was Like Christmas*, 07863 66482 2.

The most notable thing about the release of *The Twelfth Of Never* though was that it was the first previously unissued track to be used as an A side single since Elvis died in August 1977. This was not counting previously unissued versions of songs, of course.

Secondly, it was not a formal studio recording either; it was a stage rehearsal from 16 August 1974, when it was recorded at RCA Studios, Hollywood, on a non-professional tape recorder, simply for reference purposes. As such, it was never intended for release; indeed its existence was not known of until well into the 1990s. It was part of a collection of tapes owned by former Elvis photographer, Ed Bonja. However, despite imperfections in terms of its overall quality, and Elvis's less than perfect rendition of it (remembering that this was only a rehearsal), the producers felt that its rarity value far outweighed these considerations and made it the lead track on this single compiled to promote the '70s boxed set.

Incidentally, an overdubbed version of *The Twelfth Of Never*, produced by former Elvis session-man David Briggs in 1994, had been rejected by RCA in favour of the less-produced rehearsal version. This overdubbed version was included on a bootleg release entitled *From Sunset Boulevard To Paradise Road*, produced by Diamond Anniversary Editions of Germany, and issued in late 1995. The two CD set included more rehearsal material from the 16 August 1974 session and most of the opening show from 19 August 1974, recorded live at the Hilton Hotel, Las Vegas, Nevada.

The release of *The Twelfth Of Never* came, conveniently for BMG, at an interesting time. News of 'a previously unreleased recording' appeared in the UK in an article in **The Times** newspaper, dated 24 August 1995, under the front page heading 'Unknown Presley song goes up for auction'.

According to the paper, the song was found on a 10 inch acetate disc given to Dick Grob, at one time Elvis's head of security. Bonhams auction house described it as being an acoustic ballad, in the vein of **Love Me Tender**, and were quoted as saying "It's an absolutely brilliant mid-sixties classic". Bonhams thought the song was entitled **Let Me Make Believe A While.**

The Sun newspaper, in its 25 August 1995 edition, was even more enthusiastic. Their front page article suggested that the song would be a certain commercial success and quoted Roger Semon as saying, "I'm sure it could go to No. 1". On a more cautious note though, Roger was keen to prove that the song was authentic. **The Sun** even arranged a special phone line so that readers could listen to a 30 second excerpt of the song.

All this, of course, provided the perfect marketing springboard to release the previously unheard recording of **The Twelfth Of Never** on a single. And while it was never actually stated, there was a clear implication in the wording on the front of the sleeve which read '... a recently discovered sensation!', that this was the song that the newspapers had been discussing. Perhaps we will never know whether BMG had any plans to release the single had these newspaper articles never appeared. In the event, **Let Me Make Believe A While**, was ultimately discredited. It was not Elvis performing the song. However, this publicity did not hurt the promotion of **The Twelfth Of Never**, as many of the the general public may well have thought that this was the song in question.

RCA Label Change

The next RCA single, **The Twelfth Of Never**, 74321 32012 7 (**S 180**), released in October 1995, appeared with two different label designs within a matter of weeks. The last time a label colour variation occurred on an RCA single had been in 1980, when a blue label version of **Don't Be Cruel**, PB 9265 (**S 118**) appeared, although the original, orange label version, had been released in June 1978!

Obviously sales of 7 inch vinyl copies of **The Twelfth Of Never** exceeded expectations, and further copies were pressed to meet demand.

The initial copies were silver, similar to the one last used in August 1991 for the single **Are You Lonesome Tonight?**, PB 49177 (**S 177**), although some of the details had been re-positioned. The RCA logo, for example, had been moved from the top to the left of the spindle hole.

The second batch of copies appeared with a pale cream coloured label. This was the first time this had happened on a regular single release, although RCA had used the colouring previously on special promotional records, such as the Radio Promo for **I Can Help** and on **Danny**, issued by the UK Fan Club at one of their conventions in August 1990 (see the Promotional Release section for further details).

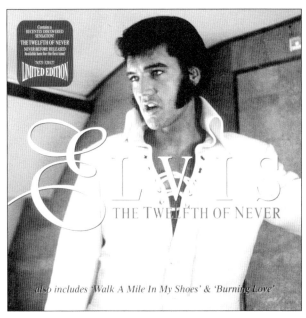

| **S 180** | **RCA** | **74321 32012 7** |

The Twelfth Of Never {U} {M} (Livingstone, Webster)
Walk A Mile In My Shoes {S} (South)
Burning Love {S} (Linde)

also includes 'Walk A Mile In My Shoes' & 'Burning Love'

Released October 1995 **Chart Entry Number 145**
Higest Chart Position 21

This single release was delayed slightly. Originally planned for the last week of September, to coincide with the release of the seventies' 5 CD set **Walk A Mile In My Shoes**, 74321 30331 2, the single did not actually appear in the shops until 9 October 1995.

The Twelfth Of Never was recorded on 16 August 1974 and coupled with **Walk A Mile In My Shoes** (the title track of the '70s boxed set), a live recording from 19 February 1970, previously available on the album **On Stage February 1970** (**LP 41**), and **Burning Love**, a studio recording from 28 March 1972, issued as the A side of a single in September 1972 (**S 84**).

All formats featured the same tracks (which had a total running time of 8.32). However, most unusually, there were two distinct variations on the 7 inch release. The first and most common one, it seems, was the silver labelled version with black script. Side A stated 45 RPM, whereas side B correctly stated 33 RPM, as the company had been advised to use this playback speed because both tracks were quite long, and the sound quality would have been impaired had they used the more conventional 45 RPM speed. This was the only one of Elvis's UK singles to have a playing speed of 33 RPM, albeit on only one side. The correct publishing dates were shown: 1995 for the A side, and 1970 and 1972 respectively for the tracks on the B side. Oddly though, despite the group Voice being credited, their name appeared using lower case letters.

The variation featured a pale cream coloured label, once again with black print. And, although the key information was the same, the RCA logo was situated nearer the centre hole; and this time 45 RPM appeared on both the A and B sides, erroneously so in the case of the latter, as the actual speed was 33 RPM.

Another significant difference was in the picture sleeves. The design remained the same but the silver labelled copies were housed in glossy sleeves front and back, while the cream coloured copies were found in a poorer finished, less glossy sleeves. Regarding the back of the covers, the glossy sleeves had a purple tinge, whereas the less glossy ones were dark blue. For the first time on an Elvis single, the individual sleeves were numbered, making each one unique. The initial batch of 10,000 copies (with the purple back) was believed to have been followed by a further pressing of 5,000 copies (with the blue back). As with the previous single, **Don't Be Cruel** (**S 179**), the sleeve pocket was on the side, not the top, as was more common.

The front cover shot was a colour photograph from 15 September 1970. The same photograph was used on the front cover of CD 3 in the '70s set. However, it was not a new photograph; many fans would remember it as the cover shot for the bootleg album **The Legend Lives On** issued in 1976. In the top left hand corner was what looked like a red sticker advertising the release as a limited edition, though it was, in fact, an integral part of the cover design. The legend ran as follows:

'Contains a RECENTLY DISCOVERED SENSATION
THE TWELFTH OF NEVER NEVER BEFORE RELEASED
Available here for the first time!'

with the limited edition note added at the end. Incidentally this was the 50th UK picture sleeve single (43 produced by RCA/BMG and 7 by Old Gold).

The back cover featured a faded image of the same photograph used on the front cover of the '70s set. Down the left were the song titles, timings, writers and publishers, followed by a brief note about each song and a list of personnel working on the tracks.

Just below the top fold over was a white oblong box with the limited edition number printed on it. Below this, printed in white, was the distribution note and the catalogue number. The BMG/RCA logo was featured at the end of the bar code information. Vocal accompaniment credits were printed below this, followed by the publishing and copyright date of 1995. Underneath the 'Made in the EEC' and trademark details, was a small advert for the seventies boxed set, showing the front cover shot in colour. Printed below this picture was a caption saying that these songs were taken from the 'forthcoming CD set' and quoting the title and catalogue number. Clearly the single had originally been intended to promote the '70s boxed set.

The single peaked at number 21 in the charts, Elvis's best chart rating since 1980, when **It's Only Love** (*S 122*) reached number three in the UK. A specially constructed video, using clips from **The Lost Performances** video, was used to promote the single, though it was not broadcast very much - in the main because the track failed to get into the top 20.

Dealers were supplied with a big poster for in-store display, showing the cover of the single, Elvis's name, the title and the legend 'Recently Discovered Sensation', followed by 'CD Single, Cassette Single & Limited Edition 7" Single'. However, unlike the cover, the poster featured the RCA and BMG logos in the bottom left and right hand corners respectively. Many outlets sold the 7 inch single for as little as 99p, though later copies were being sold for as much as £2.29.

As mentioned previously, there was also a CD version released, though this was not a limited edition (the CDs were not numbered in any way). There were, coincidentally, two variations on the CD release also. The 7 inch single was pressed in the UK and both variations had solid centres.

For more general information on this release see the notes prior to this entry.

Label Variations

SILVER LABEL/SOLID CENTRE
1   1995 PRESSING

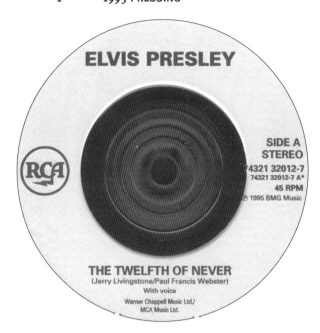

CREAM LABEL/SOLID CENTRE
2   1995 PRESSING

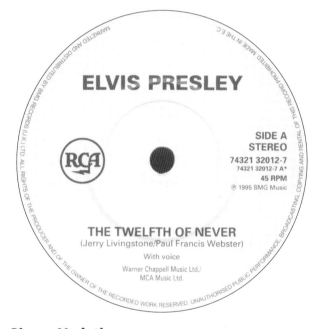

Sleeve Variations

1   Purple back
2   Blue back

Picture Sleeves

When **The Twelfth Of Never** was released in October 1995, a significant milestone was reached as it became the 50th single to be released in the UK in a picture sleeve.

We have compared the UK release pattern to American singles previously and noted that US singles appeared in picture sleeves as early as 1956 **(Hound Dog/Don't Be Cruel)**, whereas in the UK, the record industry was far less adventurous, and it was not until the release of **Suspicious Minds** (*S 70*) in November 1969, that an Elvis single was issued in a picture sleeve.

Even then, there was the strange situation of RCA using the same picture on subsequent singles, after which they reverted to normal bags. It was not until May 1977, when the 'Gold 16' singles were released, that the use of picture sleeves became standard practice for UK Elvis singles.

Of course, not all of the UK picture sleeves were issued by RCA/BMG. Had it not been for the seven singles issued by Old Gold between 1989 and 1990, then it is doubtful that the 50 sleeve landmark would ever have been achieved.

Label Design Change

The label design featured on the next RCA single release, **Heartbreak Hotel** (**S 181**), had not been featured on a UK single previously, for it was based on the design used for RCA releases in America during the '50s. It featured an RCA Victor logo, in white print, across the top of the black label although, unlike the American original design, the picture of the dog 'Nipper' peering into a gramophone was not used, as its use would have been an infringement of copyright in the UK. Instead, the round RCA logo was used. A white line ran across the label, just above the centre hole (all copies were solid centres), with the details printed below, all in white print.

Incidentally, on all the copies we saw, there was what appeared to be a fault on the label just to the right of the centre hole. This small round mark may have been intended as part of the production process, as it appeared on both sides of the record, but we have been unable to confirm this.

Just underneath the LC 0316 number on the right of the label was an unusual number - 08-016741-00 - which appeared to be some kind of matrix/file reference number, as it is also to be found machine stamped in the vinyl at the end of the run out grooves.

Heartbreak Hotel

The release of **Heartbreak Hotel** in May 1996 meant that for the first time since January 1988, BMG had released two Elvis singles within the year, the last one being **The Twelfth Of Never** (**S 180**), issued in October 1995. However the days of the autonomous single release had long since past: any single release now was tied in with the release of a special album project or special occasion. In the case of **Heartbreak Hotel**, the single was released to help promote the album **Elvis 56** (**LP 321**). This album, in turn, was celebrating Elvis having been on the RCA label for 40 years, and the release of his first RCA single in March 1956 (UK) which was, of course, **Heartbreak Hotel/I Was The One**.

The single was released in all three formats. However, having been delayed several months (it was originally scheduled for a January 1996 release), there was a strong rumour during April 1996 that the single was to have been cancelled - presumably because of this delay. In the event though, it did eventually gain a release, though it failed to make the top forty chart, peaking at 45. A 7 inch and CD version of the single was also issued in the USA.

| **S 181** | **RCA** | **74321 33686 7** |

Heartbreak Hotel {M} (Axton, Durden, Presley)
I Was The One {M} (Schroeder, DeMetrius, Blair, Peppers)
Heartbreak Hotel {U} {M} (Axton, Durden, Presley)
I Was The One {U} {M} (Schroeder, DeMetrius, Blair, Peppers)

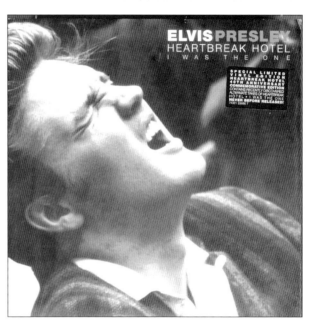

Released May 1996   **Chart Entry Number 146**
Higest Chart Position 45

The release of **Heartbreak Hotel** was significant in many ways - hence its release, of course! First of all, it was Elvis's first single release on RCA Victor in the USA, going on to become a number one hit on the pop charts in March 1956, the same month it was issued on the HMV label in the UK - though it only achieved the number 2 position in the UK. In respect of the 40th anniversary of these songs, RCA had been planning this release for some while, though originally the intended release date had been January 1996, forty years after it was first recorded and issued in the USA. Sadly though, something went dramatically wrong - for reasons which can only be guessed at (BMG refused to be specific) - and the release of the single and album was delayed almost four months. There were suggestions that it was something to do with copyright on the Wertheimer photographs used on the single and the album, but this was unconfirmed. Whatever the reason, there was no doubt that the delay did cause the company some degree of embarrassment.

For the first time RCA used both regular and unreleased performances of two songs on the same single release. **Heartbreak Hotel** and **I Was The One** (duplicating the first RCA/HMV release) were followed by recently discovered unreleased performances of the same two tracks: takes 5 and 2 respectively. Ironically, the album **Elvis 56** (**LP 321**) featuring 22 tracks recorded in 1956, was released almost simultaneously. And, although it did include the unreleased performance of **Heartbreak Hotel**, and the previously issued alternative take of **Shake, Rattle And Roll** (included on the '50s boxed set in 1992), it did not include the alternative version of **I Was The One**. Certainly some fans expressed relief at this, for they felt they could forego the album release as the two alternatives were on the single. As a marketing exercise, it seemed hard to comprehend!

Incidentally, the two unreleased performances had been found on the end of someone else's session tape (presumably the original session tape had been recorded over - a normal practice at the time - thus erasing most of the outtakes).

The actual label format for the vinyl single was quite unlike any previous UK release. The solid centred label was entirely black; the script was in white. In the top sector was the RCA Victor logo just above the small RCA logo. Slightly above the centre hole was a white line, and all other details were printed below.

The publishing/copyright date for both sides read '1996 BMG Entertainment' though, strictly speaking, side A ought to have shown 1956. It stated 'Made in EC' on the label, just above the mono legend. In the case of the two previously unreleased performances on side B, this was stated clearly and, unusually, the take numbers were given too.

The opening for the single was at the top. The front cover shot was from Alfred Wertheimer's now famous photo collection. In fact, both the front and back cover shots were the ones featured on the cover of the book **Songs Of Innocence** (Rijff, Wertheimer, van Gestel) in the summer of 1995, a collection of Wertheimer's photographs published by Tutti Frutti Productions in Amsterdam. The front shot was taken on 2 July 1956 in RCA's New York studios, during the recording of **Hound Dog**, **Don't Be Cruel** and **Any Way You Want Me (that's how I will be)**, while the back shot was taken on the train when Elvis was en route back to Memphis, following the session.

On the front, in the top right hand corner just under the song titles, was a black sticker with white printing which read:

SPECIAL LIMITED VINYL EDITION HEARTBREAK HOTEL 40TH ANNIVERSARY COMMEMORATIVE EDITION CONTAINS RECENTLY DISCOVERED ALTERNATE TAKES OF HEARTBREAK HOTEL AND I WAS THE ONE NEVER BEFORE RELEASED!

Note the reappearance of the word 'alternate', a term which had effectively been replaced by the more accurate word 'alternative' and - in recent years - by 'unreleased performance'. The sleeve itself reverted to a thin paper of the type last used in early 1988 on some copies of the **Stuck On You** single (**S 163**). However, most unusually, there was not only a label variation available, but also a sleeve variation. Indeed, the second sleeve was actually better quality than the first. Stranger still was that fact that there minor differences in design and details featured on both the label and sleeve. We have seen a spider centre copy of the second variation and firmly believe that this was not made at the original pressing plant. It is likely that such examples were prepared for juke box purposes.

As with the release of **The Twelfth Of Never**, BMG used a video clip to support and promote the release. The clip used was of Elvis singing a live version of **Heartbreak Hotel** from the Dorsey Brothers' TV show in early 1956.

There was also a CD version of this single. The vinyl version was said to be a limited edition, though the exact number is not known. And strangely, the US division also released a 7 inch version too, their first since the release of **Silver Bells** (a juke box dealers only release) in November 1993.

Once again, depending on where you bought the single, the price would vary considerably from 99p to £1.99.

All references to Bill Peppers, one of the writers of **I Was The One**, omitted the 's' in his surname.

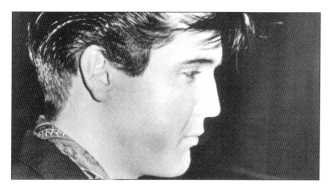

Label Variations

BLACK LABEL/SOLID CENTRE
1   1996 PRESSING

BLACK LABEL/SOLID CENTRE
2   1996 PRESSING

Sleeve Variations

1   Matt - thin paper
2   Gloss - thick paper

The Final 7 Inch Vinyl?

Although there seemed good reason to believe that **S 181** would be the last vinyl single available in the UK, almost four years later Castle Music, in conjunction with BMG, issued a boxed set vinyl edition of the original five Elvis singles issued on Sun Records, plus an EP of Sun material. Vinyl, it seemed, refused to die!

S 182 Sun Singles
Sun/Castle Music
ELVIS 101

Disc 1
SUN 209
- **That's All Right** {M} (Crudup)
- **Blue Moon Of Kentucky** {M} (Monroe)

Disc 2
SUN 210
- **Good Rockin' Tonight** {M} (Brown)
- **I Don't Care If The Sun Don't Shine** {M} (David)

Disc 3
SUN 215
- **Milkcow Blues Boogie** {M} (Arnold)
- **You're A Heartbreaker** {M} (Sallee)

Disc 4
SUN 217
- **I'm Left, You're Right. She's Gone** {M} (Kesler, Taylor)
- **Baby Let's Play House** {M} (Gunter)

Disc 5
SUN 223
- **Mystery Train** {M} (Parker, Phillips)
- **I Forgot To Remember To Forget** {M} (Kesler, Feathers)

Disc 6
Bonus EP
- **Tomorrow Night**
- **That's All Right** {M} (Crudup)
- **Harbour Lights** {M} (Kennedy, Williams)
- **Tomorrow Night** {M} (Coslow, Grosz)
- **Trying To get To You** {M} (Singleton McCoy)

Released March 2000

Castle Music, the company who had brought us the various vinyl versions of *Artist Of The Century* boxed sets in 1999 (**LPs 323** and **324**), took vinyl collectors by surprise again when they announced their plans to issue replicas of the five US Sun singles - issued originally on that famous label between July 1954 and August 1955.

Originally scheduled for release in February, a delay of a couple of weeks resulted in a March 2000 release date. Initially, up to 5,000 copies were made (the records themselves were pressed in the UK by EMI, who also handled the packaging), although it was hoped that twice that number would be sold over the three year period covered by Castle's licensing arrangement with BMG. Indeed, by the end of 2000, a total of 8,000 black vinyl sets had been made.

Of course, in some ways it was not hard to see who the driving force was behind such a release - none other than Roger Semon himself, co-producer of Elvis product throughout the world on behalf of BMG. However, this project was devised and issued by Castle Music - who Semon now worked for - though this was done in conjunction

with BMG Special Products. However, there would seem to be no doubt that it was mainly Semon's unique relationship with BMG and the Presley Estate that would have allowed this to happen. So, once again, Castle Music had come up with a quality vinyl package - another limited edition - to meet the small but nonetheless significant collectors' market.

Housed in a sturdy cardboard box, the set not only included replicas of the five Sun singles, but also had a unique EP comprising one alternative take (previously issued) and three other Sun songs not issued at the time (1954-55), and only made available once Elvis had signed to RCA. Needless to say, there never was an Elvis EP on Sun, but it was a novel idea to construct one as a bonus for this set. However, some felt that it may have been more appropriate to have used other tracks also and thus made this a complete Sun set. Certainly, by including every track known to have been recorded would have made the package even more attractive.

Each single replicated its Sun original in terms of print size and type, and the information included on the label. This extended to copying the use of upper case letters for all song titles, with the exception of *I'm Left, You're Right, She's Gone* and *Baby Let's Play House*, which appeared in upper and lower case. Produced on high quality vinyl, all of these singles had push out (spider) centres, and were in 'Sun-ray' sleeves - although they were not the type used when the originals appeared, but were more in line with those used by Sun in 1957. Incidentally, on the reverse of each singles' cover was the legend 'A Product of Sun Record Co. Inc. Memphis, Tennessee'. Of course they weren't, but in terms of authenticity, it was a neat touch.

The sixth record - the EP *Tomorrow Night* - was enclosed in an EP type laminated sleeve featuring a similar photograph to that used on the front of the box. In the top right hand corner was the mono legend, while on the back cover appeared 'Monaural Extended Play'.

Incidentally, none of the records featured a publishing or recording first published date - in keeping with practice at the time.

The front of the white box featured the Sun Records logo, and in the centre was a shot of Elvis from mid-1954 holding his guitar. The title below simply read 'Elvis Presley Sun Singles'. In the top left corner was a sticker bearing the legend 'Special Limited Edition includes 5 Sun 7" Singles Unique Bonus EP Colour Poster with Essay Elvis Presley Elvis 101'. The top and bottom of the box bore the artist's name and title.

The back of the box showed a photograph of each A and B side, alongside details of each release, which included titles, writers, music publishers, recording dates, and timings. In the top right corner was the Elvis 101 catalogue number, while parallel to the EP track details was the Castle Music logo, with the BMG and RCA logos beneath.

Below the label photographs was information pertaining to Castle Music and the bar code, bearing the 'Made in England' legend. Castle's LC number, 6448, was quoted, whereas normally Elvis product from BMG bore the LC 0316 number. Astonishingly - and clearly in error - the compact disc digital audio symbol was also shown.

Within the box was a fold out poster measuring approximately 36cm by 36cm. There was an essay by Colin Escott, a renown Sun expert, and various pictures from the time, placed alongside quotations from a number of principals involved in the recordings.

Disc 1:   Sun 209   *That's All Right*
                                      Blue Moon Of Kentucky

Both tracks were cut on 6 July 1954 and constituted Elvis's first ever single release. And, although re-issued in the USA by RCA in late 1955, this coupling never appeared in the UK. Indeed, it was not until August 1981 that the A side appeared on any UK single (*S 130*), while the B side had never appeared on a single release in the UK prior to this. *That's All Right* re-appeared as one of the tracks included on *The Last Farewell* (*S 144*) in November 1984. Its UK debut though was on **Rock 'N' Roll** (*LP 1*), issued in October 1956. **Blue Moon Of Kentucky**, however, made its first UK appearance in September 1957 on the **Good Rockin' Tonight** extended player issued on HMV (*EP 3*).

Disc 2:   Sun 210   *Good Rockin' Tonight*
                                        I Don't Care If The Sun Don't Shine

Having a follow on number from his first Sun release, this coupling featured songs cut in September 1954. Once again though, this coupling was never issued in the UK. **Good Rockin' Tonight** was not issued until September 1957 when it appeared on an EP of the same name (*EP 3*), although, ironically, **I Don't Care If The Sun Don't Shine** secured an earlier UK release as the B side of **Blue Moon** (*S 5*) in November 1956. **Good Rockin' Tonight** made its only appearance on a UK single in October 1981 when it was released on the Golden Grooves label (*S 131*).

Disc 3:   Sun 215   *Milkcow Blues Boogie*
                                        You're A Heartbreaker

Both of these tracks were recorded in December 1954. However, neither was issued on a UK single in the fifties or sixties, although the B side was one of the tracks featured on the Maximillion single, RCA 2601, released by RCA in September 1975 (*S 94*). The A side was included on the EP **Good Rockin' Tonight** (*EP 3*) in September 1957, though British fans had to wait until October 1958 to hear **You're A Heartbreaker**, when it was included on **Elvis' Golden Records** (*LP 7*).

Disc 4:   Sun 217   *I'm Left, You're Right, She's Gone*
                                        Baby Let's Play House

Strangely, the A and B sides seem to have been reversed on this release, for the general belief has always been that **Baby Let's Play House** was the top side - including Ernst Jorgensen himself in hisrecording sessions book **A Life In Music**. Whatever, **Baby Let's Play House** was recorded sometime in February 1955, while **I'm Left, You're Right, She's Gone** was cut the following month.

Ironically, it was this track which appeared first in the UK when it was included on Elvis's first album, **Rock 'N' Roll** (*LP 1*) in October 1956. **Baby Let's Play House**, on the other hand, was relegated to being a B side, in this case **Rip It Up** (*S 9*) in March 1957. From this point on it never appeared on another UK single until now, although **I'm Left, You're Right, She's Gone** was included on a Maximillion single in September 1975 (*S 94*).

Incidentally, this was the only original Sun release to use upper and lower case letters in the titles.

Disc 5:   Sun 223   *Mystery Train*
                                        I Forgot To Remember To Forget

Both of these tracks were cut in July 1955, a mere year after his first session at Sun. And, of course, they represented his final Sun release. As with Sun 217, the A and B sides appear to have been reversed, and although most fans would believe that **Mystery Train** was the A side, this was not the case.

In February 1957 **Mystery Train** was released on the HMV label backed with **Love Me** (*S 7*). Interestingly, in the same month, the original Sun coupling was also released in the UK, but primarily for export to Europe (*S 8*). However, for most UK fans, the opportunity to have **I Forgot To Remember To Forget** did not come until September 1958 when it was included on **Elvis' Golden Records** (*LP 7*). Much later, **Mystery Train** was used as a B side on Gold 534 (*S 131*), issued in October 1981.

Disc 6:   Bonus EP   *Tomorrow Night*
                                        That's All Right (alternate take)
                                        Harbour Lights
                                        Tomorrow Night
                                        Trying To Get To You

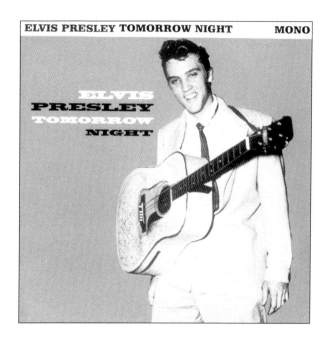

As mentioned previously, there never was an Elvis EP on Sun. Indeed, none of these tracks was released during his time on the label. Of course, **That's All Right** (an outtake) was cut at the same session as the master in July 1954, probably the same session which produced **Harbour Lights**. **Tomorrow Night** (the undubbed version from the fifties' set - **LP 318**) was believed to have been cut in September 1954, while **Trying To Get To You** was from the 11 July 1955 session.

That's All Right (alternate take) was first released on the boxed set album **A Golden Celebration** (*LP 251*), issued in October 1984. **Harbour Lights** first saw the light of day on **Elvis - A Legendary Performer Vol. 2** (*LP 87*). **Tomorrow Night** has an interesting background, for although an overdubbed version appeared on **Elvis For Everyone** (*LP 26*) in November 1965, an undubbed edit was included on **Reconsider Baby** (*LP 271*) in May 1985. However, in July 1992, fans got to hear this undubbed and complete version on **The King Of Rock 'N' Roll The Complete 50's Masters** (*LP 318*). Finally, **Trying To Get To You** had been released in the UK in October 1956 when it was included on the album **Rock 'N' Roll** (*LP 1*). In October 1957 it was the A side of a UK single (*S 15*).

Will Grosz, co-writer of **Tomorrow Night**, had surname spelt Gross, although this was the only error.

Yellow Vinyl Edition

In August 2000, following the success of the limited edition blue vinyl version of the album **Artist Of The Century** (**LP 323**), HMV music stores, in an 'exclusive' deal with Castle Music, issued **Sun Singles** in yellow vinyl, again as a limited edition, this time of 2,000 copies. This resulted in some complaints from specialist Elvis dealers, who argued that it was unfair that they were being excluded from offering special editions such as this. The same argument applied equally to collectors. As HMV chose to limit the number of their stores stocking the product - generally the larger ones - some fans found it difficult to obtain copies. Consequently, Castle Music allowed dealers, such as Elvis Presley Records By Mail, to sell copies, but they had to wait until the end of August to do so, allowing HMV 'exclusive' rights in the meantime.

As with the blue vinyl version of **Artist Of The Century** (**LP 323**), we have not allocated a separate release number to this set, even though the catalogue number had been slightly modified - with an 'X' added at the end. The only reason this had been done was to assist HMV staff distinguish between the regular and yellow vinyl versions. So, despite the fact that there was a six month gap between the versions, this was not a re-issue, but a variation of the original. Obviously, the track content was the same.

Other than being yellow vinyl, the only other noticeable differences concerned the sticker on the front of the box, which was now larger to accommodate the individual limited edition number, and a bar code sticker (showing the revised catalogue number) attached to the back of the box.

Label Variations

BLACK VINYL

1	2000 PRESSING

YELLOW VINYL

2	2000 PRESSING

S 183	**The UK No.1 Singles Collection** **RCA/Castle Music ELVIS 103**

Disc 1 RCA 1088	**All Shook Up** {M} (Blackwell, Presley) **That's When Your Heartaches Begin** {M} (Raskin, Brown, Fisher)
Disc 2 RCA 1028	**Jailhouse Rock** {M} (Leiber, Stoller) **Treat Me Nice** {M} (Leiber, Stoller)
Disc 3 RCA 1100	**One Night** {M} (Bartholomew, King) **I Got Stung** {M} (Schroeder, Hill)
Disc 4 RCA 1113	**(Now and then there's) A Fool Such As I** {M} (Trader) **I Need Your Love Tonight** {M} (Wayne, Reichner)
Disc 5 RCA 1207	**It's Now Or Never** {S} (DiCapua, Schroeder, Gold) **Make Me Know It** {S} (Blackwell)
Disc 6 RCA 1216	**Are You Lonesome Tonight?** {S} (Turk, Handman) **I Gotta Know** {S} (Evans, Williams)
Disc 7 RCA 1226	**Wooden Heart** {S} (Wise, Weisman, Twomey, Kaemfert) **Tonight Is So Right For Love** {S} (Wayne, Silver)
Disc 8 RCA 1227	**Surrender** {S} (DeCurtis, Pomus, Shuman) **Lonely Man** {S} (Benjamin, Marcus)

Disc 9 RCA 1258	**(Marie's the name) His Latest Flame** {S} (Pomus, Shuman) **Little Sister** {S} (Pomus, Shuman)
Disc 10 RCA 1270	**Rock-A-Hula Baby** {S} (Wise, Weisman, Fuller) **Can't Help Falling In Love** {S} (Peretti, Creatore, Weiss)
Disc 11 RCA 1280	**Good Luck Charm** {S} (Schroeder, Gold) **Anything That's Part Of You** {S} (Robertson)
Disc 12 RCA 1303	**She's Not You** {S} (Pomus, Leiber, Stoller) **Just Tell Her Jim Said Hello** {S} (Leiber, Stoller)
Disc 13 RCA 1320	**Return To Sender** {S} (Blackwell, Scott) **Where Do You Come From** {S} (Batchelor, Roberts)
Disc 14 RCA 1355	**(You're the) Devil In Disguise** {S} (Giant, Baum, Kaye) **Please Don't Drag That String Around** {S} (Blackwell, Scott)
Disc 15 RCA 1455	**Crying In The Chapel** {S} (Glenn) **I Believe In The Man In The Sky** {S} (Howard)
Disc 16 RCA 1974	**The Wonder Of You** {S} (Knight) **Mama Liked The Roses** {S} (Christopher)
Disc 17 PB 0998	**Way Down** {S} (Martine Jnr.) **Pledging My Love** {S} (Robey, Washington)

THE UK NO.1 SINGLES COLLECTION

Released August 2000

Although the appearance of this set may well have surprised a number of fans - and by no means all will have known anything about it, for it was a closely kept secret up to the point of it being offered for sale - in some ways its appearance was overdue and obvious.

Essentially the set was offered for sale on the QVC satellite shopping channel during a day dedicated to a whole range of Elvis material - specifically, all day 16 August 2000. As a special surprise, Roger Semon, co-producer of Elvis product throughout the world, was on hand to talk about Elvis and, of course, the products. Clearly, as with the various vinyl LP versions of *Artist Of The Century* (**LPs 323** and **324**) and then the *Sun Singles* (**S 182**), Semon had struck a deal with BMG which allowed Castle Music to issue Presley material on vinyl. This time though there were two major differences: a deal had been made with a TV channel offering them exclusive rights to this new set (believed to be for a six month period), with little or no advance information given. And, secondly, there was no BMG equivalent in vinyl or CD form.

Yet, as with most good ideas, it was not really new, but what it demonstrated was Semon's skill and flair for marketing. It had, in fact, been 23 years since a similar package had been released, comprising the then 16 number one hits in the UK. That had been in May 1977, a mere few months prior to Elvis's death. On that occasion, of course, vinyl releases were the norm, so not only was there a collectors' box of the 16 number one hits, but each record was also available individually. Not so the latest set. It only came as a set and was housed in a numbered box (it was a limited edition of 5,000 copies). Added to the original set was Elvis's final number one record to date, **Way Down**, which had been issued in July 1977 and very quickly rose to number one following Elvis's death on 16 August 1977.

The 17 records in question copied their original label formats, in general terms, and used sleeves representative of their era too. There were, however, some discrepancies and anomalies, but they are dealt with as each one is considered. Unlike many of the original singles, some standardisation had been achieved for things like the size of print, the use of a comma between writers names (as opposed to a hyphen), and so on. Equally, a number of standard features found on original releases were dropped. For example, there was no 'Made in Britain', or purchase tax codes printed on the labels. It is also worth noting that, while the publishers' names were printed in the same place as they had been on the original singles, few of the actual names remained the same.

Fans who telephoned in for the set on the day of its release were charged a shade under £40, plus about £3 for postage and packing. However, this 'introductory offer' price rose to almost £50 thereafter.

The set was housed in a sturdy box covered in a blue velour material. On one side was an image of Elvis from 1956, and underneath was printed in gold lettering **The UK No. 1 Singles Collection**. On the other side of the box was a panel which had been stuck on and which listed the tracks, gave the various credits and featured the Castle Music, RCA and BMG logos. In the bottom right hand corner was a small gold panel into which was stamped a number, indicating it was a limited edition.

Inside the box, accompanying the singles, was a fold out insert. On one side was a picture and some of Elvis's gold records as displayed on the Trophy Room wall in Graceland; a superimposed image of Elvis in his gold lamé suit from 1957, alongside a spread of UK sheet music showing nine of the releases. On the opposite side, each release was discussed in detail by writer Colin Escott. The tracks were then listed in turn, and gave the writers' names and publishers' details.

As before, when dealing with the **Sun Singles** set (**S 182**), we have chosen to deal with each record separately, drawing your attention to any relevant points of interest and, where necessary, indicating any label errors. Incidentally, all the singles were solid centres. And, of course, whilst solid centred orange label singles were not uncommon, original RCA black label singles rarely appeared with a solid centre. Of course, all of the original singles released on RCA during the fifties featured triangular centres, but these were not used for this set.

The set was mastered by Damont and pressed on 180gm vinyl, which clearly made for a substantial product with an excellent sound quality. And for the first time in many cases, those tracks which were recorded in stereo were pressed in stereo - in other words, everything from Disc 5 onwards.

Disc 1: RCA 1088   *All Shook Up*
                        That's When Your Heartaches Begin

Original Issue June 1957. HMV POP 359 (*S 11*)

Now, although this 1957 coupling represented Elvis's first UK number one, it had been released on the HMV label (HMV POP 359 - S 11), and was never issued in this form as an RCA single. However, in this instance, BMG and Castle Music exercised some artistic licence (as they made clear on the box itself and in the notes),

and used the RCA 1088 catalogue number. In fact, the original coupling on RCA 1088 (*S 23*) paired **All Shook Up** with Elvis's first RCA single release **Heartbreak Hotel** when it was issued in November 1958, some eight months after Elvis's induction into the US army.

Indeed, the original RCA 1088 gave a recording first published date as 1958 for both sides. But this reproduction used the 1957 date (technically also correct, based on the fact that the songs first appeared in that year). Similarly, while the correct matrix number appeared above the catalogue number on the A side - H2WW 0256 (indicating a 1957 recording) - the same matrix number was shown on the B side, when it ought to have been H2WW 0260.

The A side was a frequent - indeed, almost a mandatory inclusion - in Elvis's stage act throughout the late sixties and seventies. However, no live version of the B side is known to exist.

The original HMV single (*S 11*) identified the writers of **That's When Your Heartaches Begin** as Raskin, Brown, Fisher, whereas RCA releases refer to Fisher, Hill, Raskin (and sometimes just Fisher, Hill). For some unknown reason, this time the single showed Fisher, Brown, Raskin, reversing the correct order.

Disc 2: RCA 1028   *Jailhouse Rock*
                        Treat Me Nice

Original Issue January 1958. RCA 1028 (*S 18*)
Previous Re-issue May 1977. RCA 2695 (*S 101*)
Previous Re-issue January 1983. RCA 1028 (*S 136*)
Previous Re-issue January 1988. Old Gold OG 9740 (**S 164**)

This coupling, originally released in the UK in January 1958 (*S 18*), was the first single ever to enter the UK charts at number one. And although his second number one in this set, some charts (namely **Melody Maker**) had credited **Party** (*S 14*) with this distinction. Whatever, officially **Jailhouse Rock**, the title track from his third film, hit the top spot in 1958, oddly his only UK number one of that year.

This was the fifth time that these tracks had been issued together on a single. The coupling was re-issued in May 1977 (*S 101*) as part of the 16 Number Ones, and again in January 1983 (its 25th anniversary), but this time as a replica bearing the original RCA 1028 catalogue number (*S 136*). Finally, prior to their release on this new set, they were issued on Old Gold in 1988 (**S 164**).

Of course, strictly speaking, the reference to **Treat Me Nice** being from the film **Jailhouse Rock** was not exactly true. Yes, a version had appeared in the film, but this particular version on the B side had not been cut until September 1957, after the film had been released. Incidentally, this coupling was only one of two in the set written by the same writers - on this occasion Leiber and Stoller. The other one was **(Marie's the name) His Latest Flame/Little Sister**, penned by Pomus and Shuman.

Note that on the B side, **Treat Me Nice** is said to be 'From film **Jailhouse Rock**', whereas some of the original label variations used 'From the film....'.

Incidentally, the A side was a regular feature of Elvis's live act in the late sixties and seventies, while the B side was never used as part of his live performances during that era.

Disc 3: RCA 1100   *One Night*
                        I Got Stung

Original Issue January 1959. RCA 1100 (*S 25*)
Previous Re-issue May 1977. RCA 2696 (*S 102*)

The original coupling hit the number one spot in January 1959, by which time Elvis had been in the US army for 10 months. **One Night** had been cut in February 1957 and held over for release until 1958 (its US release date), while **I Got Stung** had been recorded in June 1958 at Elvis's last studio session before departing for Germany.

This coupling was re-issued on the RCA orange label in May 1977 (S 102), though it failed to chart at that time.

This replica of the original black label release gave a slightly incorrect matrix number for *I Got Stung* - H2WW 3257, which ought to have read J2WW 3257. Correctly, there was no recording first published date printed on the label. This piece of information was not shown on any of the original labels, although the practice had started prior to this release, and, of course, continued on later pressings.

The single in this set featured the correct spelling of Bartholomew, yet the variation from which the details were copied (V1) (identified by the format of the American catalogue number - 47 7410), featured the incorrect spelling Bartholemew.

One Night was heavily featured during Elvis's '68 TV Special, and later when he returned to live performances and touring in the late sixties and seventies. Sadly though, *I Got Stung* was never used as part of his live act.

Disc 4: RCA 1113 *(Now and then there's) A Fool Such As I*
I Need Your Love Tonight

Original Issue April 1959. RCA 1113 (*S 26*)
Previous Re-issue May 1977. RCA 2697 (*S 103*)

The original coupling gave Elvis his fourth UK number one (the second in a row) in April 1959 (*S 26*), although when re-issued in May 1977 (*S 103*) it failed to chart. Both songs had been cut at Elvis's June 1958 session in Nashville, his last official recordings until he returned from the army in March 1960.

As with the original black label release, the words in brackets on the A side were omitted. Correctly though, the recording first published date - 1959 - was shown. In the case of *I Need Your Love Tonight*, the number read 3235 instead of 3253. This was clearly a new error, as the originals quoted the correct number - 3253.

Once again, apart from his 1961 live shows, neither track was ever included as part of his stage act in the late sixties and then on into the seventies, although a rehearsal version of *(Now and then there's) A Fool Such As I* from 1970 was included on the revised *"That's The Way It Is"* 3 CD package, issued in July 2000, and as a 5 LP set (ELVIS 102, **LP 328**) in August of that year.

This was the last of the singles issued in this set where the original issue featured a triangular centre.

Sleeves

Strictly speaking, the replica sleeves for the first four of the singles included in this set were not actual copies of the originals. Prior to the release of **Stuck On You,** RCA 1187 (*S 28*), in April 1960, RCA sleeves did not have rectangular boxes in the top corners (these were used by staff in record shops to write in the catalogue number so that individual records could be found more easily). While the colouring was similar, the design did not feature the distinctive white band across the centre of the sleeve.

The sleeves used for the first four singles were copies of the type used by RCA from 1960 to 1968 (although there were minor colour variations during that period). These sleeves were used for re-pressings of the first four singles made during the sixties.

All of the remaining black label singles included in this set were issued in authentic looking copies of their original sleeves, although they were printed using a far superior weight of paper than the originals.

Now, in the introductory section we explained that while BMG own RCA Records, the 'RCA' trademark is owned by General Electric (their name is usually shown on all RCA releases). Our understanding was that BMG had certain restrictions placed upon them when printing the RCA logo. The letters 'R C A' were not allowed to touch the outer circle of the logo. If you check any BMG/RCA release from 1986 onwards you will see that this is, indeed, the case. Compare these to RCA black label singles in this set where the letters actually touch the sides. It is possible, therefore, that, when replicating the original sleeves, the condition imposed by General Electric was compromised.

Disc 5: RCA 1207 *It's Now Or Never*
Make Me Know It

Original Issue October 1960. RCA 1207 (*S 30*)
Previous Re-issue May 1977. RCA 2698 (*S 104*)

The release of this coupling (unique to the UK and European market in 1960) marked Elvis's third post army single, yet was the first to hit the top spot in the UK since his release from the services in March 1960. It was re-issued in May 1977 (*S 104*), but only just scraped into the top forty on that occasion. Old Gold also issued a single featuring *It's Now Or Never* (*S 165*), but not with its original B side. Instead, another UK number one A side, **Surrender**, was used.

This replica used the full title on the A side, including the Italian words in brackets *(O Sole Mio)*, and credited DiCapua as a writer.

And, despite being one of his biggest and best known hits, the A side was never a consistent inclusion in his stage act in later years, nor was it ever performed in the majestic manner of the single version. The B side was never used as part of his live act.

Disc 6: RCA 1216 *Are You Lonesome Tonight?*
I Gotta Know

Original Issue January 1961. RCA 1216 (*S 31*)
Previous Re-issue May 1977. RCA 2699 (*S 105*)

Although issued in January 1961 in the UK (*S 31*), this coupling bore a recording first published date of 1960 - the year the songs were recorded and released in the USA. Not surprisingly then, this replica also featured the 1960 date, just as the original UK issue had. Lacking consistency, the later - 1977 - re-issue (*S 105*) had shown 1961.

The format of the American catalogue number - 47 7810 - had been altered on the replica label, as it appeared in brackets, whereas the original label did not feature this detail.

Not surprisingly, the A side became a staple part of Elvis's live performances in the late sixties and early seventies. Indeed, one of his live performances of the song from August 1969 became a hit in 1982 - the so called 'laughing version' - when it reached number 25 in the UK charts (*S 133*). The B side was never used as part of his live act.

Disc 7: RCA 1226 *Wooden Heart*
Tonight Is So Right For Love

Original Issue February 1961. RCA 1226 (*S 32*)
Previous Re-issue May 1977. RCA 2700 (*S 106*)

As with the original February 1961 pairing (*S 32*), this replica showed a publishing date of 1960 - correctly so, as both titles had been released on the LP **G.I. Blues** (*LP 12*), issued in November 1960. The May 1977 release (*S 106*) barely made the charts.

Old Gold released the two A sides **Are You Lonesome Tonight?** and **Wooden Heart** as a single coupling in April 1987 (**S 157**).

And, apart from an occasional off-the-cuff rendition of the song (usually the result of someone shouting out a request for him to sing it), no proper live version of **Wooden Heart** exists. Needless to say, nor is there one of the B side either.

Disc 8: RCA 1227 *Surrender*
Lonely Man

Original Issue May 1961. RCA 1227 (*S 33*)
Previous Re-issue May 1977. RCA 2701 (*S 107*)

This release became Elvis's fourth number one in the UK since his discharge from the US army in March 1960. And, following on from the enormous success of **It's Now Or Never**, this song was also an Italian ballad with new lyrics - although **Surrender** had nothing at all to do with the original **Torna A Surriento** - roughly translated as 'Come back to Surrento', it seems.

Significantly, this replica label did not refer to the Italian composition at all, unlike most of the original RCA singles when the title **Torna a Surriento** was added (in brackets). Instead, the new label copied the details from the earliest known label variation (V1 in **Elvis UK 1956-86**) which showed the title simply as **Surrender**. Furthermore, the writers were shown as De Curtis, Arr. Pomus, Shuman, as did the original, but unlike later pressings. It is thought that later labels variations were produced to counter possible copyright restrictions, similar to those which delayed the UK release of **It's Now Or Never** in 1960.

The matrix number on the original B side was L2PW 5381, where as this replica quoted L2WW 5381. The original labels of some of the earlier singles in this set had featured brackets around the matrix numbers, but these were not shown on the replica labels. **Surrender** was the first replica label to show this detail.

The A side had been cut at the **His Hand In Mine** session in late October 1960, while the B side was a song recorded for the film **Wild In The Country**, although, as it turned out, it was never used in the film. Elvis is only known to have sung the A side live in 1969 - and even then only a snatch of it is available for fans to hear. **Lonely Man** was never used in his live act.

Disc 9: RCA 1258 *(Marie's the name) His Latest Flame*
Little Sister

Original Issue October 1961. RCA 1258 (*S 35*)
Previous Re-issue May 1977. RCA 2702 (*S 108*)

Both tracks came from the pen of Doc Pomus and Mort Shuman and were recorded in late June 1961 in Nashville. And, while Elvis frequently used **Little Sister** in his return to live performances in 1969 (usually as part of the **Little Sister/Get Back** medley), he never included **(Marie's the name) His Latest Flame** in his live act.

Originally promoted as a double A side single (one of many issued by both HMV and RCA), **(Marie's the name) His Latest Flame** became the 'lead' track and was later issued coupled with **The Girl Of My Best Friend** by Old Gold in October 1986 (**S 151**).

Disc 10: RCA 1270 *Rock-A-Hula Baby*
Can't Help Falling In Love

Original Issue January 1962. RCA 1270 (*S 36*)
Previous Re-issue May 1977. RCA 2703 (*S 109*)

This double A sided single featured two songs from the film **Blue Hawaii**, and was his third UK number one to feature songs from a movie. And, while Elvis never sang **Rock-A-Hula Baby** again, as far as anyone knows, **Can't Help Falling In Love** became the song he regularly closed his live shows with as of 1970 (although later versions were far faster than the film version). Incidentally, **Rock-A-Hula Baby** retained the 'Twist Special' legend after the title on the original label copy.

No original label copy exists with the American catalogue number in the format 47-7968. It was always shown with brackets around it.

Disc 11: RCA 1280 *Good Luck Charm*
Anything That's Part Of You

Original Issue May 1962. RCA 1280 (*S 37*)
Previous Re-issue May 1977. RCA 2704 (*S 110*)

Both tracks emanated from the October 1961 session held in Nashville. The A side was the work of Aaron Schroeder and Wally Gold, the pair who had penned the English lyrics on **It's Now Or Never**. The B side was a Don Robertson ballad of the type favoured by Elvis during the early sixties.

Neither side was ever sung again by Elvis in a live setting.

To the best of our knowledge, no original label copy variation exists with the words 'Trade Mark(s) Registered' around the logo. By the time **Good Luck Charm** was originally released, RCA label copy had been amended to read 'Trade Marks Registered Marca(s) Registrada(s). Also, no original exists showing the American catalogue number 47-7992 without brackets around the numbers.

Disc 12: RCA 1303 *She's Not You*
Just Tell Her Jim Said Hello

Original Issue August 1962. RCA 1303 (*S 38*)
Previous Re-issue May 1977. RCA 2705 (*S 111*)

Both of these songs had been cut in Nashville in March 1962, and both were the work of Leiber and Stoller, although on the A side this was a collaboration with Doc Pomus. The order of the writers' names as shown on the label was incorrect, reading Pomus, Stoller, Leiber, just as they had been on original label copy. However, on the B side only surnames were used, whereas the original single showed their names in full - Mike Stoller, Jerry Leiber - an unusual format for UK Elvis singles.

Neither song was ever used in Elvis's live act.

Disc 13: RCA 1320 *Return To Sender*
Where Do You Come From

Original Issue November 1962. RCA 1320 (*S 39*)
Previous Re-issue May 1977. RCA 2706 (*S 112*)

This was the fourth number one single in the UK to feature a song from a movie. Included in the score of **Girls! Girls! Girls!**, this was the last film song to experience such success. Thereafter, no song from a film hit the number one spot. Ironically, the B side, although cut at the original recording session, was not featured in the film.

It was only in later years that Elvis occasionally used the A side in his live act, although no 'proper' version exists on tape as it was obviously sung without being rehearsed. Not surprisingly, the B side was not used in any live concert.

Although commonplace on most (but not all) original label variations, this was only the second single in this set to feature brackets around the matrix number.

Disc 14: RCA 1355   *(You're the) Devil In Disguise*
Please Don't Drag That String Around

Original Issue June 1963. RCA 1355 (*S 41*)
Previous Re-issue May 1977. RCA 2707 (*S 113*)

Both songs were recorded in Nashville in May 1963, during an extensive session where Elvis cut a number of original (as opposed to film) songs. In fact, released in summer 1963, this song was the last in the run of number one singles (his next was not until 1965), coming as it did during the emergence of the British pop music industry. It was also Elvis's first number one in the UK to appear solely on the RCA Victor label (**Return To Sender** had started out on the RCA label, but had quickly appeared on the RCA Victor label, too).

Neither song was ever used as part of Elvis's live shows in later years.

The American catalogue number shown on the label - 47-8100 - was incorrect. In fact, this was the catalogue number of the previous single, **Return To Sender**. In the case of *(You're the) Devil In Disguise* it ought to have read 47-8188.

Disc 15: RCA 1455   *Crying In The Chapel*
I Believe In The Man In The Sky

Original Issue May 1965. RCA 1455 (*S 50*)
Previous Re-issue May 1977. RCA 2708 (*S 114*)

When issued in May 1965 (during the height of the British pop music boom), this song (recorded in October 1960 - as was the B side) became one of the most surprising hits for Elvis. None of the intervening eight single releases (since *(You're the) Devil In Disguise)* had succeeded in topping the UK charts, so it was somewhat ironic that an unreleased, quasi-religious, song from 1960 should achieve such success. Of course, in fairness, Elvis had cut virtually no original material since May 1963 (apart from a very minor session held in January 1964).

There was no American catalogue number shown on the label, whereas original labels had quoted 447-0643. Yet, astonishingly, the legend 'Made in England by the Decca Record Co. Ltd' was featured, quite inappropriately. Although this was true for the original single release, this replica was certainly not made by Decca (a company and label name long abandoned, but resurrected in late 2000), and its appearance here was unjustified, even to those seeking authenticity.

Disc 16: RCA 1974   *The Wonder Of You*
Mama Liked The Roses

Original Issue July 1970. RCA 1974 (*S 73*)
Previous Re-issue May 1977. RCA 2709 (*S 115*)

This number one hit - a live recording from February 1970 (Elvis's only live number one) - came five years after his last one. Taken from the *On Stage - February 1970* album (*LP 41*), the song was coupled with a previously unissued track from Elvis's 1969 Memphis sessions.

It was also Elvis's first number one hit on the RCA orange label. However, unlike the 1970 original hit single, this revised version was in stereo, although no mention was made of this on the label.

Unlike the original label copy, no running time was shown on either label.

Sleeves

In design terms the sleeve used for **The Wonder Of You** was a straightforward copy of the original, but, as with all of the records included in this set, the paper quality was much improved when compared to the originals.

However, the green, orange and white sleeve design was not used for all of RCA orange label output. **Way Down** was originally issued in a blue and orange coloured sleeve, with 'RCA' in white print at the

top. The copy sleeve used for **Way Down** was, therefore, not appropriate. Perhaps it made economic sense to produce the same copy sleeve for the last two singles in the set, rather than two different ones.

Disc 17: PB 0998   *Way Down*
Pledging My Love

Original Issue July 1977. RCA PB 0998 (*S 116*)

It was not until after Elvis's death in August 1977 that he registered his next (and to date last) number one hit. Taken from the **Moody Blue** album (*LP 93*), the song was released prior to Elvis's death. And although a very strong offering (cut at Graceland in October 1976), no-one will ever be able to say whether or not it would have been such a big hit had Elvis not died. It was coupled with another recording from Graceland.

Because **Way Down** was not released on a single until July 1977, it was obviously not included as part of the 16 other number one singles released in May 1977. Indeed, this was the first time that the original coupling had been available since that time, although **Way Down** was issued on a single along with **Moody Blue** on RCA's Golden Grooves label in May 1982 (**S 134**), and again on Old Gold in January 1988 (**S 172**).

This was the only label copy in the set to show the 'Stereo' legend, although all tracks from 1960 were pressed in stereo for this collection.

As with the previous single, no running times were shown on the labels, unlike original copies. Although both tracks were featured on the **Moody Blue** album (*LP 93*), re-printing this fact, and quoting the album's original catalogue number at the bottom of the label, seemed pointless.

Once again though, apart from a rare and unrehearsed live rendition of the A side, Elvis never included the song in his live act. Nor, for that matter, was the B side ever sung live.

Coloured Vinyl Edition

In July 2001, 11 months after the original version was issued, Castle Music produced a coloured vinyl edition of this set, continuing their theme of producing unusual, and collectable, product.

As with the other special editions, we have not allocated a separate release number for this item because no additional product was included, unlike, for example, **Peace In The Valley The Complete Gospel Recordings** (LP 333), which, when first issued, contained a 10 inch Christmas LP as a bonus.

On this occasion, the special edition amounted to a series of vinyl discs, each one a different colour. Never before had a coloured vinyl single been issued in the UK, although at one time they had proved very popular in other parts of the world.

The packaging and, of course, the tracks themselves were identical to the original issue. The only differences were the addition of two stickers attached to the outside of the box. The first, a light blue circular sticker (with the same image of Elvis from the centre of the box), attached to the front, bore the legend 'Limited Edition Coloured Vinyl Boxset', followed by the catalogue number. On the back, a second sticker, this time white and rectangular in shape, carried the revised ELVIS 103X catalogue number and bar code.

EPs

Introduction

At no point throughout the research and preparation for this volume of **Elvis UK** (effectively from 1990 onwards) did we once consider the possibility of there being an EP section – quite simply because there weren't any, and the likelihood of there being any was extremely remote. Indeed, as we make clear at various points in the text, the future – indeed the very existence – of vinyl releases (both singles and LPs) seemed in doubt for a number of years. How quickly things changed!

And so, in the closing stages of this book being prepared for publication (autumn 2001), came the news that Castle Music (Sanctuary) – no doubt under the auspices of Roger Semon - were about to release an eleven EP collection, entitled **The International EP Collection**. Now apart from the surprising nature of the release (International EPs), one obvious effect was to delay the publication of this book, as we felt obliged to include this very significant release. Yes, there had been an EP included in the **Sun Singles** set (**S182**) – albeit a newly created one – but this was part of a singles' set and so had no separate identity, in our view.

It is worth back-tracking a little to place this set this into its proper context. EPs – in a sense mini-albums - first appeared in the fifties, although their hey-day was during the sixties. As regards Elvis EP releases, the USA always seemed to have more than the UK did and, as became apparent with LP album releases, there was often a sharp difference between what was issued in the USA and the UK, not to mention differences in track listings also (though this occurred less with later releases i.e. from 1960 onwards).

During his lifetime, there were 22 EP releases in the UK, two of those on the HMV label (**Love Me Tender** and **Good Rockin' Tonight** – EPs 1 and 3 respectively), the others were on the RCA label. Officially the last Elvis EP in the UK was **Easy Come, Easy Go** (EP 22) in 1967, when the medium seemed to have had its day. Ironically, despite its shortcomings, both as a film and as an album, this EP actually topped the EP charts – which says much for the state of the medium at the time. Of course, RCA continued to re-press back catalogue titles on the black RCA Victor label; and later, when the company undertook its own pressings, many also appeared on the orange RCA label. Needless to say, neither of the HMV releases were re-issued by RCA during that era.

Some pundits might argue that the emergence of the maxi-singles in the seventies continued the EP format in a revised form, but we would dissent from that view. EPs were always a separate entity and were usually characterised by having four or more tracks and being housed in colourful cardboard sleeves – some of which had sleeve notes. On the other hand, maxi-singles were just what the name implied: a vehicle for issuing (certainly in Elvis's case) back catalogue material, usually former single releases.

However, in 1982, fifteen years after the last Elvis EP in the UK, Roger Semon, then of RCA in London, took the bold step of releasing not one but two 11 EP sets, both of which were hugely successful and acclaimed by collectors and critics alike. Of course, this was only the start of many extremely imaginative and well-marketed packages compiled by Semon, later joined by Ernst Jorgensen, then of RCA Denmark.

Nonetheless, as the 1980s drew to a close, most music industry 'experts' were predicting the imminent demise of all but a tiny part of the vinyl market. In fairness, it was a general view and one which we shared, albeit with some reluctance. In what seemed like an unstoppable trend, CDs had begun to dominate the market, and

while there were still some vinyl singles and LP albums, they were in the minority. Indeed, vinyl collectors were often scorned and ridiculed. And often where there was a new release being planned, it was not an automatic thing to have a vinyl equivalent: it happened only after careful consideration of its market potential. Each of the major boxed sets of the 1990s had to undergo this process and, as you will be aware, there was serious debate as to the wisdom of releasing vinyl versions of the fifties' and sixties' sets. In the event, however, both of the previously mentioned sets were made available in vinyl form (and did very well sales-wise, too). But by 1995, when the seventies' set was ready for release, no vinyl version was manufactured. Now whether or not that was to do with the view that this era (the '70s) may not have been as popular with vinyl enthusiasts, or whether conventional wisdom dictated that vinyl in general was no longer appealing is anyone's guess. Whatever the case, vinyl releases became the exception rather than the rule. That is until some shrewd marketing people in the industry sensed that specialist vinyl products were still highly sought after and, thus, saleable.

The 7 inch vinyl EP made its reappearance as part of Castle Music's **Sun Singles** (**S182**), released in March 2000. In fact, it was a piece artistic licence on the part of Roger Semon, as there never was an Elvis EP on Sun. It comprised the following tracks: **That's All Right**, **Harbour Lights**, **Tomorrow Night**, and **Trying To Get To You**.

However, as this EP came as part of a singles' set, and was not available as a separate entity, we treated it as an extra. Thus, at that time, there seemed no need to have a discrete EP section. This was also the case when Castle Music started to issue film soundtrack LPs in October 2001. The five LPs **G.I. Blues**, **Blue Hawaii**, **Loving You**, **Jailhouse Rock** and **King Creole** (**LPs 337, 338, 342, 343** and **344**) - all included, as a bonus, an EP of songs from other film soundtracks, gathered together for the first time. As these EPs came as bonus items with the albums, they too were dealt with accordingly in the LP section. We hope the logic of this makes sense to you.

Finally, it is worth noting that only one of the inclusions in this latest collection of extended players had a UK equivalent. The rest were taken from German, Italian, Japanese, Spanish, Australian, Iranian, New Zealand, French and American releases. In the course of the specific piece on the EPs themselves, your attention will be drawn to any comparisons/differences there are to UK releases.

UK EPs Listed Chronologically

Unlike the chronological Singles and LP listings there is only one entry in this section (despite comprising 11 separate EPs).

However, as with the other sections, we have maintained the chronological numbering sequence from the previous book.

It is worth noting that the twenty-two EPs that comprised both volumes of the 1982 **EP Collection**, were also available to buy individually, although the original intention was to exclude the three **Collectors Gold** EPs from this practice. In considering release numbers, we therefore allocated separate numbers to each EP, which explains the large gap between the last 'original' EP, **Easy Come, Easy Go** (EP 22) and **The International EP Collection**.

Release Number	Catalogue Number	Title	Release Date
EP 45	RCA/ Castle Music ELVIS 105	*The International EP Collection*	Aug 2001

EP 45 | The International EP Collection

RCA/Castle Music ELVIS 105

EP 1
7EG 8199
(UK)

Love Me Tender
Love Me Tender (Presley, Matson)
Let Me (Presley, Matson)
Poor Boy (Presley, Matson)
We're Gonna Move (Presley, Matson)

EP 2
EPA 9644
(Germany)

One Night With Elvis Presley
One Night (Bartholomew, King)
You're A Heartbreaker (Sallee)
I Got Stung (Schroeder, Hill)
Baby Let's Play House (Gunter)

EP 3
A72V 0074
(Italy)

Rock 'N' Roll
One-Sided Love Affair (Campbell)
Money Honey (Stone)
Shake, Rattle And Roll (Calhoun)
Lawdy, Miss Clawdy (Price)er)

EP 4
A72V 0073
(Italy)

Il Re Del Rock 'N' Roll
I Got A Woman (Charles)
I'm Gonna Sit Right Down And Cry (over you)
(Thomas, Biggs)
Just Because (B.& J. Shelton, Robin)
Trying To Get To You (Singleton, McCoy)

EP 5
SCP-1133
(Japan)

Elvis Presley
Long Tall Sally (Johnson, Blackwell, Penniman)
First In Line (Schroeder, Weisman)
How's The World Treating You (Atkins, Bryant)
How Do You Think I Feel (Walker, Pierce)

EP 6
3-21024
(Spain)

Elvis
Silent Night (Mohr, Gruber)
I Believe (Drake, Graham, Shirl, Stillman)
White Christmas (Berlin)
It Is No Secret (what God can do) (Hamblen)

EP 7
20101
(Australia)

Loving You Vol. 1
Loving You (Leiber, Stoller)
Party (Robinson)
(Let me be your) Teddy Bear (Mann, Lowe)
True Love (Porter)

EP 8
EX 4071
(Iran)

Girls! Girls! Girls!
Girls! Girls! Girls! (Leiber, Stoller)
I Don't Wanna Be Tied (Giant, Baum, Kaye)
A Boy Like Me, A Girl Like You (Tepper, Bennett)
Return To Sender (Blackwell, Scott)
The Walls Have Ears (Tepper, Bennett)
We're Coming in Loaded (Blackwell, Scott)

EP 9
RPX-1146
(New Zealand)

His Hand In Mine
His Hand In Mine (Lister)
I'm Gonna Walk Dem Golden Stairs (Holt)
Joshua Fit The Battle (Arranged and adapted Presley)
Swing Down, Sweet Chariot (Arranged and adapted Presley)

EP 10
86.557
(France)

Paradise Hawaiian Style
Scratch My Back (then I'll scratch yours)
(Giant, Baum, Kaye)
A Dog's Life (Wayne, Weisman)
Stop Where You Are (Giant, Baum, Kaye)
House Of Sand (Giant, Baum, Kaye)

EP 11
SPA-7-37
(USA)

Perfect For Parties
Love Me (Leiber, Stoller)
Anchors Away (Unknown) - Tony Cabot & His Orchestra
That's A Puente (Sommer) - Tito Puente & His Orchestra
Rock Me But Don't Roll Me (Scott) - Tony Scott And His Orchestra
Happy Face Baby (Unknown) - The Three Suns
Prom To Prom (Pell) - Dave Pell Octet

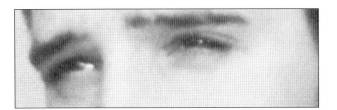

Released August 2001

Prior to the release of this set, as mentioned in the introduction to this section, there had been no Elvis EP releases since 1982 when the celebrated **The EP Collection** volumes 1 and 2 were issued. Please note, when Castle Music (by this time part of the Sanctuary Music Group) issued the vinyl albums **G.I Blues** and **Blue Hawaii** (**LPs**

337 and **338**) in October 2001 they each had a bonus EP included. Nonetheless, neither EP was available individually; they had to be bought as part of the package. Furthermore, they were newly compiled EPs, as no such albums had existed previously in the UK.

This collection of international EPs was unusual in that it sought to replicate original EP albums from around the world, in most cases different from the releases US and UK fans has seen. Some of the original albums are thought to be quite valuable, therefore their release in this format helped those fans who would never be in a position to buy the original issues. Naturally there were many to choose from, so clearly the compilers opted for variety, as well as choosing unusual compilations. The material itself ranged from Sun recordings to film soundtrack cuts, though there was no material after 1965 included.

Of course, while the idea was to offer replicas of worldwide releases, they were not intended as 'exact' replicas of the originals, as the note beneath the track listing on the back of the box made perfectly clear. Presumably this would have been too great a task, not to mention the likely problems with copyright details etc. For example, there was no way that BMG would have gained permission to replicate an HMV label, or use their logo for the *Love Me Tender* EP. Collectors, we believe, understood this constraint. Besides, the idea was to reproduce the general feeling of these mini albums, not to copy everything in minute detail. Quite aptly, the note concluded with the line 'Enjoy the Music!'.

As with the *Sun Singles* (**S 182**) and *The UK No. 1 Singles Collection* (**S 183**), we have chosen to deal with this set as an entity, as none of the EPs was available individually, at least not at the time of writing, though who knows what the future might hold. Therefore, although we write about each EP separately, it is within the one section.

Each of the label designs were the same and used a black RCA Victor logo which displayed a Z/T tax code – something that dated it to the period April – October 1962. All were solid centred EPs, too, while the original EPs usually had knockout centres. Each EP cover was fully glossed on both sides and some had two foldovers also, though not all.

Please note that any references to single, EP or LP releases in this section pertain to UK records, unless otherwise stated. Furthermore, although no recording modes appear on any of the records or sleeves, all the post-1960 tracks – as featured on EPs 8, 9 and 10 – were in stereo. Naturally, the '50s tracks were in mono, even though 'stereo' versions exist of the *Love Me Tender* songs.

The set included a fold out poster that featured a live shot of Elvis on stage in 1957 on one side and detailed the tracks on each EP on the other. Also illustrated were other Elvis releases in the Castle Music catalogue and a display of bubble gum cards.

We have reason to believe that this set sold well enough to justify a second pressing, following an initial press run of 5,000 copies, although this is unconfirmed. However, we also believe that they were indistinguishable from the first pressings.

1	7EG 8199	*Love Me Tender*
	UK	

Original Issue February 1957 *(EP 1)*
Previous Re-issue February 1982. RCA RCX 7191 *(EP 26)*

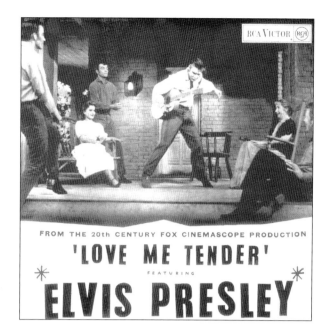

This was the only EP in the set that was an original UK issue. None of the others had been issued in the UK at all. In fact, the original release of this EP in the UK was on the HMV label, not RCA. It was actually Elvis's first EP release in the UK, issued in February 1957 *(EP 1)*. This replica used the same catalogue number as the original issue – 7EG 8199. And while the copyright date was shown as 1956, this pertained to the date the recordings were made, not their release in the UK. It ought to have read 1957, though it is worth remembering that records from this period did not display this detail anyway.

As a point of interest, in the period between March 1956 and the middle of 1957, RCA's product was released in the UK through the EMI group, using the HMV label design. However, in July 1957, new RCA product was pressed by Decca using the RCA label, although HMV continued to issue material they already had the rights to well into 1958. Incidentally, there were only two Elvis EPs on HMV; three albums and 13 singles – 14 if you include the export edition of *Mystery Train* (*S 8*). And by September 1958, HMV no longer had any rights to issue Elvis product. Therefore, once the licensing arrangement had expired, this EP was no longer available in the UK, nor was it re-pressed on the RCA label during Elvis's lifetime. However, it did appear in *The EP Collection* (as *EP 26*) in February 1982, but on that occasion it featured the US cover design.

The four tracks were the ones featured in the film. They appeared here in their original mono mode. In recent years, however, some of these recordings have appeared in stereo.

The cover shot duplicated that of the HMV release, with the notable exception that the RCA Victor logo featured on the front and back cover.

2	EPA 9644	*One Night With Elvis Presley*
	Germany	

This EP combined two Sun recordings – *You're A Heartbreaker* and *Baby Let's Play House* - with two songs released as a double A sided single in January 1959 (*S 25*), several months after Elvis went into the US army: *One Night* (recorded in February 1957) and *I Got Stung*, a recording made in June 1958. The front cover shot used the same photo (circa August 1956) as used on the UK album *Elvis* (*LP 8*) issued in March 1959.

3	A72V 0074	*Rock 'N' Roll*
	Italy	

All of these tracks had been recorded at Elvis's second session for RCA, held in New York, late January/early February 1956. Only *Lawdy Miss Clawdy* had appeared on a UK single when it was the

B side of **Trying To Get To You** (*S 15*) in October 1957, Elvis's penultimate single release on the HMV label. The front cover shot used a black and white photo from Elvis's appearance on the Steve Allen show in June 1956. Unusually, the track listing on the back cover included song timings, along with a list of other Elvis product available in Italy.

4   A72V 0073   *Il Re Del Rock 'N' Roll*
         Italy

Once again, these tracks dated from 1954 - 56, two from his Sun catalogue – **Just Because** and **Trying To Get To You** – along with **I Got A Woman** (his very first RCA recording in January 1956) and **I'm Gonna Sit Right Down And Cry (over you)**. Of these, only **Trying To Get To You** made it as an A side single in the UK in October 1957, when it was coupled with **Lawdy, Miss Clawdy** (*S15*). The front cover shot was similar to that of his first HMV album. Once again, there was a list of other Elvis product available in Italy printed on the back cover.

5   SPC-1133   *Elvis Presley*
         Japan

These four tracks were taken from Elvis's second album recorded in September 1956. They had also been issued in the USA on an EP entitled **Strictly Elvis**, issued in early 1957. This was, of course, a completely different collection of songs to those issued on the English EP of the same name (*EP 12*). Only **How Do You Think I Feel** was released on a single in the UK when it was the B side of Elvis's last HMV release, **I'm Left, You're Right, She's Gone** (*S 17*) in January 1958. The front cover shot was a coloured drawing, depicting an image from the mid -1960s.

Incidentally, this EP included the lyrics printed on the back of the cover. The words for **Long Tall Sally** include some interesting and amusing mistakes!

6   3-21024   *Elvis*
         Spain

This collection comprised four songs from the original **Elvis' Christmas Album** (*LP 5*) from 1957, two religious items alongside two Christmas songs. However, the front cover shot was circa the **Clambake** period (1967), which would seem to date the release of this EP to that period.

7   20101   *Loving You Vol. 1*
         Australia

Once again this collection had been released originally on an EP in the USA, simply entitled **Loving You**. There was no British release of this collection however, at least not until it was included in **The EP Collection** in February 1982 (*EP 27*). Three of these songs had appeared on UK singles: **(Let me be your) Teddy Bear** and **Loving You** (Elvis's first release on the RCA label in the UK) had been coupled in July 1957 (*S 12*), while **Party** (*S 14*) had been an A side when released in October 1957.

The front cover shot used one of the famous poses as featured on the back cover of **Elvis' Golden Records** (*LP 7*). The back cover of this EP listed other Elvis EPs available in Australia at the time.

Oddly, the track listing on the fold out poster listed **(Let me be your) Teddy Bear** as **Let Me Be Your (Teddy Bear)**.

8   EX 4071   *Girls! Girls! Girls!*
         Iran

This was an unusual collection in that most regions in the world did not issue an extended play release of songs from the film, opting for the LP release instead. This six track album included the single release from the film, **Return To Sender** (*S 39*). Unusually, although the front cover featured the same photo as was used on the **Girls! Girls! Girls!** album (*LP 18*) the image was in monochrome. Another odd

feature was that the back cover advertised EP releases by other artists. These tracks were in stereo.

9   RPX-1146   *His Hand In Mine*
         New Zealand

Once again, this was an unusual collection in that most fans throughout the world were only offered an LP of material from this session. Incidentally, when the LP **His Hand In Mine** (*LP 13*) was released, none of the tracks was issued a single. It was only in May 1965 when the previously unreleased **Crying In The Chapel** (*S 50*) was issued and coupled with **I Believe In The Man In The Sky** (taken from the **His Hand In Mine** album), that any other song from this album made it as a single release.

The front cover copied that of the LP version (though the tint on the colour was different) as did the back cover, complete with sleeve notes. The timings were shown for each track also. Although no mode was shown, these tracks were in stereo.

10   86.557   *Paradise Hawaiian Style*
       France

Without overstating things, few fans would hold the album **Paradise, Hawaiian Style** (*LP 29*) in very high regard, so it was strange to see that French fans were 'treated' to an EP of some songs from the film. The front cover design was very similar to that of the LP, while the back cover listed the tracks, showed the timings and gave the writers' details. Three other Elvis EPs were advertised beneath the RCA Victor logo. These tracks were in stereo.

Please note, that although **Paradise, Hawaiian Style** was shown without the comma after **Paradise**, conventionally one would be shown.

11   SPA-7-37   *Perfect For Parties*
         USA

Of course, this EP wasn't an Elvis EP at all. Originally, this collection was a promotional album for RCA Victor artists and was not available in stores. It could only be obtained by sending a newspaper coupon directly to RCA in Philadelphia (there were also radio and TV advertisements). Original copies of this EP are greatly sought after by collectors and command very high prices. Presumably, despite the national campaign, relatively few were made, as the set was only available for a couple of months in late 1956.

Featuring six artists (including Elvis), this was a promotional record of the kind rarely seen in the UK (at that time). The tracks were taken from current LPs and, incredibly, Elvis introduced all the recordings, including his own **Love Me!**.

Unlike all of the other EPs in this collection, **Perfect For Parties** played at 33 rpm.

LPs

Introduction

Retrospectively 1986 will probably be seen as a watershed in terms of Elvis Presley album releases. A quick glance at the number of album releases for any other year reveals that, by comparison, 1986 was a very lean year indeed, there being a dearth of material made available. In fact, had it not been for the release of *Essential Elvis* (**LP 280**) in December of that year, 1986 would have gone down as the year in which no 'new' releases were issued as full-priced items. The only other releases that year were three Camden albums: *The Rock Hits, Girls! Girls! Girls!, Kissin' Cousins* (**LPs 276, 278** and **279**), plus a mid-priced RCA album, *Elvis Forever* (**LP 277**).

Of course, the years from 1983-85 had seen a lot of activity in the UK and European market in terms of re-cataloguing albums, introducing new label formats, centralising the production of albums - their mastering and pressing - in Germany, as well as the huge number of re-issues. Consider also that during this time there had been some major personnel changes in the company's management structure in the USA: Joan Deary (who had been with RCA when Elvis first recorded for them in 1956), left the company quite suddenly after many years, and Gregg Geller assumed responsibility for the Presley catalogue. It was evident that changes were in the offing. Joan Deary's final project was her contribution to the six album boxed set *A Golden Celebration* (*LP 251*), although rumours had abounded that her creative judgement had been challenged and countermanded over the proposed contents of the set, resulting in significant changes to the finished product. Our theories regarding this were discussed in the relevant part of *Elvis UK 1956-86*. So, under a 'new' regime, 1985 saw a spate of releases featuring repackaged material: *A Valentine Gift For You, Reconsider Baby* and *Always On My Mind*, (*LPs 270, 271* and *272* respectively). On the other hand, 1986 was, as already discussed, barren in terms of releases. In fact from October 1985, when the company re-issued *Elvis' Christmas Album*, PL 85486 (*LP 275*), there was no other re-issue on RCA until October 1988 when *Moody Blue*, NL 90252 (**LP 296**), was issued, to tie in with a CD release of the album (ND 90252).

Meanwhile, the situation in the USA changed again: Gregg Geller left the company, and for a while there was a management vacuum in terms of who was looking after the Presley catalogue. It seemed as if the only activity regarding releases centred around re-issues and the licensing of back catalogue material by the likes of Pickwick and Old Gold - although in the case of the latter this was confined to single releases only, not to mention the occasional various artist compilation albums.

On the other hand, there were some promising signs too. The word was that the Presley Estate and RCA had resolved many of their former difficulties, and that a better level of understanding and working relationship had been fostered. And, amidst all of these changes, quietly beavering away in the background was Roger Semon, champion of the Elvis catalogue at RCA in the UK, and the major force behind the release of *Essential Elvis* (**LP 280**). His work, largely in collaboration with Ernst Mikael Jorgensen, then of RCA in Denmark, was to re-shape the pattern of Presley releases in a way few would have dared dream about previously. Undoubtedly, in our view, the release of *Essential Elvis* (**LP 280**) in late 1986, proved to be the pivotal point in determining the future of Elvis's releases, not only in the UK, but throughout the world. What was remarkable about this was that now the real centre of creative energy for most of the imaginative album releases which were to follow stemmed not from the USA but, quite clearly, from the UK division of the company. A point few people would argue with.

As looking at the releases listed for 1987 will reveal, the year produced more and better quality material, apart from a couple of interview albums - *The Elvis Tapes* (**LP 281**) and *Confidential...... Elvis* (**LP 282**), as well as several re-issues of compilations by Premier (formerly Everest). However, the key releases for the year focused around July/August to mark the tenth anniversary of Elvis's death. From the US division came *The Memphis Record* (**LP 284**), a double album of tracks cut by Elvis in Memphis in 1969 and the promising, though flawed, *The Complete Sun Sessions* (**LP 283**). But from the UK company came probably the best compilation ever, *Presley - The All Time Greatest Hits* (**LP 287**), the brainchild of Roger Semon, which went on to sell phenomenally well for many years after. Then, towards the end of the year Charly Records issued the double album of *The Complete Million Dollar Quartet* (**LP 291**) officially.

On the other hand 1988 was relatively quiet, apart from the release of *The Alternate Aloha* (**LP 294**) - a US inspired album - and a 're-issue' of *The Elvis Presley Sun Collection* (**LP 295**) in a presentation box as part of a series by the record retail outlet HMV.

However, pride of place in 1989 was devoted to the second volume of the Essential Elvis series: *Stereo '57 (Essential Elvis Volume 2)* (**LP 298**), a long-awaited follow up to *Essential Elvis* (**LP 280**). This release generated particular interest, in that the album not only comprised virtually all unreleased performances, but because they were in binaural - an early form of stereo recordings. More compilations appeared under licence from BMG, while Ocean Records released an album of interview material, and then a live performance of material recorded in Little Rock in May 1956, which had previously been available as a bootleg release. There were yet more compilations that year when Time-Life issued an album devoted to Elvis material.

In September 1989, the UK company (following the lead from USA) issued *A Date With Elvis* (**LP 304**) (featuring the same tracks as the 1959 UK compilation - *LP 9*) in CD and vinyl format, along with *For LP Fans Only* (**LP 303**). This, as most collectors know, was the title of the 1959 US 10 track release, which was never issued as such in the UK. British fans were offered instead an album entitled *Elvis*, RD 27120 (*LP 8*), which was a 14-track offering based on the US release, but with significant track differences. So, this newly titled release was simply the original UK album re-issued with the American title! In truth though, neither album was deserving of being re-issued, as the vast majority of tracks were readily available on both CD and LP. However, both albums had always generated a great deal of affection with the fans, therefore once they were issued in the US (in dreadful sound quality - it was not proper mono), it was only a matter of time before they secured a British re-release. It is worth noting that both UK albums were mastered by Bob Jones (uncredited on the covers), though in the period before pristine fifties master tapes were available, he had to work with low-grade copy tapes. Needless to say though, the sound was appreciably better than the US releases. Incidentally, all re-issues of back catalogue material were now mid-priced items.

Early 1990 saw the release of more interview material but this time on a label called Magnum Force. Of special note here is that one of the co-authors of *Elvis UK*, Gordon Minto, penned the extensive sleeve notes. But for collectors, two BMG releases were especially well-received: the third Essential Elvis release - *Hits Like Never Before (Essential Elvis Vol. 3)* (**LP 306**) - made up of unreleased performances from *King Creole* and Elvis's June 1958 recording session, and *For The Asking (The Lost Album)* (**LP 309**), comprising original material Elvis cut in Nashville in May 1963 and a couple of tracks from early 1964. This was the first occasion these tracks - many of them used as singles or 'bonus' tracks on film soundtrack LPs - had been brought together in one package. Skilfully remastered from the master tapes, the LP (and CD) were well-received. Reader's Digest also came up with another Elvis collection, **The Legend Lives On** (**LP 310**) available in LP, music cassette and CD forms. Not normally aimed at the serious collector, this release featured a couple of outtakes - in all likelihood accidentally - thus making it highly sought after.

Earlier in the year (in August 1990), the US division, in conjunction with the Presley Estate and Buena Vista Home Video, released an album entitled **The Great Performances** (**LP 308**) which for the first time had a companion release on video. The two video cassettes were popular with fans as they included previously unseen footage. For record/CD buyers though, the main virtue of the audio release was the inclusion of Elvis's private recording of **My Happiness,** made in 1953. Recently obtained from someone called Ed Leek (who had been given the acetate by Elvis in the fifties), the company issued the song once the minefield of legalities had been successfully navigated.

Towards the end of 1990, BMG re-issued the 1957 Christmas album, along with the 1971 Christmas album. However, the CD version of the latter included the single version of **If Every Day Was Like Christmas** (from 1966), and the so-called 'country rhythm' version of **I'll Be Home On Christmas Day.**

By now BMG was issuing CD versions of albums at fairly regular intervals, about three times a year. So, in February 1991, they finally released **From Elvis In Memphis** (ND 90548) and **On Stage - February 1970** (ND 90549) on CD, as well as having a vinyl release too (**LPs 313** and **314** respectively). Notably, neither album had been re-issued previously in the UK. However, the third CD of this batch (and note that in each case the batches of re-issues were linked by virtue of time), was the NBC TV Special. The CD had eight extra tracks, all bar one of which had been available officially before. The only previously unreleased track was a version of **Don't Be Cruel** from the second 'Stand-Up' show on 29 June 1968. There was no vinyl album release of this item; indeed the 'original' album i.e. the LP with the original running order was still available. There was, therefore, the strange situation where both the vinyl album and CD bore the same catalogue number, though there were significant track differences. And, although, there were precedents for this, they normally related to the likes of the **Essential Elvis** releases, whereby the CD version had additional tracks but, of course, both vinyl and CD albums had been available almost simultaneously.

Prior to its release in August 1991, there had been some doubts as to whether there would be a vinyl version of **Collectors Gold.** Happily for collectors there was. However, Roger Semon explained that this decision had been considered by the respective committee members and only sanctioned because the argument that it was worth pressing vinyl copies was persuasively put. In other words: those who needed to be convinced were assured that the decision was financially beneficial to the company. This it seems - and this really ought to be no surprise to anyone - was, literally, the bottom line, especially during a rapidly changing set of circumstances, wherein the production costs of producing vinyl records were rising - due in part to the relatively few numbers being manufactured, not to mention the fact that pressing facilities were also quickly contracting. But, as Semon explained in early 1992, the Elvis market was still strong enough to be considered separately from the rest of the industry trend. For example, at that time the percentage of vinyl sales was estimated as being below 10% - some said as low as 6 - 7%. But the Elvis market could still sustain sales anywhere in the region of 15-18%. However, perhaps this was the main thrust of 'new' or repackaged material, rather than straightforward re-issues, as the next batch of CDs to be made available demonstrated.

Whereas two of the three mid-priced CD releases from February/March 1991 had vinyl counterparts, the batch issued in October 1991 had none. This time BMG released **Promised Land** (ND 90598), **Back In Memphis** (ND 90599) (issued for the first time as a separate entity in the UK - albeit only in CD form), and

Elvis In Person At The International Hotel Las Vegas, Nevada (ND 83892). Oddly enough though, there <u>was</u> a vinyl LP copy of the latter to be found, but we are not convinced that it was intended to be a British release. (For more information see **LP 316.**)

Of course, all the while RCA/BMG were involved in restoring back catalogue material via the medium of CD - and less frequently with a vinyl equivalent - there was also a deletion programme in operation. As vinyl quickly lost its major appeal to the consumers - apart from die-hard collectors, of course - BMG, like all other record companies, had to review the situation with regard to issuing catalogue items in vinyl. Therefore, systematically old vinyl album releases were deleted. This process involved representatives from the various departments - principally marketing and production - discussing the value or otherwise of keeping particular titles on catalogue in vinyl form. And, as a look at the deletions schedules we have compiled will show, there were few surprises in terms of which went first, and which ones had sufficient sales potential to defer their demise a while longer. It is notable that many of those which stayed on catalogue were the most interesting and innovative releases - in most cases the UK inspired albums. Of course, items which were little known and hence did not sell very well, **Elvis Forever** (**LP 277**) for example, were also slow to clear.

Thereafter, the next release was **From The Heart,** PL 90642 (**LP 317**), issued in February 1992, which was available as a vinyl LP (with modified track listing), music cassette and CD (PD 90642) (with additional tracks). This had the benefit of an intensive publicity campaign, including a television advert, thus generating extremely healthy and lucrative sales for BMG. Of the formats available, vinyl had only about 8% of market sales, CD represented about 65% - the rest were cassettes.

Very shortly afterwards, three more mid-priced CD releases appeared: **Today** (ND 90660), **He Touched Me** (ND 90661), and **Elvis As Recorded At Madison Square Garden** (ND 90663), but there were no vinyl copies available. Meanwhile plans were being finalised for the definitive fifties collection (released in July 1992) and still the question regarding vinyl copies being available was being asked. In the event, BMG were persuaded to press 15,000 six LP sets of **The King Of Rock 'N' Roll The Complete 50's Masters** (**LP 318**), but this was essentially for the home market (UK), although several thousand sets were exported to the USA which did not have vinyl copies at all. There were no other LP/CD releases in 1992.

Then, in 1993 the long-awaited Double Feature releases appeared in the UK in March of that year. Eight film soundtracks (only six of which had been LP releases originally) were released on four compact disc sets. And even though the sets included some unreleased performances, there were no vinyl copies made at all.

The next major project to spawn a vinyl equivalent was **From Nashville To Memphis The Essential 60's Masters I** (**LP 319**) in September 1993, a six LP set which was also released as a 5 CD boxed set too (74321 15430 2). As with the '50s set, this was a limited edition (only 10,000 sets were made), as the major sales went to the CD market.

The next LP release proved to be unusual in that it was a single album of hits. Entitled **The Essential Collection** (**LP 320**), this album (comprising 23 tracks) was a UK only collection, and aimed squarely at the general record buying public. The appearance of a vinyl equivalent - alongside the more popular CD version (which contained five extra tracks) - was simply an acknowledgement that some potential buyers would only be equipped to buy and play vinyl.

However, the last RCA album in the UK (to date) was stunningly good. **Elvis 56** (**LP 321**) featured 22 tracks, the same number of tracks as its CD equivalent (07863 66856 2).

Ironically though, the next UK vinyl Elvis album appeared on an independent label, Stomper Time Records, who produced an album entitled **The Louisiana Hayride/Little Rock, Arkansas** (**LP 322**), which comprised material from 1954-55 and was released in October 1997. Apart from being beautifully packaged, of special interest to collectors was the fact that it revived what was thought to be a defunct medium: the 10 inch vinyl album. Then in mid-1999 came another surprise, in the form of a vinyl version of BMG's *Artist Of The Century* (**LP 323**), a 75 track release, manufactured and marketed not by BMG themselves, but by Castle Music in England. It was the brainchild of Roger Semon who, although still a co-producer of Elvis product for BMG, worked in Marketing for Castle Music. There followed a very limited edition blue vinyl version (available only through HMV outlets), and, later still, towards the end of 1999, a 5 LP picture disc version, said to be limited to 3,000 copies. Clearly, marketing executives in various record companies, had come to realise the potential of producing high quality, small quantity vinyl releases for the collectors' market. And there was more to follow.

Finally, one further point of information. In *Elvis UK 1956-86* we did not include chart positions for LPs - mainly because the information for early releases was unreliable. However, in part as a response to a request made by one of our readers - a R. Semon, late of BMG - we have now included what information we have on this subject.

UK Albums Listed Chronologically

This section lists the UK album releases from 1986 onwards and, in order to allow the number of such releases to be put into perspective, we decided to maintain the chronological numbering sequence from the previous book.

This section should, therefore, enable you to determine, for each release, its release number, label and catalogue number, whether it was a re-issue of an earlier release, and date of release. If an album is not listed here, it was not a UK issue (even though it might have been on sale in some outlets), or it was released prior to 1986 and can be found in *Elvis UK 1956-86*.

Release Number	Catalogue Number	Title	Release Date
LP 276	Camden CDS 1215	*The Rock Hits*	Apr 1986
LP 277	RCA NL 89004	*Elvis Forever*	Jul 1986
LP 278	Camden CDS 1221	*Girls! Girls! Girls!* (*re-issue*)	Sep 1986
LP 279	Camden CDS 1222	*Kissin' Cousins* (*re-issue*)	Sep 1986
LP 280	RCA PL 89979	*Essential Elvis*	Dec 1986
LP 281	Redwood RED 1	*The Elvis Tapes* (*re-issue*)	Apr 1987
LP 282	Arena ARAD 1008	*Confidential...... Elvis*	May 1987
LP 283	RCA PL 86414(2)	*The Complete Sun Sessions*	Jul 1987
LP 284	RCA PL 86221(2)	*The Memphis Record*	Aug 1987
LP 285	RCA NL 89830(6)	*Elvis Forever - 96 Hits Of The King*	Aug 1987
LP 286	Selected Marketing ANIV 10	*Tribute To Elvis*	Aug 1987
LP 287	RCA PL 90100(2)	*Presley - The All Time Greatest Hits*	Aug 1987
LP 288	Premier PMP 1011	*In Hollywood* (*re-issue*)	Oct 1987
LP 289	Premier PMP 1012	*Mess O' Blues - Volume 1*	Oct 1987
LP 290	Premier PMP 1013	*Mess O' Blues - Volume 2*	Oct 1987
LP 291	Charly SUN CDX 20	*The Complete Million Dollar Quartet*	Nov 1987
LP 292	Premier PPD 2000	*Mess O' Blues Volumes 1 & 2*	Mar 1988
LP 293	Baktabak BAK 2086	*Elvis Presley Interview Picture Disc*	Apr 1988
LP 294	RCA PL 86985	*The Alternate Aloha*	May 1988
LP 295	HMV C88 1-2	*The Elvis Presley Sun Collection*	Sep 1988
LP 296	RCA NL 90252	*Moody Blue* (*re-issue*)	Oct 1988
LP 297	RCA CL 90249(3)	*Special Edition*	Oct 1988
LP 298	RCA PL 90250	*Stereo '57 (Essential Elvis Volume 2)*	Jan 1989
LP 299	Performance PFP 1009	*20 Golden Greats*	Mar 1989
LP 300	Performance PFP 2000	*Mess O' Blues - 24 Classic Tracks*	Mar 1989
LP 301	Ocean OCNWL 2024	*The Voice Of The King*	May 1989
LP 302	Ocean OCNWL 2031	*Elvis Live*	Aug 1989
LP 303	RCA NL 90359	*For LP Fans Only*	Sep 1989
LP 304	RCA NL 90360	*A Date With Elvis* (*re-issue*)	Sep 1989
LP 305	Magnum Force MFLP 074	*The Fifties Interviews*	Nov 1989
LP 306	RCA PL 90486	*Hits Like Never Before (Essential Elvis Vol. 3)*	Jul 1990
LP 307	Time-Life RRR-E04	*The Rock 'N' Roll Era Elvis Presley: 1956 - 1961*	Jul 1990
LP 308	RCA PL 82227	*The Great Performances*	Aug 1990
LP 309	RCA NL 90513	*For The Asking (The Lost Album)*	Nov 1990

LP 310	Reader's Digest V86002 VBI	*The Legend Lives On*	Nov 1990
LP 311	RCA NL 81936	*Elvis Sings The Wonderful World Of Christmas* (re-issue)	Nov 1990
LP 312	RCA NL 90300	*Elvis' Christmas Album* (re-issue)	Dec 1990
LP 313	RCA NL 90548	*From Elvis In Memphis* (re-issue)	Feb 1991
LP 314	RCA NL 90549	*On Stage - February, 1970* (re-issue)	Feb 1991
LP 315	RCA PL 90574(3)	*Collectors Gold*	Aug 1991
LP 316	RCA NL 83892	*Elvis In Person At The International Hotel Las Vegas, Nevada*	Oct 1991
LP 317	RCA PL 90642	*From The Heart*	Feb 1992
LP 318	RCA PL 90689(6)	*The King Of Rock 'N' Roll The Complete 50's Masters*	Jul 1992
LP 319	RCA 74321 15430 1	*From Nashville To Memphis The Essential 60's Masters 1*	Sep 1993
LP 320	RCA 74321 22871 1	*The Essential Collection*	Aug 1994
LP 321	RCA 07863 66817 1	*Elvis 56*	Apr 1996
LP 322	Stomper Time Records STEN 3	*The Louisiana Hayride/ Little Rock, Arkansas*	Oct 1997
LP 323	RCA Castle Music ELVIS 100	*Artist Of The Century*	Aug 1999
LP 324	RCA Castle Music ELVIS 100P	*Artist Of The Century* (re-issue)	Dec 1999
LP 325	RCA Simply Vinyl 07863 67735 1 SVLP 185	*Elvis Presley*	Mar 2000
LP 326	RCA Simply Vinyl 07863 67736 1 SVLP 212	*Elvis*	May 2000
LP 327	RCA Simply Vinyl 07863 67462 1 SVLP 231	*Elvis' Golden Records*	Jul 2000
LP 328	RCA Castle Music ELVIS 102	*"That's The Way It Is"*	Aug 2000
LP 329	RCA Simply Vinyl 07863 67463 1 SVLP 241	*50,000,000 Elvis Fans Can't Be Wrong Elvis' Gold Records - Volume 2*	Sep 2000
LP 330	RCA Simply Vinyl 07863 67464 1 SVLP 273	*Elvis' Golden Records - Vol. 3*	Nov 2000
LP 331	RCA Simply Vinyl 74321 81102 1 SVLP 296	*The 50 Greatest Hits*	Nov 2000
LP 332	RCA Castle Music ELVIS 104X	*Peace In The Valley The Complete Gospel Recordings*	Dec 2000
LP 333	RCA Castle Music ELVIS 104	*Peace In The Valley The Complete Gospel Recordings*	Jan 2001
LP 334	RCA Simply Vinyl 07863 67465 1 SVLP 342	*Elvis' Gold Records - Volume 4*	Jul 2001
LP 335	RCA Castle Music ELVIS 108	*Live In Las Vegas*	Aug 2001
LP 336	RCA Simply Vinyl 07863 67466 1 SVLP 346	*Elvis' Gold Records - Volume 5*	Sep 2001
LP 337	RCA Castle Music ELVIS 106	*G.I. Blues*	Oct 2001
LP 338	RCA Castle Music ELVIS 107	*Blue Hawaii*	Oct 2001
LP 339	RCA Castle Music ELVIS 109	*I'll Be Home For Christmas*	Nov 2001
LP 340	RCA Simply Vinyl S125010	*Elvis Presley* (re-issue)	Dec 2001
LP 341	RCA Simply Vinyl S125039	*Elvis* (re-issue)	Dec 2001
LP 342	RCA Castle Music ELVIS 110	*Loving You*	Jan 2002
LP 343	RCA Castle Music ELVIS 111	*Jailhouse Rock*	Jan 2002
LP 344	RCA Castle Music ELVIS 112	*King Creole*	Jan 2002
LP 345	RCA Castle Music ELVIS 113	*Tickle Me*	Jun 2002

The LP section of this book shows all the details of Elvis's albums in chronological order, rather than alphabetically, to enable you to follow the developments and changes that resulted. If, however, you do not know when a particular album was released, and you are unable to find it in the chronological section, then you can use this listing to determine its location in the chronological section, and turn to the page in question where the record is discussed in detail.

Where the same title was used more than once on an album in the period covered by this book, the listings place the albums in a chronological sequence, but reference to the catalogue number will clearly distinguish between releases.

Titles	Catalogue Number	Release Number
A Date With Elvis	RCA NL 90360	LP 304
Artist Of The Century	RCA/Castle Music ELVIS 100	LP 323
Artist Of The Century	RCA/Castle Music ELVIS 100P	LP 324
Collectors Gold	RCA PL 90574(3)	LP 315
Confidential...... Elvis	Arena ARAD 1008	LP 282
Blue Hawaii	RCA Castle Music ELVIS 107	LP 338
Elvis	RCA/Simply Vinyl 07863 67736 1 SVLP 212	LP 326
Elvis (re-issue)	RCA/Simply Vinyl S125039	LP 341
Elvis 56	RCA 07863 66817 1	LP 321
Elvis Forever	RCA NL 89004	LP 277
Elvis Forever - 96 Hits Of The King	RCA NL 89830(6)	LP 285
Elvis Live	Ocean OCNWL 2031	LP 302
Elvis In Person At The International Hotel Las Vegas, Nevada	RCA NL 83892	LP 316
Elvis Presley	RCA/Simply Vinyl 07863 67735 1 SVLP 185	LP 325
Elvis Presley	RCA/Simply Vinyl S125010	LP 340
Elvis Presley Interview Picture Disc	Baktabak BAK 2086	LP 293
Elvis Sings The Wonderful World Of Christmas	RCA NL 81936	LP 311
Elvis' Christmas Album	RCA NL 90300	LP 312
Elvis' Golden Records	RCA/Simply Vinyl 07863 67462 1 SVLP 231	LP 327
Elvis' Golden Records - Vol. 3	RCA/Simply Vinyl 07863 67464 1 SVLP 273	LP 330
Elvis' Gold Records - Volume 4	RCA/Simply Vinyl 07863 67465 1 SVLP 342	LP 334
Elvis' Gold Records - Volume 5	RCA/Simply Vinyl 07863 67466 1 SVLP 346	LP 336
Essential Elvis	RCA PL 89979	LP 280
50,000,000 Elvis Fans Can't Be Wrong Elvis' Gold Records - Volume 2	RCA/Simply Vinyl 07863 67463 1 SVLP 241	LP 329
For LP Fans Only	RCA NL 90359	LP 303
For The Asking (The Lost Album)	RCA NL 90513	LP 309
From Elvis In Memphis	RCA NL 90548	LP 313
From Nashville To Memphis The Essential 60's Masters 1	RCA 74321 15430 1	LP 319
From The Heart	RCA PL 90642	LP 317
G.I. Blues	RCA Castle Music ELVIS 106	LP 337
Girls! Girls! Girls!	Camden CDS 1221	LP 278
Hits Like Never Before (Essential Elvis Vol. 3)	RCA PL 90486	LP 306
I'll Be Home For Christmas	RCA Castle Music ELVIS 109	LP 339
In Hollywood	Premier PMP 1011	LP 288
Jailhouse Rock	RCA Castle Music ELVIS 111	LP 343
King Creole	RCA Castle Music ELVIS 112	LP 344
Kissin' Cousins	Camden CDS 1222	LP 279
Live In Las Vegas	RCA Castle Music ELVIS 108	LP 335
Loving You	RCA Castle Music ELVIS 110	LP 342
Mess O' Blues - Volume 1	Premier PMP 1012	LP 289

Mess O' Blues - Volume 2	Premier PMP 1013	**LP 290**
Mess O' Blues - Volumes 1 & 2	Premier PPD 2000	**LP 292**
Mess O' Blues - 24 Classic Tracks	Performance PFP 2000	**LP 300**
Moody Blue	RCA NL 90252	**LP 296**
On Stage - February, 1970	RCA NL 90549	**LP 314**
Peace In The Valley *The Complete Gospel Recordings*	RCA/Castle Music ELVIS 104X	**LP 332**
Peace In The Valley *The Complete Gospel Recordings*	RCA/Castle Music ELVIS 104	**LP 333**
Presley - The All Time Greatest Hits	RCA PL 90100(2)	**LP 287**
Special Edition	RCA CL 90249(3)	**LP 297**
Stereo '57 (Essential Elvis Volume 2)	RCA PL 90250	**LP 298**
"That's The Way It Is"	RCA/Castle Music ELVIS 102	**LP 328**
The Alternate Aloha	RCA PL 86985	**LP 294**
The Complete Million Dollar Quartet	Charly SUN CDX 20	**LP 291**
The Complete Sun Sessions	RCA PL 86414(2)	**LP 283**
The Elvis Presley Sun Collection	HMV C88 1-2	**LP 295**
The Elvis Tapes	Redwood RED 1	**LP 281**
The Essential Collection	RCA 74321 22871 1	**LP 320**
The Fifties Interviews	Magnum Force MFLP 074	**LP 305**
The 50 Greatest Hits	RCA/Simply Vinyl 74321 81102 1 SVLP 296	**LP 331**
The Great Performances	RCA PL 82227	**LP 308**
The King Of Rock 'N' Roll *The Complete 50's Masters*	RCA PL 90689(6)	**LP 318**
The Legend Lives On	Reader's Digest V86002 VBI	**LP 310**
The Louisiana Hayride/ *Little Rock, Arkansas*	Stomper Time Records STEN 3	**LP 322**
The Memphis Record	RCA PL 86221(2)	**LP 284**
The Rock Hits	Camden CDS 1215	**LP 276**
The Rock 'N' Roll Era *Elvis Presley: 1956 - 1961*	Time-Life RRR-E04	**LP 307**
The Voice Of The King	Ocean OCNWL 2024	**LP 301**
Tickle Me	RCA/Castle Music ELVIS 113	**LP 345**
Tribute To Elvis	Selected Marketing ANIV 10	**LP 286**
20 Golden Greats	Performance PFP 1009	**LP 299**

Sample Of Detail Included

As in ***Elvis UK 1956-86***, by choosing to discuss Elvis's UK LPs in chronological order, rather than alphabetically, we have been able to discuss any changes in label and sleeve design, along with the information they contain as, and when, they occurred. In addition, comparisons between consecutive releases are brought to your attention easily and in a more meaningful manner.

For each album we have included the following information.

LP 277 — The chronological number of release. This maintains the numbering system from ***Elvis UK 1956-86*** for the sake of continuity. This number immediately tells you how many Elvis albums have been released in the UK. (See the chronological listing for further details.)

RCA — The record label on which the album was released.

NL 89004 — The album's UK catalogue number.

Elvis Forever — The album's title.

Song Listing — The full and correct song titles as they ought to appear. Frequently the label (and sleeve) titles a song incorrectly. Where this occurs, the nature of the error is drawn to your attention in the text.

Writers — The song's composers. These are also the subject of many label errors. The correct writers are shown, irrespective of the labels' claim, and, as with song titles, errors are noted in the text.

Release Date — The month and year that each record was released in the UK.

Deletion Date — The month and year that each record was deleted in the UK. When the exact date is not known (usually in the case of non-BMG releases), this is noted.

Original Issue — Where an album is a re-issue of an earlier release, the month and year of the original issue is noted. A re-issue is defined as an album which contains the same track listing as a previous release. Previous re-issues are also noted.

Following the title block with the above features, each record is discussed in detail with any important or interesting information listed, including the song title and writing credit errors referred to above.

For each record we have given details of the known variations in label design, colour and layout, logo changes etc. Where these variations occur, we have placed them in the order in which they appeared.

To further assist identification, we have shown the year in which each variation appeared and indicated the actual mode (this is not necessarily the same as claims made on labels and sleeves).

In addition, we have given details of the sleeve variations for each release.

For further information on label and sleeve variations, see the notes below. These refer to RCA albums only. Releases by other companies are dealt with individually.

1 Label Colour

(A) German Black

We used the term German black labels in *Elvis UK 1956-86* to distinguish them from the earlier RCA black labels. German black labels were first used on albums in October 1983, when records pressed in Germany began to appear in the UK.

(B) Various

For some special releases - the *Collectors Gold*, PL 90574(3) (**LP 315**), boxed set, for example - different coloured labels were used. These were not part of BMG's corporate identity profile, but were used to co-ordinate with the sleeves as part of the overall presentation. Such examples are dealt with in the notes accompanying the release in question.

2 Type Of Logo

(A) Computer Style

This logo appeared printed down the left hand side of the label reading upwards from the bottom of the label. It was originally designed as 'computer' style print, and this is how we refer to it. This logo was first introduced in 1969 with RCA's orange label and was used consistently thereafter. It was the standard logo in use in 1986 and is, therefore, the starting point for variations in logo design.

(B) Round RCA logo at top of label

In December 1986 RCA released the album *Essential Elvis*, PL 89979 (**LP 280**), and used a label design which copied the original black label design from the 1950s. In doing so, they used a round RCA logo situated at the top of the label.

(C) Round RCA logo on left of label

A new label design first introduced in November 1990 when *Elvis Sings The Wonderful World Of Christmas*, NL 81936 (**LP 311**), was released, showed the round RCA logo on the left hand side of the label.

D) Various

As with label colour, special edition releases, such as *Collectors Gold*, PL 90574(3) (**LP 315**), different label designs have been used, and, consequently, different logo formats have appeared. Where this has occurred, all the relevant details are noted.

This book starts with an album issued in April 1986. Therefore, to provide continuity and, for the benefit of readers unfamiliar with our descriptions and terminology, we have included a photograph of the label of the last RCA album to be issued prior to this date - *Elvis' Christmas Album*, PL 85486 (*LP 275*), issued in October 1985. This will provide a starting point for identifying changes in design, layout, and features such as the type of logo used for all subsequent releases.

Album Deletions - March 1986

On 1 March 1986 a total of thirteen albums were deleted in a programme which concentrated on film soundtrack albums. These are listed below, in catalogue number order for ease of reference, along with their date of release and release number.

PL 80504	*The First Year*	Jan 1985	*LP 259*
NL 82558	*Harem Holiday*	Apr 1984	*LP 222*
NL 82559	*Frankie And Johnny*	Aug 1984	*LP 241*
NL 82560	*California Holiday*	Nov 1984	*LP 255*
NL 82564	*Double Trouble*	Sep 1984	*LP 244*
NL 82565	*Clambake*	Apr 1984	*LP 223*
NL 82568	*It Happened At The World's Fair*	Sep 1984	*LP 247*
NL 83338	*Girl Happy*	Sep 1984	*LP 248*
NL 84115	*Kissin' Cousins*	Sep 1984	*LP 249*
NL 89010	*Paradise, Hawaiian Style*	Apr 1984	*LP 215*
NL 89014	*Fun In Acapulco*	Nov 1984	*LP 257*
NL 89048	*Girls! Girls! Girls!*	Jun 1984	*LP 229*
NL 89049	*Roustabout*	Aug 1984	*LP 240*

It is worth pointing out the short life of ***The First Year***, PL 80504 (*LP 259*), which seems to suggest that sales were poor. Perhaps this was only to be expected as its contents - live recordings at the Eagles Hall in 1955, and Scotty Moore's narration of the first year with Elvis - had been available on bootleg and on the official Golden First Editions, KING 1, album released in November 1979 (*LP 118*). The full price tag, it must be said, cannot have helped sales either.

The rest of the deleted albums were all film soundtrack recordings, now out of vogue, and the majority of these were never to see release on vinyl again. Some film soundtrack albums (and we are discounting ***That's The Way It Is***, NL 84114 - *LP 224* - here) though continued to sell, as they always have done, and the following remained on catalogue until the nineties. These were:

NL 81515	*Loving You*	Apr 1984	*LP 210*
NL 83683	*Blue Hawaii*	Aug 1984	*LP 238*
NL 83733	*King Creole*	Apr 1984	*LP 212*
NL 83735	*G.I. Blues*	Jan 1984	*LP 206*

So far we have accounted for sixteen out of the total of seventeen film soundtrack albums released in the fifties and sixties. But what of ***Speedway***, NL 89012 (*LP 228*)? Sadly, we have been unable to confirm precisely when this album was deleted, although there are indications that it too was deleted in March 1986, making the total thirteen deleted film soundtrack LPs in that month. If that was indeed the case, then it would not tie in with the suggestion that twelve film soundtrack albums were to be released by Pickwick on

the Camden label, who, as it turned out, only released two such albums - ***Girls! Girls! Girls*** (**LP 278**) and ***Kissin' Cousins*** (**LP 279**). For further details on this, see the LP introduction and notes on Camden releases below. Most of the film soundtracks were to remain unavailable until late March 1993 when, as part of the restoration programme, the first batch of Double Feature CDs were issued.

Camden

In ***Elvis UK 1956-86,*** the LP section ended with the April 1986 Camden release ***The Rock Hits***, CDS 1215 (**LP 276**), which, to that point, had been the only release of any kind in 1986. Released during the final stages prior to the printing of ***Elvis UK 1956-86,*** the LP was not listed in either the chronological or alphabetical listings which were already typeset, though details of the record itself were included. Therefore, we thought it only sensible to reproduce the details again, with some additional text, as this volume clearly overlaps the earlier book.

Although we did not know this at the time, ***The Rock Hits*** turned out to be the last Elvis compilation album produced by Pickwick; nor were we aware that Pickwick intended to pull out of the market altogether to concentrate on other things. After the huge volume of material which appeared in the previous year, 1986 was a very sparse year for releases. The lack of any material - albums or singles - produced by RCA during 1986 clearly suggested that they had other things on their mind, and, as we have already discussed in the LP introduction, these had a direct impact on the amount and type of material being issued.

Up to September 1986 only one album, ***The Rock Hits*** (**LP 276**), had been released, not by RCA, but by Pickwick, who followed this with two further albums during September. These albums were a significant departure from the material with which Pickwick were normally associated, in that the records were re-issues of deleted RCA film soundtrack material, again an indication of the lack of planning apparent within RCA. At the time there was talk of Pickwick issuing as many as ten or twelve soundtrack albums - a sizeable proportion of RCA's original album material - although these albums never appeared.

In terms of the new partnership between RCA and Ariola, the lack of RCA material meant that it was left to Pickwick to show the first reference to this fact on the sleeve of ***The Rock Hits***. The notes on the back referred to the licensing arrangement between Pickwick and RCA/Ariola Records, whereas the label simply showed RCA Records. The two albums released in September detailed - on both sleeve and label - a modified reference: RCA/Ariola International.

Label Colour/Design

The colour of label used on all Camden albums - including the three included in this book - was a light blue, which we have called turquoise. All of the titles, track details, artist's name and publishing details were printed in black, with the name Camden running down the left hand side, printed in white along with the licensing details which covered four lines at the bottom of the label.

The three Camden albums included in this book all featured a similar layout of the track details and, typically, three of the song titles, writers and publishers were printed above the spindle hole, with the remainder below. Side two of ***Girls! Girls! Girls!***, CDS 1221 (**LP 278**), was an exception to this as four tracks were printed above the spindle hole because of the number of tracks involved, and the length of the song titles.

No recording mode was shown on the label and the earlier practice of showing the playing speed in a triangle at the bottom of the label had ceased to be shown. There was also a reference to the fact that the records were made in the UK.

Sleeves

Camden sleeves had a gloss finish and featured a bar code in the top right hand corner on the back of the sleeve. (To facilitate reading, notice how the bar code had to be printed in a white box on ***Kissin' Cousins*** (**LP 279**) because the back of the sleeve was coloured blue.) The catalogue number was also shown on the front of the sleeve.

LP 276	The Rock Hits
	Camden CDS 1215

Side 1

1   **Shake, Rattle And Roll** (Calhoun)
2   **Rip It Up** (Blackwell, Marascalco)
3   **Blue Suede Shoes** (Perkins)
4   **Ready Teddy** (Blackwell, Marascalco)
5   **Lawdy, Miss Clawdy** (Price)
6   **What'd I Say** (Charles)

Side 2

1   **Long Tall Sally** (Johnson, Blackwell, Penniman)
2   **(Let me be your) Teddy Bear** (Mann, Lowe)
3   **Jailhouse Rock** (Leiber, Stoller)
4   **C'mon Everybody** (Byers)
5   **Hi Heel Sneakers** (Higgenbotham)
6   **Guitar Man** (Hubbard)

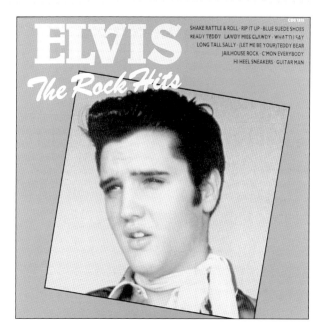

Released April 1986   Deleted end of 1988

Camden releases had, if nothing else, a certain mysterious quality, in that they turned up in the shops unannounced and often disappeared just as quickly and quietly. However, this album, released in April 1986, did have one claim to fame previously denied other Camden releases: it was the first Elvis UK release of any kind in 1986. Indeed, the last official release had been **Elvis' Christmas Album**, PL 85486 (*LP 275*), in October 1985. Some legal wrangles between RCA and the Elvis Presley Estate resulted in a veritable famine of releases after the welter of material issued between January and October 1985. Consequently, **The Rock Hits** - a modest release by any standards - found itself elevated to fame quite unexpectedly.

As the title implied, all the tracks were true rock 'n' roll songs; eight pre-army tracks; and four other tracks from the sixties. Also, four of the songs had been featured in films. All the pre-army tracks were in mono: tracks 1-5, side one; tracks 1-3, side two. The others, with the exception of **Hi Heel Sneakers**, were in stereo. However, no modes were indicated, either on the record label or the sleeve.

Only four of the publishing dates given were correct, the remainder being inaccurate and, moreover, inconsistent. For example, tracks 5 and 6 on side 2, which appeared back to back on a single (RCA 1688 - *S 62* -

in February 1968), were given different publishing dates. And, suggesting a recording first published date of 1977 for **What'd I Say**, was beyond comprehension.

Originally, we thought that this album was mastered in 1984 at the same time as another Camden release **The First Ten Years**, CDS 1213 (*LP 246*), but we now know for certain that **The Rock Hits** was actually mastered on 3 March 1986, just prior to its release in April.

As it turned out, this album proved to be the final Camden compilation album, although the company responsible - Pickwick - did issue two further albums: the deleted **Girls! Girls! Girls!** and **Kissin' Cousins**, the first time that film soundtrack albums had been treated in this way. For further information see the notes on *LPs 278* and *279*.

No printing date was given on the cover, which featured a blurred close-up shot of Elvis in his cowboy suit from **Loving You**, and a black and white publicity shot from **It Happened At The World's Fair** on the back of the sleeve. Both the sleeve and label stated **Shake Rattle & Roll**, omitted the comma after **Shake**, and used an ampersand instead of the word **And**. **Lawdy, Miss Clawdy** appeared without the comma. However, the best error was in the liner notes which read: 'Since Elvis' tragic death in July 1977......'

Label Variations

TURQUOISE LABEL

1   **1986 PRESSING: STEREO/MONO**
         3 up/3 up

Sleeve Variations

1   **Gloss**

US Only Release: Return Of The Rocker

In June 1986 the US division issued this release in LP (5600-1-R) and CD (5600-2-R), in effect making it a **Rocker** Volume 2. However, RCA in the UK elected not to release it. For interest though we have listed the tracks included.

King Of The Whole Wide World	*Little Sister*
(Marie's the name) His Latest Flame	*A Mess Of Blues*
Like A Baby	*I Want You With Me*
Stuck On You	*Return To Sender*
Make Me Know It	*Witchcraft*
I'm Comin' Home	*Follow That Dream*

Oddly though, three tracks were in mono: the previously unreleased extended version of **King Of The Whole Wide World**, **Little Sister** and **Follow That Dream**. Also, the introduction to **Make Me Know It** was spoiled by an electronic 'glitch', as it was on the first pressing of the UK CD **Elvis Is Back!**, ND 89013, released in March 1989.

LP 277   Elvis Forever
RCA 89004(2)

Side 1
1 **My Baby Left Me** (Crudup)
2 **Heartbreak Hotel** (Axton, Durden, Presley)
3 **Blue Suede Shoes** (Perkins)
4 **Hound Dog** (Leiber, Stoller)
5 **Love Me Tender** (Presley, Matson)
6 **Got A Lot O' Livin' To Do** (Schroeder, Weisman)
7 **(Let me be your) Teddy Bear** (Mann, Lowe)
8 **All Shook Up** (Blackwell, Presley)

Side 2
1 **Don't** (Leiber, Stoller)
2 **Hard Headed Woman** (DeMetrius)
3 **King Creole** (Leiber, Stoller)
4 **Jailhouse Rock** (Leiber, Stoller)
5 **A Big Hunk O' Love** (Schroeder, Wyche)
6 **I Got Stung** (Schroeder, Hill)
7 **One Night** (Bartholomew, King)
8 **Stuck On You** (Schroeder, McFarland)

Side 3
1 **Fever** (Davenport, Cooley)
2 **It's Now Or Never** (DiCapua, Schroeder, Gold)
3 **Are You Lonesome Tonight?** (Turk, Handman)
4 **Wooden Heart** (Wise, Weisman, Twomey, Kaempfert)
5 **Surrender** (DeCurtis, Pomus, Shuman)
6 **Wild In The Country** (Peretti, Creatore, Weiss)
7 **Rock-A-Hula Baby** (Wise, Weisman, Fuller)
8 **Can't Help Falling In Love** (Peretti, Creatore, Weiss)

Side 4
1 **Good Luck Charm** (Schroeder, Gold)
2 **Return To Sender** (Blackwell, Scott)
3 **(You're the) Devil In Disguise** (Giant, Baum, Kaye)
4 **Crying In The Chapel** (Glenn)
5 **Guitar Man** (Hubbard)
6 **In The Ghetto** (Davis)
7 **Suspicious Minds** (James)
8 **There Goes My Everything** (Frazier)

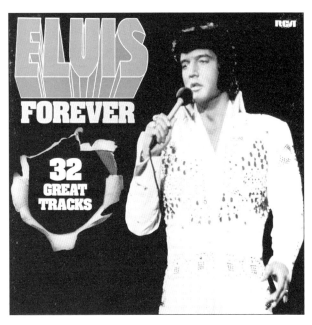

Released July 1986   Deleted November 1992

The **Elvis Forever** series had been initiated by the German division of RCA in 1983, and had run to four volumes by the end of 1986. Many of these albums had been imported into the UK and were widely distributed, but their exact status, right up to July 1986 when this album was released, was that they were imports and not UK issues.

The first three volumes were shown in the RCA catalogue of 1985, but volumes 2 and 3 were noted as not being available in the UK. Actually they were, but only as imports. However, in July 1986, RCA UK chose to issue the first volume in the series, **Elvis Forever**, NL 89004(2), as a UK album. The reason why RCA suddenly decided to make this move was quite simple: they were looking around for a good compilation album with a reasonable track selection to issue in the UK. The suggestion that the reason was closely related to the general lack of 'new' product available at the time may have been a consideration, but this seems unlikely. RCA, basically, thought there was a gap in the market, and this album was 'adopted' by the UK division to fill it. Some of you will think this a strange decision given the nature of the tracks which, it has to be said, bore a close resemblance to albums like **Elvis's 40 Greatest Hits**, PL 42691(2) (*LP 105*), and, of course, they were bound to - both were 'hits' compilations. It has to be remembered though that **Elvis's 40 Greatest Hits** was no longer available, although the two **20 Greatest Hits** packages, comprising the same tracks, were still on catalogue. Nevertheless, to issue an album which was designed to appeal to casual buyers clearly represented a good move, and it must have paid off, for the album remained on catalogue well into the nineties.

Closer inspection of the tracks in comparison to those featured on **Elvis's 40 Greatest Hits** revealed the true origins of **Elvis Forever**. Obviously it had fewer tracks, but the running order of those included was the same. For completeness, the eight songs included on **Elvis's 40 Greatest Hits**, but omitted from **Elvis Forever**, were:

Party

Old Shep

(Now and then there's) A Fool Such As I

I Need Your Love Tonight

(Marie's the name) His Latest Flame

There's Always Me

She's Not You

Don't Cry Daddy

However, whatever the reason was, the album attained UK issue status, a fact that may surprise, and annoy, many collectors who considered this an unnecessary purchase at the time. Granted, the UK price code - HH - was shown, but as we have pointed out many times, the use of price codes was so unreliable that the inclusion of this alone was no guarantee that the product was intended as a UK issue.

Throughout the mid-eighties RCA's German division seemed to be quite active, in that several new compilation albums were produced. Among these were albums like *The Complete Bonus Songs*, *Elvis In Germany*, *Elvis Sings Mort Shuman And Doc Pomus*, and many others, and some of these were 'imported' by RCA themselves through their own special import services. It was understandable, therefore, that the general public were unaware of changes in distribution and availability of certain product. A similar situation applied to dealers who, it has to be said, must also have been confused regarding the status of this and some of the other albums circulating at the time. To conclude: in the case of the *Elvis Forever* series only the first of these - this album - should have had a UK price tag, with the others attracting the higher, import price.

The album survived remarkably well, despite obvious competition, and wasn't deleted until 16 November 1992, but no CD version was issued in the UK, although imported copies were selling for a costly £24.

In terms of content, the track listing was a remarkably strong one, with the thirty-two tracks covering the period 1956-70. Later volumes failed to maintain this standard, and nor could they in terms of hits, suggesting that initially, at least, there had been no intention to run the series to four volumes. As mentioned earlier, RCA UK chose not to issue any further volumes, but a collection of the first three volumes, gathered together under the title *Elvis Forever - 96 Hits Of The King*, NL 89830(6) (**LP 285**), did appear as a UK release.

The original German *Elvis Forever* album, 26 28103 (a picture of which appeared in the 1985 RCA UK Elvis catalogue), was issued on the International label, as this album was. However, on the front of the cover, under the title, the words '32 Hits and the story of a King' were displayed. This turned out to be a series of photographs of album covers as issued in Germany. These were retained on the UK issue, but the wording on the front of the sleeve had been amended to read '32 Great Tracks'.

The back of the sleeve was taken up entirely by track details, along with the normal features like the bar and price codes, and the date the sleeve was printed was shown at the bottom - 7/86 - which was also the date of issue. The labels claimed that all the tracks were in stereo which, of course, they were not. In fact, there was a mixture of mono, stereo and electronic stereo. Apart from *Stuck On You* on LP 1, which was genuine stereo, all other tracks were in electronic stereo. On LP 2, all tracks except *Wild In The Country* and *Suspicious Minds* were in stereo. These two were in mono.

The catalogue number on the label was slightly different from other issues, in that the digits were smaller than the NL prefix. Even more oddly, there was a publication date of 1974 shown at the bottom of the label. However, as *Elvis Forever* appeared to be based on *Elvis's 40 Greatest* (*LP 73*), 1974 may have been a reference to the release date of the latter, which was issued in that year. As far as we are aware the *Elvis Forever* compilation did not appear until 1983.

While there were a number of errors, there was a high degree of consistency between the details on the label and those on the sleeve - both had the same errors!

In terms of 'classic' errors, listing *All Shook Up* as *I'm All Shook Up* must rank highly. However, on a more positive note - *Got A Lot O' Livin' To Do!* was correctly, and almost uniquely, shown with an exclamation mark (!). While on side 2, track 2, the writer of *Hard Headed Woman*, Claude DeMetrius, suffered the normal misspelling of his name - DeMetruis.

On side 3, track 2, *It's Now Or Never*, omitted the name DiCapua, and, similarly, DeCurtis was not shown on track 5, *Surrender*.

Side 4, track 3, omitted the brackets in *(You're the) Devil In Disguise*, and Jerry Reed's surname - Hubbard - was shown, correctly, for *Guitar Man*. Finally, the writer of track 6, *In The Ghetto*, was Scott Davis, and not two separate people - Scott, Davis.

Label Variations

GERMAN BLACK LABEL

1   1986 PRESSING: MONO/STEREO/
     ELECTRONIC STEREO
     BIEM above GEMA; both in separate boxes

Sleeve Variations

1   7/86

LP 278	*Girls! Girls! Girls!*
	Camden CDS 1221

Side 1

1 **Girls! Girls! Girls!** (Leiber, Stoller)
2 **I Don't Wanna Be Tied** (Giant, Baum, Kaye)
3 **Where Do You Come From** (Batchelor, Roberts)
4 **I Don't Want To** (Torre, Spielman)
5 **We'll Be Together** (O'Curran, Brooks)
6 **A Boy Like Me, A Girl Like You** (Tepper, Bennett)

Side 2

1 **Earth Boy** (Tepper, Bennett)
2 **Return To Sender** (Blackwell, Scott)
3 **Because Of Love** (Batchelor, Roberts)
4 **Thanks To The Rolling Sea** (Batchelor, Roberts)
5 **Song Of The Shrimp** (Tepper, Bennett)
6 **The Walls Have Ears** (Tepper, Bennett)
7 **We're Coming In Loaded** (Blackwell, Scott)

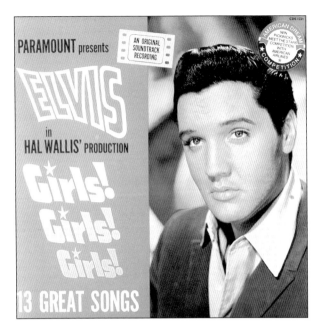

Released September 1986   Deleted end of 1988
Original Issue February 1963. RCA RD/SF 7534 (LP 18)
Previous Re-issue October 1977. RCA PL 42354 (LP 94)
Previous Re-issue August 1981. RCA International INTS 5107 (LP 158)
Previous Re-issue June 1984. RCA International NL 89048 (LP 229)

It was suggested that when RCA deleted many of the film soundtrack albums during the mid 1980s that they would be re-issued on the Camden label, which would have ensured an extended run in stores like Woolworths, and in supermarkets. Whatever the plans were, they were never realised, as only two of the deleted film soundtracks were released by Pickwick. These were *Girls! Girls! Girls!* and *Kissin' Cousins*, which RCA had deleted in September 1986, after two years of availability on the German black label. Incredibly, this was the fifth time that both these albums had been released in the UK.

Pickwick issued several albums in addition to the Elvis titles in the Autumn of 1986, and ran a promotional competition entitled 'American Dream - fly to the USA - meet the stars', the first prize being a trip to America with an opportunity to see Don Williams in person and in concert. A sticker appeared on the front of all these albums advertising the competition. Actually, the competition itself was quite unusual, in that the promotional leaflet contained twelve questions, one for each of the new album releases with the answer contained somewhere in the lyrics of one of the songs featured on the album in question. The question for *Girls! Girls! Girls!* was 'What hangs on the tree?', and for *Kissin' Cousins*, 'When you've got no one to call your own, its..?'. The answers can be found in the text for the next album, *Kissin' Cousins* (**LP 279**).

The artwork for the sleeve was largely the same as all the previous issues, but the colour tone on the front was a distinct improvement over the very dark NL 89048 (*LP 229*) German produced sleeve. The back of this sleeve had been tidied up and was actually the better for it, losing the adverts for other albums which had been included on the German release, as they simply had no relevance to Pickwick. Further slight adjustments to the left hand photograph made the picture complete.

There was one feature of this album which made it unique - certainly no other album has been treated in the same way in the UK. This was because Pickwick had a problem with the total playing time, as each side of the original album varied widely, being approximately 16 and 11 minutes respectively. Pickwick wanted the running time for sides 1 and 2 to be much more even, not for artistic reasons, but for the cassette version. To achieve this, the final song from side 1, *Earth Boy*, was moved to become the first song on side 2, producing a more evenly balanced running time. This decision proved to be unpopular with many people, including, we have to say, some of the people who

were responsible for its production. The principal objection being that the original concept had been altered, and that this was unacceptable. However, such a move provided fans and collectors with a highly desirable item, though many may have dismissed it as being just another re-issue. The album was mastered by Bob Jones in early August 1986, a month before its release, and it was pressed in the UK by CBS, as was *Kissin' Cousins*.

There were two song title errors on the sleeve, where *I Don't Wanna Be Tied* became the more anglicised *I Don't Want To Be Tied* and *We'll Be Together* was shown as *We'll Get Together*! Many of the song titles included words with the first letter in lower case, some of which had been copied from the previous albums, although some errors previously included had been corrected, with new ones introduced.

The label errors contained the same song title mistakes as the sleeve, and the co-author of *I Don't Want To*, Torre, had his name incorrectly spelt as Tarre. The writers of tracks 4 and 5, side 2, were reversed and were normally shown as Tepper, Bennett.

The contents on this LP were finally made available on CD in March 1993, when *Kid Galahad/Girls! Girls! Girls!*, 74321 13430 2, was issued as part of the Double Feature programme.

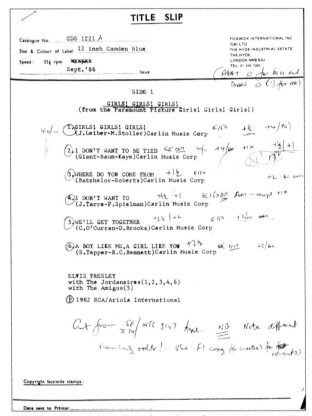

The title and track details for Girls! Girls! Girls! sent to the printer. The technical notes were made by Bob Jones. Note the label errors.

Label Variations

TURQUOISE LABEL
1   1986 PRESSING: STEREO
           3 up/3 up

Sleeve Variations

1   Gloss

LP 279 — Kissin' Cousins

Camden CDS 1222

Side 1

1   **Kissin' Cousins (No. 2)** (Giant, Baum, Kaye)
2   **Smokey Mountain Boy** (Rosenblatt, Millrose)
3   **There's Gold In The Mountains** (Giant, Baum, Kaye)
4   **One Boy, Two Little Girls** (Giant, Baum, Kaye)
5   **Catchin' On Fast** (Giant, Baum, Kaye)
6   **Tender Feeling** (Giant, Baum, Kaye)

Side 2

1   **Anyone (could fall in love with you)** (Benjamin, Marcus, DeJesus)
2   **Barefoot Ballad** (Fuller, Morris)
3   **Once Is Enough** (Tepper, Bennett)
4   **Kissin' Cousins** (Wise, Starr)
5   **Echoes Of Love** (Roberts, McMains)
6   **(It's a) Long Lonely Highway** (Pomus, Shuman)

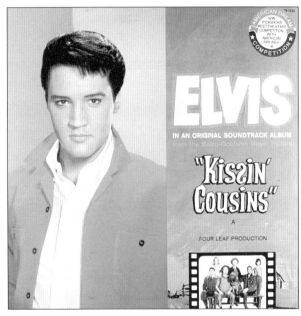

Released September 1986   Deleted end of 1988

Original Issue June 1964. RCA RD/SF 7645 (LP 22)
Previous Re-issue October 1977. RCA PL 42355 (LP 95)
Previous Re-issue August 1981. RCA International INTS 5108 (LP 159)
Previous Re-issue September 1984. RCA International NL 84115 (LP 249)

This turned out to be the final Elvis album produced by Pickwick for release on the Camden label, and less than two years later Pickwick pulled out of the market altogether after seventeen years. We have discussed the contribution made by Pickwick in a separate section to be found at the end of 1988.

Kissin' Cousins was released simultaneously with *Girls! Girls! Girls!*, appearing only two years after the RCA German black label version was released, and very soon after it was deleted. Bob Jones mastered this album on 6 August 1986, and, as with *Girls! Girls! Girls!*, it was pressed by CBS in the UK.

The front of the sleeve featured the same 'American Dream' competition sticker, as did all the other Pickwick albums of the period. This competition closed on 31 December 1986, so that albums bought after that date were unlikely to carry the sticker, although some inevitably did.

Interestingly, in the bottom right hand corner on the back of the sleeve, details of the printer and printing date (RWG681JU) could clearly be seen. This was not the date when this sleeve was printed, but the date of the RCA International INTS 5108 (*LP 159*) album released in August 1981. Obviously the artwork used for the INTS album was re-used, but this detail was not amended.

Incidentally, the answers to the competition questions were:

Girls! Girls! Girls! - *Dried fish* - **Thanks To The Rolling Sea**, *Kissin' Cousins* - **(It's a) Long Lonely Highway**.

Minor, but long standing errors from previous releases were perpetuated here, with *Kissin' Cousins (No. 2)* still being shown as *(Number 2)* on both label and sleeve, and the comma being omitted from *One Boy, Two Little Girls*.

This soundtrack was finally made available in June 1994 as part of the Double Feature CD programme, when it was combined with *Clambake* and *Stay Away, Joe*, 07863 66362 2.

Label Variations

TURQUOISE LABEL

1   1986 PRESSING: STEREO
    3 up/3 up

Sleeve Variations

1   Gloss

RCA New Label Design

RCA UK had issued two singles, **Jailhouse Rock** (*S 136*) and **(You're so square) Baby I Don't Care** (*S 138*), in the early part of 1983 which had featured a label design based on the original UK RCA releases of the 1950s. The next RCA album, **Essential Elvis**, PL 89989 (**LP 280**), issued in December 1986, took up this theme and used a label design which contained many of the old details long since abandoned. Of course, **Essential Elvis** was a UK inspired release, but it was good to see a UK idea being converted into actual product on an album pressed in Germany.

Of course, not all of the detail included on the label was authentic to the early label details - compilation dates and song times were never featured, and the label included some now standard features of German produced albums - but the overall feel was good, and it was particularly pleasing to see the old round RCA logo prominently displayed once again. As with the two singles referred to above, the material contained on the album was of the right period - 1956/7 - and the label did much to evoke the spirit of the times. Having said that, there were, of course, no releases on the RCA label in the UK until July 1957, after their marketing arrangement with HMV had expired (although HMV were allowed to release product for several months after this), but this is a minor point.

The round RCA logo was also used on the sleeve for the first time in many years.

Essential Elvis was also the first RCA LP to show details of the RCA/Ariola partnership.

The Essential Elvis Series

In November 1983 RCA released what was to be the last in their **Legendary Performer** series, **Elvis - A Legendary Performer, Vol. 4**, PL 84848 (*LP 204*). The previous three volumes had been issued in February 1974 (*LP 70*), January 1976 (*LP 87*), and January 1979 (*LP 106*).

The series spanned nine years and was held in great affection by fans in general, probably because it was the company's first, albeit distinctly modest, attempt to cater for the collectors' market. And certainly it is more likely that the series will be remembered for its excellent packaging, containing, for the first time, session details (in the form of actual tape logs), along with outtakes and the occasional unreleased song. The accompanying booklets were beautifully produced, quite frequently exceeding the album's contents in terms of interest, mainly because the audio material was so well-known.

Looking at the series in total, there is probably little argument that it actually improved as time went on, in that more outtakes or unreleased material were featured with each subsequent volume. In particular, volume 4 (*LP 204*), represented good value as it featured twelve previously unreleased tracks. Consequently, although there was no formal announcement as such, fans were generally disappointed when it became evident that there would be no more releases in the series. This seemed to coincide with Joan Deary's sudden departure from the company in the mid-1980s. And, of course, as might be expected, there were numerous rumours circulating among the fans during this time (always a problem when trying to discern fact from fiction). Deary had been implicitly involved in the series, so her leaving RCA signalled the end of the series which, anyway, some felt had outlived its usefulness. Indeed, much later, in early 1992, Roger Semon, still working for BMG at the time, acknowledged this to be the case.

Perhaps one of the key areas of difference of opinion centred around the apparently random nature of the tracks included on the **A Legendary Performer** series, which led to the ludicrous situation of tracks being repeated, albeit in the form of different versions. The series spanned many years and as many styles and, despite a notional theme **The Early Years**, or whatever, the series lacked any real coherence. On the other hand, many fans perceived these drawbacks as unimportant and, if nothing else, allowed the company an opportunity to release tracks recently 'discovered', without requiring them to wait pending a suitable release in terms of an appropriate period - as later **Essential Elvis** releases did. Perhaps a good example of this was the discovery of **Danny,** issued on **Elvis - A Legendary Performer Vol. 2**, CPL1 1349 (*LP 87*), in 1976. Had it not been for the series, the company may well have been thwarted as to how to market the song. Indeed, with the advent of the **Essential Elvis** series - not to mention other albums claiming to be 'complete' or 'definitive' - that still remains a problem for the company, as further unreleased material is uncovered. And, although less likely now, that still remains a possibility - indeed, for many, an optimistic hope! Obviously though, there is no clear right or wrong answer here: each person had his/her own point of view on this subject; and, if nothing else, whether people agreed with the company or not, the decision to end the series was made.

It was not for another three years that another series emerged which catered for collectors (although it had been planned and worked on for a couple of years previously), and which was to go on to be enormously popular with fans. This was, of course, the **Essential Elvis** series. However, there were some very important and significant differences from all the series which had gone before. What made the **Essential Elvis** series so radically different was that, unlike all other series - **Golden Records, A Legendary Performer** etc. - it originated in the UK under the auspices of Roger Semon (then of BMG UK), and Ernst Mikael Jorgensen (also of BMG - the Danish division - at the time and highly regarded co-author of the **A Life In Music** book). Both men had proved their worth and interest in Elvis in a variety of ways: Jorgensen through his work on researching Elvis's recording sessions, and Semon through his first class efforts in marketing Elvis product imaginatively in the UK, despite a lot of indifference on the part of others. Perhaps his first major success was the release of two EP Collections, in 1982, comprising no less that twenty-two EPs. Conceived, planned, mastered, produced and marketed in the UK, the first collection went on to sell something like 39,000 copies, while volume 2 still sold about 28,000 copies. This was nothing short of remarkable and, no doubt, set the scene for more ambitious projects which were not only received favourably, but which were a commercial success. To have achieved this fine balance did much to raise Semon's personal reputation among fans and the company, paving the way for other projects. It also boosted the UK division's credibility throughout the world.

Without doubt, part of the thinking behind the **Essential Elvis** series was not only to play the bootleggers at their own game, but to go on and better them in a way no-one had attempted to do before. In some ways it was a risk for, without doubt, the number of people buying Elvis product was falling rapidly; and while bootleggers thrived on low-run, high profit margin releases (paying no tax, royalties or whatever), major companies still had to consider the economics of what was to be a collectors' (and, therefore, almost by definition, limited) release. And, of course, since Elvis's death, bootleg releases had proliferated in a staggering way - some excellent, others simply awful. But what they had shown was that there was a significant appetite to be met by way of collectors wanting outtakes. Having given up on the idea of there being lots of unreleased songs, collectors had developed an almost obsessional interest in outtakes. Semon and co.'s idea was to attempt to meet this need by issuing quality product in all respects; proper research, good audio reproduction and high quality packaging. The other main consideration was to produce a package which had a discernible theme.

Now although Joan Deary left the company in 1985, apparently she proved to be an enormously useful ally to Semon both before she left and since. What is more, Gregg Geller was also very supportive about the projects the UK division were planning, and was a great help in assisting with tape searches, for example. In fact, it was really the start of a growing level of co-operation between the US and UK companies - all of which paid massive dividends in all sorts of ways, both for the company and fans.

Perhaps the biggest coup of all with this new series was that it was launched in the UK first, and not released in the US for an appreciable time after - over a year. In fact, it was because of its success and critical acclaim - many copies were imported into the US - that there was a pressure created and growing demand for it to be released in the US. All of this was tremendously good news for BMG in the UK and paved the way for subsequent volumes in the series. Incidentally, when interviewed in early 1992, both Roger Semon and Ernst Mikael Jorgensen expressed the view that this series had not only been artistically and commercially successful, but also that it would continue indefinitely.

Only the first three volumes of the *Essential Elvis* series have appeared in vinyl (and CD) form - 1986, 1989 and 1990 - subsequent volumes were released on CD, though often there was a considerable time gap between releases.

Sleeve Detail Change

The back of the sleeve of *Essential Elvis* (**LP 280**) showed, for the first time on an Elvis LP, a diagrammatical representation of the three formats - vinyl, cassette and compact disc - in which the album was issued. Previously only a cassette symbol had been used.

The back of the sleeve also showed the round RCA logo.

LP 280	Essential Elvis
	RCA PL89979

Side 1

1. **Love Me Tender** (Presley, Matson)
2. **Let Me** (Presley, Matson)
3. **Poor Boy** (Presley, Matson)
4. **We're Gonna Move** (Presley, Matson)
5. **Loving You** (Leiber, Stoller)
6. **Party** (Robinson)
7. **Hot Dog** (Leiber, Stoller)
8. **(Let me be your) Teddy Bear** (Mann, Lowe)
9. **Loving You** (Leiber, Stoller)
10. **Mean Woman Blues** (DeMetrius)
11. **Got A Lot O' Livin' To Do!** (Schroeder, Weisman)

Side 2

1. **Loving You** (Leiber, Stoller)
2. **Party** (Robinson)
3. **Lonesome Cowboy** (Tepper, Bennett)
4. **Jailhouse Rock** (Leiber, Stoller)
5. **Treat Me Nice** (Leiber, Stoller)
6. **Young And Beautiful** (Silver, Schroeder)
7. **Don't Leave Me Now** (Schroeder, Weisman)
8. **I Want To Be Free** (Leiber, Stoller)
9. **(You're so square) Baby I Don't Care** (Leiber, Stoller)
10. **Jailhouse Rock** (Leiber, Stoller)
11. **Got A Lot O' Livin' To Do!** (Schroeder, Weisman)
12. **Love Me Tender** (Presley, Matson)

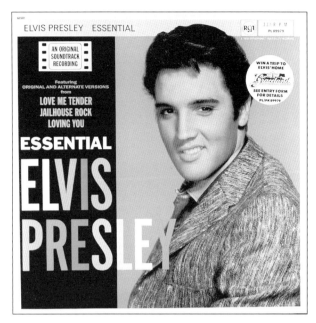

Released December 1986   Deleted December 1992

If one album had to be chosen to represent a turning point in the company's attitude towards Elvis Presley releases in the post-1977 era, surely it would be this one.

Its claim to fame can be explained thus. It was the first completely original UK album release to feature outtakes; it was a quality package (well packaged, well researched and beautifully mastered), which was aimed at the dual market of collectors and the general record buying public; and it was to set the tone of what was to follow for the next few years, whereby innovative, quality releases were compiled by Semon and Jorgensen culminating, in the summer of 1992, with the release of the highly acclaimed fifties' boxed set (**LP 318**).

Incredibly this release was the only full-price release of 1986. In fact, it had been delayed so frequently that it almost did not make 1986 at all. Indeed, the CD version was not available until February 1987. So what was the attraction of this release?

First of all - and there is no reason to suppose that this was anything other than accidental - the album's delay in appearing effectively hyped its release to new heights. The concept had been talked about and mulled over for some time. And certainly, part of the private thinking behind its release was to take on the bootleggers at their own game and produce an album of quality for collectors - only to do it better. The company had long been urged to do this, but thus far had not responded positively to such ideas.

The delays surrounding this release were ascribed to several problems: principally though, questions regarding royalty payments, and troubles with the sleeve design contributed to its delay. There was even a rumour - unconfirmed we have to say, that the sleeve had to be reprinted. Whatever the fine qualities of the album, its actual release was also fraught with difficulties. Some retailers obtained copies about 14 December - traditionally a very difficult time to issue product because of its closeness to Christmas - while others did not get their copies until January 1987. Some, indeed, knew nothing about it at all - a clear indication of the shortcomings of the communications and distribution systems at RCA. Consequently, despite healthy interest in the album - it was said that RCA were distributing 500 copies a day - it failed to chart, possibly because its sales were spread over a few months. Another reason may well have been because many fans - well in excess of 1,000 we are told - bought copies from the Elvis Record Centre, then based at Heanor, Derbyshire - an outlet which did not count when chart surveys were compiled. There was an irony here, in that the Fan Club, anxious of course to get Elvis into the charts had, on various occasions, encouraged buyers to buy from shops which made chart returns - the likes of Virgin, HMV etc. Incidentally, one of the adverts for the forthcoming album in *Elvis Monthly* claimed that the version of *Love Me Tender* was to be the one from the 9 September 1956 Ed Sullivan TV Show. It wasn't: the company issued the standard version. The same advert made no mention of *We're Gonna Move* being included either.

The album comprised all of the tracks from Elvis's first three films: *Love Me Tender* (1956), *Loving You* and *Jailhouse Rock* (1957), although a number of them were hitherto unreleased versions - at least officially, as several had been on bootlegs over the years. In fact the album did not include the standard versions of the following songs: *Loving You*, *Mean Woman Blues*, *Treat Me Nice*, *Jailhouse Rock*, or *Young And Beautiful*. However, the CD release did contain an extra four tracks: the regular undubbed version of *Treat Me Nice,* along with *Mean Woman Blues*, plus two extra *Loving You* out-takes (take 1 of the slow cut and take 8 of the fast version). This was at a time when CD buyers were being wooed by being offered extra tracks over the vinyl album version. Incidentally, the end title version of *Love Me Tender* was taken directly from a video cassette, as no master could be found.

Now, although Roger Semon had been responsible for a number of excellent releases in the early to mid 1980s - most notably the two EP Collection volumes - this was the first album to bear his name as producer. Equally, it was the first release to mention Ernst Mikael Jorgensen's name too - and it was to be the first of the many excellent collaborative efforts between the two. On this occasion Jorgensen and the English Fan Club President, Todd Slaughter, shared the honours on project research. The mastering of the set was handled by Boppin' Bob Jones at CTS Studios, Wembley on 18 November 1986. As usual, he signed his name in the run-out groove of the record, and added the cryptic and personal message 'Love and Real Rock'. Incidentally, the LP was pressed in the UK by CBS.

The vinyl album, featuring 23 tracks, ran for 50 minutes and was excellent value for money. The cover (a gatefold sleeve - the first on a new album from RCA since the release of *Elvis In Concert* - LP 100 - in 1977) was in beautiful colour. The actual photograph used on the front cover was the same one used on the cover of *Elvis' Golden Records*, RB 16069 (*LP 7*), except that this time it was a larger image and there was more of it. In the top left corner was the 'Mono' legend, while underneath it simply said 'ELVIS PRESLEY ESSENTIAL', although lower down it said 'ESSENTIAL ELVIS PRESLEY'. However, the spine of the sleeve (top and side) and the label correctly read *Essential Elvis*. Remember, rather like *Elvis' Golden Records* originally, there was no mention of volume - it was only when subsequent volumes were issued that the tag 'Volume One' was added - incorrectly, albeit understandably. The back featured four photographs, one of him in the famous 'cowboy' suit

from *Loving You* and three others, one each from the recording sessions concerned. The track listing noted which were 'alternate' or unreleased versions, adding take numbers where known. Generally, subsequent releases changed the references from 'alternate' to 'unreleased performances'. The sleeve notes were written by Roger Semon himself. One particular line is worthy of being quoted: 'It's the most exciting single album release since his untimely death in 1977'. We endorse that entirely - something which its success in the UK and Europe, and later in the USA, was to vindicate in ways which, at the time, few would have believed possible.

The inner gatefold featured more shots from the three films and included not only a synopsis of each one, but brief session notes (added by Ernst Mikael Jorgensen, we believe). There was, however, a slight error in the *Love Me Tender* session notes: Thorne Nogar's studio (Radio Recorders) was wrongly referred to as 'Radio Records'. Whatever though, the quality of the artwork, designed by 'Mainartery' of London and printed in Germany, was outstandingly good. Incidentally, attached to the front cover was a sticker advertising a competition to win a trip to Graceland. The entry forms required competitors to answer three questions and send in the their replies to the OEPFC of Great Britain. The question (and answers) were as follows:-

1. Graceland is situated on Highway 51 South Memphis. What is the name of this boulevard?

    Elvis Presley Boulevard.

2. Name Elvis' legendary manager.

    Colonel Tom Parker.

3. What do the letters RCA stand for?

    Radio Corporation of America.

For this release the company reverted to the old style RCA logo design (circa 1957-1960) with parallel lines above and below the centre hole. The 'Long Play' legend straddled either side of the RCA logo. However, necessarily, there were differences: for example, the use of BIEM and GEMA, LC 0316 and, of course, the reference to 'Mono', which did not need to appear on most fifties' albums, and certainly none of Elvis's. Sensibly (and usefully for collectors), the compilation date for the set was given as 1986, although the original publishing dates were also given - 1956 for the *Love Me Tender* material and 1957 for the others. Strictly speaking though, the unreleased versions (alternates, as they were then referred to) ought to have been dated 1986, the year of their release (and publication, of course). Other label errors are dealt with at the end of this section.

Without doubt the album - in beautiful mono sound - was a tremendous effort by all concerned. It is hard, and perhaps not entirely fair, to pinpoint precisely whose idea this was. No doubt the English Fan Club could take some credit for constantly badgering the company to produce releases along the lines of the most successful bootleg releases. However, all of this would have counted for naught if the company had not been inclined to listen. And here the role of Roger Semon had to be pivotal, for had he not been so well-placed, not to mention convinced of the project's viability and commercial potential, then there is little chance it would have ever materialised. Even so, at the time of its release, the company (Semon and Co.) included all of the relevant out-takes available to them. Subsequent tape vault searches revealed other material, but this had to be included in later works.

Indeed, this was a problem for the compilers: the knowledge that once having prepared an album dealing with a specific period there was always the chance that more material might turn up later, and thus pose the problem of how it could be best marketed. Some argued that this was a strength of the now defunct *A Legendary Performer* series: the facility for including odds and ends which appeared from time to time. A case in point would be the appearance of *Reconsider Baby*, the version from 4 December 1956, which ought to have been part of *The Million Dollar Quartet* album, but which turned up too late to be included - hence its appearance on the fifties' boxed set (**LP 318**). On the other hand, the approach taken by the producers of the ***Essential Elvis*** series was, we believe, correct in that it offered much more rationale and coherence than the ***A Legendary Performer*** series ever did.

Earlier we made much of the delay there was in this album materialising. But few, if any, were disappointed when it finally appeared. Perhaps as consumers/fans we do not have much interest in the whys and wherefores regarding why releases are delayed - for most the real interest lies, sensibly, in the grooves. On the other hand, some fans delight in the minutiae of background detail, deriving almost as much enjoyment from the tasty titbits as they do from listening to the releases. And so, for them, here is the intended original running order of the album to compare with what was actually released.

Side 1		Side 2	
1	*Party*	1	*Loving You*
2	*Loving You*	2	*Lonesome Cowboy*
3	*Treat Me Nice*	3	*Hot Dog*
4	*Don't Leave Me Now*	4	*Got A Lot O' Livin' To Do!*
5	*Young And Beautiful*	5	*Mean Woman Blues*
6	*Loving You*	6	*Loving You* (fast version: takes 4, 5)
7	*(Let me be your) Teddy Bear*	7	*I Want To Be Free*
8	*Jailhouse Rock*	8	*Jailhouse Rock* (take 5)
9	*Love Me Tender*	9	*(You're so square) Baby I Don't Care*
10	*Poor Boy*	10	*Treat Me Nice*
11	*We're Gonna Move*	11	*Loving You* (fast version: take 8)
12	*Let Me*	12	*Party*
		13	*Love Me Tender*

As you will see, the running order varied considerably from the final product. Of special note was the intention to include takes 4 and 5 of ***Loving You*** - fast version.

*The original compilation and running order for ***Essential Elvis***. Roger Semon's handwritten notes.*

To help promote this new album and the birth of a series - a promo LP (ESSEL 1) was produced, full details of which appear in the Promotional Records section. Broadly speaking, it was intended as a media statement: sign-posting what the company was doing with Presley product and giving it a high-profile to show the level of commitment the company held for Presley material. Conversely though, it did represent a gamble too: and had ***Essential Elvis*** failed, then who knows what might have happened. Thankfully though it did not fail. On the contrary, it was hugely popular with fans and

sold far better than expected.

As a measure of its success copies were exported to the US division, as it was not available there. In fact, it did not secure a US release until a year or so later, when it was sub-titled ***The First Movies***. But when it did, it was acclaimed there too, thus providing a big boost for the UK company and in particular for its producer, Roger Semon. Undoubtedly, the success of this release paved the way for later volumes; but more than that it set the tone and direction of Presley releases which followed, characterised as they were by care and quality. Moreover, it opened up a host of new opportunities for the producers, not least of which was the opportunity to engage in systematic and thorough searches in RCA vaults.

Evidence of the album's success lies in the fact that the original 20,000 copies sold quickly, and it had to be re-pressed. Interest and enthusiasm were expressed on a world-wide basis.

Only one previous album, ***Elvis' Christmas Album***, PL 85486 (*LP 275*), had used the price code SS. Its appearance on ***Essential Elvis*** was its final one to date.

Despite being a release of outstanding merit, there were still irritating label and sleeve errors, although we have to say that our own efforts in the past may have contributed to some of these. Up until the release of the fifties' boxed set in 1992 we considered the writers of the four songs from ***Love Me Tender*** should have been shown as Matson, Presley (the way they were shown on this album's labels). However, prompted by the fifties' set, we revised the order to Presley, Matson to correspond to BMG's thinking. Alas, this modification puts this label in error. We can, however, still point a finger at the omission of the words in brackets from ***(Let me be your) Teddy Bear*** and ***(You're so square) Baby I Don't Care***; the use of the small 'm' in DeMetrius and the missing exclamation mark in ***Got A Lot O' Livin' To Do!*** Note also that ***Mean Woman Blues*** was not an 'Alternative Film Version', but the standard version overdubbed. The sleeve errors were exactly the same.

The label gave no take numbers or indicated which were alternative versions. And while the publishing dates of 1956/57 were correct for standard versions, the outtakes ought to have read 1986. The term 'Unreleased Version' appeared on the back of the album cover, but as 'Alternate Versions' on the front.

One final point, the CD version (not issued until February 1987) featured four more tracks, two of them out-takes, as mentioned earlier: ***Loving You*** (two unreleased versions, one fast and one slow), and the standard versions of ***Mean Woman Blues*** and ***Treat Me Nice***. It also had a different catalogue number, PD 89980, in keeping with the directive from MCPS that where track differences occurred between vinyl and CD versions of albums, then they ought to have different catalogue numbers. As we discuss elsewhere, this directive was honoured more in the breach than in the observance, in that subsequently - no matter what differences there were - vinyl and CD albums carried the same number, the only difference occurring in the prefix - PL or PD.

Sadly, the vinyl format of ***Essential Elvis*** was deleted on 23 December 1992.

Significantly, during the early 1990s, the songs from ***Love Me Tender*** were discovered in binaural form - as recorded by 20th Century Fox in 1956. These versions were included on the CD ***Jailhouse Rock***, 07863 67453 2, released in April 1997, which also included other outtakes from the ***Jailhouse Rock*** movie. A vinyl version of this CD was issued by Castle in January 2002 (**LP 343**).

Finaly, as proof that the search for unreleased versions of songs was on-going, ***Silver Screen Stereo***, a 2001 CD release in the Collectors Label series, included binaural versions of ***Loving You*** (fast version, take 14), ***Jailhouse Rock*** (take 5), and ***Don't Leave Me Now*** (takes 16, 17 & 18). According to Ernst Jorgensen, the company had the masters of these tracks and others in binaural also.

Label Variations

GERMAN BLACK LABEL

1	1986 PRESSING: MONO
	Round RCA logo at top of label
	BIEM above GEMA - no boxes

Sleeve Variations

1   Gloss

Catalogue Numbers

Sharp-eyed readers may have noted that the catalogue numbers of the LP and CD release of ***Essential Elvis*** (**LP 280**) were different. The reason for this was simple. BMG management were directed by MCPS to observe the rule that if the track listing on an LP and CD version of a release differed, then they had to assign different catalogue numbers. Hence on ***Essential Elvis***, the numbers were as follows:

LP = PL 89979
CD = PD 89980

However, this ruling appeared to be ignored thereafter, as subsequent album releases - whether or not there were any differences - carried the same numbers, although the prefix continued to determine the type of release it was: PL = vinyl album; PD = compact disc; PK = music cassette. (The 'P' signified a full-priced release, whereas an 'N' indicated that it was a mid-priced release.)

The situation regarding singles was noticeably different from that of albums, however. All RCA singles released in both 7 and 12 inch formats, had (in the period covered by this book) been assigned different catalogue numbers, and all 12 inch releases included additional tracks to their 7 inch equivalents. This seemed to suggest two policies were being pursued, depending on the type of release, but, as we have pointed out in the Singles' Section, as far as sales and chart positions were concerned, the 7 and 12 inch versions were classed as the same single.

Track Sequencing

Since the advent of album releases bearing a number of out-takes, or 'alternates' as they were often referred to, collectors have noticed one or two things about track sequencing which have puzzled them.

One question frequently posed is why, for example, on an album containing three unreleased performances of the same song, the takes used did not run in numerical order i.e. takes 3, 7 and 12, in the order they were recorded? The answer is simple and, in a way, obvious: the producers of any artistic package have to give considerable thought as to how a product is assembled. In the case of a film, it involves sequencing scenes in the order in which they are most effective to maximise dramatic impact. Compiling a collection of recordings into an album requires similar skill too: how tracks are sequenced calls for judgement on how best to deliver a product, bearing in mind things such as pace, mood, audience response, and so on. So too with outtakes. A producer has to judge what is appropriate at what point in the album. A later, incomplete take of a song may well suit the mood of an album early in its track listing, whereas an earlier, complete take may sound better placed later in the running order. As with many other things, of course, it calls for the use of judgement and depends on what the producer is trying to 'say' in the album. So while we might not always understand why certain tracks are sequenced in the way they are, rest assured that a lot of thought goes into the process, even if the running order needs to be chronological for reasons of historical accuracy. Normally though, there is nothing random or unplanned about such things.

Perhaps on a final note we ought to remember the parallel made earlier with film making. When we watch a film, although we see a narrative unfold - often towards a climax of some sort - we have to remember that probably little, if any, of the story was filmed in sequence. It was probably filmed in short scenes and assembled later in the order which creates the best dramatic impact. Knowing that ought not to spoil our enjoyment of it as a piece of art; equally the same case can be argued for songs and how they are sequenced. The ***Essential Elvis*** series are the best examples of careful sequencing on Elvis albums. And for those of you who are particularly interested look at the provisional track listing for ***Essential Elvis***, PL 89979 (**LP 280**), and then compare it with the final running order.

Elvis - A Legendary Performer Vol.5

The series ***A Legendary Performer*** ended up featuring four volumes from its inception in January 1974 to its demise in November 1983. Their release dates were as follows:

Volume 1 (*LP 70*) February 1974   Volume 2 (*LP 87*) January 1976
Volume 3 (*LP 106*) January 1979   Volume 4 (*LP 204*) November 1983

As discussed elsewhere, by the mid-1980s it was obviously felt, by those whose opinions carried authority in RCA, that the series had outlived its usefulness. In effect, the ***Essential Elvis*** series succeeded ***A Legendary Performer*** as a vehicle for issuing collectors' material, albeit as a mainstream release. And while some may have challenged the philosophy behind the new policy, it remains a fact that late 1983 saw the end of another series.

However, since that time rumours abounded that there was another volume of ***A Legendary Performer*** scheduled for release at some undetermined date. We can now state with some degree of certainty - courtesy of Ernst Mikael Jorgensen who investigated this for us - that there was no such release planned. Of course, Joan Deary, whose project ***A Legendary Performer*** was, may have intended a future release, but as she left the company in 1985 on less than amicable terms, nothing further was ever heard of the idea. Incidentally, Joan Deary died on 2 October 1999.

LP 281 | The Elvis Tapes

Redwood Red 1

Side 1

1   Introduction And Press Conference, Vancouver 1957

Side 2

1   Press Conference And Description Of Pre-Concert
     Scene, Vancouver 1957

Released April 1987
Original Issue April 1977. Redwood RED 1 (LP 91)

We were undecided as to whether or not give this album a chronological release number and include full details. The reason for this was because it contradicted our own ruling of what constituted a new album. To all intents and purposes, this release appeared to be merely a new variation of the 1977 original issue, as it retained its original catalogue number, even though the sleeve had been re-worked. In the end we settled for describing it as a re-issue, despite the catalogue number. Note that the album was issued exactly ten years after the original.

Actually there was an earlier example of a record which used the same catalogue number as its original, thereby creating the precedent. That distinction belonged to the 1983 single *Jailhouse Rock* (S 136), which used the same RCA 1028 catalogue number found on the 1958 original (S 18).

Whilst the sleeve of this album had been slightly re-designed, the original sleeve notes were retained and were, therefore, hopelessly out of date. It seems pointless to produce an album, remaster it, modify the sleeve and then print something that opens with 'It's been twenty years since I first met Elvis Presley.' Bearing in mind that the interview and actual concert were recorded in 1957, would it have been asking too much just to amend the number of years referred to?

The only good thing really about the album was that it had been re-mastered in November 1986 (five months before it was issued) by Bob Jones, who, with his usual care and attention, had managed to remove some of the clicks (caused by hitting the microphone at the time of the recording), and improve the overall sound quality.

Although the label retained the Redwood Music logo, the album was actually marketed by Ace Records, who advertised many of their other products on the inner bag. The album cost approximately £4.50 when it was released. No CD format was available initially, but one was released in July 1991.

Label Variations

CREAM LABEL

1   1987 PRESSING: MONO

Sleeve Variations

1   Gloss

LP 282 Confidential...... Elvis

Arena ARAD 1008

Side 1

1 **WMPS, Memphis,** with Bob Neal, 31 August 1955
2 **San Antonio, Texas,** with Charlie Walker, 15 April 1956
3 **Warwick Hotel, New York,** with Robert Carlton Brown 24 March 1956

Side 2

1 **Warwick Hotel, New York,** with Robert Carlton Brown 24 March 1956 (continued)
2 **County Coliseum, Texas,** with Al Hickock, 14 October 1956
3 **Honolulu, Hawaii,** with Tom Moffett and Peter Noone, 18 August 1965

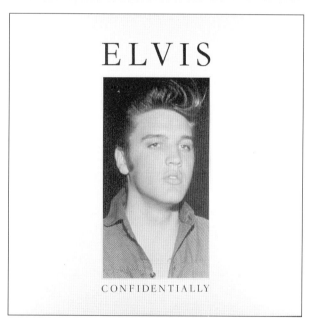

Released May 1987   Deleted: unknown

The material contained on this album first appeared on the Buttons label release, BUT 2, entitled *Elvis Answers Back* (*LP 145*). The interviews on that album were featured in a different order to those listed here. The same interviews were also used on a subsequent release *Personally Elvis*, AFESD 1032 (*LP 186*), which added instrumental versions of some of Elvis's songs, as well as vocals by other artists.

Actually, the record was well presented with a good shot of Elvis from 1956 framed in a white background. Inside the gatefold sleeve was a series of photographs from the 1950s, some of which were not often seen. All of the photographs were provided by Bill Williams and Gary Wallington, who with Williams, also wrote the sleeve notes. You may recall that both had written liner notes for some earlier Elvis albums, the Camden releases *Elvis Presley*, CDA 1201 (*LP 142*), and *The Wonderful World Of Elvis*, PDA 073 (*LP 143*).

The interview details on the back of the sleeve contained one glaring error, where it was claimed that the Peter Noone 'interview' took place on 20 March 1966, when the actual date was 18 August 1965. In fairness, the *Personally Elvis* album also got it wrong, claiming 29 April 1966. And there was also a printing error in the notes for interview two, side 1, where reference was made to a Milton Berle Show in 1950 when it should have been 1956.

The sleeve referred to the album title as being *Elvis Confidentially*, whilst the record label stated **Confidential......Elvis**, and added *Rare Elvis Interviews*. As you know we prefer to stick to the title as shown on the label, but the sub-title here seems more like a statement (and an inaccurate one), rather than an integral part of the title.

The label, falsely, claimed that the recordings were in stereo. They were not. No CD format version was produced. Finally, the album was priced at £4.99 when it was first released, and it was pressed by Spartan in the UK.

As with a number of other non-BMG albums, no firm deletion date is known for this release.

Label Variations

BLUE LABEL

1   **1987 PRESSING: MONO**

Sleeve Variations

1   **Gloss**

Price Codes

The release of **The Complete Sun Sessions**, PL 86414(2) (**LP 283**), in July 1987, saw the introduction of a new price code - DD - to UK albums. Despite being a double album, the price code failed to use the multiplier i.e. 2 x, which was normally a feature of such issues. However, **The Memphis Record**, PL 86221(2) (**LP 284**), released in August, did utilise the full code - 2 x DD.

Label Detail Change

The album **The Complete Sun Sessions**, PL 86414(2) (**LP 283**), released by RCA on 31 July 1987, continued to use the normal style RCA German black label design which had been in use, with minor modifications, from the early days of centralised production in 1983. It was, therefore, the standard design as featured on *Elvis Forever*, NL 89004 (**LP 277**), this being the first RCA album featured in this book and, therefore, our starting point. In December 1986 *Essential Elvis*, PL 89979 (**LP 280**), on the other hand, made use of a revised copy of the original RCA label but, as we have said, this was a deliberate move to achieve authenticity made by the company's UK division.

The label of **The Complete Sun Session** was the first to carry the reference to the fact that the material was now being published by BMG Music, but most of the other details were the same as previous albums. Two label features need to be drawn to your attention here, as they provided important clues to dating amendments to label details.

The first concerned the way in which the two Mechanical Rights organisations - BIEM and GEMA - were shown. On this label they were shown one above the other with a single box around them. The second feature is the record's playing speed - 33 (revolutions per minute) - shown in a triangle towards the right of the spindle hole. Now, these details were amended on the next RCA album, **The Memphis Record**, PL 86221(2) (**LP 284**), which, despite having a lower catalogue number, was released after **The Complete Sun Sessions**, although some stores received both albums at the same time.

On **The Memphis Record**, BIEM and GEMA were shown, not together in one box, but in smaller boxes of their own, and the 33 symbol had moved from the right to the bottom of the label. These, apparently innocent, changes became vital indicators in the identification of pressing dates, not so much for albums released in this period, but for earlier issues.

Despite including the label detail amendments described above, the labels of **The Memphis Record** did not refer to BMG Music but, instead, noted RCA/Ariola International, which (when considered along with the lower catalogue number) suggested that it was in preparation - and possibly production - before **The Complete Sun Sessions**. Reference to the details in the run-out grooves of the vinyl supports this, as **The Memphis Record** had a mastering date of June, compared to July for **The Complete Sun Sessions**.

We can, therefore, conclude from all of this that conversion to showing the Mechanical Rights Societies in two separate boxes dates from around July 1987, and any label with this feature was produced after this date.

A final point about the sleeves of these albums. Both were consistent, in that they showed the RCA 'computer' style logo; referred to copyright BMG Music; and, for the first time on an album sleeve, pointed out that RCA was 'A Bertelsmann Music Group Company'.

LP 283 — The Complete Sun Sessions
RCA PL 86414(2)

Side 1

1 **That's All Right** (Crudup)
2 **Blue Moon Of Kentucky** (Monroe)
3 **Good Rockin' Tonight** (Brown)
4 **I Don't Care If The Sun Don't Shine** (David)
5 **Milkcow Blues Boogie** (Arnold)
6 **You're A Heartbreaker** (Sallee)
7 **Baby Let's Play House** (Gunter)
8 **I'm Left, You're Right, She's Gone** (Kesler, Taylor)

Side 2

1 **Mystery Train** (Parker, Phillips)
2 **I Forgot To Remember To Forget** (Kesler, Feathers)
3 **I Love You Because** (Payne)
4 **Blue Moon** (Rodgers, Hart)
5 **Tomorrow Night** (Coslow, Grosz)
6 **I'll Never Let You Go (little darlin')** (Wakely)
7 **Just Because** (B. & J. Shelton, Robin)
8 **Trying To Get To You** (Singleton, McCoy)

Side 3

1 **Harbour Lights** (Kennedy, Williams)
2 **I Love You Because** (Payne)
3 **That's All Right** (Crudup)
4 **Blue Moon Of Kentucky** (Monroe)
5 **I Don't Care If The Sun Don't Shine** (David)
6 **I'm Left, You're Right, She's Gone** (Kesler, Taylor)
7 **I'll Never Let You Go (little darlin')** (Wakely)
8 **When It Rains, It Really Pours** (Emerson)

Side 4

1 **I Love You Because** (Payne)
2 **I Love You Because** (Payne)
3 **I Love You Because** (Payne)
4 **I'm Left, You're Right, She's Gone** (Kesler, Taylor)
5 **I'm Left, You're Right, She's Gone** (Kesler, Taylor)
6 **I'm Left, You're Right, She's Gone** (Kesler, Taylor)
7 **I'm Left, You're Right, She's Gone** (Kesler, Taylor)
8 **I'm Left, You're Right, She's Gone** (Kesler, Taylor)
9 **I'm Left, You're Right, She's Gone** (Kesler, Taylor)

Released July 1987   Deleted December 1992

While Elvis was at Sun Records i.e. between July 1954 and November 1955 when he signed for RCA Victor, he recorded a mere 18 tracks that are known of. In fact, Sam Phillips only released ten of these tracks on five single releases in that time. The pairings were as follows:

That's All Right/Blue Moon Of Kentucky
Good Rockin' Tonight/I Don't Care If The Sun Don't Shine
Milkcow Blues Boogie/You're A Heartbreaker
I'm Left, You're Right, She's Gone/Baby Let's Play House
I Forgot To Remember To Forget/Mystery Train

The rest were eventually issued by RCA between 1956-1983. The link piece following this release discusses all of Elvis's Sun recordings in more detail. There was no Sun LP of Elvis material during his time at the company, nor was there when Elvis signed for RCA. Previously issued and unissued Sun tracks appeared on RCA albums alongside RCA recordings - indeed for many years some fans were not sure which was which. In fact, it was not until July 1975 that RCA in the UK, compiled an album devoted to Elvis's Sun material, **The Elvis Presley Sun Collection** on Starcall HY 1001 (*LP 80*). This album, modified slightly to include 'new' finds such as **Harbour Lights**, was re-released on a number of occasions (*LPs 108, 201* and **295**). Incredibly, however, it was not until 1987, to tie in with the tenth anniversary of Elvis's death, that a US inspired collection of Sun material was commissioned. Using the somewhat contentious title *The Complete Sun Sessions* (in that as doubts remain about what was, or was not, cut at Sun, it seemed foolish to make such an assertion) the album set out to offer fans all the known Sun masters, plus a number of outtakes, some previously unissued, others not.

Another Sun track, *Tomorrow Night*, first issued in an overdubbed form in 1965 on *Elvis For Everyone*, RD/SF 7752 (*LP 26*), was issued in its undubbed (and then thought to be original) form on *Reconsider Baby*, PL 85418 (*LP 271*), in May 1985. However, it was not until the release of *The King Of Rock 'N' Roll The Complete 50's Masters*, PL 90689(6), in July 1992 (**LP 318**), that the original Sun recording was issued as it was cut. In brief, the 1985 version had been edited by Rick Rowe and bits of the song left out and re-jigged. We can only suppose that the version on the fifties' set was the original.

Also included was the previously issued outtake of *That's All Right*, which had first appeared on *A Golden Celebration*, PL 85172(6) (*LP 251*), in October 1984, along with *Harbour Lights, I Love You Because*, the slow *Blue Moon Of Kentucky*, false starts on *I Don't Care If The Sun Don't Shine*, the slow version of *I'm Left, You're Right, She's Gone* (which had also been called *My Baby's Gone*), *I'll Never Let You Go (little darlin')*, and *When It Rains, It Really Pours*, first issued in November 1983 on *Elvis - A Legendary Performer Vol. 4*, PL 84848 (*LP 204*).

Collectors were catered for on side 4 of the double album release, in that it featured outtakes of two songs: takes 3, 4 and 5 of *I Love You Because*, and takes 7, 8, 10, 11, 12 and 13 of *I'm Left You're Right, She's Gone (My Baby's Gone)*. However, there were a couple of problems.

First of all side 3, 'The Outtakes', included take 1 of *I Love You Because* - albeit a false start, which was previously unissued. Strictly speaking, it ought to have been on side 4, along with the other previously unissued material, although its natural place was on side 3 as a lead in to take 2. More problematical though was the situation regarding *I'm Left, You're Right, She's Gone (My Baby's Gone)*. The use of the alternative title was to make it easier to discriminate between the standard released version - the up-tempo country song - and the slower, bluesier version. Now, although track six quoted take 9 (which it probably was), the previously issued version, available for years on innumerable bootlegs, then finally made generally available on *A Golden Celebration* (*LP 251*) in October 1984, was actually take 11, included on side 4 and quoted as being previously unreleased.

However, if this seems confusing, the situation regarding the CD issue of this album went even further. Apart from featuring fewer outtakes, those compiling the CD made a major blunder. Track 18, listed as take 2 of *I Love You Because*, was, in fact, take 3 which was repeated on track 25! So, CD buyers were, in a sense, cheated further as they only obtained two outtakes of *I Love You Because* (takes 3 and 5), and only three outtakes of *I'm Left, You're Right, She's Gone (My Baby's Gone)* (takes 7, 9 and 12). Take 11 was not issued on CD until it was included as part of *The King Of Rock 'N' Roll The Complete 50's Masters* (**LP 318**). This still meant, of course, that takes 8, 10 and 13, were not available on CD.

The terminology used was also somewhat confusing. *Harbour Lights* and *When It Rains, It Really Pours* were not, strictly speaking, outtakes. Although not made available for many years, they were, in a sense, master recordings, as no previous master had been issued. And as it became clear in 1992 with the release of the fifties set, *Tomorrow Night* was not really the master take.

The sequencing of the album was interesting also, for the first ten tracks represented the five Sun single couplings. The rest were issued at various points later. (For more information on this see the link piece following this release.)

The albums came in a gatefold sleeve featuring various early photographs of Elvis with key personnel at the time. All the shots were tinted. Gregg Geller supplied a Sun sessions abstract, including the inaccurate reference to take 9 of *I'm Left, You're Right, She's Gone* being previously issued. There was also a quote from Sam Phillips on the back cover, and Peter Guralnick provided extensive notes on Elvis's time at Sun Records. The album, which cost £7.99, also came with a beautiful colour poster of Elvis from 1956, although this was not included in all of the albums.

Each of the labels displayed a grievous error: all stated Stereo! And, although the sound quality of album one (mastered by Rick Rowe and Jack Adelman) was a point of controversy for many fans, (basically they did not like what had been done to the tracks - some sounding too bassy or too echoey) the sound quality on sides 3 and 4 was acceptable to most.

Perhaps the worst label error was the crediting of *That's All Right* on side 1 to J. Kennedy and H. Williams, the writers of *Harbour Lights*. A comma was incorrectly included after *Baby* in *Baby Let's Play House*, on both label and sleeve. Also, somewhat oddly, track 8 on side 1, *I'm Left, You're Right, She's Gone* wrongly added *My Baby's Gone*, yet omitted it in all other label references where it was appropriate!

Incidentally this was the last Presley project to feature Gregg Geller as A+R Director. In the UK this album was released on 31 July 1987, not August as was often claimed, although the CD version was released in August. To be fair though, most stores received copies of this album and *The Memphis Record* at the same time during August which is why, presumably, both are credited with an August release date. What is certain is that both *The Complete Sun Sessions* and *The Memphis Record* shared the same deletion date - 23 December 1992.

The CD version of this album did, as mentioned previously, include fewer outtakes. As a result, it was re-titled *The Sun Sessions CD*, although it still bore the same catalogue number PD 86414. Note that the sleeve of the vinyl album displayed the CD symbol, but no catalogue number was shown. The release of an outtake of *Blue Moon* in 1992 on the fifties' set (**LP 318**), and another on the *Platinum A Life In Music* CD, 07863 67469 2, in July 1997, heightened the absurdity of using the term 'Complete' for the vinyl album.

Label Variations

GERMAN BLACK LABEL
1   1987 PRESSING: MONO
BIEM above GEMA in a single box

2 **1987 PRESSING: MONO**
BIEM above GEMA in separate boxes

Sleeve Variations

1   Gloss

The Sun Recordings

Decades on from when Elvis Presley first made commercial recordings at Sam Phillips' Sun Records in 706 Union Avenue, Memphis, Tennessee, there are still unresolved issues surrounding the sessions. The main one, of course, centres around what else Elvis did, or did not, record while working for Sam.

Several things make the likelihood of complete clarification highly unlikely:

1. Sam Phillips kept the minimum of paperwork at that time, so session information is quite sparse.

2. No-one is completely sure just what was handed over to RCA in late 1955 when they bought Elvis's contract; RCA's notes are also incomplete.

3. Neither Sam nor RCA's logging system for what was on which tape was at all efficient - hence 'finds' - usually unexpected - many years on.

4. RCA's policy - not unique to them, of course - of disposing of or erasing unwanted or apparently redundant session tapes - hence the lack of outtakes for the critical 1954-1958 period. Despite exhaustive tape vault searches by the likes of Roger Semon and Ernst Mikael Jorgensen in the late 1980s and early 1990s, few were actually located; and most of those which did turn up were included on the definitive '50s masters boxed set.

5. A number of key people who may have been able to elucidate on the issues are no longer alive; those who have survived have forgotten much or, alternatively, have confused and sometimes contradictory memories.

Therefore, with grateful acknowledgement to the compilers of *The King Of Rock 'N' Roll The Complete 50's Masters* (**LP 318**), we would like to remind you of the Sun recordings known so far and explain when each track first appeared in the UK and where. This, in fact, supercedes the information printed on page 462 of *Elvis UK 1956-86*. The list below details the track information in the running order of the album *The Complete Sun Sessions* (**LP 283**) and does actually deviate at times from the actual order of being recorded or released.

	Recording Date	First Appearance In The UK
That's All Right	5/6 July 1954	October 1956 *Rock 'N' Roll* (*LP 1*) HMV CLP 1093
Blue Moon Of Kentucky	5/6 July 1954	September 1957 *Good Rockin' Tonight* (*EP 3*) HMV 7EG 8256
Good Rockin' Tonight	Sept 1954	September 1957 *Good Rockin' Tonight* (*EP 3*) HMV 7EG 8256
I Don't Care If The Sun Don't Shine	Sept 1954	November 1956 (*S 5*) HMV POP 272
Milkcow Blues Boogie	Nov/Dec 1954	September 1957 *Good Rockin' Tonight* (*EP 3*) HMV 7EG 8256
You're A Heartbreaker	Nov/Dec 1954	October 1958 *Elvis' Golden Records* (*LP 7*) RCA RB 16069
Baby Let's Play House	Feb 1955	March 1957 (*S 9*) HMV POP 305
I'm Left, You're Right, She's Gone	March 1955	October 1956 *Rock 'N' Roll* (*LP 1*) HMV CLP 1093
Mystery Train	11 July 1955	October 1956 *Rock 'N' Roll* (*LP 1*) HMV CLP 1093
I Forgot To Remember To Forget	11 July 1955	February 1957 (*S 8*) HMV 7MC 42 *

*This was an export single also on sale in the UK. Its first UK album appearance was in October 1958 on RB 16069, *Elvis' Golden Records* (*LP 7*).

I Love You Because	5/6 July 1954	October 1958 *Elvis' Golden Records* (*LP 7*) RCA RB 16069
Blue Moon	19 Aug 1954	November 1956 (*S 5*) HMV POP 272
Tomorrow Night (undubbed) **	10 Sept 1954	May 1985 *Reconsider Baby* (*LP 271*) RCA PL 85418

** An overdubbed version first appeared in the UK in November 1965 on *Elvis For Everyone*, RD/SF 7752 (*LP 26*). What is now thought to be the original version appeared in July 1992 on *The King Of Rock 'N' Roll The Complete 50's Masters* (**LP 318**). Aural checks revealed that the version included in *The Complete Sun Sessions* (**LP 283**) did not correspond with the later version - which implied that the '1985' version had been edited by Rick Rowe.

I'll Never Let You Go (little darlin')	10 Sept 1954	October 1958 *Elvis' Golden Records* (*LP 7*) RCA RB 16069
Just Because	Sept 1954	September 1957 *Good Rockin' Tonight* (*EP 3*) HMV 7EG 8256
Trying To Get To You	11 July 1955	October 1956 *Rock 'N' Roll* (*LP 1*) HMV CLP 1093

Harbour Lights	5/6 July 1954	January 1976 **Elvis - A Legendary** **Performer Vol. 2** (*LP 87*) RCA CPL1 1349
When It Rains, It *Really Pours*	Nov 1955	November 1983 **Elvis - A Legendary** **Performer Vol.4** (*LP 204*) RCA PL 84848

Outtakes/Alternatives

I Love You Because (take 2)	February 1974 **Elvis - A Legendary** **Performer Vol. 1** (*LP 70*) RCA CPL1 0341
I Love You Because (takes 1, 3, 4 and 5)	July 1987 **The Complete Sun Sessions** (**LP 283**) PL 86414(2)
That's All Right	October 1984 **A Golden Celebration** (*LP 251*) RCA PL 85172(6)
Blue Moon Of Kentucky	October 1984 **A Golden Celebration** (*LP 251*) RCA PL 85172(6)
I Don't Care If The Sun Don't Shine	October 1984 **A Golden Celebration** (*LP 251*) RCA PL 85172(6)
I'm Left, You're Right, She's Gone *(My Baby's Gone)* (take 11)	October 1984 **A Golden Celebration** (*LP 251*) RCA PL 85172(6)
I'll Never Let You Go *(little darlin')*	October 1984 **A Golden Celebration** (*LP 251*) RCA PL 85172(6)
I'm Left, You're Right, She's Gone (takes 7, 8, 9, 10, 12 and 13)	July 1987 **The Complete Sun Sessions** (**LP 283**) RCA PL 86414(2)
Blue Moon	July 1992 **The King Of Rock 'N' Roll** **The Complete 50's Masters** (**LP 318**) RCA PL 90689(6)
Blue Moon (unknown take)	**Platinum A Life In Music** CD July 1997 07863 67469 2
Blue Moon (unknown take and two false starts)	**Sunrise** CD February 1999 07863 67675 2

Two other, non-commercial, recordings, made by Elvis at Memphis Recording Service were released in 1990 and 1992 respectively. *My Happiness* was included on **The Great Performances** album, PL 82227 (**LP 308**), while Elvis's first known recording of **That's When Your Heartaches Begin** (the other side of *My Happiness*) was first issued in July 1992 on **The King Of Rock 'N' Roll The Complete 50's Masters**, PL 90689(6) (**LP 318**). Both were believed to have been recorded in the summer of 1953.

Then in July 1997, **I'll Never Stand In Your Way**, thought to have been recorded in January 1954, was released on the CD **Platinum A Life In Music**, 07863 67469 2. The other side, **It Won't Be The Same Without You**, was finally issued on the **Sunrise** double CD, 07863 67675 2, in February 1999, forty five years after it had been

cut for private purposes at the Memphis Recording Service - better known to everyone as the home of Sun Records. Incidentally, the release also included some previously unreleased live recordings from the same era: **That's All Right**, **Money Honey**, **Tweedle Dee**, **I Don't Care If The Sun Don't Shine**, along with another alternative take of **Blue Moon**, and a live version of a previously unreleased song, **Hearts Of Stone**.

LP 284	**The Memphis Record**
	RCA PL 86221(2)

Side 1

1 **Stranger In My Own Home Town** (Mayfield)
2 **Power Of My Love** (Giant, Baum, Kaye)
3 **Only The Strong Survive** (Gamble, Huff, Butler)
4 **Any Day Now** (Hilliard, Bacharach)
5 **Suspicious Minds** (James)

Side 2

1 **Long Black Limousine** (Stovall, George)
2 **Wearin' That Loved On Look** (Frazier, Owens)
3 **I'll Hold You In My Heart (till I can hold you in my arms)** (Arnold, Horton, Dilbeck)
4 **After Loving You** (Miller, Lantz)
5 **Rubberneckin'** (Jones, Warren)
6 **I'm Movin' On** (Snow)

Side 3

1 **Gentle On My Mind** (Hartford)
2 **True Love Travels On A Gravel Road** (Owens, Frazier)
3 **It Keeps Right On A-Hurtin'** (Tillotson)
4 **You'll Think Of Me** (Shuman)
5 **Mama Liked The Roses** (Christopher)
6 **Don't Cry Daddy** (Davis)

Side 4

1 **In The Ghetto** (Davis)
2 **The Fair's Moving On** (Fletcher, Flett)
3 **Inherit The Wind** (Rabbitt)
4 **Kentucky Rain** (Rabbit, Heard)
5 **Without Love (there is nothing)** (Small)
6 **Who Am I?** (Goodman)

Released August 1987   **Deleted December 1992**

Not surprisingly, two particular periods of time in Elvis's recording career inspired close public attention and critical acclaim: his time at Sun Records in Memphis, between July 1954 and November 1955, and, secondly, his marathon sessions held at Chip Moman's American Sound Studios, also located in Memphis, during January and February 1969. For many, they represented Elvis Presley at his best.

Once again to coincide with the proposed celebrations and expected media attention on the occasion of the tenth anniversary of his death, RCA in the USA, marketed a series of albums to promote their artist fully. Two albums were devoted to presenting hits packages, another claimed to present the definitive Sun collection, while the other collection, *The Memphis Record*, aimed to present a large chunk of the material Presley recorded at American in early 1969.

It is known that Elvis recorded 32 tracks during the two sessions, which spawned several single successes and two long-playing albums: *From Elvis In Memphis* (*LP 38*), and *Back In Memphis*, which was originally issued in the UK as a companion volume to *In Person* under the title *From Memphis To Vegas From Vegas To Memphis* (*LP 39*).

The Memphis Record featured 23 tracks (including the twelve which comprised *From Elvis In Memphis*), although the following songs had not appeared on either of the original albums referred to above:

Suspicious Minds

Don't Cry Daddy

Rubberneckin'

Mama Liked The Roses

Kentucky Rain

Who Am I?

This, of course, meant that several tracks were omitted from the new collection. They were:

Hey Jude

I'll Be There (if ever you want me)

If I'm A Fool (for loving you)

This Is The Story

A Little Bit Of Green

Do You Know Who I Am

And The Grass Won't Pay No Mind

From A Jack To A King

My Little Friend

As had become common by now there was a CD version of this release; and although there were no track differences or additions (indeed the CD ran for 72.09 - supposedly very close to what was thought to be the maximum running time for a CD at that time), this was the first time any of the Memphis material (as a session, that is) had appeared on compact disc. Its appearance though fuelled a couple of criticisms: a) why, as the company had tried to do with the Sun period, all of the tracks were not issued on one package; and b) why so many tracks had been remixed when there seemed to be no obvious problems with the original mixes. In fact, a couple of songs in particular featured at least partly different vocal tracks: *Inherit The Wind*, *I'm Movin' On*, *Wearin' That Loved On Look*, as well as an abridged version of *Suspicious Minds* (3.24), although this was the correct length of the original studio cut, the single version having had the ending spliced on to make it longer when it was issued as a single.

At the time of its release none of the nine tracks omitted from the album was available in the UK. (However, in January 1999, all of the Memphis 1969 recordings were included on a double CD entitled *Suspicious Minds*, 07863 67677 2.)

When it became apparent that the two US 'hits' albums would not be granted a UK release (following the rumours that Roger Semon had been working on a more comprehensive package), hopes were raised that he would similarly amend the Memphis album to include the other songs. How true this rumour was, and how far the idea was considered, is not really known. Consequently, *The Memphis Record* was marketed in its US form in the UK and the rest of the world. Perhaps on the value-for-money theme, it is worth remembering that *Presley - The All Time Greatest Hits* (**LP 287**) which boasted 45 tracks, sold for the same price (£7.99) as *The Memphis Record*, which featured only 23. Certainly of the three albums marketed almost simultaneously, *The Memphis Record* was the least appealing in terms of value, especially as *Presley - The All Time Greatest Hits* did so well sales-wise, a situation which continued well into the nineties.

As with the two other releases at the time - *The Complete Sun Sessions* (**LP 283**) and *Presley - The All Time Greatest Hits* (**LP 287**) - *The Memphis Record* also came in a gatefold sleeve. Elvis events were set in the context of world events on the black and white cover which used a newspaper format. The liner notes were by Peter Guralnick who also compiled the notes on *The Complete Sun Sessions* (**LP 283**) album. The sleeve also listed the session musicians used - in itself a very rare feature. Guralnick's extensive notes dealt with Elvis's sessions at American Sound in detail, giving lots of background information.

Of the 23 tracks featured, nine had been used as singles, either as A or B sides.

In The Ghetto b/w *Any Day Now* (*S 68*).

The Fair's Moving On - B side of *Clean Up Your Own Backyard* (*S 69*).

Suspicious Minds b/w *You'll Think Of Me* (*S 70*).

Don't Cry Daddy b/w *Rubberneckin'* (*S 71*).

Kentucky Rain (*S 72*).

Mama Liked The Roses - B side of *The Wonder Of You* (*S 73*).

Strangely, all of the tracks were given a publishing date of 1987, the year the album was released, and not when the songs were first published. The errors concerning song titles and writers' names were few, and mainly of a minor nature. *Only The Strong Survive* was one of those songs where the order in which the names of the writers concerned presented us with some problems in the past. We now believe that the order shown here - Gamble, Huff, Butler - to be correct and we amended the index accordingly. RCA seemed to have similar difficulties with *Any Day Now*: they listed Bacharach, Hilliard on the sleeve and Hilliard, Bacharach on the label. We believe the latter to be correct.

A spelling mistake occurred with the surname of one of the writers of *I'll Hold You In My Heart (till I can hold you in my arms)*, where Dilbeck was spelt Dilback on the label, but it was spelt correctly on the sleeve. Also, the order in which the writers' names appeared should be Arnold, Horton, Dilbeck, not Dilbeck, Horton, Arnold.

On side 4, both label and sleeve incorrectly changed the title of **The Fair's Moving On** to read **The Fair Is Moving On**.

The album was deleted, along with a number of others, on 23 December 1992. To the surprise of many fans, the album was re-issued on CD only (74321 18754 2) as a mid-line release in February 1994.

In April 1999, BMG released a double CD entitled **Suspicious Minds** (07863 67677 2) which included all of the above master recordings, as well as all the other tracks cut at the sessions. In addition though, CD 2 included previously unreleased performances of the following:

After Loving You
Without Love
I'm Movin' On (alternative mix/vocal)
It Keeps Right On A Hurtin'
True Love Travels On A Gravel Road
Power Of My Love
You'll Think Of Me
Kentucky Rain

Additionally, two other previously issued outtakes of **Suspicious Minds** and **In The Ghetto** (as featured on the CD **Platinum A Life In Music**, 07863 67469 2) were included, along with a snatch of **Poor Man's Gold**. Finally, a number of other previously unreleased performances, along with undubbed master takes of some tracks were issued in 2001 on **Memphis Sessions**, a CD only Collector's Label album.

Label Variations

GERMAN BLACK LABEL

1   1987 PRESSING: STEREO
     BIEM above GEMA in separate boxes

Sleeve Variations

1   Gloss

Record 1
Side 1

1   **My Baby Left Me** (Crudup)
2   **Heartbreak Hotel** (Axton, Durden, Presley)
3   **Blue Suede Shoes** (Perkins)
4   **Hound Dog** (Leiber, Stoller)
5   **Love Me Tender** (Presley, Matson)
6   **Got A Lot O' Livin' To Do!** (Schroeder, Weisman)
7   **(Let me be your) Teddy Bear** (Mann, Lowe)
8   **All Shook Up** (Blackwell, Presley)

Side 2

1   **Don't** (Leiber, Stoller)
2   **Hard Headed Woman** (DeMetrius)
3   **King Creole** (Leiber, Stoller)
4   **Jailhouse Rock** (Leiber, Stoller)
5   **A Big Hunk O' Love** (Schroeder, Wyche)
6   **I Got Stung** (Schroeder, Hill)
7   **One Night** (Bartholomew, King)
8   **Stuck On You** (Schroeder, McFarland)

Record 2
Side 1

1   **Fever** (Davenport, Cooley)
2   **It's Now Or Never** (DiCapua, Schroeder, Gold)
3   **Are You Lonesome Tonight?** (Turk, Handman)
4   **Wooden Heart** (Wise, Weisman, Twomey, Kaempfert)
5   **Surrender** (DeCurtis, Pomus, Shuman)
6   **Wild In The Country** (Peretti, Creatore, Weiss)
7   **Rock-A-Hula Baby** (Wise, Weisman, Fuller)
8   **Can't Help Falling In Love** (Peretti, Creatore, Weiss)

Side 2

1   **Good Luck Charm** (Schroeder, Gold)
2   **Return To Sender** (Blackwell, Scott)
3   **(You're the) Devil In Disguise** (Giant, Baum, Kaye)
4   **Crying In The Chapel** (Glenn)
5   **Guitar Man** (Hubbard)
6   **In The Ghetto** (Davis)
7   **Suspicious Minds** (James)
8   **There Goes My Everything** (Frazier)

Record 3
Side 1

1   **Don't Be Cruel** (Blackwell, Presley)
2   **I Want You, I Need You, I Love You** (Mysels, Kosloff)
3   **Too Much** (Rosenburg, Weinman)
4   **Loving You** (Leiber, Stoller)
5   **Treat Me Nice** (Leiber, Stoller)
6   **I Beg Of You** (McCoy, Owens)
7   **Ain't That Loving You Baby** (Otis, Hunter)
8   **Wear My Ring Around Your Neck** (Carroll, Moody)

Side 2

1. **Such A Night** (Chase)
2. **A Mess Of Blues** (Pomus, Shuman)
3. **I Gotta Know** (Evans, Williams)
4. **Kiss Me Quick** (Pomus, Shuman)
5. **Little Sister** (Pomus, Shuman)
6. **No More** (Robertson, Blair)
7. **I Feel So Bad** (Willis)
8. **King Of The Whole Wide World** (Batchelor, Roberts)
9. **(Such an) Easy Question** (Blackwell, Scott)

Record 4

Side 1

1. **Bossa Nova Baby** (Leiber, Stoller)
2. **Mexico** (Tepper, Bennett)
3. **Witchcraft** (Bartholomew, King)
4. **What'd I Say** (Charles)
5. **Kissin' Cousins** (Wise, Starr)
6. **Viva Las Vegas** (Pomus, Shuman)
7. **Ask Me** (Modugno, Giant, Baum, Kaye)
8. **It Hurts Me** (Byers, Daniels)

Side 2

1. **I've Lost You** (Howard, Blaikley)
2. **I Just Can't Help Believin'** (Mann, Weil)
3. **Love Letters** (Young, Heyman)
4. **You Don't Have To Say You Love Me** (Pallavicini, Donaggio, Wickham, Napier-Bell)
5. **The Wonder Of You** (Knight)
6. **Burning Love** (Linde)
7. **My Way** (Thibault, Francois, Revaux, Anka)

Record 5

Side 1

1. **Blue Moon** (Rodgers, Hart)
2. **Money Honey** (Stone)
3. **I Got A Woman** (Charles)
4. **Tutti Frutti** (LaBostrie, Penniman)
5. **Long Tall Sally** (Johnson, Blackwell, Penniman)
6. **Blueberry Hill** (Lewis, Stock, Rose)
7. **Mean Woman Blues** (DeMetrius)
8. **Your Cheatin' Heart** (Williams)

Side 2

1. **Dixieland Rock** (Schroeder, Frank)
2. **(Now and then there's) A Fool Such As I** (Trader)
3. **Lover Doll** (Wayne, Silver)
4. **Doncha' Think It's Time** (Otis, Dixon)
5. **Make Me Know It** (Blackwell)
6. **Fame And Fortune** (Wise, Weisman)
7. **The Girl Of My Best Friend** (Ross, Bobrick)
8. **Lonely Man** (Benjamin, Marcus)

Record 6

Side 1

1. **Blue Hawaii** (Robin, Rainger)
2. **(Marie's the name) His Latest Flame** (Pomus, Shuman)
3. **Aloha-oe** (Arr. and adapted Presley)
4. **Anything That's Part Of You** (Robertson)
5. **Night Rider** (Pomus, Shuman)
6. **Suspicion** (Pomus, Shuman)
7. **She's Not You** (Pomus, Leiber, Stoller)
8. **Santa Lucia** (DiCapua)

Side 2

1. **(It's a) Long Lonely Highway** (Pomus, Shuman)
2. **Please Don't Drag That String Around** (Blackwell, Scott)
3. **Memphis, Tennessee** (Berry)
4. **Little Egypt** (Leiber, Stoller)
5. **Do The Clam** (Wayne, Weisman, Fuller)
6. **Indescribably Blue** (Glenn)
7. **Gentle On My Mind** (Hartford)
8. **Any Day Now** (Hilliard, Bacharach)

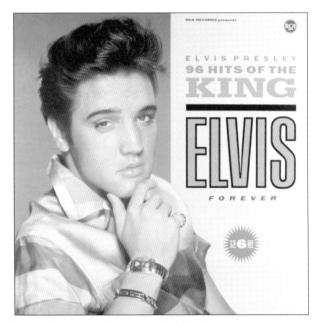

Released August 1987   Deleted March 1993

In December 1986 RCA Germany issued a 6 LP (and cassette) boxed set as a limited edition of 20,000 copies (each one individually numbered), under the title ***Elvis Forever - 96 Hits Of The King***. The set comprised the first three volumes of their ***Elvis Forever*** series, but what made this particular compilation unique was that the box front featured a 3-dimensional full colour illustration of Elvis. Copies of the set appeared in selected stores in the UK as imports, and ***Elvis Monthly*** advertised it for almost £46 plus postage. This was, therefore, an expensive item, but a popular one nevertheless, and one which is still sought after by collectors, although copies rarely turn up on the second-hand market.

As with many of the other RCA Germany albums produced in the mid-eighties, this was not a UK issue, but an import. RCA UK had adopted the first ***Elvis Forever*** volume for issue in the UK in July 1986 (**LP 277**) when they were looking for suitable compilation material for release, but the second, third and fourth volumes (the latter being the final release in the series, also issued in Germany in December 1986), failed to secure UK status, as the market for this type of release contracted, in favour of more collectors' orientated albums.

However, in 1987, when RCA prepared to saturate the market with a host of releases such as ***The Complete Sun Sessions*** (**LP 283**), ***The***

Memphis Record (**LP 284**) and, of course, *Presley - The All Time Greatest Hits* (**LP 287**), part of their marketing strategy was to issue a 'mail order only' set designed to appeal to the casual record buyer who did not regularly visit record stores, and who, consequently may not have been aware of, or indeed wished to purchase, the regular releases. Not surprisingly, *Presley - The All Time Greatest Hits* (**LP 287**) had universal appeal which, through TV advertising, went on to out-sell the other two releases many times over. But despite the wide-spread advertising, there would be some potential customers who would either not see the TV promotion, or would not wish (or be able) to visit record stores. The idea of a mail order only release was a good one, in that it enabled a new audience to be reached at relatively low cost and RCA knew, of course, that fans and collectors would also wish to buy this kind of product.

Producing a six album set was a major undertaking, even allowing for the fact that this was a combination of three separate double albums. Confining it to chart material - hits - rendered the project even more difficult. A prolonged series of 'hits' packages was bound to grow weaker as the series progressed and the hits were used up, and even by the third volume the producers were experiencing difficulties in collecting the required 32 tracks, and so were turning their attention to EPs and LPs for their material. The fourth volume (not represented here) was, therefore, the weakest of the series, and a weak compilation when compared to the original volume. This suggested (like other series in the past), that there had been no intention originally of running to four volumes. If there had been, the strongest material would not have been used up so quickly, but would, instead, have been utilised more carefully. Presumably the decision to extend the series was based on the success of the earlier volumes.

Taking the package as a whole revealed some interesting statistics: all the UK number one hits were included, with the exception of *Way Down* from 1977. Remember though, that this album was produced prior to the programme of joint co-operation between BMG and the Estate, when releasing material from 1973 onwards was somewhat restricted. The bulk of the number one hits were concentrated on records 1 and 2 (the original *Elvis Forever*), and appeared mainly in a chronological sequence. Record 4 *Elvis Forever Vol. 2* featured only one chart topping single - *The Wonder Of You*, while records 5 and 6 (*Elvis Forever Vol. 3*) contained *(Now and then there's) A Fool Such As I*, *(Marie's the name) His Latest Flame* and *She's Not You*. In the script for *Elvis Forever*, NL 89004 (**LP 277**), we pointed out that the album was, in fact, derived from the UK issue *Elvis's 40 Greatest Hits* (*LP 73*), a package which dated back to October 1974. Eight tracks were, however, omitted when *Elvis Forever* was released, three of which were number one hits (listed above) now found on records 5 and 6, accounting for the lack of chronology.

The same kind of statistics applied to the rest of the material. Albums 1 and 2 had only one LP track, *Fever*, and two B sides, one of which (*Got A Lot O' Livin' To Do!*) was a UK hit in its own right, while all the remaining 27 tracks (including double A sides) were UK A sides. The number of A sides on albums 3 and 4 was down to 17, with only 6 appearing on the final two albums, which featured mainly LP tracks.

The cream coloured box featured the same publicity still photograph (showing Elvis with his natural hair colouring) which had been used inside the gatefold sleeve of *Personally Elvis*, AFESD 1032 (*LP 186*), in March 1982. The album title was also shown, along with the round RCA logo. The back of the box listed the tracks, showed a bar code and UK price code of 4 x DM, and featured a grainy black and white image of Elvis from late 1960.

Inside was a single sheet which listed the tracks and indicated when a particular song was taken from a film. Vocal accompaniment credits were also provided. The records themselves (all standard German black label albums), were in plain white paper sleeves.

Apart from *Stuck On You* on LP 1, which was in stereo, all other tracks were in electronic stereo. On LP 2 all tracks except *Wild In The Country* and *Suspicious Minds* were in stereo. These two were in mono, despite the existence of stereo versions.

On LP 3, side 1, all these fifties' tracks were in mono, while on side 2 all tracks apart from *Little Sister* and *King Of The Whole Wide World* were in stereo. Both the latter tracks were in mono.

On LP 4, *Bossa Nova Baby*, *Kissin' Cousins* and *Viva Las Vegas* were in mono (stereo versions existed), while all other tracks were in stereo. *I've Lost You* was the live stereo version. Up to that point a stereo version of the studio cut had not been released. *Love Letters* was the 1970 recording of the track.

As regards LP 5, once again all the fifties' tracks (i.e. everything apart from *Make Me Know It*, *Fame And Fortune*, *The Girl Of My Best Friend* and *Lonely Man* which were in proper stereo) were presented here in electronic stereo. All tracks on album 6 were in stereo.

In terms of errors, there were many, typifying the sloppy attitude that was all too often found on this kind of release. The writers were only shown on the label, so all references to writers' names refer to that source.

Record 1

The back of the box omitted the exclamation mark at the end of *Got A Lot O' Livin' To Do!*. Co-writer Lowe was missing from *(Let me be your) Teddy Bear*. Only the label showed *All Shook Up* - the insert and the back of the box referred to the song as *I'm All Shook Up*.

Record 2

The label omitted the question mark at the end of *Are You Lonesome Tonight?* The co-writer of *Wild In The Country*, Hugo Peretti, had his surname spelt Parettie (yet it was spelt correctly on the same label under *Can't Help Falling In Love*). None of the references to *(You're the) Devil In Disguise* were correct. The insert and back of the box omitted the brackets altogether, while the label included them around *(You're)* only. The name Scott was incorrectly added to that of Davis on *In The Ghetto*.

Record 3

The back of the box correctly listed *Don't Be Cruel*, while the insert and label referred to *Don't Be Cruel (to a heart that's true)*. The co-writer of *I Want You, I Need You, I Love You*, Kosloff, was shown as Koslof, but two n's were added to Weinman, co-writer of *Too Much*. The co-writer of *I Beg Of You*, McCoy, had his name spelt McCay. *(La Paloma)* was unnecessarily added to *No More*.

Record 4

Modugno normally preceded Giant, Baum, Kaye on *Ask Me*. The writers of *Love Letters* should have been Young, Heyman - not the other way around. The writers of *You Don't Have To Say You Love Me* were in the wrong order, and Thibault was not included with the other writers of *My Way*.

Record 5

The writers of *Long Tall Sally* were in the wrong order. The back of the box omitted the words in brackets in *(Now and then there's) A Fool Such As I*, though all other references were correct. No apostrophe was shown after *Doncha'* in *Doncha' Think It's Time*.

Record 6

The words in brackets were omitted from *(Marie's the name) His Latest Flame* on the back of the box only. The label mis-spelled *Aloha-oe*, reading *Aloha-De*, and there was no reference to DiCapua on *Santa Lucia*, which referred to the song as being 'Traditional/Arr. Presley'. The label omitted the comma in *Memphis, Tennessee*.

Label Variations

GERMAN BLACK LABEL

1 1987 PRESSING: STEREO/MONO
Computer Style logo
BIEM above GEMA in separate boxes

Box Variations

1 Gloss

LP 286 — Tribute To Elvis

Selected Marketing ANIV 10

Side 1

1 **Heartbreak Hotel** (Axton, Durden, Presley)
2 **I Want You, I Need You, I Love You** (Mysels, Kosloff)
3 **Hound Dog** (Leiber, Stoller)
4 **Don't Be Cruel** (Blackwell, Presley)
5 **Love Me Tender** (Presley, Matson)
6 **Love Me** (Leiber, Stoller)
7 **Too Much** (Rosenberg, Weinman)
8 **All Shook Up** (Blackwell, Presley)
9 **(Let me be your) Teddy Bear** (Mann, Lowe)
10 **Jailhouse Rock** (Leiber, Stoller)

Side 2

1 **Don't** (Leiber, Stoller)
2 **I Beg Of You** (McCoy, Owens)
3 **Wear My Ring Around Your Neck** (Carroll, Moody)
4 **Hard Headed Woman** (DeMetrius)
5 **One Night** (Bartholomew, King)
6 **I Got Stung** (Schroeder, Hill)
7 **(Now and then there's) A Fool Such As I** (Trader)
8 **I Need Your Love Tonight** (Wayne, Reichner)
9 **A Big Hunk O' Love** (Schroeder, Wyche)

Side 3

1 **Stuck On You** (Schroeder, McFarland)
2 **It's Now Or Never** (DiCapua, Schroeder, Gold)
3 **Are You Lonesome Tonight?** (Turk, Handman)
4 **Surrender** (DeCurtis, Pomus, Shuman)
5 **I Feel So Bad** (Willis)
6 **Little Sister** (Pomus, Shuman)
7 **(Marie's the name) His Latest Flame** (Pomus, Shuman)
8 **Can't Help Falling In Love** (Peretti, Creatore, Weiss)
9 **Good Luck Charm** (Schroeder, Gold)
10 **She's Not You** (Pomus, Leiber, Stoller)

Side 4

1 **Return To Sender** (Blackwell, Scott)
2 **(You're the) Devil In Disguise** (Giant, Baum, Kaye)
3 **Bossa Nova Baby** (Leiber, Stoller)
4 **Crying In The Chapel** (Glenn)
5 **In The Ghetto** (Davis)
6 **Suspicious Minds** (James)
7 **Don't Cry Daddy** (Davis)
8 **The Wonder Of You** (Knight)
9 **Burning Love** (Linde)

Released August 1987

This double album picture disc set was produced by Selected Marketing (a company based in Newbury, Berkshire) under licence from RCA. The company promoted the album extensively and it was advertised widely in the Sunday newspaper colour supplements. The advertisement claimed that all of the tracks were 'Top Ten Hits', although a note in smaller print clarified this, saying that this was based on information supplied by Billboard, indicating that these were American top ten hits which, of course, they were. Not only that though, this album was identical to the US album **The Top Ten Hits** which was widely distributed in the UK at the time, as was **The Number One Hits**, which contained much of the same material, but which was an eighteen track single album. The advert also claimed that this was the first time a picture disc had been used for Elvis records! We beg to differ. It was not. The first UK picture disc was **Elvis - A Legendary Performer Vol. 3** (*LP 107*) issued in January 1979.

Significantly, it was possible to buy **The Top Ten Hits** for £13.50 whereas this UK picture disc cost £14.95 although, admittedly, this included post and packaging, as the album could not be bought in any shop.

Selected Marketing claimed that they had been able to select the tracks for inclusion on the album, but this would seem very unlikely, and would have made little economic sense either to themselves or RCA. Being able to use existing tapes prepared for *The Top Ten Hits* would have been much more sensible. Selected Marketing were, however, able to choose the pictures for the record which RCA provided, although the choice was fairly limited. Indeed, the picture on side 2, first used on the original UK release of *Elvis' Christmas Album* (*LP 5*) in November 1957, also formed the front cover of *The Top Ten Hits*. Side 1 featured a picture from 1956, as used on the cover of *Romantic Elvis* (*LP 192*). Side 3 showed a photograph from the *Jailhouse Rock* era, as used on the *(You're so square) Baby I Don't Care* single (*S 138*). Side 4 showed a photograph from 1972, circa *Elvis On Tour*.

The timing of this album was perfect in terms of sales to the general public, despite fierce competition provided by RCA's own tenth anniversary release, *Presley - The All Time Greatest Hits* (*LP 287*), which contained many of the tracks available here. Selected Marketing were confident of success, ordering an initial press run of 10,000 copies, which they claimed had been exhausted by the end of August. Further pressings were made later. However, as with all releases of this kind, it was very difficult to estimate what the demand was likely to be, yet there was no doubt that this record did particularly well, riding as it did on a tide of nostalgia, but being countered by RCA's heavy TV advertisements for their own product. Inevitably, Selected Marketing were left with unsold copies on their hands from the later pressings (which, incidentally, were identical to the first pressings), and these later turned up for sale in Elvis Monthly in November 1989 at the reduced price of £8.99, plus post and packaging. Later still, in 1991, the final copies were being sold off by the same source for £4.99, plus a further £1.50 postage.

There were, not surprisingly, some errors. Incorrectly, sides 1 and 2 were shown as stereo. They were all in mono, as they dated from the 1956-58 era. On side 1 there was some inconsistency where a comma was used to separate writers' names on tracks 4 and 5, when a hyphen was used elsewhere on the album. The writers of *Love Me Tender* were shown in the wrong order; *(Let me be your) Teddy Bear* was listed minus the words in brackets, as was *(Now and then there's) A Fool Such As I* and *(Marie's the name) His Latest Flame*. On track 4, side 2, DeMetrius was spelt De Metrius. There was no question mark after *Are You Lonesome Tonight?* Mort Shuman had his surname spelt Schuman on tracks 6 and 7, side 3. The writers of *She's Not You* were in the wrong order.

The were errors too in the publication dates quoted. *Crying In The Chapel* (recorded in 1960) was not published in 1961, but 1965; *I Feel So Bad* was not published in 1960, but in 1961 (when it was recorded); *Too Much* was first published in 1957; and, *Jailhouse Rock* was first published in the UK in 1958, not 1957.

Label Variations

PICTURE DISCS
1   1987 PRESSING: STEREO/MONO

Sleeve Variations
1   Clear plastic sleeve

Sleeve Detail Change

On the back of the sleeve of the next RCA album, *Presley - The All Time Greatest Hits*, PL 90100(2) (*LP 287*), a new feature was the inclusion the round RCA logo, which was to become a regular feature of all the company's UK releases. Note that whilst being very similar to the original logo found on black label releases in the fifties and early sixties, it had been slightly modified. It is said that BMG had to do this because they were not allowed to use the logo if it touched the side of the circle around the outside! RCA, as the sleeve pointed out, was a registered trademark of the RCA Corporation who were owned by General Electric.

The sleeve also showed that the tracks had been digitally remastered - the first time this claim had been made on an album. The sleeve boasted proudly: 'Digitally Remastered Analogue Recordings'.

Unlike the sleeve, the label showed no significant changes from those featured on *The Memphis Record*, PL 86221(2) (*LP 284*); and despite references on the sleeve to Bertelsmann, the label still quoted 'Marketed by RCA Records'.

LP 287 — Presley - The All Time Greatest Hits

RCA PL 90100(2)

Side 1

1. **Heartbreak Hotel** (Axton, Durden, Presley)
2. **Blue Suede Shoes** (Perkins)
3. **Hound Dog** (Leiber, Stoller)
4. **Love Me Tender** (Presley, Matson)
5. **Too Much** (Rosenberg, Weinman)
6. **All Shook Up** (Blackwell, Presley)
7. **(Let me be your) Teddy Bear** (Mann, Lowe)
8. **Paralyzed** (Blackwell, Presley)
9. **Party** (Robinson)
10. **Jailhouse Rock** (Leiber, Stoller)
11. **Don't** (Leiber, Stoller)
12. **Wear My Ring Around Your Neck** (Carroll, Moody)
13. **Hard Headed Woman** (DeMetrius)
14. **King Creole** (Leiber, Stoller)

Side 2

1. **One Night** (Bartholomew, King)
2. **(Now and then there's) A Fool Such As I** (Trader)
3. **A Big Hunk O' Love** (Schroeder, Wyche)
4. **Stuck On You** (Schroeder, McFarland)
5. **The Girl Of My Best Friend** (Ross, Bobrick)
6. **It's Now Or Never** (DiCapua, Schroeder, Gold)
7. **Are You Lonesome Tonight?** (Turk, Handman)
8. **Wooden Heart** (Wise, Weisman, Twomey, Kaempfert)
9. **Surrender** (DeCurtis, Pomus, Shuman)
10. **(Marie's the name) His Latest Flame** (Pomus, Shuman)
11. **Can't Help Falling In Love** (Peretti, Creatore, Weiss)
12. **Good Luck Charm** (Schroeder, Gold)

Side 3

1. **She's Not You** (Pomus, Leiber, Stoller)
2. **Return To Sender** (Blackwell, Scott)
3. **(You're the) Devil In Disguise** (Giant, Baum, Kaye)
4. **Crying In The Chapel** (Glenn)
5. **Love Letters** (Young, Heyman)
6. **If I Can Dream** (Brown)
7. **In The Ghetto** (Davis)
8. **Suspicious Minds** (James)
9. **Don't Cry Daddy** (Davis)
10. **The Wonder Of You** (Knight)

Side 4

1. **I Just Can't Help Believin'** (Mann, Weil)
2. **An American Trilogy** (Arr. Newbury)
3. **Burning Love** (Linde)
4. **Always On My Mind** (James, Carson, Christopher)
5. **My Boy** (Francois, Bourtayre, Martin, Coulter)
6. **Suspicion** (Pomus, Shuman)
7. **Moody Blue** (James)
8. **Way Down** (Martine Jnr.)
9. **It's Only Love** (James)

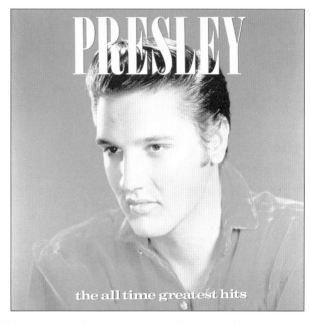

the all time greatest hits

Released August 1987   Deleted December 1994

August 1987, the tenth anniversary of Elvis's death, predictably proved to be a busy time for fans in terms of product offered for sale - whether it was video, audio, books or magazines. Two double albums - *The Complete Sun Sessions*, PL 86414(2) (**LP 283**), and *The Memphis Record*, PL 86221(2) (**LP 284**) - arrived from the USA. In the UK though, an imaginative (and what was to prove a phenomenally successful) double album was launched - *Presley - The All Time Greatest Hits*, a 45 track compilation put together by Roger Semon of the UK division. It is worth looking at the history of this release carefully.

In the USA, to coincide with the release of the two above-named albums, RCA had issued two 'hits' packages: *The Top Ten Hits* and *The Number One Hits*, the first one bearing 38 tracks and the second featuring Elvis's 18 number one hits in the USA. Inevitably, there was a high number of common tracks (see listing below) which, from a buyer's point of view, made little sense. However, it is worth noting at this point that it was a fact (supported by healthy sales figures), that the US market has always been better disposed to what some fans may refer to as 'random hits packages' than the UK or European market. In other words such packages do sell. A good example of this was the release of *Elvis' Worldwide 50 Gold Award Hits, Vol. 1* on CD in 1988 in the US. Despite featuring no new material, the set sold in excess of 150,000 copies. It was not issued in the UK because those responsible for the UK releases felt, quite justifiably, that its release offered nothing new and was, thus, superfluous. This, in a nutshell, was Roger Semon's view of the two US inspired 'hits' albums in 1987. Although well packaged, they did not meet the needs of the UK market. Hence, he began modifying the releases accordingly, ending up with a 45 track double album (on both vinyl and CD).

In fact, apart from the *Elvis' Golden Records* series, the flawed *Worldwide 50 Gold Award Hits Volumes 1 and 2* (they were in mono!), RCA themselves had not tried to produce a definitive hits package for many years - this had been left to the likes of Reader's Digest and Arcade (who produced the phenomenally successful *Elvis's 40 Greatest* (LP 73) in 1974). Yet what made *Presley - The All Time Greatest Hits* different from any of its predecessors were two main things: for the first time a collection of hits spanned the full period of his time on RCA i.e. 1956-1977, including songs from the post 1973 era. This had been a major point of difference and acrimony between RCA and the Estate in the years following Elvis's death, because of deeply complicated legal wrangles over royalty payments for songs. As a consequence of this, virtually no releases for ten years bore tracks recorded after 1973, as the Estate would have earned royalties from them. The second important difference was that *Presley - The All Time Greatest Hits* was extremely well prepared sound-wise, being digitally remastered in the UK by Bob Jones at CTS Studios, Wembley, London, between 21 and 24 July 1987. So, not only was the package beautifully presented, but it also sounded wonderful and was, moreover, extremely well received by fans and the media alike. Clearly the company had adjudged that the market was ready for another 'hits' package (a phenomenon which occurs every four/five years for many major artists, it seems. For example, *The Essential Collection* (LP 320) in August 1994, which had 27 of the tracks featured on this album, but Semon's acumen ensured that the UK market (and fans) would be offered a better deal. And what a deal it was! The albums offered a fraction under two hours playing time.

As a point of comparison, the US albums on which *Presley - The All Time Greatest Hits* was based, included the following tracks.

The Top Ten Hits

Side A   *Heartbreak Hotel**
*I Want You, I Need You, I Love You**
*Hound Dog**
*Don't Be Cruel**
*Love Me Tender**
Love Me
*Too Much**
*All Shook Up**
*(Let me be you) Teddy Bear**
*Jailhouse Rock**

Side B   *Don't**
I Beg Of You
Wear My Ring Around Your Neck
*Hard Headed Woman**
One Night
I Got Stung
(Now and then there's) A Fool Such As I
I Need Your Love Tonight
*A Big Hunk O' Love**

Side C   *Stuck On You**
*It's Now Or Never**
*Are You Lonesome Tonight?**
*Surrender**
I Feel So Bad
Little Sister
(Marie's the name) His Latest Flame
Can't Help Falling In Love
*Good Luck Charm**
She's Not You

Side D   *Return To Sender*
(You're the) Devil In Disguise
Bossa Nova Baby
Crying In The Chapel
In The Ghetto
*Suspicious Minds**
Don't Cry Daddy
The Wonder Of You
Burning Love

Note that the last track featured - *Burning Love* - was a hit from 1972.

The other album, *The Number One Hits*, included the eighteen tracks above bearing an asterisk. However, we should also point out that a double picture disc album containing these tracks was issued in the UK, not by RCA, but by the mail order company Selected Marketing (LP 286).

And so, armed with permission to include post-1973 material on a compilation release for the first time, Roger Semon produced what was to prove a great perspective on Elvis's career, a release which was excellent value in all respects. It was also the first Elvis album to be advertised on TV since the 1985 Telstar *Ballads* album, STAR 2264 (LP 274), and the first Elvis one to be promoted thus by RCA themselves. It seems though that budget restrictions dictated that the TV advertisements were shown for a only short time, although they appeared in the Yorkshire and Granada TV areas for two weeks. There were a number of competitions organised in conjunction with this release, and an in-store promotional sampler album was produced primarily for record shops. This is dealt with more fully in the section on promotional records. Unfortunately, many copies of the promotional album did not reach their intended audience and were, instead, to be found on sale at record fairs and in specialist shops where the asking price far exceeded that of the actual double album! Such was the allure of promotional items. Nonetheless, the standard release sold exceptionally well, reaching number 4 and spending 20 weeks in the UK album charts. And, by early 1992, it had sold in excess of 600,000 units (all formats) in the UK alone. In fact, in August 1992, as public interest in the fifties' boxed set was running very high, aided by positive and sincere media attention, *Presley - The All Time Greatest Hits* entered the BBC Radio 2's album chart again - six years after its release! Also 1992 saw its release in Australia and South Africa, too, where it did extremely well, earning revenue and kudos for BMG in the UK, and praise for Roger Semon himself.

Now, as a close look at the track listing will reveal, the compilation was not based on chart placings alone - despite its title. Instead, Semon opted for what seemed to be the strongest possible package, including songs most identifiable with Elvis, and excluding some top ten items based on UK chart placings. For example, the following songs appeared in the UK top ten (their positions are noted) yet they were not included in the set:

Title	Release Number	Year	Chart Placing
Blue Moon	S 5	1956	9
Santa Bring My Baby Back (to me)	S 16	1957	7
Wild In The Country	S 34	1961	4
Rock-A-Hula Baby	S 36	1961	1
Kissin' Cousins	S 45	1964	10
Clean Up Your Own Backyard	S 69	1969	2
I've Lost You	S 74	1970	9
You Don't Have To Say You Love Me	S 75	1971	9
There Goes My Everything	S 76	1971	6
Rags To Riches	S 77	1971	9
Until It's Time For You To Go	S 82	1972	5
Promised Land	S 92	1975	9
My Way	S 117	1977	9

It could also be argued that several other hits were omitted - those which had originally formed the other side of double A sided singles. For example, *I Got Stung*, which was released with *One Night* (S 25).

On the other hand, *Love Me Tender* (S 6) was included, as was *If I Can Dream* (S 67), even though both songs only reached number 11 in the charts. A further 'grey' area was the inclusion of *The Girl Of My Best Friend* from 1960, as the A side was *A Mess Of Blues*. However, as it was a number 9 hit in 1976, when it was an A side, it seemed sensible to include it.

It is also known that the original label copy listed **Don't Be Cruel** but at the last moment a decision was made to use **Hound Dog** instead. Of course, such omissions/amendments were inevitable; there was no way everything eligible could have been included, given the parameters Semon had to work within - therefore decisions had to be taken on what was in and what was omitted.

The UK compilation, therefore, included the following tracks not featured on either of the US releases:

Blue Suede Shoes	*Paralyzed*
Party	*The Girl Of My Best Friend*
Wooden Heart	*Love Letters*
If I Can Dream	*I Just Can't Help Believin'*
An American Trilogy	*Always On My Mind*
My Boy	*Suspicion*
Moody Blue	*Way Down*
It's Only Love	

On the other hand, **The Top Ten Hits** included the following songs not on the British album:

I Want You, I Need You, I Love You	*Don't Be Cruel*
Love Me	*I Beg Of You*
I Got Stung	*I Need Your Love Tonight*
I Feel So Bad	*Little Sister*
Bossa Nova Baby	

ELVIS PRESLEY - "THE ALL TIME GREATEST HITS" - NL/NK/ND 90100.

SELECTION TITLE	RECORDING DATE	CHART DEBUT	UK	US
SIDE A.				
1. HEARTBREAK HOTEL	10.1.56	11.5.56	2	1
2. BLUE SUEDE SHOES	30.1.56	25.5.56	9	-
3. DON'T BE CRUEL (Hound Dog)	2.7.56	21.9.56	2	1
4. LOVE ME TENDER	2.8.56	7.12.56	11	1
5. TOO MUCH	2.9.56	10.5.57	6	1
6. ALL SHOOK UP	12.1.57	14.6.57	1	1
7. TEDDY BEAR	24.1.57	12.7.57	3	1
8. PARALYSED	2.9.56	30.8.57	8	-
9. PARTY	2.57	4.10.57	2	1
10. JAILHOUSE ROCK	30.4.57	24.1.58	1	1
11. DON'T	6.9.57	28.2.58	2	1
12. WEAR MY RING AROUND YOUR NECK	12.2.58	2.5.58	3	2
13. HARD HEADED WOMAN	15.1.58	25.7.58	2	1
14. KING CREOLE	15.1.58	3.10.58	2	-
SIDE B.				
1. ONE NIGHT	23.2.57	23.1.59	1	4
2. A FOOL SUCH AS I	10.6.58	24.4.59	1	2
3. A BIG HUNK O' LOVE	10.6.58	24.7.59	4	1
4. STUCK ON YOU	21.3.60	7.4.60	3	1
5. THE GIRL OF MY BEST FRIEND	4.4.60	28.7.60	2	-
6. IT'S NOW OR NEVER	3.4.60	3.11.60	1	1
7. ARE YOU LONESOME TONIGHT?	4.4.60	19.1.61	1	1
8. WOODEN HEART	28.4.60	9.3.61	1	-
9. SURRENDER	30.10.60	25.5.61	1	1
10. HIS LATEST FLAME	26.6.61	2.11.61	1	4
11. CAN'T HELP FALLING IN LOVE	23.3.61	1.2.62	1	2
12. GOOD LUCK CHARM	15.6.61	10.5.62	1	1
SIDE C.				
1. SHE'S NOT YOU	19.3.62	30.8.62	1	5
2. RETURN TO SENDER	.3.62	29.11.62	1	2
3. (YOU'RE THE) DEVIL IN DISGUISE	26.5.62	4.7.62	1	3
4. CRYING IN THE CHAPEL	31.10.60	27.5.65	1	3
5. LOVE LETTERS	26.5.66	7.7.66	6	19
6. IF I CAN DREAM	30.6.68	26.2.69	11	12
7. IN THE GHETTO	21.1.69	11.6.69	2	3
8. SUSPICIOUS MINDS	23.1.69	29.11.69	1	1
9. DON'T CRY DADDY	15.1.69	28.2.70	8	6
10. THE WONDER OF YOU	19.2.70	11.7.70	1	9
SIDE D.				
1. I JUST CAN'T HELP BELIEVIN'	.8.70	4.12.71	6	-
2. AN AMERICAN TRILOGY	9.4.72	17.6.72	8	66
3. BURNING LOVE	28.3.72	30.9.72	7	2
4. ALWAYS ON MY MIND	29.3.72	16.12.72	9	20
5. MY BOY	13.12.73	16.11.74	5	20
6. SUSPICION	19.3.62	25.12.76	9	-
7. MOODY BLUE	4.2.76	5.3.77	6	31
8. WAY DOWN	29.10.76	13.8.77	1	18
9. IT'S ONLY LOVE	20.5.71	30.8.80	3	51

*The original label copy. Note the substitution of **Hound Dog** instead of **Don't Be Cruel** and the mid-price prefix NL. Bob Jones's handwritten notes indicate the tape source were those prepared for various CDs.*

An interesting feature of this album was that some of the tracks sounded different from what they had done previously. For example, although **The Wonder Of You** was the standard live version (recorded in Las Vegas on 19 February 1970), as used on the **On Stage February** 1970 (LP 41) album, the mix on **Presley - The All Time Greatest Hits** was noticeably different, particularly on the music leading up to the guitar instrumental, where James Burton's 'fills' can be heard prior to the break itself. More importantly though, a few of the fifties' tracks had been remastered without the use of compression (a technique commonly used on early singles, whereby the frequency range of the songs was narrowed to give a more 'punchy' sound when played on the likes of home record players or juke boxes). Without going into the technicalities at this stage, the effect of using compression tended to lessen the clarity of the song. Conversely, when reduced or removed entirely, the result was a song

which sounded 'cleaner' - you could hear the instruments and voice more clearly - though some of the original 'punch' may have been diminished. The songs which sounded different were: **Wear My Ring Around Your Neck**, **(Now and then there's) A Fool Such As I**, and **A Big Hunk O' Love**. Incidentally, this was how Bob Jones received the tracks from the USA: it was not a phenomenon peculiar to the UK release alone. Jones cut the albums at CTS in Wembley on 21, 23 and 24 July 1987.

Careful listeners will also be aware that some of the versions used on the album were not the original single versions. **Suspicious Minds**, for example, was the edited/remixed version - arguably the original version as there was no repetitious fade out. **An American Trilogy** was not the single version from February 1972, but one recorded at Hampton Roads on 9 April 1972, as used in **Elvis On Tour**. This version was first released in April 1981 on the **This Is Elvis** soundtrack, RCALP 5029 (LP 150). **Always On My Mind** was the 'stringed' version, first issued in 1985 on the album of the same name, PL 85430 (LP 272). Finally, whilst **Moody Blue** was the standard version, it featured the mix used on **Elvis' Gold Records Volume 5**, PL 84941 (LP 261), with the prominent female voice on the chorus.

The gatefold sleeve was lavish and most eye-catching, featuring a colour shot from 1956. Inside was a montage of LP covers and bits of UK memorabilia, while on the back cover the tracks were listed, quoting their recording dates and release dates, along with the highest US and UK chart placings. In fact, although done briefly, it was the first UK release to list session dates. The audio restoration was credited to Bob Jones (from the UK) and Rick Rowe (from the USA). The set was the first UK compilation to bear the legend 'Digitally Remastered' on the cover.

The price coding on the album denoted DD, meaning that at the time of issue the dealer price was £4.86 for the double vinyl album and £10.33 for the CD.

Now, while everything about the release exuded care and quality, there were some errors on the label information. On side 1, for instance, the publishing date for **Jailhouse Rock** was given as 1957, whereas it was not issued in the UK until January 1958, as the cover correctly stated. Then on side 2, the label read mono. Now while this was true for tracks 1-3, the rest were in stereo and no reference was made to this. Oddly, the three tracks in question were asterisked as if the intention had been to say stereo at the top of the label, with a footnote indicating that these three were in mono. Indeed, this was precisely what happened with later labels featuring the round RCA logo on the left of the label. Here the label read stereo, whilst the first three tracks, again asterisked, were correctly identified as being mono recordings.

The sleeve referred to Sides Three and Four of the release, whereas the second record, used Side 1 and 2 again. Once again, there were some errors in dates given. **Suspicion** was released in the UK in 1962 on the album **Pot Luck** (LP 16), not 1961 - in fact it was not even recorded until March 1962; **It's Only Love**, while being a 1971 recording, was not issued in the UK until 1977 on the **Elvis In Demand** album (LP 90); and, finally, the date given for **Moody Blue** - 1976 - was incorrect: it ought to have been 1977 when it first appeared in the UK.

There was the usual crop of label and sleeve errors relating to song titles and writers' names. On side 1, **Love Me Tender** showed the writers in the wrong order - Matson, Presley - and we suggest you refer to the notes following **The King Of Rock 'N' Roll The Complete 50's Masters** (LP 318) for a full explanation of this. The co-writer of **Too Much**, Lee Rosenberg, had her surname spelt Rosenburg, and the words in brackets were omitted from **(Let me be your) Teddy Bear**. Similarly, the words in brackets were missing on **(Now and then there's) A Fool Such As I**, on side 2.

There were no errors on side 3, but on side 4 the writers of **My Boy** were in the wrong order. The writer of **Way Down**, Martine, was omitted in favour of Martin, Kennedy on the label and, on the sleeve, Martin Kennedy, suggesting one person. Finally a new error occurred on **It's Only Love**, where the name Tyrell was printed on the label, but not on the sleeve.

150

Overall the number of errors were minor, and given that the track listing contained some perennial errors, clearly some effort had gone into clarifying some long standing mistakes.

Confirmation of the success of **Presley - The All Time Greatest Hits** can be found by reference to the label variations listed below: this was one of the few albums from this period to have been re-pressed. In fact, several re-pressings were made, and, as one of these coincided with a modification to the RCA label, a label variation resulted.

An enquiry to BMG in April 1994 revealed that only 200 copies were left in stock! The album was finally deleted in December 1994.

Label Variations

GERMAN BLACK LABEL
1   1987 PRESSING: MONO/STEREO
Computer style logo
BIEM above GEMA in separate boxes

2   1990 PRESSING: MONO/STEREO
Round RCA logo at side of label
BIEM above GEMA in separate boxes

Sleeve Variations
1   Gloss

LP 288	In Hollywood

	Premier PMP 1011

Side 1
1   **Jailhouse Rock** (Leiber, Stoller)
2   **Rock-A-Hula Baby** (Wise, Weisman, Fuller)
3   **G.I. Blues** (Tepper, Bennett)
4   **Kissin' Cousins** (Wise, Starr)
5   **Wild In The Country** (Peretti, Creatore, Weiss)
6   **King Creole** (Leiber, Stoller)
7   **Blue Hawaii** (Robin, Rainger)
8   **Fun In Acapulco** (Weisman, Wayne)
9   **Follow That Dream** (Wise, Weisman)
10   **Girls! Girls! Girls!** (Leiber, Stoller)

Side 2
1   **Viva Las Vegas** (Pomus, Shuman)
2   **Bossa Nova Baby** (Leiber, Stoller)
3   **Flaming Star** (Wayne, Edwards)
4   **Girl Happy** (Pomus, Meade)
5   **Frankie And Johnny** (Gottlieb, Karger, Weisman)
6   **Roustabout** (Giant, Baum, Kaye)
7   **Spinout** (Wayne, Weisman, Fuller)
8   **Double Trouble** (Pomus, Shuman)
9   **Charro** (Strange, Davis)
10   **They Remind Me Too Much Of You** (Robertson)

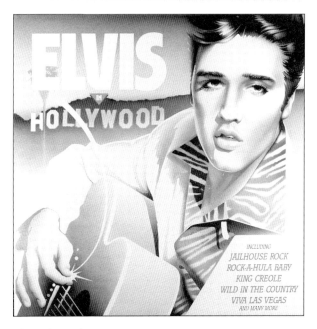

Released October 1987

An album entitled **Elvis In Hollywood**, containing identical tracks, was released in July 1982, Everest CBR 1014 (*LP 191*). This album was subsequently re-issued in January 1985 on Premier Records, CBR 1014 (*LP 268*).

Another album with identical tracks entitled **20 Golden Greats** was released on Performance Records, PFP 1009, in March 1989 (**LP 299**).

There was no doubt that albums like **In Hollywood** would always serve a useful purpose in the market, representing, as this album did, a strong collection of largely film title tracks in the 'greatest hits' mould. For first time buyers they were a useful introduction to the Elvis world, and must be considered in this light. At £3.49 for the twenty tracks the album represented value for money but, in all honesty, whilst there were some very strong recordings included, the overall feel for this album was slightly downmarket and more likely to appeal to casual buyers. Of course for long-time fans and serious collectors the album offered nothing new; these were familiar tracks in a familiar format. Indeed, this was the third issue of the album, which had an interesting and chequered history.

Originally issued on the Everest label in 1982, the sleeve had a number of photographs of Elvis on the back. This sleeve was later withdrawn, it is said, because Colonel Parker objected to *Elvisly Yours* claiming credit for supplying them. True or not, the sleeve re-appeared minus the photographs. A second issue came in 1985, this time on the Premier label who used the same sleeve design initially. This was later completely revised with a drawing of Elvis playing a guitar replacing the photograph. The back of the sleeve featured three pictures of the drawing in close up.

Now entitled *In Hollywood*, and thereby becoming a new release rather than a re-issue according to our definition (see the introductory section for further details), although to be absolutely certain that no-one is confused by this, we have classed it as a re-issue in the chronological listing. The sleeve had been subjected to further modifications. Most noticeable was the removal of the '20 tracks' legend on the front, and a re-styling of Elvis's name. The three identical images found on the back of the 1985 sleeve had been reduced to one, allowing room for a much clearer listing of the songs.

Nine of the tracks featured on the album had been issued as singles in the UK, eight of them A sides. The 'other' version of *Kissin' Cousins* had been an A side in 1964. The tracks were placed in a random, non-chronological sequence, and only two tracks, *Jailhouse Rock* and *King Creole*, were pre-army recordings. On side 1 tracks 1, 6 and 9 were in mono (track 9 ought to have been in stereo but no master could be found), while all tracks on side 2 were in stereo, although there was poor separation on *Frankie And Johnny* and *Flaming Star*.

New errors on both label and sleeve were created, the most obvious of which was turning *Jailhouse Rock* into *Jail House Rock*. On the sleeve, an end bracket }), instead of a /, was used between the writers of track 2, side 1, Weisman and Fuller. The label, on the other hand, failed to put a / between Wise and Wiseman on the same song! There were some significant errors though! Giant, Baum, Kaye did not write the version of *Kissin' Cousins* featured here, it was Wise and Starr. There were two writers of *Blue Hawaii* - Robin and Rainger - not one man - Robin Rainger - as both sleeve and label would have us believe. The writers of *Fun In Acapulco* were the wrong way round; *Girls! Girls! Girls!* ought to have had exclamation marks, not commas; and Mann and Weil had no involvement in writing *Bossa Nova Baby*; and an ampersand should not have been used in *Frankie And Johnny*.

Label Variations

LIGHT BLUE LABEL

    1   1987 PRESSING: STEREO/MONO

Sleeve Variations

    1   Gloss

LP 289   *Mess O' Blues - Volume 1*

Premier PMP 1012

Side 1
1. **Trouble** (Leiber, Stoller)
2. **Reconsider Baby** (Fulson)
3. **A Mess Of Blues** (Pomus, Shuman)
4. **Give Me The Right** (Wise, Blagman)
5. **Such A Night** (Chase)
6. **When It Rains, It Really Pours** (Emerson)

Side 2
1. **Trying To Get To You** (Singleton, McCoy)
2. **Like A Baby** (Stone)
3. **I Want To Be Free** (Leiber, Stoller)
4. **Mean Woman Blues** (DeMetrius)
5. **Ain't That Loving You Baby** (Otis, Hunter)
6. **One Night** (Bartholomew, King)

Released October 1987

A double album entitled *Blue Rhythms*, EPC 1000 (*LP 205*), was released in December 1983 on Everest Records, and re-issued as PPD 2001 (*LP 269*) in January 1985 by Premier. *Blue Rhythms* contained the same tracks as *Mess O' Blues - Volume 1* and its companion *Mess O' Blues - Volume 2* (**LP 290**). Later both volumes were repackaged and released together in March 1988 as *Mess O' Blues - Volumes 1 & 2* with a catalogue number PPD 2000 (**LP 292**). Later still, in March 1989, the albums were made available again and entitled *Mess O' Blues - 24 Classic Tracks*, PFP 2000 (**LP 300**), a double album.

It will be quite apparent after reading the notes above that the collection of songs contained on this and its companion volume had been released in various guises over the years. Indeed, the twenty four 'blues' tracks had become the most frequently re-packaged Elvis set in UK history. The songs formed the basis of a whole series of album releases spread over a six year period; and whilst there was no doubt about the quality of the recordings (for they rank amongst the finest Elvis recorded), the sheer proliferation of variously titled albums containing the same material could be considered exploitation of the worst kind.

Released on Everest Records, the songs first appeared together in December 1983, when they appeared as a double album entitled *Blue Rhythms* (*LP 205*) which was pressed, initially, on blue vinyl. Two years later, in January 1985, the album was re-issued on regular black vinyl, this time by Premier (*LP 269*).

Mess O' Blues - Volume 1 contained the twelve tracks which comprised the first album of the *Blue Rhythms* set, in exactly the same running order. But the sleeve design was new, featuring a painting of Elvis performing live, though it was uncredited. A smaller, different painting appeared on the back of the sleeve.

The sleeve notes which had accompanied *Blue Rhythms* did not re-appear here, contributing to the overall impression of a reduction in quality. This was unfortunate because the songs themselves deserved better.

Some of the label and sleeve errors found on the *Blue Rhythms* album had been corrected, but many remained. No comma was shown in *When It Rains, It Really Pours*, and the song was written by Robert William Emerson - one person - and not three separate people. An interesting new error concerned *Like A Baby*, which was credited on both sleeve and label to Stone and Campbell. The correct writer was Jesse Stone, the name Campbell having come from the name of the song's publishers - Campbell Connelly & Co Ltd. Claude DeMetrius, writer of *Mean Woman Blues*, had his name spelt De Meteruis.

Label Variations

LIGHT BLUE LABEL

Sleeve Variations

1   Gloss

LP 290 — Mess O' Blues - Volume 2

Premier PMP 1013

Side 1

1 **Little Sister** (Pomus, Shuman)
2 **So Glad You're Mine** (Crudup)
3 **Big Boss Man** (Smith, Dixon)
4 **I Want You With Me** (Harris)
5 **Baby, What You Want Me To Do** (Reed)
6 **Santa Claus Is Back In Town** (Leiber, Stoller)

Side 2

1 **Stuck On You** (Schroeder, McFarland)
2 **I Feel So Bad** (Willis)
3 **What'd I Say** (Charles)
4 **Tomorrow Night** (Croslow, Grosz)
5 **It Feels So Right** (Wise, Weisman)
6 **Merry Christmas Baby** (Baxter, Moore)

Released October 1987

A double album entitled **Blue Rhythms**, EPC 1000 (*LP 205*), was released in December 1983 on Everest Records, and re-issued as PPD 2001 (*LP 269*) in January 1985 by Premier. **Blue Rhythms** contained the same tracks as **Mess O' Blues - Volume 1** (**LP 289**) and its companion **Mess O' Blues - Volume 2**. Later both volumes were repackaged and released together in March 1988 as **Mess O' Blues - Volumes 1 & 2** with a catalogue number PPD 2000 (**LP 292**). Later still, in March 1989, the albums were made available again and entitled **Mess O' Blues - 24 Classic Tracks**, PFP 2000 (**LP 300**), a double album.

The cost of this album was, like volume 1, £3.49, and with the obvious exception of the track listing, catalogue number and the fact that this was the second volume, the front and back of the sleeves were identical. The colouring was, however, noticeably different, with the sleeve of this album having a distinctive purple tint compared to the blue of the first volume.

Obviously, **Mess O' Blues - Volume 2** contained the twelve tracks which went to make up the second album of the **Blue Rhythms** (*LP 205*) set. Of the 24 tracks featured on the two volumes, only one song, **Merry Christmas Baby**, dated from the 1970s. There were 10

recordings from the '50s, and 13 from the '60s spread over both albums.

Overall the number of label and sleeve errors had been reduced and there was, happily, a consistency between the two. No comma was shown in **Baby, What You Want Me To Do**, and the writers of **Stuck On You** were shown as Schroeder/Leslie/McFarland, when Leslie McFarland was actually one person.

Label Variations

LIGHT BLUE LABEL

1   **1987 PRESSING: STEREO/MONO**

Sleeve Variations

1   **Gloss**

LP 291 — The Complete Million Dollar Quartet

Charly SUN CDX 20

Side 1

1 **You Belong To My Heart** (Gilbert, Lara)
2 **When God Dips His Love In My Heart** (Traditional)
3 **Just A Little Talk With Jesus** (Derricks)
4 **Jesus Walked That Lonesome Valley** (Traditional)
5 **I Shall Not Be Moved** (Morris)
6 **(There'll be) Peace In The Valley (for me)** (Dorsey)
7 **Down By The Riverside** (Traditional)

Side 2

1 **I'm With A Crowd But So Alone** (Tubb, Story)
2 **Farther Along** (Traditional)
3 **Blessed Jesus (hold my hand)** (Traditional)
4 **On The Jericho Road** (Traditional)
5 **I Just Can't Make It By Myself** (Brewster)
6 **Little Cabin On The Hill** (Monroe, Flatt)
7 **Summertime Is Past And Gone** (Monroe)
8 **I Hear A Sweet Voice Calling** (Monroe)

9   **Sweetheart You Done Me Wrong** (Monroe, Flatt)
10   **Keeper Of The Key** (Stewart, Howard, Devine, Guynes)
11   **Crazy Arms** (Mooney, Seals)
12   **Don't Forbid Me** (Singleton)
13   **Too Much Monkey Business** (Berry)
14   **Brown Eyed Handsome Man** (Berry)
15   **Out Of Sight, Out Of Mind** (Hunter, Otis)
16   **Brown Eyed Handsome Man** (Berry)

Side 3

1   **Don't Be Cruel** (Blackwell, Presley)
2   **Don't Be Cruel** (Blackwell, Presley)
3   **Paralyzed** (Blackwell, Presley)
4   **There's No Place Like Home** (Traditional)
5   **When The Saints Go Marching In** (Traditional)
6   **Softly And Tenderly** (Traditional)

Side 4

1   **Is It So Strange** (Young)
2   **That's When Your Heartaches Begin** (Raskin, Brown, Fisher)
3   **Brown Eyed Handsome Man** (Berry)
4   **Rip It Up** (Blackwell, Marascalco)
5   **I'm Gonna Bid My Blues Goodbye** (Snow)
6   **Crazy Arms** (Mooney, Seals)
7   **That's My Desire** (Loveday, Dresa)
8   **End Of The Road** (Lewis)
9   **Black Bottom Stomp** (Morton)
10   **You're The Only Star In My Blue Heaven** (Autry)
11   **Elvis Farewell**

Released November 1987

An album entitled *The Million Dollar Quartet*, SUN 1006 (*LP 152*), released by Charly in July 1981, contained some of the tracks found on this album. The 'new' tracks were tracks 1 and 2, side 1; and all the tracks after *Don't Forbid Me* (track 12, side 2).

Six and a half years after Charly had released their first single album instalment in the Million Dollar Quartet saga, came this double album, said to be the complete Million Dollar Quartet recordings from December 1956. Listening to the record appears to support this view, for at least there was a definite ending regarding our main

interest in the session i.e. when Elvis left the studio, but even this did not prevent widespread speculation that other tracks had been recorded in the earlier part of the session. And, as it turned out, this was justified when RCA released a hitherto unheard rendition of *Reconsider Baby* on *The King Of Rock 'N' Roll The Complete 50's Masters*, PL 90689(6) (**LP 318**), in July 1992. No-one seemed to know quite how, or why, this song was separated from the rest of the session.

The problem for all concerned is that the precise details about this impromptu session will probably never be known, with claims and counter-claims causing confusion and contradiction about what was, or was not, recorded. Note the use of the word 'recorded'. Other songs may have been sung, but whether they were recorded is quite a different matter.

One thing that was confirmed by the release of these particular songs, was that there was no clear aural evidence that Johnny Cash sang on the recordings, and his presence at the photo session was probably no more than a piece of opportunism, engineered by Sam Phillips. Of course, it was quite possible that Johnny Cash did sing on some numbers, and there have been some titles suggested, but, again, these may not have been recorded. The accompanying sleeve notes, by Martin Hawkins, suggested that another Sun artist, Smokey Joe Baugh, can be heard on certain passages. Whether this was true or not is unimportant, but it does underline the uncertainty and mystery that still shrouds this session.

In the same way that Charly's *The Million Dollar Quartet* album first appeared on bootleg, so too had this double album; and what was more, fans were paying up to £25 for the privilege of owning a copy. Charly's double album retailed at just £8.49.

The packaging itself was quite attractive with some appropriate photographs of those involved, and the sleeve notes (credited to Martin Hawkins) were informative. The title of the album on the sleeve was given as *The Complete Million Dollar Session*, whereas the label referred to *The Complete Million Dollar Quartet*. Charly issued the recordings on CD in December 1987 (CD Charly 102).

Finally, in 1990, RCA issued, on vinyl, their version of this album, entitled *The Million Dollar Quartet*, PL 90465, but only in Europe, not in the UK. (It was not until May 1993 that the recordings were issued on CD - 74321 13830 2 - in the UK by RCA.) The recordings had been digitally remastered in November 1989 in New York, and probably represented the best quality yet available. What interested us greatly about the album was that it provided some further clarification of the song titles and writers' names - never a strong point on either Charly release. When compiling *Elvis UK 1956-86* we were concerned about certain inaccuracies on the original single album issued by Charly, particularly the use of someone called Young who, it was claimed, was responsible for many of the arrangements. This would seem quite unlikely given the nature of the jam session. However, without additional references, we were unable to corroborate the information provided, and, in accordance with our own guidelines, we were obliged to include what was shown on the label.

On the RCA release, several of the titles had been modified and, having reviewed these, it seemed more sensible for us to accept these as being more accurate than those given by Charly (and the bootleggers). The fact that RCA had provided most of the writers' names suggested that more thorough research had gone into this process than had occurred previously, and this, above all, was the governing factor. We now, therefore, consider that the Charly albums contain some song title and writer errors, and, in addition to amending the song title index at the back of the book, we have listed below the discrepancies between the Charly and RCA releases, as well as indicating errors on more established songs. What we now believe to be the correct titles and writers are given in the header block for this release.

When God Dips His Love In My Heart - Charly credited Stephenson, whereas RCA listed the song as being 'Traditional'.

Just A Little Talk With Jesus - Charly listed the song as 'Traditional. Arranged by H Young', a name they applied to all the 'traditional' songs. RCA identified Clevant Derricks.

Jesus Walked That Lonesome Valley - Charly titled the song **Walk That Lonesome Valley,** though both companies identified it as being 'Traditional'.

I Shall Not Be Moved - Charly said 'Traditional'. RCA named Homer Morris.

(There'll be) Peace In The Valley (for me). Charly omitted the brackets. RCA omitted the words in brackets.

I'm With A Crowd But So Alone - Charly named the song *I'm In The Crowd But Oh So Alone*.

Blessed Jesus (hold my hand) - Charly listed the title as **Blessed Jesus, Hold My Hand**.

On The Jericho Road - Charly listed the title as **As We Travel Along The Jericho Road**, as did RCA on their **Million Dollar Quartet** CD (74321 13840 2). It was not until the song appeared on **Peace In The Valley The Complete Gospel Recordings** (**LP 332**) that the correct title was used.

I Just Can't Make It By Myself - Charly said 'Traditional'. RCA identified Clara Ward, but later collections - **Peace In The Valley** (**LP 332**), for example - quoted Herbert Brewster. We have used Brewster.

Summertime Is Past And Gone - Charly entitled the song **Summertime Has Passed And Gone** and said 'Traditional'. RCA credited Bill Monroe.

Sweetheart You Done Me Wrong - Charly said 'Traditional'. RCA listed Bill Monroe and Lester Flatt.

Keeper Of The Key - Charly identified the writers Howard, Devine, Guynes, Stewart. So did RCA, but in a different order - Stewart, Howard, Devine, Guynes.

Too Much Monkey Business. Charly did not list the song at all. Admittedly, it was very brief (timed at 5 seconds by RCA), but the song was there, although apparently Elvis made no contribution!

Out Of Sight, Out Of Mind - Charly said 'Traditional'. RCA credited Ivory Joe Hunter and Clyde Otis.

Don't Be Cruel - Both Charly and RCA showed Blackwell, Presley in the wrong order.

Paralyzed - Both Charly and RCA showed Blackwell, Presley in the wrong order, and Charly spelt **Paralyzed** with an 's'.

There's No Place Like Home - Charly showed the title as **There Is No Place Like Home**, and credited Rodgers and Hammerstein. RCA stuck to 'Traditional'.

Softly And Tenderly - Charly credited J Hendrix. RCA said 'Traditional'.

That's When Your Heartaches Begin - Charly listed Keith Potger and RCA listed Fisher, Hill, Raskin. Both should have read Raskin, Brown, Fisher.

Black Bottom Stomp - Charly called this **Jerry's Boogie**.

Label Variations

YELLOW SUN LABEL

1   1987 PRESSING: MONO

Sleeve Variations

1   Gloss

Greatest Hits: Elvis Presley

Telstar THPA 1234

Despite the fact that this was a cassette and booklet package, we felt it was appropriate to include brief details of this Telstar release - for the simple reason that it was the first time a package of this sort had been made for Elvis product in the UK.

This was the fourth release in the series of six 'Greatest Hits And Pics', and the only one to feature Elvis. The other artists were Five Star, Spandau Ballet, Samantha Fox, Mel & Kim, with the final release being a various artists compilation.

The cassette featured six songs, all number one hits, with the exception of **Heartbreak Hotel**. The other tracks were **Jailhouse Rock, All Shook Up, It's Now Or Never, Wooden Heart** and **Are You Lonesome Tonight?**.

The booklet, 48 pages long, contained notes written by Chris Charlesworth.

The package, which was released in November 1987, was priced, initially, at £7.99 and was described by **Elvis Monthly** as a souvenir with a short shelf life, meaning that they anticipated demand being high. In fact, the set was officially deleted in January 1988, two months after it was issued, but, as was often the case with this type of material, production outweighed demand and throughout 1988, and later in certain cases, copies were to be found in discount stores nationwide for as little as £0.99.

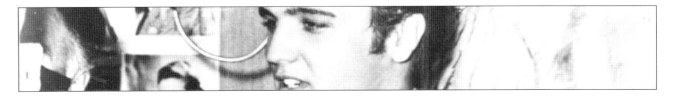

LP 292 | Mess O' Blues - Volumes 1&2
Premier PPD 2000

Side 1

1   **Trouble** (Leiber, Stoller)
2   **Reconsider Baby** (Fulson)
3   **A Mess Of Blues** (Pomus, Shuman)
4   **Give Me The Right** (Wise, Blagman)
5   **Such A Night** (Chase)
6   **When It Rains, It Really Pours** (Emerson)

Side 2

1   **Trying To Get To You** (Singleton, McCoy)
2   **Like A Baby** (Stone)
3   **I Want To Be Free** (Leiber, Stoller)
4   **Mean Woman Blues** (DeMetrius)
5   **Ain't That Loving You Baby** (Otis, Hunter)
6   **One Night** (Bartholomew, King)

Side 3

1   **Little Sister** (Pomus, Shuman)
2   **So Glad You're Mine** (Crudup)
3   **Big Boss Man** (Smith, Dixon)
4   **I Want You With Me** (Harris)
5   **Baby, What You Want Me To Do** (Reed)
6   **Santa Claus Is Back In Town** (Leiber, Stoller)

Side 4

1   **Stuck On You** (Schroeder, McFarland)
2   **I Feel So Bad** (Willis)
3   **What'd I Say** (Charles)
4   **Tomorrow Night** (Croslow, Grosz)
5   **It Feels So Right** (Wise, Weisman)
6   **Merry Christmas Baby** (Baxter, Moore)

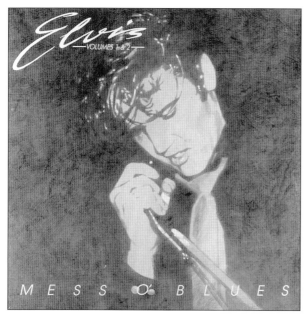

Released March 1988

This album was previously entitled **Blue Rhythms**, EPC 1000 (*LP 205*), first released in December 1983 by Everest Records, and re-issued as PPD 2001 (*LP 269*) in January 1985 by Premier. In

October 1987, two separate single albums were released entitled **Mess O' Blues - Volume 1** and **Mess O' Blues - Volume 2**, PMP 1012 (**LP 289**) and PMP 1013 (**LP 290**), which contained the same tracks. A year later, in March 1989, the set was made available again, this time on Performance Records, and entitled **Mess O' Blues - 24 Classic Tracks**, PFP 2000 (**LP 300**).

There are no prizes for guessing that this double album was actually the two single albums combined to restore the original **Blue Rhythms** (*LP 205*) album to its full twenty four track listing. However, we do not consider this to be a re-issue, because of the change in title, but, to all intents and purposes, this was the same album.

Released barely six months after the two single albums, this was a very unusual and, in many respects, unique release, which could well become quite a collectors' item in years to come.

Premier had a new sleeve prepared which was really an enlarged single album sleeve, not a gatefold one, into which they placed the volume 1 and volume 2 single albums, PMP 1012 and PMP 1013, complete with their own sleeves. By retaining the single album sleeves, this new release presented a packaging format never before used on a UK Elvis album. The new outer sleeve was given a new catalogue number of PPD 2000, a number which bore more than a passing resemblance to the PPD 2001, allocated to the January 1985 re-issue of **Blue Rhythms** (*LP 205*).

We can only speculate as to why this re-packaging took place. Premier were either forced to make this move because sales of volumes 1 and 2 as separate albums were low, and this was a good marketing ploy to sell off stocks, or the idea was to sell even more records (containing the same material) because some die-hard fans would buy this as an extra set at reduced cost. Whilst this may be true to some extent, it could not have been the main reason. Our belief is that the former is much more likely, for two main reasons. Firstly, why would Premier bother to produce more single album sleeves if they intended to use a new outer sleeve? Secondly, the price of the set was around £5, substantially less than it cost to buy the records individually (£7). So, all in all, it seemed highly likely that Premier were simply out to get what they could from this material. What confused the issue slightly was that the tracks on this album re-appeared again in March 1989 on a different label, but still under the control of the same people responsible for all the other releases of the album.

Other than the reference to volumes 1 and 2 on the front of the sleeve, it was identical to the single album issues, but the full track listing on the back appeared at the expense of the small painting found on the single albums.

All of the errors found on the two single albums appeared in identical fashion on this album. (See **LPs 289** and **290**).

Label Variations

LIGHT BLUE LABEL

1   1987 PRESSING: MONO/STEREO

Sleeve Variations

1   Outer sleeve around individual album sleeves

LP 293   *Elvis Presley Interview Picture Disc*

Baktabak BAK 2086

Side 1

1   **WPMS, Memphis,** with Bob Neal, 31 August 1955
2   **San Antonio, Texas,** with Charlie Walker, 15 April 1956
3   **Warwick Hotel, New York,** with Robert Carlton Brown, 24 March 1956

Side 2

1   **Warwick Hotel, New York,** with Robert Carlton Brown, 24 March 1956 (continued)
2   **Honolulu, Hawaii,** with Tom Moffett and Peter Noone 18 August 1965

Released April 1988

During April 1988, Baktabak released a collection of Elvis interviews on four picture disc singles (**S 174**), a CD single, and this picture disc album. (Note: some sources quote a March release date for this album.) The basis for the whole collection was the material found on the Silhouette album ***Personally Elvis***, first issued in America and, subsequently, licensed by Buttons Records for release in the UK as ***Elvis Answers Back*** during 1981 (*LP 145*). Later still, in March 1982, the American album was also released in the UK (*LP 186*), followed by more re-issues.

The singles and the album contained the same material, except that the 'interview' with Peter Noone of Herman's Hermits only appeared on this album. The material was, in the main, duplicated across both formats, but at the time of purchase there was no way of knowing this, for neither the album, nor singles, gave any clue as to the contents, other than vague references on the singles to it being 'A rare interview with Elvis Presley: 1956'. The 'label' was even less revealing, stating only that it was a limited edition picture disc. The only attraction for fans/collectors seemed to be that it was a picture disc, using two colour photographs from ***Stay Away, Joe*** and ***Roustabout***.

Incidentally, Elvis was not the only artist featured in the series. Baktabak had produced a comprehensive repertoire of these interview picture discs since their initial release in 1987, including The Beatles, Madonna and Elton John. Under the umbrella title of

Talking Pictures, there were 10 and 12 inch picture disc albums, and picture disc CDs, as well as the picture disc 7 inch collections.

The use of the phrase 'Limited Edition' has often been open to abuse, as fans discovered to their cost in the past. Its appearance on any Elvis release was rightly questioned. Baktabak claimed that this was a genuine limited edition (of 15,000 copies incidentally) would 'not be exceeded'. However, 15,000 copies was a lot of albums, and many record companies would be grateful for the income that generated. We believe that the use of the term 'limited edition' ought to be accompanied by the number of records actually being made. We are not blaming Baktabak for this: they were simply doing their job. Incidentally, the initial press run was for 5,000 copies which appeared in a clear plastic sleeve. Later runs were issued firstly in marble effect white and blue sleeve and, later, in a black sleeve. By doing so, three sleeve variations were created and, it could be argued, the 'limited edition' phrase became more pertinent. There was, however, no discernible difference in any pressing of the disc itself.

The card sleeves provided more details of the other titles available and showed that Tabak Marketing, Baktabak's parent company, did not own the copyright on the Elvis material featured on the album.

Picture Disc Variations

1   1988 PRESSING: MONO

Sleeve Variations

1   Clear plastic
2   Blue/white marble effect
3   Black

Album Deletion - April 1988

The First Live Recordings, PG 89387, issued in July 1984 (*LP 234*), was deleted in April 1988.

Price Codes

All full priced RCA albums from *The Alternate Aloha*, PL 86985 (**LP 294**), until the boxed set *Collectors Gold*, PL 90574(3) (**LP 315**), released in August 1991, made use of the HH price code - the original code first used in 1974.

Mid priced items - albums with the NL catalogue number prefix - continued to use YY.

Sleeve Detail Change

A new detail appeared for the first time on *The Alternate Aloha*, PL 86985 (**LP 294**). This was the BMG logo printed at the bottom of the back of the sleeve, next to the round RCA logo. Note that under the letters BMG was the word 'MUSIC' which would disappear on later albums, and be replaced by the words 'A Bertelsmann Music Group Company', although some of the subsequent albums did not show a BMG logo of any kind.

There were no other changes to either sleeve or label details.

LP 294	The Alternate Aloha
	RCA PL 86985

Side 1
1   **See See Rider** (Broonzy)
2   **Burning Love** (Linde)
3   **Something** (Harrison)
4   **You Gave Me A Mountain** (Robbins)
5   **Steamroller Blues** (Taylor)
6   **My Way** (Thibault, Francois, Revaux, Anka)
7   **Love Me** (Leiber, Stoller)
8   **It's Over** (Rodgers)
9   **Blue Suede Shoes** (Perkins)
10   **I'm So Lonesome I Could Cry** (Williams)

Side 2
1   **What Now My Love** (Delanoe, Becaud, Sigman)
2   **Fever** (Davenport, Cooley)
3   **Welcome To My World** (Winkler, Hathcock)
4   **Suspicious Minds** (James)
5   **I'll Remember You** (Lee)
6   **An American Trilogy** (Arr. Newbury)
7   **A Big Hunk O' Love** (Schroeder, Wyche)
8   **Can't Help Falling In Love** (Peretti, Creatore, Weiss)
9   **Blue Hawaii** (Robin, Rainger)

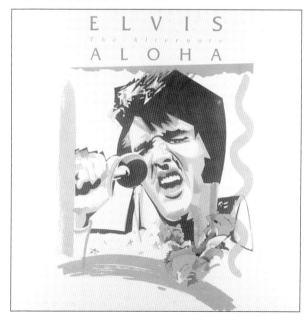

Released May 1988   **Deleted May 1991**

For many years it had been known that in addition to recording the **Aloha From Hawaii Satellite TV Special** on 14 January, 1973, a dress rehearsal or 'back-up' show had been taped on 12 January, 1973, in case anything went wrong during the recording, and transmission of this historic show. Happily nothing did, but not long after Elvis died, unofficial video copies of the so-called 'back-up' show became available. Indeed, some were even on sale openly and, apparently, officially. Audio copies of the show were made available to fans via the bootleg industry. The first copies of the bootleg originated from 1980.

However, in May 1988, the concert finally secured an official release, fifteen years after the event. Apparently the original idea had been to issue it in January to coincide exactly with the fifteenth anniversary. Obviously, this did not happen.

This, in fact, was one of the few US inspired albums to secure worldwide release in the post-1986 period. The executive producer for this project was Don Wardell, a high-ranking marketing manager for RCA in the USA. Unusually, he was credited on the album label.

Great emphasis was placed on the fact that the concert had been digitally remastered, and subjected to all manner of technical wizardry to obtain the best possible sound. Indeed, the sleeve notes, penned by engineer and producer Rick Rowe, waxed lyrical about the process used when remixing this album. All of which proved to be quite ironic, as the end result was, for many, very unsatisfactory. And, while mixing or remixing is crucial to the success of a product, it is also highly subjective. However, in keeping with our policy of minimising personal comment on the value or worth of a product/release, suffice it to say the release was not critically acclaimed, and many fans believed that while the instrumentation was clear, Elvis's voice image was too far back in the mix. Some even professed to have found the bootleg better in its overall sound quality, despite the fact that it had been issued in mono sound only.

Unusually, the album did boast quite elaborate technical sleeve notes - in itself a first on an Elvis album - as well as general background notes. The trouble was that for many people their meaning was extremely hard to follow, especially as the language was obscure and jargon-ridden. Indeed, it is known that Bob Jones himself found what was written incomprehensible - even as a remastering engineer of international repute.

It is widely known that following the broadcast of the actual show (14 January 1973), and once the audience had left the auditorium, Elvis and the band returned to the stage and recorded a further five songs: **Blue Hawaii**, **Ku-U-I-Po**, **No More**, **Hawaiian Wedding Song** and **Early Mornin' Rain**. None of these songs was used on the original soundtrack album, but they were included in the US TV broadcast when it was televised in May 1973. Quite simply, the idea was to insert these extra songs into the show at various points to extend the show to one and a half hours (including adverts). In fact, only one of these extra songs was available in the UK until they were included on **The King.... Elvis**, CDS 1190 (**LP 123**), released in January 1980. **Blue Hawaii** had been on **Elvis - A Legendary Performer Vol 2**, CPL1 1349 (**LP 87**), issued in January 1976. Incidentally, with the exception of **Early Mornin' Rain**, all of these songs had originally been included in the film **Blue Hawaii** (though not these versions, of course). Elvis's studio version of Gordon Lightfoot's **Early Mornin' Rain** had been cut in Nashville in March 1971 and included on the May 1972 album **Elvis Now** (**LP 61**). The live version from the post-show sessions had only been available on **The King.... Elvis**, in the UK. Subsequently, **Early Mornin' Rain**, **Hawaiian Wedding Song**, **Ku-U-I-Po** and **No More** were also on **Rare Elvis** (**LP 263**), released in January 1985.

There were slight track differences between this album and the actual 14 January concert. Apparently changes were made when the timing of the rehearsal show revealed that more musical items were needed to fill the time available. Added to the 14 January show were: **Johnny B. Goode**, **I Can't Stop Loving You** and a medley of **Long Tall Sally/Whole Lotta Shakin' Goin' On**.

Ironically, while **The Alternate Aloha** vinyl album only included one of the extra songs - **Blue Hawaii** - one of the songs sung during the concert itself, **Hound Dog**, was cut from the album, as were the introductions to the band. The CD version though included the following: **Hound Dog**, **Hawaiian Wedding Song** and **Ku-U-I-Po**. **Early Mornin' Rain** and **No More** were not included. It is worth noting that along with the extra tracks there was incidental 'chat' between the songs, and a false start to **Hawaiian Wedding Song**.

All references to the album title on the sleeve appeared as **Elvis The Alternate Aloha**, whereas the record label simply stated **The Alternate Aloha**, with 'Elvis Presley' printed beneath. The cover itself did not feature a photograph of Elvis, but had instead a sketch of him (from the show) by Cynthia Marsh.

And, as this was a US originated album, the main producer credits went to Don Wardell and Rick Rowe. However, among the credits on the LP inner bag were acknowledgements to Roger Semon of BMG in London, and Todd Slaughter of the Official Elvis Presley Fan Club of Great Britain.

Incidentally, as the inner bag also mentioned, only two of these versions had been released officially before: **Blue Hawaii** on **Elvis - A Legendary Performer Vol. 2** (**LP 87**), and **Steamroller Blues** which first appeared in the UK on **The Sound Of Your Cry**, RCALP 3060 (**LP 185**), in January 1982. Actually the sources were not quoted on the vinyl album cover, but the US sources were mentioned on the CD version.

The label and sleeve errors were old ones. Elvis was correctly identified with the arrangement on **See See Rider**, but there was no reference to the song's writer - Bill Broonzy. **My Way** was credited incorrectly to Anka, Revaux, Francois, and **What Now My Love** credited Sigman, Becaud, not Delanoe, Becaud, Sigman. **An American Trilogy** omitted the **An** on both label and sleeve, and **A Big Hunk O' Love** omitted the **A** on the sleeve only.

The Alternate Aloha LP was deleted on 24 May 1991.

Label Variations

GERMAN BLACK LABEL

1   1988 PRESSING: STEREO
     Computer style logo
     BIEM above GEMA in separate boxes

Sleeve Variations

1   Gloss

LP 295 The Elvis Presley Sun Collection

HMV C88 1-2

Side 1

1 **That's All Right** (Crudup)
2 **Blue Moon Of Kentucky** (Monroe)
3 **I Don't Care If The Sun Don't Shine** (David)
4 **Good Rockin' Tonight** (Brown)
5 **Milkcow Blues Boogie** (Arnold)
6 **You're A Heartbreaker** (Sallee)
7 **I'm Left, You're Right, She's Gone** (Kesler, Taylor)
8 **Baby Let's Play House** (Gunter)

Side 2

1 **Mystery Train** (Parker, Phillips)
2 **I Forgot To Remember To Forget** (Kesler, Feathers)
3 **I'll Never Let You Go (little darlin')** (Wakely)
4 **I Love You Because** (Payne)
5 **Trying To Get To You** (Singleton, McCoy)
6 **Blue Moon** (Rodgers, Hart)
7 **Just Because** (B & J Shelton, Robin)
8 **I Love You Because** (Payne)
9 **Harbour Lights** (Kennedy, Williams)

Released September 1988
Original Issue October 1983. RCA NL 89107 (LP 201)

An album with the same title, but minus **Harbour Lights**, was released in July 1975 on RCA Starcall HY 1001 (*LP 80*). This album was re-issued in March 1979, RCA NL 42757 (*LP 108*).

HMV record stores had dabbled previously in producing their own collectors items, of which the most successful was a Beatles CD set which went on to attract very high prices. For their 'Classic Collection', HMV had negotiated with many of the major record companies to produce a series of sixteen boxed special edition releases, which included this Elvis album, and included such artists as Fleetwood Mac, Led Zeppelin, The Eagles, etc.

At the outset, we ought to make it quite clear that there was nothing special about the record itself: this was the standard RCA product of

the time, a German black album and sleeve. However, what made the release so interesting and appealing was that HMV had prepared a special presentation box to hold the record.

Each album in the series came in a box with a black bottom section. It was padded so that the album did not move about - a feature which ought to have been standard for this kind of release, for it allowed the overall thickness of the box to be large enough to create the impression that the contents were substantial, and yet, at the same time, it had a practical use. The cream coloured lid had a sticker applied in the top right hand corner showing the price (£7.99) and series title, which was repeated on another sticker in the lower left hand corner. In the bottom right hand section was the individual number of the LP, and the total number produced - 3500. It is worth pointing out that the CD version cost £12.99, and, as with the LP, 3,500 copies were produced. The price, of both LP and CD, in effect meant that £4 had been added to the normal price for the booklet and packaging - a price, it seems, which was worth paying, for all available copies were quickly sold. And, as copies rarely turned up on the second hand market, we can only assume that it was collectors who were buying the product.

The central section of the cover was a replica of the original sleeve artwork, with the words 'originally released July 31st 1975' underneath. Actually this claim was slightly misleading because whilst there was indeed an album with this title released on that date, it wasn't this album exactly. The reason for this was that an additional track, **Harbour Lights**, was added to the original sixteen track compilation when the album re-appeared in October 1983 (*LP 201*). In fact, the song in question had not been released until January 1976, when it appeared on the album **Elvis - A Legendary Performer Vol. 2** (*LP 87*), having only recently been discovered.

Inside the box was a note about the series and, more importantly, a twelve page booklet which was written by Roy Carr who had been responsible for the notes on the back of **The Elvis Presley Sun Collection** sleeve. These were entertaining and informative, although there was more than a hint of speculation presented as though it were fact. This was particularly noticeable in the way he authoritatively stated that **Uncle Penn** was recorded in September 1954 at the session which produced **Good Rockin' Tonight**. Even Ernst Mikael Jorgensen, who has had more access to Elvis material and documentation than anyone else, could not confirm this as fact.

Reference to *LP 201* in **Elvis UK 1956-86**, will reveal that the label of this 'HMV' release was a variation of the one we described in our earlier work. This variation, produced in 1988, was identical in every respect, with the exception of the way the mechanical rights societies were printed.

Because this was really the RCA NL 89107 album, the errors found on that release remained the same here. Of particular note was the way in which RCA used inaccurate publishing dates for the songs (see the notes following **The Complete Sun Sessions** - **LP 283** - for precise dates).

Label Variations

GERMAN BLACK LABEL

1   1988 PRESSING: MONO
Computer style logo
BIEM above GEMA in separate boxes

Sleeve Variations

1   Matt Box

Album Deletion - October 1988

Reconsider Baby, PL 85418 (*LP 271*), a compilation album from May 1985, was deleted on 2 October 1988.

Label Detail Change

The label for **Moody Blue,** NL 90252 (**LP 296**), amended the 'Marketed by...' details to read 'Marketed by BMG Records'.

The sleeve had no BMG logo on the back, but the round RCA logo was still shown.

LP 296	Moody Blue
	RCA NL 90252

Side 1

1   **Unchained Melody** (North, Zaret)
2   **If You Love Me (let me know)** (Rostill)
3   **Little Darlin'** (Williams)
4   **He'll Have To Go** (J & A Allison)
5   **Let Me Be There** (Rostill)

Side 2

1   **Way Down** (Martine Jr.)
2   **Pledging My Love** (Robey, Washington)
3   **Moody Blue** (James)
4   **She Thinks I Still Care** (Lipscomb)
5   **It's Easy For You** (Webber, Rice)

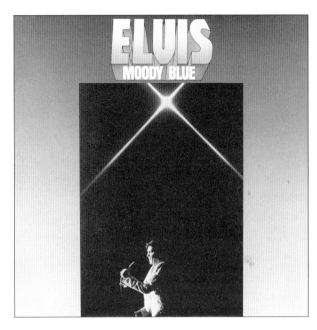

Released October 1988   Deleted March 1992
Original Issue August 1977. RCA PL 12428 (*LP 93*)
Previous Re-issue September 1981. RCALP 3021 (*LP 178*)
Previous Re-issue January 1985. RCA PL 82428 (*LP 260*)

This was the fourth time **Moody Blue** had been released since the original issue in 1977. When we discussed the 1985 RCA PL 82428 issue (*LP 260*), an album produced in Germany on RCA's new black label, in **Elvis UK 1956-86**, we pointed out that its price of £5.49 was £2 more that the original album had cost. Yet, whereas all of the previous issues had been full priced albums, this release was placed in the mid-price range and cost £3.99, representing a mere fifty pence increase in price over the cost of the original issue. So, if you were buying **Moody Blue** for the first time then it represented real value for money. This, then, was a mid-priced album (indicated by the NL prefix) which replaced the full priced PL 82428 album, which had been deleted three months earlier in July 1988.

The sleeve was virtually the same as all the previous issues, with a number of minor amendments, including a revised bar code and price code layout, along with modified ownership and distribution details. The most significant change though was the removal of the old RCA computer style logo on the spine and front and back of the sleeve, which were replaced by the inclusion of the round RCA logo on the back of the sleeve only.

The label featured a revised layout from that included on the 1985 version of the album. Elvis's name was printed above the title, the playing speed - 33 - moved from the bottom to the right of the spindle hole, and the track details were presented both above and below the centre, instead of all below.

In keeping with many RCA albums of that time, the date the record was mastered could be found engraved into the vinyl between the run-out grooves, reading 9/88.

The album was issued in all formats: LP, CD and cassette.

In 1990, the album was re-pressed, making it one of the few albums from this period to achieve this status. Instead of the computer style RCA logo on the left of the label, the round RCA logo was used instead. All other details remained the same, with the exception of the marketing and copyright information, although the September mastering date was no longer shown between the run-out grooves. There is one point we would like to clear up regarding what we have previously considered to have been an error. We had constantly referred to the writers of **Unchained Melody** to be the wrong way round when, in fact, the order had always been shown North and Zaret. The song index has been amended.

The album was deleted in March 1992.

Label Variations

NEW BLACK LABEL

1   **1988 PRESSING: STEREO**
     Computer style RCA logo
     BIEM above GEMA in separate boxes

2   **1990 PRESSING: STEREO**
     Round RCA logo on left of label

Sleeve Variations

1   **Gloss**

RCA Catalogue Numbers

Up to this point the Elvis albums issued by RCA since 1987 had adopted the following pattern: PL for full price albums and NL for mid-price releases. Two other prefixes had been used but only on one occasion each - BL had appeared on the May 1984 release of **This Is Elvis**, BL 84031(2) (*LP 226*), and PG had made its only appearance on **The First Live Recordings**, PG 89387 (*LP 234*), issued in July 1984.

The next RCA album, a three record boxed set, entitled **Special Edition**, CL 90249(3) (**LP 297**), was a departure for the company, in that it was a mail order release and, to distinguish it from the regular releases, it was allocated a different, and new, prefix: CL. To date this was the only Elvis record to use this prefix, although the normal five digit catalogue number followed the same pattern as regular releases.

LP 297	Special Edition
	RCA CL 90249(3)

Side 1
1   **Heartbreak Hotel** (Axton, Durden, Presley)
2   **Blue Suede Shoes** (Perkins)
3   **I Want You, I Need You, I Love You** (Mysels, Kosloff)
4   **My Baby Left Me** (Crudup)
5   **Hound Dog** (Leiber, Stoller)
6   **Don't Be Cruel** (Blackwell, Presley)
7   **Love Me Tender** (Presley, Matson)
8   **All Shook Up** (Blackwell, Presley)
9   **That's When Your Heartaches Begin** (Raskin, Brown, Fisher)

Side 2
1   **Paralyzed** (Blackwell, Presley)
2   **Lawdy, Miss Clawdy** (Price)
3   **I'm Left, You're Right, She's Gone** (Kesler, Taylor)
4   **I Forgot To Remember To Forget** (Kesler, Feathers)
5   **Just Because** (B. & J. Shelton, Robin)
6   **Jailhouse Rock** (Leiber, Stoller)
7   **(Let me be your) Teddy Bear** (Mann, Lowe)
8   **Party** (Robinson)
9   **Got A Lot O' Livin' To Do!** (Schroeder, Weisman)

Side 3
1   **Wild In The Country** (Peretti, Creatore, Weiss)
2   **(Marie's the name) His Latest Flame** (Pomus, Shuman)
3   **Rock-A-Hula Baby** (Wise, Weisman, Fuller)
4   **Good Luck Charm** (Schroeder, Gold)
5   **She's Not You** (Pomus, Leiber, Stoller)
6   **(You're the) Devil In Disguise** (Giant, Baum, Kaye)
7   **Crying In The Chapel** (Glenn)
8   **Ain't That Loving You Baby** (Otis, Hunter)

163

Side 4

1. **Indescribably Blue** (Glenn)
2. **Love Letters** (Young, Heyman)
3. **Long Legged Girl (with the short dress on)** (McFarland, Scott)
4. **There's Always Me** (Robertson)
5. **You Gotta Stop** (Giant, Baum, Kaye)
6. **You'll Never Walk Alone** (Rodgers, Hammerstein II)
7. **Your Time Hasn't Come Yet Baby** (Hirchhorn, Kasha)
8. **Almost In Love** (Bonfa, Starr)

Side 5

1. **Guitar Man** (Reed)
2. **Hi Heel Sneakers** (Higgenbotham)
3. **U.S. Male** (Hubbard)
4. **Memories** (Strange, Davis)
5. **In The Ghetto** (Davis)
6. **Suspicious Minds** (James)
7. **Kentucky Rain** (Rabbitt, Heard)
8. **I've Lost You** (Howard, Blaikley)

Side 6

1. **I Just Can't Help Believin'** (Mann, Weil)
2. **Until It's Time For You To Go** (Sainte-Marie)
3. **The Wonder Of You** (Knight)
4. **I'm Leavin'** (Jarrett, Charles)
5. **Burning Love** (Linde)
6. **The Next Step Is Love** (Evans, Parnes)
7. **My Way** (Thibault, Francois, Revaux, Anka)
8. **An American Trilogy** (Arr. Newbury)

Released October 1988   Deleted March 1995

Those readers with long memories (or access to *Elvis UK 1956-86*) will, perhaps, recognise this three album boxed set as being the same fifty track compilation as the 1981 Imperial Records (actually K-tel) release *American Trilogy*, DR 1124 (*LP 151*). Imperial originally advertised the album on TV as a mail order package, although towards the end of 1981, copies turned up in record shops.

RCA decided to issue the set themselves in 1988, again as a kind of mail order release. Dates next to the matrix number in the run-out grooves show that mastering was done in August and September

1988, just before the album was released in October. The set was advertised for one day only in the Daily Express, and was available also via various record clubs. To all intents and purposes, the only place it was not available was in normal record shops, although occasionally copies did turn up. RCA's intention was to fill a gap in the market, and they thought that collections such as this served a useful purpose. Similar sets were produced for other RCA artists, such as Jim Reeves and Glenn Miller.

In all, 5,000 copies of the album were produced, and, by mid-1992, around 3,500 had been sold. For the casual buyer, this set represented good value, even at the 1991/92 price of less than £14. Most of the tracks had been released on singles over the years, and obviously most of them were hits. However, for fans, most of what was included offered nothing new. But in 1988, when the set was issued, there had been some radical changes in the amount of Elvis material available, and certain songs could not be readily obtained in any format in the UK. So, if you just happened to be searching for tracks like *Almost In Love* or *Your Time Hasn't Come Yet Baby*, then perhaps this album fitted the bill. For collectors, it has to be said, this should have been an essential purchase simply because it was a unique RCA package with a relatively small press run. At the time though, no CD format was available, and when the album was released on CD in February 1991, it also attracted little attention. The CD (and cassette versions) were handled in exactly the same way as the earlier vinyl copies: being sold through mail order outlets and specialist retailers like Argos, who sold the cassettes for £12.99 and the CDs for £19.99. They also referred to the set as *The Elvis Presley Collection* in their catalogue.

The box was grey and, in terms of quality and layout, evoked a general air of being a fairly cheap 'European' album from somewhere like Portugal or Denmark. Much slimmer than the later RCA box sets such as *Collectors Gold* (**LP 315**), it prevented the albums inside from moving about too much. Emblazoned across the top were the words THREE ALBUM SET, Elvis's name, the album's title, and the fact that it contained fifty tracks - all good marketing 'bullet points'. The back of the box, which listed the tracks (the original Imperial album failed to do so), was quite plain. There was a bar code, but no price code, although many of the regular features were included - LC 0316, and the round RCA logo. The spine did not mention the title, just the catalogue number (minus the (3), indicating a three record set), Elvis's name and, again, three record set.

No modes were mentioned on either label or on the box. The tracks were, in fact, a mixture of mono and stereo recordings. On LP 1, all of the tracks were mono, as they ought to have been, and on LP 2 all of the tracks were in stereo, except for *Ain't That Loving You Baby* which was in mono. *You Gotta Stop* was also in mono, although it was recorded in stereo. All of the tracks on LP 3 should have been in stereo, but the following were presented in mono: *Hi Heel Sneakers*, *I've Lost You* and *I'm Leavin'*. As regards versions, *Suspicious Minds* was the full single version with the extended ending; *My Way* was from the Aloha show (January 1973); while *An American Trilogy* was the single version from 14 February 1972. A 'first published' and copyright date of 1988 was shown. The mastering was done by Mike Brown on 2 September 1988, a date which could be seen between the run out grooves, although on side four this was shown as 2/8 (August). We believe this to be a mistake.

The albums were standard RCA German black labels and used the normal design. There were, however, two interesting features worth noting. The sides were numbered one to six, not album 1, side 1 etc., but each album had an additional digit applied to the catalogue number to indicate which particular record it was i.e. CL 90249(3)-1. Also, there was a note at the bottom of each label which was quite unusual, reading 'Original Sound Recordings Made By BMG Records (UK) Ltd.'

In terms of errors, there were quite a few, as perhaps we had come to expect with these multi-album releases, and many were identical to those found on the Imperial Records set.

On the label - side 1, track 1 - Tommy Durden had his name misspelt Durdon. Once again, Fisher, Hill and Raskin were credited with writing **That's When Your Heartaches Begin**. Both the label and sleeve spelt **Paralyzed** with an *'s'*. On the label only (no writing credits were shown on the box), the writers of **I'm Left, You're Right, She's Gone** were incorrectly identified as Kesler, Feathers. This pair wrote the next track, **I Forgot To Remember To Forget**, so perhaps this was where the error originated. The correct writers were Kesler, Taylor. Both the label and sleeve omitted the exclamation mark at the end of **Got A Lot O' Livin' To Do!**.

On side 3, track 2, the additional word *'of'* was incorrectly inserted in **(Marie's the name) His Latest Flame**. The writers of track 5, **She's Not You**, usually appeared in a different order, and on both label and sleeve, track 6, **(You're the) Devil In Disguise**, was listed without the brackets.

On side 4, track 7, no comma appeared in **Your Time Hasn't Come Yet, Baby**, again on both the label and sleeve.

On side 5, track 2 (but on the sleeve only), **Hi Heel Sneakers** was listed as **High Heel Sneakers**.

Finally, **My Way**, had the usual error of showing the writers in a different order.

Label Variations

GERMAN BLACK LABEL

1 1988 PRESSING: MONO/STEREO
Computer style RCA logo
BIEM above GEMA in separate boxes

Sleeve Variations

1 Grey box, matt finish

Pickwick - Camden Releases

Towards the end of 1988 Pickwick, the company responsible for issuing Elvis's Camden record releases under contract from RCA, deleted their entire LP catalogue, including all their Elvis records. There were three reasons for this. The most significant reason being that they wished to concentrate on compact disc releases, and they intended to direct their attention towards the increasing demand for the children's market for talking books. Secondly, the company felt that the market had been saturated with budget price material, leased from whatever source, a fact that was particularly true of Elvis material. Finally, RCA themselves had begun to question the whole principle of leasing material to other companies.

The contribution made by Pickwick to the Elvis market should not be underestimated, for despite limitations in the amount of material which they had at their disposal, Pickwick regularly produced high quality product, using sleeves which stood out well compared to their full priced RCA equivalents. Pickwick had cornered a regular slice of the market and were able to reach a wider customer base, with outlets in supermarkets and chain stores, enabling them to release a succession of interesting compilations which would not have seen the light of day had they been left solely in the hands of RCA. To their credit Pickwick also released a couple of film soundtrack albums which would otherwise have remained deleted in the UK.

However, as a result of their decision to pull out of the record market, further releases of film soundtrack albums - previously pencilled in - were cancelled. This was a shame, as it meant that in order to obtain this kind of material, previously deleted by RCA, it was necessary to buy expensive imports.

At this point, we thought it would be useful to present a full listing of all Camden releases, and to summarise some of the more important points regarding these releases.

Complete listing of Camden LPs

			Release Date	Release Number
1.	CDM 1088	*You'll Never Walk Alone*	Mar 1971	*LP 48*
2.	CDS 1110	*Elvis Sings Hits From His Movies*	Oct 1972	*LP 64*
3.	CDS 1118	*Separate Ways*	May 1973	*LP 67*
4.	CDS 1146	*Easy Come Easy Go*	Feb 1975	*LP 76*
5.	CDS 1150	*The U.S. Male*	Jun 1975	*LP 78*
6.	CDS 1155	*Elvis' Christmas Album*	Oct 1975	*LP 81*
7.	CDS 1154	*I Got Lucky*	Nov 1975	*LP 84*

Please note: two three-album sets, comprising various Camden albums, were released via mail order catalogues only towards the end of 1975. These were existing albums re-packaged in a special sleeve. See **Elvis Presley** (*LP 85*), and **Elvis Presley Vol. 2** (*LP 86*).

			Release Date	Release Number
8.	PDA 009	*The Elvis Presley Collection*	Aug 1976	*LP 89*
9.	PDA 042	*The Elvis Presley Collection Vol. 2*	Jun 1978	*LP 103*
10.	CDS 1175	*Please Don't Stop Loving Me*	Apr 1979	*LP 109*
11.	CDS 1185	*Flaming Star*	Apr 1979	*LP 110*
12.	PDA 054	*The Elvis Presley Collection Vol. 3*	Apr 1979	*LP 111*
13.	CDS 1182	*Double Dynamite Vol. 1*	Jan 1980	*LP 120*
14.	CDS 1188	*Double Dynamite Vol. 2*	Jan 1980	*LP 121*
15.	PDA 057	*Double Dynamite*	Jan 1980	*LP 122*
16.	CDS 1190	*The King...Elvis*	Jan 1980	*LP 123*
17.	CDS 1200	*Return To Sender*	Jan 1981	*LP 141*
18.	CDS 1201	*Elvis Presley*	Feb 1981	*LP 142*
19.	PDA 073	*The Wonderful World Of Elvis*	Jan 1981	*LP 143*
20.	CDS 1203	*It's Now Or Never*	Aug 1981	*LP 163*
21.	CDS 1204	*Heartbreak Hotel*	Aug 1981	*LP 164*
22.	CDS 1206	*Suspicious Minds*	Apr 1982	*LP 188*
23.	CDS 1207	*Are You Lonesome Tonight?*	Apr 1982	*LP 189*
24.	CDS 1210	*Can't Help Falling In Love & Other Great Movie Hits*	May 1983	*LP 197*
25.	CDS 1211	*Love Songs*	Aug 1983	*LP 199*
26.	CDS 1212	*The Legend*	Oct 1983	*LP 202*
27.	CDS 1213	*The First Ten Years*	Sep 1984	*LP 246*
28.	CDS 1215	*The Rock Hits*	Apr 1986	**LP 276**
29.	CDS 1221	*Girls! Girls! Girls!*	Sep 1986	**LP 278**
30.	CDS 1222	*Kissin' Cousins*	Sep 1986	**LP 279**

Most of the earlier albums had been deleted for many years, but two had survived throughout the period. They were the first Camden release, CDM 1088, **You'll Never Walk Alone** (*LP 48*), and the seasonal **Elvis' Christmas Album** (*LP 81*). At the end of 1988, by which time a lot of the albums listed above were deleted, only eleven others (in addition to the two releases referred to above) remained on catalogue, and many of these were difficult to locate as shops reduced stock. Basically, those still available were the later releases from CDS 1200, **Return To Sender** (*LP 141*) to the end of the list, with the exception of CDS 1201, **Elvis Presley** (*LP 142*) and PDA 073, **The Wonderful World Of Elvis** (*LP 143*), which were only available for a short period of time.

The first Camden release, **You'll Never Walk Alone** (*LP 48*), was an essential purchase when it was released in March 1971, as it contained previously unreleased material in the form of **Who Am I?** and **Let Us Pray**, as well as restoring to catalogue some previously deleted items.

You'll Never Walk Alone was never deleted throughout its seventeen year history, and was the only Camden album to carry the catalogue number prefix CDM, because it comprised several mono recordings. However, in May 1987, the album was re-mastered in stereo by Bob Jones, except of course for the tracks originally recorded in mono. Sadly, this went by almost unnoticed - certainly there was no promotion - which was not entirely unexpected, but there was no indication of this situation on the sleeve, which still carried the CDM mono prefix. However, the label was re-catalogued CDS for stereo and, of course, Bob had scratched the new catalogue number in the vinyl. The sleeve, however, claimed the record was mono.

CDS 1110, **Elvis Sings Hits From His Movies** (*LP 64*), was thought to have had more masters prepared for it than any other UK album, and was possibly the most re-pressed UK Elvis album of all time.

CDS 1118, **Separate Ways** (*LP 67*), was interesting in that it featured the title track - the B side of **Always On My Mind**, which was also included on the album - the point being that the single had only been released a few months earlier, in December 1972, (*S 85*). This was an interesting departure, whereby a successful single (it reached number 9 in the charts) was featured on a budget album, as opposed to a 'greatest hits' type package for release by RCA themselves.

Pickwick's policy of releasing single albums which were then re-packaged and re-issued as a double album (often simultaneously with the single albums), was a feature unique to them. This meant **You'll Never Walk Alone** (*LP 48*) and **Elvis Sings Hits From His Movies** (*LP 64*) became **The Elvis Presley Collection** (*LP 89*), while **Separate Ways** (*LP 67*) and **Easy Come Easy Go** (*LP 76*) became **The Elvis Presley Collection Vol. 2** (*LP 103*). For the third volume, **Please Don't Stop Loving Me** (*LP 109*) and **Flaming Star** (*LP 110*) were combined to produce **The Elvis Presley Collection Vol. 3** (*LP 111*), released at the same time. Later, in January 1980, two **Double Dynamite** single albums (*LP 120* and *LP 121*) were issued together under the imaginative title **Double Dynamite** (*LP 122*).

The King...Elvis, CDS 1190 (*LP 123*), released in January 1980, was another essential purchase at the time because it contained material not available elsewhere i.e. the four songs recorded after the actual show for inclusion in the 1973 **Aloha From Hawaii** TV Special. A fifth song, **Blue Hawaii**, also included, had been released previously on **Elvis - A Legendary Performer Vol. 2** (*LP 87*) in January 1976. Although many fans bought the American import album **Mahalo From Elvis**, first released in September 1978 (which contained identical tracks), this did not detract from the importance of **The King...Elvis**.

Flaming Star, CDS 1185 (*LP 110*), was a re-issue of the RCA International, INTS 1012, album from June 1969 (LP 37), while **Elvis Presley** (*LP 142*) and **The Wonderful World Of Elvis** (*LP 143*), a double album, were new compilations of existing Camden material mixed with newly leased tracks. Both albums were re-issues

of what became extremely rare albums sold exclusively in Marks & Spencer stores (*LPs 137* and *138*).

Pickwick made extensive use of the tracks which formed **Elvis's 40 Greatest** (*LP 73*), first released on Arcade ADE P 12, and later on RCA PL 42691(2) (*LP 105*), as all forty tracks were spread over four albums along with other tracks. The albums in question were **It's Now Or Never** (*LP 163*), **Heartbreak Hotel** (*LP 164*), **Suspicious Minds** (*LP 188*) and **Are You Lonesome Tonight?** (*LP 189*).

After these came a series of 'theme' albums - **Can't Help Falling In Love & Other Great Movie Hits** (*LP 197*), **Love Songs** (*LP 199*), **The Legend** (LP 202), **The First Ten Years** (*LP 246*) and **The Rock Hits** (**LP 276**), none of which offered any unusual material for collectors, but all of which had reasonably attractive sleeves.

The final two albums, discussed at length at the beginning of the LP section, were **Girls! Girls! Girls!** (**LP 278**) and **Kissin' Cousins** (**LP 279**), both of which were important releases as they were film soundtrack albums and the only original RCA albums to be issued in this way. The track listing on **Girls! Girls! Girls!** was modified slightly, with one track being moved from side 2 to side 1 for this release. However, plans to issue more back catalogue film soundtrack albums never materialised, as Camden releases came to an end in 1988.

Label Detail Change

The label design used for **Stereo '57 (Essential Elvis Volume 2)**, PL 90250 (**LP 298**), was, like **Essential Elvis** (**LP 280**), a copy of the original RCA black label design, although additional wording was introduced, reading 'Product of BMG Music Ltd'.

Sleeve Detail Change

The legend underneath the BMG logo had been amended to read 'A Bertelsmann Music Group Company'.

Price Codes

Unlike **Essential Elvis**, which carried the price code SS, **Stereo '57 (Essential Elvis Volume 2)** (**LP 298**) used HH - the normal price code for full-priced albums.

RCA PL 90250

Side 1

1   **I Beg Of You** (McCoy, Owens)
2   **Is It So Strange** (Young)
3   **Have I Told You Lately That I Love You** (Wiseman)
4   **It Is No Secret (what God can do)** (Hamblen)
5   **Blueberry Hill** (Lewis, Stock, Rose)
6   **Mean Woman Blues** (DeMetrius)
7   **(There'll be) Peace In The Valley (for me)** (Dorsey)
8   **Have I Told You Lately That I Love You** (Wiseman)

Side 2

1   **Blueberry Hill** (Lewis, Stock, Rose)
2   **That's When Your Heartaches Begin** (Raskin, Brown, Fisher)
3   **Is It So Strange** (Young)
4   **I Beg Of You** (McCoy, Owens)
5   **(There'll be) Peace In The Valley (for me)** (Dorsey)
6   **Have I Told You Lately That I Love You** (Wiseman)
7   **I Beg Of You** (McCoy, Owens)

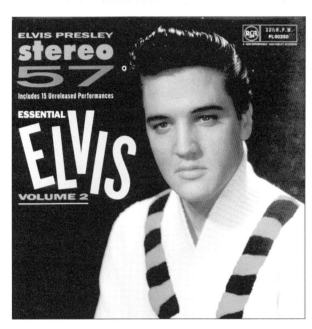

Released January 1989   Deleted October 1993

Readers of the much acclaimed *Recording Sessions* (Jorgensen, Mikkelsen, Rasmussen) book had been intrigued to read that in 1957 a number of Elvis's sessions had been recorded in a medium called binaural - generally speaking, an early form of stereo, whereby vocalists' and musicians' performances could be separated and subsequently mixed to achieve the desired balance. (For more in depth and, we hope, understandable information on this see Modes in the Introductory Section.)

However, as the book's authors found, all the indications were that these particular session tapes had not survived; indeed they published photographs of tape boxes bearing the legend 'Binaural', but with the word 'Erase' written through it. At the time (the mid-eighties) it seemed as if these historic tapes had been lost forever. Miraculously though - and contrary to what was company policy at the time - some tapes survived the injunction that they be erased and, almost thirty years on, were found. And remember miraculous is not an

overstatement here, because it has to be remembered that binaural copies were largely experimental at this stage and were merely backup, safety copies, of no use or value, it was probably thought, once the tracks had been mixed and mastered. Further details regarding these 'lost' tapes can be found in the notes following this release.

And while the album contained no unreleased songs, there were no fewer than 15 unreleased versions of the eight songs included, some of which were false starts and incomplete takes. All had been recorded in January 1957 at Radio Recorders in Hollywood. Ironically five other songs, also recorded at the same sessions, were not found in their binaural form, but the mono versions were included in the CD version of this album. The tracks not found in binaural were: *I Believe*, *Tell Me Why*, *Got A Lot O' Livin' To Do!*, *All Shook Up*, and *Take My Hand, Precious Lord*.   However, perhaps the most significant find of all was a version of *I Beg Of You* which differed in style from the standard released version and which was cut at a later session (23 February 1957) and which ended up as the B side of *Don't*, RCA 1043 (*S 19*). The new version had been heard on a bootleg recording in the early 1980s but it was of very poor quality. Besides, these recordings were in binaural, with clear separation of information on the tracks. Incidentally, when BMG issued The *King Of Rock 'N' Roll The Complete 50's Masters*, PL 90689(6) (**LP 318**), in 1992, they included a mono mix (done at the original session) of Take 12 of the song, which was the last item of *Stereo '57 (Essential Elvis Volume 2)*. This suggested that this version was considered for issue at the time of its recording.

With the exception of *Mean Woman Blues* - also in binaural and with a definite end rather than the customary fade out - the producer (Roger Semon) and mastering engineer (Bob Jones) had all the outtakes of the seven songs to work from to prepare this release. For the first time ever, Jones was able to work with original RCA master tapes (for Elvis material) in Britain. The final selection of which takes were used and how they were sequenced resided with Semon. The actual mastering was done at CTS studios in Wembley. Only the tracks used on the album were remixed and mastered. The other takes were not worked on, and all the tapes were then returned to the USA. This was the only occasion original session tapes were allowed to leave the USA. Incidentally, the LP was mastered from the CD master.

The preparation for the album had gone on throughout 1988. It had been slated for release in October 1988 but, as with *Essential Elvis* (**LP 280**), hold-ups of various kinds occurred. However, irritating though it was for the fans eagerly awaiting its release, when it was actually issued the careful preparation paid off. Once again, it was a quality package, matched not only by historic 'long-lost' recordings, but by superlative sound. The release had inputs not only from Semon and Jones, but benefited from specialist research by Ernst Mikael Jorgensen and Bones Howe, and photographic contributions from Dutch author/fan Ger Rijff. Bones Howe, a tape operator on a number of Elvis's early sessions, had, in fact, submitted personal notes from his memories of the sessions in question but, in the event, the gatefold sleeve featured notes by Roy Carr, then of NME (he who had pestered RCA into issuing *The Elvis Presley Sun Collection* (*LP 80*) in the mid-1970s). Carr used a number of direct quotations from Howe in his liner notes. On the back cover, Bob Jones made a rare appearance in print, giving a brief technical note about binaural. Incidentally the notes used were Jones's second attempt: the first set were considered to be too technical! So the final version, using some of Bones Howe's remarks, were completed in November 1988. All agreed Jones had made an excellent job of mixing the original 2-track masters (used simply as back-up copies originally from which engineers would mix the final mono masters). Jones literally stamped his name on the run-out groove of the record with the legend: 'Jones the Binaural' - but this was only on the UK issue, not the US one. As regards the five tracks added to the CD version, Bob Jones was not working with the master tapes but with copies of who-knows-what generation. Consequently, he was not at all happy about the sound on *Tell Me Why*, in particular. He wished it to be made clear that re-mastering could only achieve so much; in this case good engineering could not compensate for a poor quality source tape.

The labels were prepared and supplied by BMG in the UK and were authorised in August 1988. Notice how the label read both 'Made in Germany' and 'Made in England' near the bottom. It was an old-style label but had 'stereo' in small print to the upper-left of the centre hole. The LC number was on the right hand side. The publishing date was given as 1988, even though the record did not appear until January 1989. Alongside each of the tracks the take numbers were given, as well as the running times. In fact much of this information was hard to read, as the print was both small and faint, and all of the detail was printed in a cream colour.

Without doubt the behind-the-scenes preparation and research for this project was intensive. Semon readily admitted that the project was only possible with the full support - in all senses - of the US division. Belatedly they (the US division) had acknowledged the value and success of *Essential Elvis* (which was not issued in the USA until just over a year after its UK release), and so supported the second in the series. Indeed, the fact that RCA in the USA not only helped with the funding but also sanctioned the master tapes coming to London was a clear indication of their interest level. Originally the US division had wanted a simultaneous release date with the UK, but in the event the UK release still appeared first.

This album was well received by both fans and media alike. Even Radio One devoted time to playing tracks and, what is more, raved about them! BMG issued a single from the album comprising the full version of *Mean Woman Blues* and *I Beg Of You* on the 7 inch, with two additional tracks on the 12 inch version - *Party* and a 'dub' mix of *Mean Woman Blues* (whereby Bob Jones edited part of Elvis's vocal from the binaural tape - thus making it sound like a partial instrumental).

The dealer price for the vinyl and cassette was £3.85 (about £6.75 retail), while the CD was priced at £7.29 (£11.99 retail).

As with *Essential Elvis* (**LP 280**), this release came in a gatefold sleeve. The cover shot, thought to be previously unseen, was in colour and dated not from 1957 but almost certainly from 1958 (note the hairstyle - circa *King Creole* - and lack of sideburns). The jumper Elvis is wearing was identical to that featured on the picture sleeve of the April 1958 American single release of *Wear My Ring Around Your Neck*. Given that the photographs were very similar (the only real difference being that Elvis is smiling on the single's sleeve shot), it seems a safe bet that the two photographs were taken at the same session early in 1958. Inside the gatefold, arranged around the liner notes, were 9 candid shots (all in black and white), dating from 1956 through to 1958. Certainly, at least three of the session photos were from the *King Creole* recording sessions in 1958.

It is also worth pointing out that this was the first album to make reference to 'unreleased performances'.

The only label and sleeve errors occurred on side 2, which listed *(There'll be) Peace In The Valley (for me)* without the words in brackets, although they were shown correctly on side 1, and the continued reference to Fisher, Hill, Raskin (instead of Raskin, Brown, Fisher) on *That's When Your Heartaches Begin*.

Please note: in 2001, a previously unreleased binaural version of *It Is No Secret (what God can do)* (take 9) appeared on the Collectors Label CD, *Easter Special*. Later in the year, another Collectors Label release - *Silver Screen Stereo* - included more binaural versions of songs, this time from the films *Loving You* and *Jailhouse Rock*.

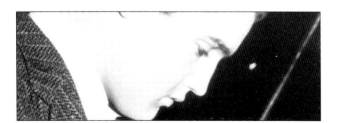

Label Variations

GERMAN BLACK LABEL

1   **1989 PRESSING: STEREO**
       Round RCA logo at top of label
       BIEM above GEMA - no boxes

Sleeve Variations

1   **Gloss**

An early 'mock-up' of the album cover is shown. Note the legend at the bottom of the picture: 'Ask for the Essential Elvis Volume 1 LP album - At your favourite dealer'. Also the 'mock-up' of the logo (top right) gave the catalogue number for *Essential Elvis* (**LP 280**)!

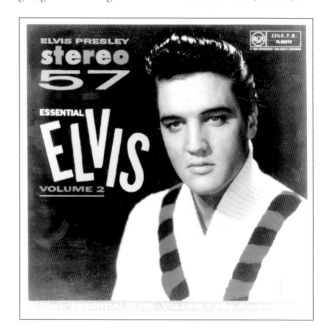

Stereo '57 - Sales Notes

BMG issued a sales note for the album *Stereo '57 (Essential Elvis Volume 2)* (**LP 298**) to help promote the album in record shops. In it they described how the tapes came to be in existence (despite the order that they be destroyed), and some background history to binaural and Elvis's stereo recordings, in addition to track listings and administrative detail. In view of unique nature of this collection, and the informative background which these notes provided, we thought it would be useful to reproduce part of them here.

The notes started:

'RCA is proud to announce the release of **Stereo 57**, a unique, historical collection of previously unreleased performances by The King for his fans throughout the world.

Until now, the earliest stereo recordings by Elvis Presley, were from 1960 onwards. His first stereo single was **'Stuck On You'**. The recent location of these priceless session tapes from 1957 is sure to excite fans throughout the world. They were originally recorded as part of RCA's binaural technique in the late 50's. In addition to the 15 inch per second mono tapes, a 2 track protection copy was made at the same time with Elvis's voice on track 1 and everything else on track 2 - this was in case a remix was needed to bring Elvis's voice out of the overall production for commercial release.

However, these binaural tapes were rarely used and if the original master tape was suitable, then the 2 track tape was discarded. Many valuable tapes were lost because of this procedure. This seems like an extremely harsh decision, but at that time, no one really believed that Rock & Roll should be released in stereo!

These recently discovered masters have been in the possession of Bones Howe who during his career has also produced acts like Jerry Lee Lewis, 5th Dimension and Sergio Mendes. Bones Howe was an engineer at the Radio Recorders Studio in L.A. during the late 50's and worked on all of Elvis's sessions with producer Thorne Nogar. The tape boxes that have been supplied to RCA are in their original form and have the word 'erase' in crayon. Fortunately, Bones decided to keep these tapes for old time's sake. They are the only 2 track binaural stereo masters to exist today. The songs were recorded on January 12th, 13th and 19th 1957.

Stereo 57 continues the highly successful **Essential Elvis** series and the music will be complemented by deluxe packaging, great photos and informative sleeve notes.

The original tapes have been digitally mastered for optimum sound quality. This really is the most exciting album for collectors since Elvis's untimely death in 1977.

SELLING POINTS!!!

*   Stereo recordings from 1957!

*   All performances previously unreleased!

*   Deluxe packaging
       - Informative sleeve notes
       - Great Pics!

*   Digitally mastered

*   High profile media coverage assured

*   Compact disc features five bonus tracks

*   Press Advertising
       - *Record Collector*
       - *Now Dig This*

*   National press co-op

*   Instore poster

*   Single release'

Background to Stereo '57

The full story concerning how the tapes which formed the tracks found on **Stereo '57 (Essential Elvis Volume 2)** finally came to be released will probably never be told. Suffice it to say that when news was finally announced that RCA had the tapes and were prepared to release them, it was greeted with intense interest from fans, although the fact that they existed originally was generally known to readers of **Recording Sessions** - especially as they had produced photographs of the tape boxes (the binaural copies) with the word 'ERASE' printed across them in red crayon. In fact Ernst Mikael Jorgensen first became aware of their existence in 1980 - courtesy of Bones Howe. The tapes were bought for RCA by Greg Geller, although it was Jorgensen who negotiated the price.

It seems that in 1959 executives with RCA had ordered a clear out of tapes - or, more likely, that old tapes were erased and re-used, presumably for reasons of economy and space. Remember that at this stage RCA had the master recordings they wanted: binaural tapes were simply back-up, safety copies to be used if, for some reason, something went wrong with the mixing of a particular track. Of course, we should also remember that these were experimental recordings - the industry had yet to standardise on the stereo recordings we know today. But, in 1959, two years after the recordings had been made and issued, no-one would have believed them to be of any value - in any sense of the word. Hence the decision to erase the material.

What happened next is unclear. But somehow the tapes - at least some of them - survived. And, of course, the fact that photographs of the tape boxes were published in the mid-1980s, suggests that if they were there to be photographed then the tapes themselves may well have also been there. Surely if they had been erased - as instructed - then the boxes would also have been re-stickered or discarded. It is a confusing business, especially as the tape boxes in question seemed to contain only the master take (in binaural) of each song. The tracks which formed **Stereo '57 (Essential Elvis Volume 2)**, and other takes of the same songs, had obviously come from other boxes, for they not only contained the master takes, but also all other takes of the songs in question. Indeed, we now know that somehow the tapes came into the possession of Bones Howe, who at that time was a tape operator at Radio Recorders, and who worked on Elvis's sessions in the late fifties and went on to be the music producer for the 1968 NBC TV Special.

At this stage we thought it appropriate to list the songs from these sessions at Radio Recorders, showing the number of takes made and which takes were featured on the album. In all cases the master take was the final take number noted. The songs are listed in the order in which they were recorded.

Date	Title	Number Of Takes Recorded	Take Numbers Used
12/1	*I Believe*	9	9 (mono) on CD only. Note: the CD track listing quoted take No. 4, when the take used - the master take - was take 9).
	Tell Me Why	5	5 (mono) on CD only
	Got A Lot O' Livin' To Do!	9	9 (mono) on CD only
	All Shook Up	10	10 (mono) on CD only
13/1	*Mean Woman Blues*	14	14
	(There'll be) Peace In The Valley (for me)	9	2, 3, 7, 9
	I Beg Of You	12	1, 6, 8, 12
	That's When Your Heartaches Begin	7	4, 5, 6
	Take My Hand, Precious Lord	14	14 (mono) on CD only
19/1	*It Is No Secret (what God can do)*	13	1, 2, 3
	Blueberry Hill	9	2, 7
	Have I Told You Lately That I Love You	15	2, 12, 13
	Is It So Strange	12	1, 7, 11

The five mono only tracks had not been located in binaural, and the use of the master take with no alternative takes of **Mean Woman Blues** suggested that this was the only take actually located. All of the other songs featured at least two takes but, importantly, only two songs included the master take in binaural - **(There'll be) Peace In the Valley (for me)** and **I Beg Of You**. The remaining five songs used alternative takes without including the master take. Note also that four of the five mono only tracks come from the first day of recording - the 12th.

Perhaps the complete story about these tapes will never be fully known - not necessarily because those who have survived from that era wish to deceive - but simply because the sequence of events (then thought to be of little or no consequence) have been blurred by the mists of time. But then, interesting though it is, some would argue that it does not really matter.

In the notes accompanying the album itself, we mentioned that the sleeve notes were done by Roy Carr. However, the source for some of what was included was a fax message sent to RCA in the UK from Bones Howe himself, dated 15 October 1988. For reasons of historical interest we have included a transcript of what Howe had to say about Elvis's pre-army recording sessions at Radio Recorders, Hollywood. To our knowledge, these notes have never been published previously anywhere.

'I started my professional career in 1956 at Radio Recorders in Hollywood as an apprentice recordist (what is now known as a tape operator). I began mixing some jazz and R&B sessions one year later. During these first years, I worked frequently as the recordist on Elvis' Hollywood recording sessions.

To the best of my recollections Radio Recorders was owned by two recording engineers named Harry Bryant and Ernie Dummell; and two businessman named H. Dovoe Ray and Howard Hutchinson. It was located at 7000 Santa Monica Boulevard in Hollywood, California. The building still stands, with Studio-B still very much as it was then, the last time I was in it (around 1980-81). The annex was located one street west on Sycamore St. - the new Record Plant studios stand on that site today.

The following is the scenario for most of Elvis' sessions at Radio Recorders prior to his leaving for the army in 1958:

One of the large studios (the annex or Studio-B) would be blocked-out for Elvis sessions for about four weeks (the studio would be reserved by RCA for Elvis only, so that the recording set-up in the studio could be left up for the duration of the recording, and Elvis could work as late as he wished). Block-booking was very unusual in those days, so this drew a lot of attention from the recording community.

Elvis drove to L.A. from Memphis in the same stretch Cadillac sedan that he toured in with the guys in his band - Bill Black, D.J. Fontana and Scotty Moore. The Jordanaires would fly in from Nashville, or wherever they were working at the time.

I have always maintained that Elvis was the first self-produced rock artist because the recording sessions were always under his control alone - he chose the songs to record, worked out the arrangement with the band, and chose the final takes.

Here is how it went:

Elvis' music publishers would attend the sessions and would bring several boxes of 78-rpm "dubs" (demo recordings) to play for Elvis who never listened to songs outside of the studio prior to the sessions. In the control booth next to the tape machines the recordist would have a turntable on which he could play the demos put in the studio for Elvis. The demos would be played, Elvis would signal back to the booth by tapping the top of his head if he wanted to hear it again "from the top"; or he would make the "throat cutting" sign with his finger if he wanted it cut off and the next demo to be played. When he finally heard a song he liked, he would have it played over and over, and the guys in the band would

begin to play along with the demo, learning the song with Elvis. As the band learned the song, Elvis worked on the arrangement with them.

Thorne Nogar was the recording mixer on all of Elvis' recording sessions in Hollywood. He worked with Elvis getting the sound Elvis wanted for each song. An RCA representative, usually Steve Sholes, was always present; but Elvis called all the shots on creative and sound matters. The RCA Rep. took care of the A&R paperwork and timed the takes. His role was that of "Ambassador from RCA."

Elvis would keep working on a song - getting the arrangement right, adding the Jordanaires for background vocals; making one take after another. He listened back to each take standing directly in front of the big playback speaker at the end of the studio; moving to the music.

Elvis said that when he heard a take back that made him feel like moving, that was the take - it was the feel that was the important thing, no matter if there were mistakes - if it felt good and it made him feel like moving, that was it!

All of these recordings were made directly to 15-ips mono tape. A 2-track protection was made at the same time with Elvis' voice on track-1 and everything else on track-2, in case a re-mix was needed to bring Elvis' voice out more. There were no stereo records in those days, so as soon as the mono master was approved, the 2-track tape was discarded. Many very valuable tapes were probably lost because of this procedure.

In a time when pop recordings were made live/direct to mono tape, four songs in each 3-hour session, an album in 3 sessions, Elvis' sessions seemed quite unusual; but they provided him with the freedom and relaxed atmosphere he needed to make the great recordings!'

LP 299 | 20 Golden Greats

Premier PFP 1009

Side 1

1. **Jailhouse Rock** (Leiber, Stoller)
2. **Rock-A-Hula Baby** (Wise, Weisman, Fuller)
3. **G.I. Blues** (Tepper, Bennett)
4. **Kissin' Cousins** (Wise, Starr)
5. **Wild In The Country** (Peretti, Creatore, Weiss)
6. **King Creole** (Leiber, Stoller)
7. **Blue Hawaii** (Robin, Rainger)
8. **Fun In Acapulco** (Weisman, Wayne)
9. **Follow That Dream** (Wise, Weisman)
10. **Girls! Girls! Girls!** (Leiber, Stoller)

Side 2

1. **Viva Las Vegas** (Pomus, Shuman)
2. **Bossa Nova Baby** (Leiber, Stoller)
3. **Flaming Star** (Wayne, Edwards)
4. **Girl Happy** (Pomus, Meade)
5. **Frankie And Johnny** (Gottlieb, Karger, Weisman)
6. **Roustabout** (Giant, Baum Kaye)
7. **Spinout** (Wayne, Weisman, Fuller)
8. **Double Trouble** (Pomus, Shuman)
9. **Charro** (Strange, Davis)
10. **They Remind Me Too Much Of You** (Robertson)

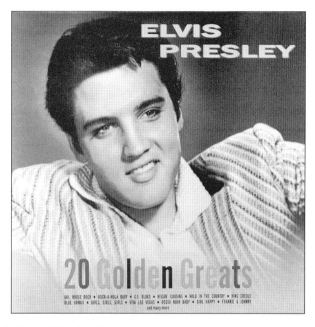

Released March 1989

An album containing identical tracks entitled *Elvis In Hollywood* was released in July 1982, Everest CBR 1014 (*LP 191*). This album was subsequently re-issued in January 1985 on Premier Records, CBR 1014 (*LP 268*), and again, also on Premier, in October 1987, when it was entitled *In Hollywood* (**LP 288**).

The notes above show that this particular track compilation had been featured on three occasions previously when the album was entitled *Elvis In Hollywood*, or simply *In Hollywood*. As with the blues collection *Blue Rhythms* (*LP 205*), the album had been re-titled - *20 Golden Greats* - and given a new lease of life, although the contents remained the same. The sleeve, which featured a black and white photograph of Elvis from the *Jailhouse Rock* EP cover, was a major improvement over all of the previous issues of the album, tempting some fans to buy, even though they had the material many times over. The back of the sleeve, too, had been re-designed, again with a black and white photograph and sleeve notes by Todd Slaughter who focused on Elvis's film successes, pointing out that the bulk of the songs featured were title tracks from Elvis's movies. Unfortunately, the reference to Elvis's 'last two dramatic roles in 1971' is inaccurate. Elvis made no more dramatic films after 1969. Indeed, his last scripted film was *Change Of Habit*.

There was no reference to the modes on the sleeve, but the label quoted, falsely, stereo. While it was true that some songs were indeed in stereo, there was, in fact, a mixture of stereo and mono recordings (see **LP 288** for details).

Only the song titles were shown on the sleeve and label (there were no writing credits), however the following errors occurred in song titles, and both label and sleeve were consistent in this. Incidentally, nor were any publishing details shown either, the first time these details had not been shown on any Elvis release in the UK. *Jailhouse* was shown as two separate words - *Jail House Rock*. There were no exclamation marks shown in *Girls! Girls! Girls!*, and an ampersand should not have been used in *Frankie And Johnny*.

Label Variations

CREAM LABEL

1   **1989 PRESSING: STEREO/MONO**

Sleeve Variations

1   **Gloss**

LP 300   *Mess O' Blues - 24 Classic Tracks*

Performance PFP 2000

Side 1

1 **Trouble** (Leiber, Stoller)
2 **Reconsider Baby** (Fulson)
3 **A Mess Of Blues** (Pomus, Shuman)
4 **Give Me The Right** (Wise, Blagman)
5 **Such A Night** (Chase)
6 **When It Rains, It Really Pours** (Emerson)

Side 2

1 **Trying To Get To You** (Singleton, McCoy)
2 **Like A Baby** (Stone)
3 **I Want To Be Free** (Leiber, Stoller)
4 **Mean Woman Blues** (DeMetrius)
5 **Ain't That Loving You Baby** (Otis, Hunter)
6 **One Night** (Bartholomew, King)

Side 3

1 **Little Sister** (Pomus, Shuman)
2 **So Glad You're Mine** (Crudup)
3 **Big Boss Man** (Smith, Dixon)
4 **I Want You With Me** (Harris)
5 **Baby, What You Want Me To Do** (Reed)
6 **Santa Claus Is Back In Town** (Leiber, Stoller)

Side 4

1 **Stuck On You** (Schroeder, McFarland)
2 **I Feel So Bad** (Willis)
3 **What'd I Say** (Charles)
4 **Tomorrow Night** (Croslow, Grosz)
5 **It Feels So Right** (Wise, Weisman)
6 **Merry Christmas Baby** (Baxter, Moore)

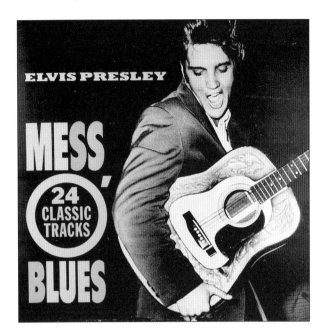

Released March 1989

This album was previously entitled **Blue Rhythms,** EPC 1000 (*LP 205*), first released in December 1983 and re-issued as PPD 2001 (*LP 269*) in January 1985 by Premier. Two single albums, **Mess O' Blues - Volume 1** and **Mess O' Blues - Volume 2**, PMP 1012 (**LP 289**) and PMP 1013 (**LP 290**), were issued in October 1987 and contained the same tracks. Later both albums were repackaged and released together in March 1988 as **Mess O' Blues - Volumes 1 & 2** with a catalogue number PPD 2000 (**LP 292**).

Once again the twenty four track which originally formed **Blue Rhythms** (*LP 205*) were re-presented on this album, now entitled **Mess O' Blues - 24 Classic Tracks**, exactly one year after their last appearance on the Premier record label. This, then, became their fifth appearance on either a different label (three in total: Everest, Premier and Performance), or in a different sleeve or packaging, making the set one of the most used track listings in Elvis's UK record history. However, although the albums contained the same material, it would be inaccurate to call the later albums re-issues, for each release had been re-titled, but the notes following the track listing (above) should enable the complex release pattern to be traced.

In case you were wondering why these tracks had been the subject of so many changes in label, we should explain that all of these albums were produced by the same people, and that the Whittington Entertainment Group (WEG) (referred to on the sleeve of this Performance record) was in fact the company which owned the Performance and Premier labels. Indeed, they also produced the original Everest album, after which they changed their name to Premier, which accounts for why the original artwork was retained for the second release on Premier. Ron Winter, the man responsible for the compilation of these tracks (or so the sleeves of all the records claimed) was actually the managing director of Performance.

Of course, we are not suggesting that there was anything untoward in all of this, merely discussing the background to these unusual releases that have appeared over the years. Clearly WEG were extremely active in getting as much mileage as possible out of a

relatively small number of songs included on this series of releases, and on the **Elvis In Hollywood/20 Golden Greats** (*LP 191* and *LP 299*) albums for which they were also responsible. Some would call their practices aggressive marketing, others exploitation.

However, the sleeve of this album featured a completely new design from its earlier counterparts and came in a single pocket, but the LPs themselves came in plain white bags. The front featured an early shot of Elvis in live performance, whilst the back saw the return of the sleeve notes found inside the gatefold of the original **Blue Rhythms** album (*LP 205*). The spine gave the title as being **Mess O' Blues**.

All the tracks were featured in their correct modes - mono for the pre-1960 tracks (although **When It Rains, It Really Pours** was very 'echoey'), and stereo for the post-1960 material.

WEG came up with a rather unusual way of reducing the number of label errors: no writers were shown! Nor were any of the songs' publishers referred to.

The label errors that remained were minor, both concerning punctuation, as the commas had been left out of **When It Rains, It Really Pours** and **Baby, What You Want Me To Do**. However, the claim that all tracks were in stereo was incorrect.

Label Variations

CREAM LABEL

1   1989 PRESSING: MONO/STEREO

Sleeve Variations

1   Gloss

LP 301	**The Voice Of The King**
	Ocean OCNWL 2024

Side 1

1   **WPMS, Memphis,** with Bob Neal, 31 August 1955
2   **St. Petersburg, Florida,** with Bob Hoffer, 7 August 1956
3   **Wichita Falls, Texas,** with Jay Thompson, 9 April 1956
4   **New Orleans, Louisiana,** with Jim Stewart, 10 July 1956
5   **Memphis (Part 1),** 25 February 1961

Side 2

1   **Memphis (Part 2),** 25 February 1961
2   **Houston, Texas,** 27 February 1970
3   **Madison Square Garden,** New York, 9 June 1972

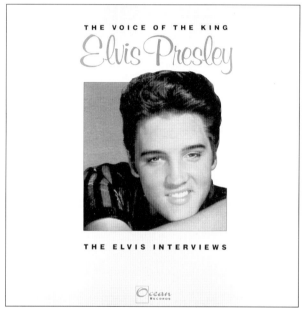

Released May 1989

Some sources claim that this LP was released in July 1989. However, copies existed prior to this and, as it was reviewed in the June 1989 issue of **Elvis The Man And His Music**, we believe a release date of April/May much more likely.

This was a collection of seven, not eight, interviews, as the one from Memphis was continued on side two. The material spanned a seventeen year period from 1955 to 1972. And while there have been many interview records issued in the UK over the years, the strength of this release was that it featured some lesser known items, although all of them had been available at some time previously. There were, of course, some old favourites repeated here for the umpteenth time. The first interview featured (actually not so much an interview, but an opportunity to promote a concert) from 1955 with Elvis's former manager Bob Neal, had been a regular inclusion on such releases from its first appearance in the UK on **Elvis Answers Back**, BUT 2 (*LP 145*), in February 1981. On the other hand, the Memphis interview had previously only been found on the Hammer LP, **The King Speaks**, HMR 9005 (*LP 115*), and its subsequent re-issue HMS 6002 (*LP 147*) - now an extremely rare and very collectable item.

Some of the other interviews were not as common or as easy to locate as one might initially have thought: the Houston and Madison Square Garden Press Conferences (the New York interview) had made fleeting appearances, but neither had been consistently featured on a regular basis. This album, then, provided a good

example of what could be done within this limited field and, its price of around £4 or less, represented excellent value for money. Of course, as with all interview discs, there was a limit on just how many times you would wish listen to the material included. Elvis 'interviews' were never particularly revealing or informative, but they did offer some background and, seen in this light, were often very enjoyable.

Rather cheekily, the two photographs of Elvis (one on the front and one on the back cover) seemed to have come from the earlier interview albums **Elvis Answers Back**, BUT 2 (*LP 145*) and **Personally Elvis**, AFESD 1032 (*LP 186*), although credit was given, for the cover shot, at least, to Stephen Holland Inc.. Bill Williams, who had been responsible for liner notes on several Elvis albums, notably **Blue Rhythms**, EPC 1000 (*LP 205*), and some of the Pickwick/Camden releases, was credited as Executive Producer.

The etchings found in the run-out grooves mentioned Damont and a reference LYN 23124. We believe that this referred to Damont Audio, who presumably did the mastering, if not the production, and to Lyntone who, you may recall, were responsible for many of the flexi-discs of Elvis interviews produced for the UK Fan Club in the mid-eighties. Incidentally, the Lyntone factory closed down at the end of December 1991, their work being transferred to its sister factory Damont Audio Ltd, based in Hayes, Middlesex.

The inner bag carried adverts for ten other Ocean releases, but there was no reference to the other Ocean/Elvis album, **Elvis Live** (**LP 302**).

Label Variations

BLUE/GREY LABEL

1   1989 PRESSING: MONO

Sleeve Variations

1   Gloss

Album Deletion - May 1989

A significant number of vinyl albums were deleted during 1989. The first of these - in May - was **The First Live Recordings**, PG 89387 (*LP 234*), which dated from July 1984.

Elvis Gospel 1957-1971: Known Only To Him

PL 90355

Around July 1989, copies of this German black label album began to circulate in the UK, with some stores selling copies for around £8 (the normal price for PL releases), while others treated it as an import and charged a higher price. **Elvis Monthly** advertised it as an American import at a cost of £11.25 for the vinyl format and £18.99 for the CD. Unbelievably, some shops sold vinyl copies at the then standard UK mid-price of either £3.99 or £4.49, depending on the shop. In fact, despite the inclusion of a UK price code on the back of the sleeve - HH, which normally signified full price for a PL single album - this was not a UK issue. Certainly, the album had been considered for UK release, but had been rejected. One reason for this was that it was felt that to do so would have merely served to provide unnecessary duplication of tracks at a time when there was a concentrated, and successful, effort towards rationalisation. The point being that most of the tracks included on this compilation album were readily available on albums like **His Hand In Mine**, NL 83935 (LP 214), and **How Great Thou Art**, NL 83758 (LP 235). Admittedly other tracks were more difficult to locate - **We Call On Him**, for example, which had not been available in the UK for many years. Another factor for not releasing the album in the UK was simply that this kind of material did not sell particularly well. This was in contrast to America, where items of a religious nature have always enjoyed healthy sales. Finally, at the time, releasing the album would have only complicated the release schedules. Strangely enough though, a CD only version (74321 18753 2) was issued in the UK in February 1994.

The vinyl album (catalogue number 9586-1-R) originated in America and was first released there in April 1989. It contained a selection of fourteen of Elvis's religious recordings covering the period 1957 to 1971.

No photograph of Elvis appeared on the front of the sleeve which, instead, featured a plain design with the title being prominent. There was, however, a small picture on the back.

Jay Orr, of the Country Music Foundation, compiled the album and was also responsible for the sleeve notes. Additional comments by Gordon Stoker of The Jordanaires included an amusing anecdote of Elvis singing spirituals at a film soundtrack recording session.

The label featured more or less the standard RCA label of the time, but both the BMG and round RCA logo appeared on the back of the sleeve. Incidentally, the BMG logo had neither 'MUSIC' nor 'A Bertelsmann Music Group Company' underneath it.

The complete track listing was as follows:

Side 1
    (There'll be) Peace In The Valley (for me)
    Take My Hand, Precious Lord
    I'm Gonna Walk Dem Golden Stairs
    I Believe In The Man In The Sky
    Joshua Fit The Battle
    Swing Down, Sweet Chariot
    Stand By Me

Side 2
    Run On
    Where Could I Go But To The Lord
    So High
    We Call On Him
    Who Am I?
    Lead Me, Guide Me
    Known Only To Him

Album Deletions - July 1989

In July 1989 RCA deleted a considerable number of albums from their catalogue, including some quite important releases. The deletions are listed below, in catalogue number order for ease of reference, with the date of their original release and release number.

PL 84848	*Elvis - A Legendary Performer Vol. 4*	Nov 1983	*LP 204*
PL 84941	*Elvis' Gold Records Volume 5*	Jan 1985	*LP 261*
PL 85182	*The Rocker*	Jan 1985	*LP 262*
PL 85486	*Elvis' Christmas Album*	Oct 1985	*LP 275*
NL 89025	*It Won't Seem Like Christmas Without You*	Oct 1984	*LP 252*
PL 89051	*Rare Elvis Vol. 3*	Jan 1985	*LP 264*
NL 89099	*Elvis Presley Sings Leiber & Stoller*	Apr 1984	*LP 217*
PL 89119	*Rare Elvis Vol. 2*	Jan 1985	*LP 265*

LP 302   Elvis Live

Ocean OCNWL 2031

Side 1

1. **Heartbreak Hotel** (Axton, Durden, Presley)
2. **Long Tall Sally** (Johnson, Blackwell, Penniman)
3. **I Was The One** (Schroeder, DeMetrius, Blair, Peppers)
4. **Money Honey** (Stone)
5. **I Got A Woman** (Charles)
6. **Blue Suede Shoes** (Perkins)
7. **Hound Dog** (Leiber, Stoller)
8. **Little Rock, Arkansas,** with Ray Green, 16 May 1956

Side 2

1. **Good Rockin' Tonight** (Brown)
2. **Baby Let's Play House** (Gunter)
3. **Blue Moon Of Kentucky** (Monroe)
4. **I Got A Woman** (Charles)
5. **That's All Right** (Crudup)
6. **Tweedle Dee** (Scott)
7. **Maybellene** (Berry)

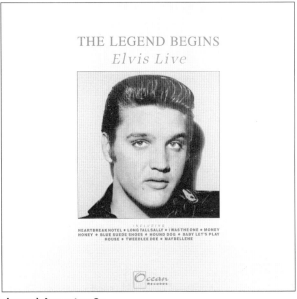

Released August 1989

For those fans/collectors who had been denied access to, or had been unable to afford, the Bilko bootleg release *Elvis Rocks Little Rock*, issued in June 1989, then this album must have appeared as a welcome, yet surprising, addition to their collection. We say surprising for there was, and still is, for that matter, some doubt as to the legitimacy of this collection; for side one comprised a live concert from 16 May 1956, recorded at Little Rock, Arkansas, when Elvis was firmly established with RCA who, to all intents and purposes, 'owned' his recorded voice. It would appear that Ocean released this record without consultation with, or the approval of, BMG. We have no indication as to how this was viewed by BMG, nor were there any signs that action was ever taken against Ocean. Indeed, BMG may not have owned the rights to this material; but whatever the truth of the matter was, the album had the air of illegality about it. Even more strange was the fact that the record was distributed by BMG, but that was the limit of their involvement. It was unlikely that anyone at BMG would have bothered to check the contents and, even if they had, the likelihood was that the material would have been considered previously issued Louisiana Hayride tracks, and therefore perfectly normal inclusions. Many fans may find it hard to understand how BMG could have missed this, but the truth of the matter was that BMG is a very big company, and no matter how obvious the error seemed to us, it would have required someone at BMG with specialist knowledge to have halted the process.

Another factor was that the record was available for a short time only and Ocean, who, we believe, were also involved selling computer software, disappeared without trace shortly afterwards. Perhaps, by the time someone at BMG noticed that the Little Rock concert was included, it was too late. Nevertheless, the appearance of these tracks in 'official' form, represented the first time that fans were able to buy the product in normal outlets. There was good news too, in that the record sold for £3.99, considerably cheaper than the bootleg price, and with the added benefit of additional tracks - albeit previously issued.

The sound quality of the Little Rock concert was another matter: there was a definite reduction in the overall sound when compared to the bootleg - the implication being that the set was simply copied from that source, and much the same can be said about the tracks which comprised side 2. Unlike the contents of side 1, side 2 contained previously released material drawn from Elvis's live appearances on the Louisiana Hayride, all of which <u>had</u> appeared on RCA/BMG albums, again throwing into question the legitimacy of this album. Incidentally, the final track on side 1 was referred to as the *Little Rock Radio Interview*. We have given what we think is the correct title, with additional detail added.

Side 2 opened with the five songs Elvis recorded at the Eagles Hall, Houston, in March 1955, which had appeared on several releases previously, the most notable being the Virgin KING 1 album, *The First Year* (*LP 118*), in November 1979. Since then they had been issued on a variety of albums and seemed to have been constantly available. The remaining two songs, *Tweedle Dee* and *Maybellene*, from April and August 1955 respectively, had also been used on various albums, including an appearance on RCA - *The First Live Recordings*, PG 89387 (*LP 234*), in July 1984.

The sleeve design was attractive enough: a white border around a black and white photograph of Elvis (from 1956) over a yellow background. This was the same image as used on the HMV album *Rock 'N' Roll No. 2* (*LP 2*). The album title, *Elvis Live*, appeared under the words 'The Legend Begins' as though this was intended to be the actual title, but it was not mentioned on the record label. Some of the tracks were listed under the photograph.

On the back of the sleeve were notes outlining the events leading up to Elvis's time at Sun, his live appearances and the move towards national stardom which, while being interesting enough, offered no new information. Note that D.J. Fontana was referred to as Fonana.

Etched between the run-out grooves were two messages - 'For Lisa-Marie' and 'A Porky Prime Cut', messages from the mastering engineer. Closer inspection also revealed '9JU8' which, we would guess, could stand for June 89 when the record was mastered.

We have come to expect errors when any of the songs featured here are used; the same error being 'copied across', or so it would appear. And, sure enough, this record was no exception.

The writers of *Long Tall Sally* were shown in the wrong order, and on *I Was the One* no / appeared between Blair and Peppers, suggesting that Blair Peppers was one person. The writer of *Money Honey*, Jesse Stone, was referred to as Jene.

On side 2, *Good Rockin' Tonight* appeared as *There's Good Rockin' Tonight* on the label and without the apostrophe on the sleeve. *That's All Right* was shown as *That's Alright Mama* and *Tweedlee Dee* (it ought to have read *Tweedle*) was uncredited, when it was known that Winfield Scott wrote the song.

Label Variations

BLUE/GREY LABEL

1	1989 PRESSING: MONO

Sleeve Variations

1	Gloss

Album Deletion - August 1989

The only album to be deleted in August 1989 was the August 1984 release of *A Date With Elvis*, NL 89097 (*LP 242*). One month later, the album re-appeared with a different catalogue number (NL 90360) and, more importantly, a revised track listing. Further details can be found in the notes for **LP 304**.

Label Design

When issued in September 1989, both *For LP Fans Only*, NL 90359 (**LP 303**), and *A Date With Elvis*, NL 90360 (**LP 304**), used a copy of the original RCA black label. On the sleeves, however, there was no BMG logo.

LP 303 | For LP Fans Only

RCA NL 90359

Side 1

1 **That's All Right** (Crudup)
2 **Lawdy, Miss Clawdy** (Price)
3 **Mystery Train** (Parker, Phillips)
4 **Playin' For Keeps** (Kesler)
5 **Poor Boy** (Presley, Matson)
6 **Money Honey** (Stone)
7 **I'm Counting On You** (Robertson)

Side 2

1 **My Baby Left Me** (Crudup)
2 **I Was The One** (Schroeder, DeMetrius, Blair, Peppers)
3 **Shake, Rattle And Roll** (Calhoun)
4 **I'm Left, You're Right, She's Gone** (Kesler, Taylor)
5 **You're A Heartbreaker** (Sallee)
6 **Trying To Get To You** (Singleton, McCoy)
7 **Blue Suede Shoes** (Perkins)

Released September 1989   Deleted March 1992

An album entitled **Elvis**, RCA RD 27120 (*LP 8*), released in March 1959, contained identical tracks.

In certain respects, the release of **For LP Fans Only** marked the end of an era, as the original issue of the album, actually entitled **Elvis**, RD 27120 (*LP 8*), released in March 1959, was one of the very few RCA albums released prior to 1972 never to have been re-issued. Technically, at least according to our own guidelines, this album should not have been considered a re-issue, as it did not use the original title. The truth of the matter was, of course, that this was a re-issue; indeed RCA themselves referred to it as being the 'original UK compilation', and really the use of the original American album title, **For LP Fans Only**, was more about reducing the number of albums entitled **Elvis** than anything else. Perhaps it would have been more appropriate to re-name the others and retain the title on this 'original' compilation. Nevertheless, the release of this album did restore to catalogue a collection which had been deleted for almost twenty years and for reasons of nostalgia, if nothing else, it was good to have it back.

It is perhaps worth reminding people that the original UK version, **Elvis**, differed from the original American release, in that it contained fourteen, not ten tracks.

The sleeve's artwork was almost identical to that of the original issue - an early shot on the front from 1956, before Elvis dyed his hair black, with a pose in army uniform on the back. Unlike the original, more of Elvis's uniform could be seen, complete with medals! A black box in the right hand corner on the front of the sleeve contained the title and track listing. A sticker 'Quality By BMG - Special Price' was applied to the front cover and the album cost £3.99 when it was released.

It was believed that there was some pressure to get this and its companion volume **A Date With Elvis**, NL 90360 (**LP 304**), into the shops quickly, and that they were both mastered by Bob Jones, who was unhappy about the overall quality of the tapes he had to work with. Despite this, the songs are in mono, not electronic stereo, as other compilations featuring some of these tracks had been. The back of the sleeve boasted 'ORIGINAL MONO RECORDINGS'. Also on the back of the sleeve was the round RCA logo situated in the bottom left hand corner, just above the distribution details. The publishing dates were quite interesting, reading 1954, 1955 and 1956 on the sleeve, which, although accurate, did not refer to individual tracks. The label did though, but rather confused and spoiled the issue by quoting 1956, 1957 and 1958 which referred to UK publishing dates i.e. when the songs were released in the UK.

A compact disc version was issued at the same time (ND 90359) and was also available as a mid-priced item. The US market had a CD release of **For LP Fans Only** in April 1989 (RCA 1990-2-R), but there was no vinyl version.

A new error appeared, in that there was no apostrophe used in **That's All Right**. The old error concerning the correct title of **Playin' For Keeps** cropped up again here. When the song first appeared in the UK it was on an HMV single, POP 330 (*S 10*), released in April 1957, the title used was **Playin' For Keeps** i.e. with an apostrophe in **Playin'**. The HMV album **The Best Of Elvis**, DLP 1159 (*LP 4*), released in October 1957, retained the apostrophe. However, on the song's first appearance on RCA - on the **Elvis** album we have been discussing - both label and sleeve referred to **Playing**. We have, therefore, always concluded that to use a 'g' was an error. To confuse matters even more this release correctly placed an apostrophe in the title on the label, but not on the sleeve, the front and back read **Playing**. We consider the correct title to be **Playin' For Keeps**.

A similar error involved the omission of the comma in **Lawdy, Miss Clawdy** on both label and sleeve. **Poor Boy** was credited to Matson, Presley in the order which we once believed to be correct, but having reviewed this further we now consider that Presley, Matson to be correct. For further information on this topic see the label and sleeve error notes following **LP 318**, and in the song index.

The inexcusable error of listing **Money Honey** as **Money Money**, first found on the EP **Heartbreak Hotel**, RCX 7189 (*EP 24*), appeared again here, but only on the sleeve.

Claude DeMetrius had his name spelt DeMetruis on side 2, track 2, as it was on the original **Elvis** album.

This album, along with **A Date With Elvis**, was deleted on 24 March 1992.

Label Variations

GERMAN BLACK LABEL

    1   1989 PRESSING: MONO
            Round RCA logo at top of label

Sleeve Variations

    1   Gloss

LP 304   A Date With Elvis

RCA NL 90360

Side 1

1. **Blue Moon Of Kentucky** (Monroe)
2. **Milkcow Blues Boogie** (Arnold)
3. **Baby Let's Play House** (Gunter)
4. **I Don't Care If The Sun Don't Shine** (David)
5. **Tutti Frutti** (LaBostrie, Penniman)
6. **I'm Gonna Sit Right Down And Cry (over you)** (Thomas, Biggs)
7. **I Got A Woman** (Charles)

Side 2

1. **Good Rockin' Tonight** (Brown)
2. **Is It So Strange** (Young)
3. **We're Gonna Move** (Presley, Matson)
4. **Blue Moon** (Rodgers, Hart)
5. **Just Because** (B. & J. Shelton, Robin)
6. **One-Sided Love Affair** (Campbell)
7. **Let Me** (Presley, Matson)

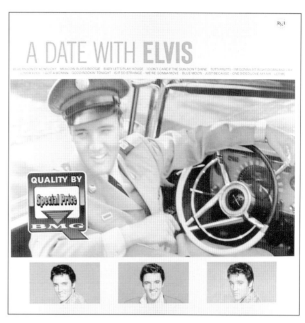

Released September 1989   Deleted March 1992
Original Issue July 1959.   RCA RD 27128 (LP 9)

An album with this title but with different tracks was released in August 1980: RCA International INTS 5032 (*LP 127*). This LP was re-issued in August 1984: RCA International NL 89097 (*LP 242*).

The album **A Date With Elvis** had a long and chequered history which, when analysed, illustrated perfectly how changes in company policy over the years had affected the end product. This was a copy of the July 1959 original version of the album, a unique UK compilation of fourteen tracks, which had not been available since the late sixties, early seventies. An album with the same title had been issued on the International label, INTS 5032 (*LP 127*), in August 1980, and re-issued in August 1984, NL 89097 (*LP 242*). However, these albums were copies of the ten track original American issue.

In 1959, a year after the end of the arrangement between RCA and HMV to produce and distribute RCA records in the UK, there was still confusion over the availability of certain tracks, some of which had been deleted with the HMV Elvis catalogue. At a time when there was little new product available for release, and in an attempt to restore certain tracks to the catalogue, RCA compiled the fourteen track version of **A Date With Elvis**, which represented a better product in terms of track content (*Is It So Strange* had not been released in the UK previously). For fans this was a good arrangement and, as with **Elvis**, RD 27120 (*LP 8*), offered much better value for money. After being deleted for around ten years, the album was again made available, but this time the track listing was the same as the American original i.e. ten tracks, not fourteen. This move was made in order to rationalise the product for the period covered by this and other albums, and to bring UK releases more in line with those of the rest of Europe. For the benefit of readers who do not have access to the earlier albums, it seems sensible at this point to list the tracks on the American original so that the differences are more apparent.

    Side 1   *Blue Moon Of Kentucky*
                   Young And Beautiful
                   (You're so square) Baby I Don't Care
                   Milkcow Blue Boogie
                   Baby Let's Play House

    Side 2   *Good Rockin' Tonight*
                   Is It So Strange
                   We're Gonna Move
                   I Want To Be Free
                   I Forgot To Remember To Forget

When, in 1989, BMG were looking to issue compact discs to represent these formative years, the prospect of releasing the 1980 album as a ten track CD with such a short running time was far removed from the 'value for money' policy which the company was striving for. Thus, the decision was made to re-compile the album with the original fourteen tracks to accompany the release of *For LP Fans Only* (**LP 303**), the new title (for the UK at least) of the original *Elvis* album.

The history of *A Date With Elvis* was unique, and presumably entailed quite a lot of work in the recompilation of the tracks from various sources. No doubt most of this work fell on Bob Jones, who mastered the album on 7 July 1989, the same day that he cut *For LP Fans Only* (**LP 303**).

Yet, having gone to the trouble of preparing the tracks, it was strange then that the sleeve notes written by Roger Semon for the 1980 (and 1984) issue remained intact. It seems odd to produce an album such as this without considering a revision to the sleeve notes, when parts of these were no longer relevant. For instance, there was reference to *I Forgot To Remember To Forget* being 'featured on this album' and, of course, a further four Sun recordings were now included which were not referred to in the notes.

A number of revisions from the 1984 NL series album had taken place. On the back of the sleeve the most noticeable omission was the picture of *Elvis Presley Sings Leiber & Stoller* album (LP 217), along with advertisements for other International releases, as these were long deleted. The RCA computer style logo had been replaced on both the front and back of the sleeve by the round logo, whilst the label used the 'original' RCA logo at the top.

It was pleasing to see that the publishing dates of the songs now showed the dates when the songs were actually released, not in the UK, of course, but in America. Still, it was better than simply showing a compilation date, as the International sleeves had done. The label gave the publishing dates for each song, but, remarkably, these were the dates when the songs were first released in the UK, so that *Is It So Strange* was, quite rightly, quoted as being published in 1959. The sleeve proudly boasted that the tracks were 'ORIGINAL MONO RECORDINGS'.

There were very few errors, but it was disappointing to see *Good Is Rocking Tonight*, and the less important omission of the hyphen in *One-Sided Love Affair*. However, these errors occurred on the sleeve only, not on the label, which we believe to be error free!

The LP *A Date With Elvis* was deleted on 24 March 1992. Incidentally, this album was released in America in January 1989 (RCA 2011-2-R), but on CD only. However, as with the American CD issue of *For LP Fans Only*, the tracks were in electronically reprocessed stereo. The UK CDs were in mono.

Label Variations

GERMAN BLACK LABEL

1   1989 PRESSING: MONO
        Round RCA logo at top of label

Sleeve Variations

1   Gloss

LP 305 — *The Fifties Interviews*

Magnum Force MFLP 074

Side 1

1 **The Truth About Me** Monologue August 1956
2 **Jacksonville, Florida,** with Mae Axton, 28 July 1955
3 **WMPS, Memphis,** with Bob Neal, 31 August 1955
4 **Wichita Falls, Texas,** with Jay Thompson, 9 April 1956
5 **LaCrosse, Wisconsin,** 14 May 1956

Side 2

1 **Little Rock, Arkansas,** with Ray Green, 16 May 1956
2 **KLAC TV, Memphis,** with Wink Martindale, 16 June 1956
3 **WNOE Radio, New Orleans, Louisiana,** 9 July 1956
4 **New Orleans, Louisiana,** with Jim Stewart, 10 July 1956
5 **St. Petersburg, Florida,** with Bob Hoffer 7 August 1956

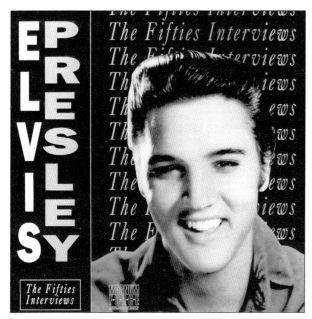

Released November 1989

The idea for this release came from Nigel Molden himself, the owner of Magnum Music Group. And although a number of other companies had, over the years, issued interview records, this release attempted to establish an accurate chronology and concentrated on interviews conducted in the fifties.

The interviews themselves were actually conducted in 1955 and 1956, not between 1955 and 1958 as the promotional leaflet stated. The tape sources were from the Official Elvis Presley Fan Club of Great Britain and Trevor Cajiao, editor of the monthly Rock 'n' Roll magazine *Now Dig This* and the quarterly Elvis Presley magazine, *Elvis The Man And His Music*. And, as the company used only Elvis's spoken voice and not his singing voice, there was no copyright problem and no need to consult BMG on this release.

At the time of its original release it appeared only as a vinyl album; the CD release did not appear until at least a year later. And up to early 1992, sales of the vinyl version were around 5,000. The set was mastered by Bob Jones at CTS and pressed at the Wimbledon based PR factory. The album artwork was done by Alex Arthur and the front cover featured the colour photograph of Elvis as used on the original cover of *Elvis*, RD 27120 (*LP 8*), superimposed on the album's title.

On the back was the list of the interviews included, although track one on side one was not actually an interview: it was a promotional piece done in August 1956, entitled *The Truth About Me*. Underneath the listing were reprints of adverts from that period of time. The main body of the rear cover was taken up with extensive sleeve notes by Gordon Minto, co-author of *Elvis UK*, who placed the interviews in their correct running order and discussed them within the context of what was happening to Elvis at that time. For the first time the Elvis/Bob Neal interview (always quoted as being from 6 May 1955) was correctly dated as being from 31 August 1955. Other discrepancies were also dealt with in the detailed notes.

Now although the release was said to be October 1989, the sleeve notes were dated November 1989, and the promotional material quoted 24 November 1989 as the release date. Even more mysterious was the fact that the back cover of the album gave the publishing and copyright dates as being 1990!

Magnum Force sales sheet.

A CD version was released in February 1991.

Some fans claimed to have difficulties in obtaining this album, suggesting either that shops did not stock it or else there was a distribution problem by Magnum Music Group. However, this latter theory was dismissed by Nigel Molden, who stated that there were no distribution problems at all. Incidentally, Molden also said he hoped to do similar albums for sixties and seventies interviews too, though they never materialised.

Label Variations

CREAM LABEL

1   **1989 PRESSING: MONO**

Sleeve Variations

1   **Gloss**

Hits Like Never Before

The last full-priced BMG vinyl album, comprising 'new' or unreleased material, was *Stereo '57 (Essential Elvis Volume 2* (**LP 298**), issued over 18 months previously in January 1989.

LP 306 — Hits Like Never Before (Essential Elvis Vol. 3)

RCA PL 90486

Side 1

1. **King Creole** (Leiber, Stoller)
2. **I Got Stung** (Schroeder, Hill)
3. **(Now and then there's) A Fool Such As I** (Trader)
4. **Wear My Ring Around Your Neck** (Carroll, Moody)
5. **Your Cheatin' Heart** (Williams)
6. **Ain't That Loving You Baby** (Otis, Hunter)
7. **Doncha' Think It's Time** (Otis, Dixon)
8. **I Need Your Love Tonight** (Wayne, Reichner)
9. **Lover Doll** (Wayne, Silver)
10. **As Long As I Have You** (Wise, Weisman)

Side 2

1. **Danny** (Wise, Weisman)
2. **King Creole** (Leiber, Stoller)
3. **Crawfish** (Wise, Weisman)
4. **A Big Hunk O' Love** (Schroeder, Wyche)
5. **Ain't That Loving You Baby** (Otis, Hunter)
6. **I Got Stung** (Schroeder, Hill)
7. **Your Cheatin' Heart** (Williams)
8. **Wear My Ring Around Your Neck** (Carroll, Moody)
9. **Steadfast, Loyal And True** (Leiber, Stoller)
10. **I Need Your Love Tonight** (Wayne, Reichner)

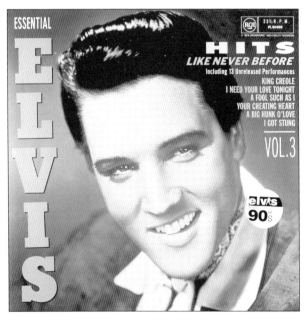

Released July 1990   Deleted April 1993

Inspired by the resounding success of the two previous volumes of *Essential Elvis*, messrs Semon and Jorgensen continued their efforts to find and release unissued Presley material. This time though there was an important difference: the pair had the moral support and financial backing of the US division of the company who, albeit belatedly, recognised the quality and commercial viability of their previous efforts. Consequently, they were allowed the time to search through RCA New York's tape vaults looking for unreleased Presley material, as well as tracking down apparently long-lost masters. The fruits of their efforts were to be found not only in this release, but in the likes of *For The Asking (The Lost Album)* (**LP 309**) and, of course, the now legendary fifties boxed set issued in July 1992 (**LP 318**).

Continuing the theme of sorting through and using unreleased versions from the fifties' sessions, the focus of attention for this release centred on two main areas: the *King Creole* recording sessions from early 1958, and the June 1958 sessions, held after Elvis was inducted into the US army, and not long before his posting to Germany in September 1958. In fact, the job of locating the complete June 1958 session outtakes was relatively straightforward; it was the *King Creole* material which proved more problematical, resulting in the set being subjected to some delay. Hence, only six songs from the film were used on this album.

The set itself, unlike the two previous volumes, was mastered by RCA employees in their New York studios, principally Chick Crumpacker, who had worked for the company for a very long time and had, indeed, engineered some of Elvis's early sessions work in New York during the fifties. The decision to master the set in America, rather than allow it to be done by Bob Jones in the UK, was one which puzzled and disappointed some fans. However, whatever political manoeuvering went on behind the scenes, we are unlikely to ever find out the precise reason why (bearing in mind the quality of Jones's work) he was not assigned the task. On the other hand, the answer may be quite simple: the master tapes were in New York so why, when the company had the personnel to do this job there, bother incurring extra expense, not to say the risk, of shipping master tapes from the USA to the UK? Obviously, if we are objective about this, then this 'answer' made some sense. Perhaps another reason was that since the US company had been of great help to the producers of the set in terms of time and financial support, then it would have been neither prudent nor right to offer the job elsewhere.

Oddly enough though, prior to the release of the album (remember it had been mastered in the USA) Bob Jones was approached by Roger Semon, then of BMG in the UK, to re-sequence the tracks and work on the sound quality. However it is understood that although he agreed to do some work on the project, little was completed in the short time available for the task to be done. And certainly some fans felt that the aural quality of this release did not match that of the previous two volumes - though that was, of course, a matter of opinion.

All the material was from sessions held in 1958 - the two January sessions (15-16 January and 23 January); the 1 February session (both at Radio Recorders, Hollywood) and the 10-11 June sessions held in RCA's Nashville studios. As mentioned earlier, the producers had experienced difficulty locating some of the *King Creole* session tapes; consequently several songs were not featured: *Hard Headed Woman*, *Trouble*, *New Orleans*, *Dixieland Rock*, and *Don't Ask Me Why*. On the other hand, the complete session tapes from the June 1958 dates were located, giving the producers complete choice of what to include.

The set boasted 13 unreleased performances, although technically the inclusion of the complete version of *Crawfish* (with Kitty White's vocal introduction) would suggest 14. The previously issued songs were *Wear My Ring Around Your Neck* - the overdubbed single version - (*S 20*); *Your Cheatin' Heart* (take 9), which was the version issued on the US Reader's Digest set and later included in *The EP Collection Vol. 2* in 1982; and the 'regular' version - take 10 - as found on *Elvis For Everyone* (*LP 26*). There was also the alternative *Doncha' Think It's Time* (take 40) which was not the single version, but the one inadvertently included on *Elvis' Golden Records Vol. 2* (*LP 10*) in 1960. *Lover Doll* was the original undubbed version - minus the Jordanaires - as released on the EP *King Creole Vol. 1* (*EP 6*) issued in October 1958. Finally, the set also included *Danny* which had not been released until January 1979 on *Elvis - A Legendary Performer Vol. 3* (*LP 106*). The actual number of previously released performances was, therefore, in excess of the number quoted in the March 1990 editorial in *Elvis Monthly*, which read 'apart from just two tracks these recordings are all previously unissued'. A number of other misleading statements were also made, particularly the reference to the overdubbed version of **Wear My Ring Around Your Neck** with Elvis slapping his guitar. The implication was that this too was unreleased, when, in fact, it was the original single version.

As regards the **King Creole** outtakes used, it was firmly believed that they were not so much session outtakes as alternative recordings made for use in the film. A number of them were made from acetates (hence their poorer sound quality), as the original session masters could not be located at that time. In fact, one of the versions of **King Creole** (take 3) was used again on the fifties' set in 1992, as a better quality tape had been found. A number of these outtakes or, to be more precise, alternative film versions, had appeared on various bootlegs over the years. This, however, was not true of any of the June 1958 session outtakes: they were entirely new to the fans and were taken directly from original master tapes.

As had happened with the two previous volumes of **Essential Elvis**, the CD version of this LP had four more tracks included. There was the 'regular' single version of **Doncha' Think It's time** (*S 20*) - said to be a splice of takes 40, 47 and 48 - along with another unreleased performance of **I Got Stung** (take 12); **As Long As I Have You** (take 8 - the 'N' version); and a short instrumental version of **King Creole**, given on the sleeve as take 8 but on the CD label as take R-6.

Delays concerning the release of all the **Essential Elvis** volumes were commonplace. Originally it was thought that the album would appear in May 1990 when, in fact, it was not issued until July. The album was going to be called **I Got Stung**. The title **Hits Like Never Before** (a play on words: Hits - like never before), was suggested by Don Wardell. And while, in a sense, it was quite apt, there was a belief that it capitalised on the idea that 'hits' compilations sold to the general public. Accordingly - and possibly because of this - dealer interest was high and the set became a good seller across the board when, in truth, it was an album almost solely aimed at the collectors' market in terms of content. This was especially true when, despite the familiarity of many of the titles listed, only one - **Wear My Ring Around Your Neck** - was the hit version (remember the undubbed version was also included). Not surprisingly then, there was no single released from this package. However, in August 1992, when BMG issued the single **Don't Be Cruel/All Shook Up/Jailhouse Rock** (**S 179**), another unreleased performance of **I Need Your Love Tonight** (take 9) was added.

Please note, the CD only release **Platinum A Life In Music** (07862 67469 2), released in July 1997, featured another unreleased performance of **I Need Your Love Tonight** (take 7), as well as another take of **A Big Hunk O' Love** (take 4).

Of course, **Essential Elvis Vol. 3** was in mono. Indeed, the label instruction from BMG read 'Please ensure MONO appears on CD label'. Its dealer price was £7.29. All label films, sleeve artwork, tapes and lacquers were supplied by the UK, even though the set had been mixed and mastered in New York.

The gatefold cover featured a colour shot from early 1958, and listed six songs included on the album (underneath the **Hits Like Never Before** legend). Note that the spine did not mention **Hits Like Never Before**, referring only to **Essential Elvis Volume 3**. Oddly, one of the songs, **Your Cheatin' Heart** (shown as **Cheating**), was never issued as a single and could hardly be described as a hit. The cover had an 'Elvis in the 90's' sticker added. Inside the gatefold was the famous shot of Elvis posing 'knock-kneed' with guitar in hand, as used on the back of **Elvis' Golden Records** (**LP 7**) along with six smaller photographs. Sleeve notes, by Richard Peters, were written in diary form, detailing key dates from December 1957 (when Elvis received his draft papers) up until January 1959. The back cover listed the tracks, their times and take numbers, indicating also whether or not the version was previously unissued. Each of the four session dates from 1958 were listed (including personnel) along with extra recording data. All key people involved in the project were credited, and it was noted that the mastering had been done in New York in March 1990.

The label, which used the old style RCA logo, gave the track information in detail, including take numbers, timings (said to be approximate) and the writers. On side 1 the compilation publishing date was correctly shown as 1990, but the copyright date erroneously quoted 1958. Certainly, the recordings were made in 1958 but not all appeared in that year. Outtakes ought to have stated 1990, while others, such as **Your Cheatin' Heart** and **Doncha' Think It's Time**, ought to have read 1982 and 1960 (their respective UK release dates).

Similarly with side 2: **Danny** was issued in 1979, while take 10 of **Your Cheatin' Heart** was released in 1965 and **Wear My Ring Around Your Neck** (single version) in April 1958. The other tracks - all outtakes/alternative versions - were all first published in 1990.

The only errors concerned **Your Cheatin' Heart**, shown as **Cheating**, (although the correct spelling was used in the session log on the back of the sleeve), and on **(Now and then there's) A Fool Such As I**, where the words in brackets were omitted.

Hits Like Never Before (Essential Elvis Vol. 3) was deleted in April 1993.

Label Variations

GERMAN BLACK LABEL
1   1990 PRESSING: MONO
     Round RCA logo at top of label

Sleeve Variations
1   Gloss

Side 1

1 **Wooden Heart** (Wise, Weisman, Twomey, Kaempfert)
2 **Heartbreak Hotel** (Axton, Durden, Presley)
3 **Hound Dog** (Leiber, Stoller)
4 **Love Me Tender** (Presley, Matson)
5 **Don't Be Cruel** (Blackwell, Presley)
6 **All Shook Up** (Blackwell, Presley)

Side 2

1 **I Want You, I Need You, I Love You** (Mysels, Kosloff)
2 **Jailhouse Rock** (Leiber, Stoller)
3 **Stuck On You** (Schroeder, McFarland)
4 **(Let me be your) Teddy Bear** (Mann, Lowe)
5 **Too Much** (Rosenberg, Weinman)
6 **Hard Headed Woman** (DeMetrius)

Side 3

1 **One Night** (Bartholomew, King)
2 **Wear My Ring Around Your Neck** (Carroll, Moody)
3 **(Now and then there's) A Fool Such As I** (Trader)
4 **Don't** (Leiber, Stoller)
5 **A Big Hunk O' Love** (Schroeder, Wyche)
6 **Are You Lonesome Tonight?** (Turk, Handman)

Side 4

1 **It's Now Or Never** (DiCapua, Schroeder, Gold)
2 **I Got Stung** (Schroeder, Hill)
3 **I Need Your Love Tonight** (Wayne, Reichner)
4 **Party** (Robinson)
5 **A Mess Of Blues** (Pomus, Shuman)
6 **Blue Suede Shoes** (Perkins)

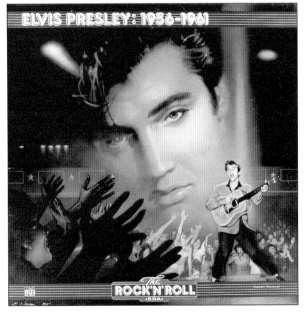

Released July 1990

The Time-Life Rock 'N' Roll Era Elvis release was similar in many respects to those of Reader's Digest, in that both companies were

originally formed in America to publish magazines, and had then diversified into other markets. Both companies had negotiated licencing arrangements with BMG to release Elvis recordings for issue on a mail-order basis which, at the time the Time-Life album was released, was possibly the only reason that the company were able to acquire the necessary rights. The point being that mail-order releases were not in direct competition to BMG's own product. Note that the back of the sleeve said that the compilation was published in 1989 by BMG Music, suggesting that preparation for the release had taken place well in advance of the actual event.

The major difference between this release and those issued by Reader's Digest (aside from the number of tracks involved), was that the Time-Life album was part of a series of releases under the overall umbrella title of **The Rock 'N' Roll Era** which, in addition to including albums covering individual years, branched out to incorporate various 'theme' albums. These included **U.S. Number Ones**, **Great Instrumentals**, **Teen Idols**, and so on. Also, albums were devoted to some of the great recording artists: Cliff Richard, Buddy Holly, The Everly Brothers and, of course, Elvis, whose album was the first to deviate from the year-by-year pattern. In all, the years 1955-1964 were covered. Clearly considerable effort had gone into the planning of this series, which ran for over two years, and the release programme was sufficiently detailed to have established the release dates for almost the entire series, although indication of intent could not be taken as a guarantee that what was planned would eventually be released. Later releases in the series were planned at an early stage, but were subject to change, depending on the outcome of negotiations with the various record companies.

The first release - 1959 - was widely advertised in the national press and in various magazines. Interestingly, in a colour booklet advertising the series, the picture showing the Elvis release displayed **'Elvis Presley 1954-1962'**, whereas the album actually covered the period 1956 to 1961. It is difficult to explain why these dates were quoted but, perhaps, the reason lies with the album's US origins, where the double album covered the period 1954-1961, although this still fails to satisfactorily explain the 1962 date.

The American album was released much earlier than the UK issue - in March 1988 - and was clearly the basis for the UK version, although it contained only 22 tracks, two fewer than its UK counterpart. The following tracks were included in the UK issue, but not on the American album :

Wooden Heart
I Got Stung
I Need Your Love Tonight
Party
A Mess Of Blues
Blue Suede Shoes

The US album contained the following, which were not included on the UK version:

That's All Right
Love Me
Little Sister
Can't Help Falling In Love

It was possible that the latter track created the confusion regarding the 1962 date quoted in an UK advert for the album. **Can't Help Falling In Love** was released in the UK (on a single with **Rock-A-Hula Baby** - S 36) in January 1962 (although the album **Blue Hawaii** - LP 15 -, which contained both songs, was released in December 1961). It was, therefore, possible that modifications to the original track listing were carried out after the advert was designed.

All three formats, LP, CD and cassette, were available, all identically priced at £11.99 plus £1.95 post and packing, which made the total cost quite high for a 24 track double album, although this was not untypical for this kind of mail-order release.

The Elvis album was entitled **Elvis Presley: 1956-1961**, suggesting the possibility of a further volume in the series, but no such release was forthcoming. A second set, entitled **Elvis, The King: 1954-1965**, was issued in America in 1990, but this was not available in the UK. For information, the complete track listing of this album was as follows:

Good Rockin' Tonight
My Baby Left Me
Any Way You Want Me
Blue Suede Shoes
Lawdy, Miss Clawdy
That's When Your Heartaches Begin
Mystery Train
Treat Me Nice
Money Honey
(You're so square) Baby I Don't Care
Loving You
Party
I Feel So Bad
Return To Sender
(You're the) Devil In Disguise
I Got Stung
I Need Your Love Tonight
(Marie's the name) His Latest Flame
Such A Night
Good Luck Charm
A Mess Of Blues
Crying In The Chapel

Although the bulk of the tracks on **Elvis Presley: 1956-1961** were from the fifties, five sixties' tracks, featuring songs like **Are You Lonesome Tonight?** and **Wooden Heart**, were included. Perhaps the only two things worthy of note here were: a) that the Rock 'n' Roll era went through to 1961, according to Time-Life, and b) that **Wooden Heart** should be deemed worthy of inclusion. In fact, the most striking (and unusual) feature of the album was the strange running order of the tracks. Certainly, normal conventions like placing tracks in chronological sequence were ignored, and moving from **A Big Hunk O' Love** into **Are You Lonesome Tonight?** and from **It's Now Or Never** back to **I Got Stung** proved disconcerting, jumping as it did from mood to mood. Presumably some attempt to produce an album of cohesion and style had been made, but at times this was difficult to follow.

The reason for the unusual track sequence undoubtedly originated with the decision to change the American listing for issue in the UK (and Europe). For example, amending 1954 to 1956 took **That's All Right** out of the frame, and it was substituted with **Wooden Heart**. So, what was formerly a straightforward chronological sequence - **That's All Right** into **Heartbreak Hotel** - became the anachronistic **Wooden Heart** into **Heartbreak Hotel**. Having said that, the US album was not strictly chronological either, but the insertion of 'replacement' tracks and the inclusion of additional material appeared haphazard and lacked cohesion.

Nevertheless, most of the tracks were standard fare being, it seems, mandatory inclusions on this type of 'hits' package. And, speaking of hits, the back of the gatefold sleeve included a track discography which was quite informative, and gave highest chart positions for both the US and UK, but it was not without errors. For instance, the claim that **Wooden Heart** was a 1961 US number one was wildly inaccurate, as the song was not released on a single there until 1965, and it was not a number one hit then either. As regards personal details, the main factual error concerned the statement that Elvis bought Graceland in 1956. He didn't; it was 1957.

The front cover art, featuring a picture and live action design, was by Ernie Norcia and was dated 1985. Inside the gatefold sleeve were notes by Bill Williams, who had been responsible for similar text on other Elvis albums, such as the sleeve notes for **Blue Rhythms**, EPC 1000 (*LP 205*). Also included were some black and white

photographs of Elvis from the fifties and, according to the credits, Paul Gambaccini acted as consultant for the series. And whilst the UK/European issue came in a gatefold sleeve, the American equivalent appeared in a hinged lid box.

There was no indication of the modes of the tracks on either the label or sleeve, but they were, in fact, a combination of mono and stereo. Indeed, the sound was very good, displaying excellent clarity. The front of the sleeve boasted that the tracks were 'Digitally Mastered'. A reference on the label to the Dutch Mechanical Rights Society STEMRA (Stichting Exploitatie Mechanische Rechten Auteurs) was quite unusual, as it was not normally found on albums issued in the UK. Its appearance here was because Time-Life were based in Amsterdam, Holland, and the record itself was pressed and produced there.

The labels listed the song titles only, without reference to the writers or publishers, which were mentioned on the back of the sleeve only and included many errors.

The co-writer of **Heartbreak Hotel**, Mae Boren Axton, was referred to as May Boren, and there was no mention of Elvis's name on **Don't Be Cruel**. The words in brackets were omitted from both **(Let me be your) Teddy Bear** and **(Now and then there's) A Fool Such As I**. **Are You Lonesome Tonight?** had no question mark, and **It's Now Or Never** did not mention DiCapua. There were several other discrepancies in the order in which writers' names were shown, but these were less obvious than usual because the credits were given in note form. The errors relating to song titles on the sleeve were also found on the labels which, additionally, omitted the commas in **I Want You, I Need You, I Love You**.

Label Variations
BLUE/WHITE LABEL
1   1990 PRESSING: MONO/STEREO

Sleeve Variations
1   Gloss

Catalogue Numbers

The use of a catalogue number PL 82227 for the next album **The Great Performances** (**LP 308**), was different from those of other albums issued during the previous three or four years. For some time, the pattern of issue had been quite normal, with an incremental number appearing on each subsequent release so that, for example,

Presley - The All Time Greatest Hits (**LP 287**), issued in August 1987 with a catalogue number 90100(2), was followed by *Moody Blue* (**LP 296**), in October 1988, which used 90252. All seemingly normal. Of course, there were minor anomalies where items like *Stereo '57 (Essential Elvis Volume 2)* (**LP 298**), released in January 1989, had a catalogue number of 90250 - sequentially lower than that of *Moody Blue*. Nevertheless, there would appear to be an explanation for this, in that *Stereo '57 (Essential Elvis Volume 2)* had been assigned a catalogue number in readiness for a planned October 1988 release date. The fact that the album was delayed by three months did not affect its assigned catalogue number.

Some of the later BMG albums, such as *Elvis Sings The Wonderful World Of Christmas*, NL 81936 (**LP 311**), and *Elvis In Person At The International Hotel Las Vegas, Nevada*, NL 83892 (**LP 316**), were 'old' albums assigned these numbers years previously when they were issued in Europe. So, despite being 'new' UK issues, they still fitted into the overall pattern, albeit being an older one to the one in operation at the time they were issued.

Even *The Alternate Aloha* (**LP 294**), which used 86985, followed the pattern started by *The Memphis Record*, PL 86221(2) (**LP 284**), and *The Complete Sun Sessions*, PL 86414(2) (**LP 283**), given the gap of ten months before the release of *The Alternate Aloha* in May 1988. All three of these albums originated in America, not the UK or Europe, and with the addition of the initial digit (8), were identical to the American catalogue number - 6985, 6221 and 6414.

The Great Performances (**LP 308**), on the other hand, was markedly different. Its catalogue number - 82227 - did not fit any of the patterns described above. It was a new compilation, so the use of a number which was closer to the 'older' black label albums would seem inappropriate. It originated in America, not Europe. So why wasn't a number which fitted into the 86xxx series used? The answer, it seemed, was that the catalogue number assigned in America - 2227 - fitted the pattern operating at the time the album was issued.

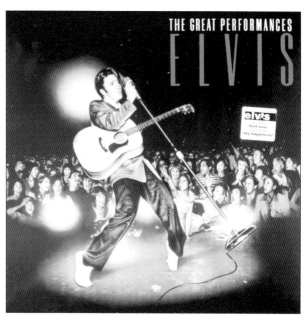

Released August 1990   Deleted February 1995

This was one of the very few US inspired releases of the late eighties, early nineties. In fact the vinyl and CD album (which bore the same track listing) was tied into the release of the videos of the same title, released by Buena Vista Home Video. *The Great Performances* turned out to be the last vinyl album officially issued in America as a standard release.

The album, however, comprised twenty tracks, highlights of the videos, and featured, by and large, previously issued material. However, the major selling point of the album was the inclusion of the hitherto unissued *My Happiness*, said to be Elvis's first non-professional recording, made for his mother in 1953 at Sam Phillips' studio in Memphis. Apparently the acetate recording - thought to have been long lost - was in the possession of Ed Leek, whom Elvis is said to have given it to very early on in his career. Various luminaries - including Phillips himself - assessed the recording and vouched for its authenticity - not that any fans who heard it ever had any doubt: it was undoubtedly Elvis. All formats of the album bore a sticker advertising the inclusion of *My Happiness*, on the front cover.

Most of the contents were standard fare. However, *Shake, Rattle And Roll/Flip, Flop And Fly* was the live, undubbed version from Elvis's first appearance on the Dorsey Brothers Stage Show of 28 January 1956, while the cut of *Ready Teddy* was the live version from the Ed Sullivan Show, broadcast on 9 September 1956. *Treat Me Nice* was unusual, in that while it was basically the film soundtrack version from *Jailhouse Rock*, which had first been issued officially on *Essential Elvis*, PL 89979 (**LP 280**), in December 1986, it was listed as a stereo recording. Certainly, there was aural evidence of information separation on the track, but careful listening on headphones revealed that it was not a stereo track at all, rather the mono track with an overdubbed guitar added. In fact, subsequent to its release, Ernst Mikael Jorgensen did confirm that the overdub was done at the film studio, and that in all likelihood the version used was from the 35mm print of the film. Therefore, the track hardly justified its stereo tag.

Always On My Mind was the 'acoustic version' as used on the *This Is Elvis* album (**LP 150**), while *Unchained Melody* was the live, undubbed version recorded at Rapid City on 21 June 1977. The version of *An American Trilogy* was from 14 January 1973 - the Aloha concert.

And although the track sequence was virtually chronological, the set closed with *Memories* from the 1968 NBC TV Special. The song had also closed the film *Elvis On Tour* (for which there had been no official soundtrack album) and later, in 1981, the film *This Is Elvis*.

| LP 308 | The Great Performances |
| | RCA PL 82227 |

Side 1

1   **My Happiness** (Peterson, Bergantine)
2   **That's All Right** (Crudup)
3   **Shake, Rattle And Roll** (Calhoun)
    Flip, Flop And Fly (Turner, Calhoun)
4   **Heartbreak Hotel** (Axton, Durden, Presley)
5   **Blue Suede Shoes** (Perkins)
6   **Ready Teddy** (Blackwell, Marascalco)
7   **Don't Be Cruel** (Blackwell, Presley)
8   **(Let me be your) Teddy Bear** (Mann, Lowe)
9   **Got A Lot O' Livin' To Do!** (Schroeder, Weisman)
10 **Jailhouse Rock** (Leiber, Stoller)
11 **Treat Me Nice** (Leiber, Stoller)

Side 2

1   **King Creole** (Leiber, Stoller)
2   **Trouble** (Leiber, Stoller)
3   **Fame And Fortune** (Wise, Weisman)
4   **Return To Sender** (Blackwell, Scott)
5   **Always On My Mind** (James, Carson, Christopher)
6   **An American Trilogy** (Arr. Newbury)
7   **If I Can Dream** (Brown)
8   **Unchained Melody** (Zaret, North)
9   **Memories** (Strange, Davis)

Although the title of the project was **The Great Performances** (suggesting it would reflect all stages of Elvis's career), of the twenty tracks used, thirteen were from the fifties, only three were from the sixties (the early sixties at that), and four were from the seventies. All tracks were mastered in New York in May 1990.

There was a reference to the modes on the album cover - 'All tracks are mono unless * for stereo'. However, both sides of the label said 'Stereo', even though all tracks on side one were mono, with the exception of **Treat Me Nice** which affected to be stereo. Reference to the modes on the label reversed the explanation on the sleeve, reading '* MONO recording. All others are stereo'.

The label itself was the old style black label. Song timings appeared on both cover and labels. An 'Elvis' sticker - a variant of the 'Elvis in the 90's' sticker - was located under Elvis's name on the front cover. It read 'Including first ever recording **My Happiness**'.

The album cover was in black and white. The front cover was a drawing from an original photograph taken by Bob Moreland in Florida, August 1956. The drawing excluded Bill Black and featured an audience in the background. Keen observers would note the similarities to the cover of **Elvis - The '56 Sessions Vol. 2**, PL 42102 (*LP 113*), issued in June 1979. The rear cover shot, also in black and white, was of Elvis walking away from Graceland in the early sixties, most probably not long after his return from the army.

The inner bag had sleeve notes on one side, along with track details, while the reverse side featured a few shots of Elvis (in black and white, of course) performing **Blue Suede Shoes** at his screen test for Paramount Pictures in late March/early April 1956.

The sleeve notes were in two sections: one by Andrew Solt, co-producer of **Elvis On Tour**, **This Is Elvis** and **Elvis '56**, and the other by Jerry Schilling, former friend/bodyguard of Elvis, then an employee of Elvis Presley Enterprises. Both men had collaborated in the production of the two videos and the resulting album release. Schilling's notes attested to his long-standing friendship with Elvis, dating back to 1954, and related briefly how this current project originated. This was the first time that the Estate had issued product of this kind in conjunction with BMG.

A promotional poster, featuring a photograph of the cover shot, was distributed to dealers. It listed some of the tracks featured on the album: **My Happiness**, **That's All Right**, **Blue Suede Shoes**, **(Let me be your) Teddy Bear** and **Jailhouse Rock**.

There were quite a few errors relating to both song titles and writers, although there was consistency between cover, inner bag and labels, all of which featured the song titles. Both **Shake, Rattle And Roll** and **Flip, Flop And Fly** made use of a ampersand (&) instead of the word **And**. The words in brackets in **(Let me be your) Teddy Bear** were missing, as was the exclamation mark at the end of **Got A Lot O' Livin' To Do!**. **An American Trilogy** omitted the word **An**.

Presumably the writers' names were taken from American sources, as full names were used on the inner bag, a departure from the normal UK/European practice of using initials and surname on the labels.

Both label and inner bag credited Jesse Stone as the writer of both **Shake, Rattle And Roll** and **Flip, Flop And Fly**, which was technically correct, but as Stone wrote these songs under the pseudonym Charles Calhoun (which was how the songs were normally credited), we had to consider this to be an error. Furthermore, **Flip, Flop And Fly** should have also credited co-writer Lou Willie Turner. The writers of **Ready Teddy** were normally shown the other way around. On the label, side 2, track 4, Otis Blackwell had his name spelt Blackweel; **Always On My Mind** was credited to James, Thompson, Christopher; and **An American Trilogy** failed to make it clear that Mickey Newbury arranged the song - he did not write it. Finally, the writers of **Memories** were usually shown the other way around.

Video Releases

Although Elvis video releases had always been enormously popular with the fans - mainly his feature films, plus the likes of **That's The Way It Is**, **Elvis On Tour**, and **This Is Elvis** (and witness the number of times they have been repackaged!) - there had never been a simultaneous release of audio and video material until the release of **The Great Performances**. Certainly, most collectors would have the likes of the **'68 Comeback Special**, **One Night With You**, **Aloha From Hawaii** and **Elvis '56**, but until this point there had never been a planned and mutually supportive release, a joint venture between BMG and the Presley Estate. It was a new and potentially very exciting concept, promising much for the future.

However, as could be seen from the track listing, there were only twenty tracks featured on the album (vinyl and CD) version (which had a running time of 51.03), while the combined running times of the two videos **Centre Stage** and **The Man And The Music** was 107 minutes. Clearly the audio release merely took highlights from the video release. Moreover, the running order varied too. So, what follows are the video track listings. The ones marked with an asterisk are the songs included on the audio release. Where necessary, notes have been added where the versions differ in some way, especially between a live performance and a studio cut.

Centre Stage

Money Honey	Live version from 24 March 1956 Dorsey Brothers Stage Show.
***That's All Right**	Standard version played over film footage from 1955-57.
***Hound Dog**	From 5 June 1956 Milton Berle Show. Note: the album version was the studio cut.
I Want You, I Need You, I Love You	Live from Steve Allen's 1 July 1956 TV Show.

*Blue Suede Shoes	Studio version which he mimed to for his Hollywood screen test in late March/early April 1956.
Love Me Tender	The record version used over the actual film soundtrack.
*Heartbreak Hotel	While the audio version was the studio cut, the video had a live version from the Milton Berle Show of 3 April 1956.
*Ready Teddy	Both audio and video used the live version from the 9 September 1956 Ed Sullivan TV Show.
*(Let me be your) Teddy Bear	The record version was used in the video and film, but without audience overdubs found in the original film of *Loving You*.
*King Creole	The record version used over candid footage, though once again, without overdubs.
*Jailhouse Rock	An edited version of the record was used in the video, and there were no overdubs as there were in the original film. The album used the full studio version.
Guitar Man	As used in the opening section of the 1968 TV Special.
Suspicious Minds	The *This Is Elvis* version i.e. an edited cut from the Aloha Special.
Mystery Train	The original version, played over candid footage.
*Unchained Melody	Live from Rapid City, 21 June 1977.
All Shook Up	Live from the 1968 TV Special.

The Man And The Music

*An American Trilogy	This was the little used *Aloha From Hawaii* version from 14 January 1973.
*My Happiness	The video version, played over stills, was edited to about 1.40, compared to the record version which ran for 2.30.
*Shake, Rattle And Roll/ Flip, Flop And Fly	Live version from Elvis's first appearance on the Dorsey Brothers Show on 28 January 1956.
Blue Suede Shoes	Live from Milton Berle's 3 April 1956 TV Show.
*Don't Be Cruel	The record cut was the studio version; the video was of Elvis's appearance on the Ed Sullivan Show in January 1957.
*Got A Lot O' Livin' To Do!	The video was the *Loving You* - end sequence - film version; the album used the studio cut.
*Trouble	From the film *King Creole*.
Mean Woman Blues	The edited film version as used in *This is Elvis*.
*Treat Me Nice	From the film *Jailhouse Rock*; the album version purported to be stereo, but it was the mono version overdubbed.

G.I. Blues	From the film, plus army footage.
*Fame And Fortune	The album featured the studio cut; on the video we saw Elvis performing this on the May 1960 Frank Sinatra TV Show.
Return To Sender	Record version, plus overdubs, as used in the film *Girls! Girls! Girls!*.
*Memories	Played over live footage.
You Gave Me A Mountain	From *Aloha From Hawaii*.
*Always On My Mind	From *This Is Elvis*, plus movie clips. On record, the 'acoustic' version i.e. no lead guitar or strings featured, was used.
*If I Can Dream	The closing song from the 1968 NBC TV Special.

LP 309 For The Asking (The Lost Album)

RCA NL 90513

Side 1

1 **(It's a) Long Lonely Highway** (Pomus, Shuman)
2 **Western Union** (Tepper, Bennett)
3 **Witchcraft** (Bartholomew, King)
4 **Love Me Tonight** (Robertson)
5 **What Now, What Next, Where To** (Robertson, Blair)
6 **Please Don't Drag That String Around** (Blackwell, Scott)
7 **Blue River** (Evans, Tobias)
8 **Never Ending** (Kaye, Springer)

Side 2

1 **(You're the) Devil In Disguise** (Giant, Baum, Kaye)
2 **Finders Keepers, Losers Weepers** (D. & O. Jones)
3 **Echoes Of Love** (Roberts, McMains)
4 **Slowly But Surely** (Wayne, Weisman)
5 **It Hurts Me** (Byers, Daniels)
6 **Memphis, Tennessee** (Berry)
7 **Ask Me** (Modugno, Giant, Baum, Kaye)

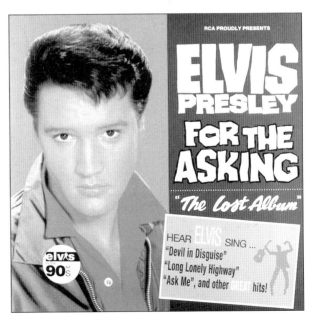

Released November 1990   Deleted April 1993

If ever fans wanted evidence that BMG were making serious attempts to rationalise Elvis's back catalogue releases, then this release proved it.

For many years innumerable fans/writers had written about how RCA had 'thrown away' most of the original songs recorded during the May 1963 sessions, by using them as 'bonus tracks' or B sides, when they ought to have been collected and issued as an album at the time. Indeed, articles had appeared over the years suggesting such a format and RCA themselves had made an effort to collate the so-called bonus songs into an album format with **The Complete Bonus Songs** package, NL 89115(2), a collection not officially released in the UK.

The idea for the release then was not a new one, as Ernst Mikael Jorgensen, who wrote the brief sleeve notes, would have agreed. Compiling these tracks on an album of their own was not only long overdue but absolutely correct in artistic terms, as it gave them the status and recognition they had been denied previously by the manner of their release - details of which are dealt with later. In fact, for a year or so prior to this release, rumours had circulated that BMG were going to issue an album of outtakes from this era. Whatever the truth of this was, perhaps we will never know. What is known though is that when Semon, Jorgensen and Rijff made their now historic visit to RCA's vaults in New York in November/December 1989, all manner of treasure was discovered. Principal among these were first generation three-track master tapes of these sessions - i.e. May 1963 and January 1964 - both held in Nashville. Thus, once having located these masters, the decision was taken to issue this material in the form of a 'lost' album to 'plug the gap', as it were, between **Pot Luck**, RD 27265/SF 5135 (LP 16), in July 1962, and the **Elvis For Everyone** collection in November 1965, RD/SF 7752 (LP 26). It was, in fact, a compilation album with a difference: instead of being a 'hits' package, or an assorted collection of odd tracks from various sessions, sometimes spanning many years, the bulk of the album comprised material recorded at the same session, thus providing a thematic and sound quality consistency lacking in random collections. Certainly, many of these tracks had been brought together on the likes of bonus songs collections issued in Europe, but no-one had ever compiled an album solely from the two sessions in question.

Apparently, the title of the album was coined by Jan van Gestel, the Dutch writer, who had written many of the texts which accompanied Ger Rijff's photo journals. Indeed, the colour photograph used on the front of the album cover, and the black and white one featured on the back cover (though not on the CD), were both supplied by Ger Rijff. The concept, both in its artwork and choice of photograph, was to replicate as far as possible a sixties' album. We believe this was successfully achieved. A bonus for fans was that this album was retailed as a mid-priced release in all formats. It was, therefore, quite possible to pay £4.99 or thereabouts for the vinyl copy, or between £8 - £9 for the CD version. Some outlets were cheaper still, making the album excellent value for money.

As for the songs themselves, they were remixed and remastered from the original three track master tapes by Chick Crumpacker in New York. And although they were not remixed in a drastically different way from the originals, there was no doubt that the real quality of the recordings was heard for the first time in this collection. Most tracks sounded clearer than they had previously though, as a result of mixing from three track (rather than two track stereo masters), some differences were evident to the listener. Most notable of these was the introduction to **Please Don't Drag That String Around**, where Elvis's humming could be heard much clearer than ever before. Perhaps the biggest surprise though was **Blue River**, which ran for a mere 1 minute 31 seconds, indicating clearly that the original single version (S 52) had obviously been spliced to give it a longer running time. Also, although there was a sort of fade out, the track actually did come to a definite stop.

It has come to light that the original label/sleeve copy information for this release included the master serial and take numbers for each of the songs. For some reason, however, the information was not included on the finished article. The release date quoted on the same sheet was September 1990 when, in fact, the album was not released until November 1990. Early advertisements for the album in **Elvis Monthly** gave the take numbers and described the tracks as being 'All previously unreleased alternative takes'. However, later adverts removed this erroneous claim, but made no reference to the fact that these were the original versions.

For your information we have included the master serial and take numbers here:-

ppa4 0303	**(It's a) Long Lonely Highway**	Take 2
ppa4 0305	**Western Union**	Take 4
ppa4 0295	**Witchcraft**	Take 3
ppa4 0297	**Love Me Tonight**	Take 8
ppa4 0294	**What Now, What Next, Where To**	Take 1
ppa4 0291	**Please Don't Drag That String Around**	Take 6
ppa4 0307	**Blue River**	Take 2
ppa4 0293	**Never Ending**	Take 3
ppa4 0292	**(You're the) Devil In Disguise**	Take 6
ppa4 0296	**Finders Keepers, Losers Weepers**	Take 3
ppa4 0290	**Echoes Of Love**	Take 10
ppa4 0306	**Slowly But Surely**	Take 5
rpa4 1006	**It Hurts Me**	Take 5 (from January 1964)
rpa4 1004	**Memphis, Tennessee**	Take 6 (from January 1964)
rpa4 1005	**Ask Me**	Take 11 (from January 1964)

Incidentally, this was not the order in which the songs were recorded. The master serial number in the left column indicated that **Echoes Of Love** (ppa4 0290) was the first song cut. The full order in which the songs were recorded can be found in the table below.

It was interesting to note how many of the songs were completed in relatively few takes, compared to earlier sessions. Further, there was little evidence of over-dubbing on these sessions and, to the best of our knowledge, no spliced takes.

On a point of order, the album cover stated that tracks 1-12 were published in 1963, and tracks 13-15 in 1964. Strictly speaking, this was not true in all cases, as we would like to explain. Remember, the publishing date ought to refer to when the song, or version of a song, was released in this form in the country of issue. It should not, therefore, be assumed that the year a song was recorded automatically corresponds with the year it was published. Obviously in many cases it does, but not always. And so, for accuracy and, we hope, interest, we have constructed a table to show where each of the songs first appeared and when. Of course, we are referring to UK releases here.

The table below, therefore, shows the tracks (placed in what is believed to be the order in which they were recorded), the recording date, details of where the song was originally released in the UK (including the release number) and, finally, the date of the original release.

Title	Recording Date	First UK Release	Release Date
Echoes Of Love	26.5.63	**Kissin' Cousins** (LP 22)	Jun 1964
Please Don't Drag That String Around	26.5.63	Single B side (S 41)	Jun 1963
(You're the) Devil In Disguise	26.5.63	Single A side (S 41)	Jun 1963
Never Ending	26.5.63	Single B side (S 46)	Aug 1964
What Now, What Next, Where To	26.5.63	**Double Trouble** (LP 32)	Aug 1967

187

Witchcraft	26.5.63	Single B side (*S 42*)	Oct 1963
Finders, Keepers, Losers Weepers	26.5.63	*Elvis For Everyone* (*LP 26*)	Nov 1965
Love Me Tonight	26.5.63	*Fun In Acapulco* (*LP 20*)	Dec 1963
(It's a) Long Lonely Highway	27.5.63	*Kissin' Cousins* (*LP 22*)	Jun 1964
Western Union	27.5.63	*Speedway* (*LP 35*)	Aug 1968
Slowly But Surely	27.5.63	*Fun In Acapulco* (*LP 20*)	Dec 1963
Blue River	27.3.63	Single A side (*S 52*)	Feb 1966
Memphis, Tennessee	12.1.64	*Elvis For Everyone* (*LP 26*)	Nov 1965
Ask Me	12.1.64	Single B side (*S 47*)	Oct 1964
It Hurts Me	12.1.64	Single B side (*S 45*)	Jun 1964

Please note: alternative versions of **Memphis, Tennessee** and **Ask Me** were also recorded at the May 1963 session. These were not issued until August 1991 when they were included in the three-album set **Collectors Gold**, PL 90574(3) (**LP 315**).

As had been the case with the **Essential Elvis** series, the label format replicated the early 1960s RCA logo. The sub-title, **The Lost Album**, appeared on the label in brackets in smaller print. Unusually, the original A+R man (Artists and Repertoire), Chet Atkins, was credited on the album sleeve and label, as was Ger Rijff, who did the art and design work. Chick Crumpacker was also credited on both sleeve and label (as Digital Producer), as was Dick Baxter, the Digital Engineer. Ernst Mikael Jorgensen, however, who wrote the sleeve notes and was responsible for compiling the release, only received a credit as co-compiler with Chick Crumpacker on the label, not the sleeve. The original recording engineers, Bill Porter and Ron Steele, were mentioned on the sleeve. Finally, the song timings were given on the label, but not on the cover. No mention was made anywhere on this release to BMG's UK representative, Roger Semon. His contribution, therefore, is not known.

Oddly, the top and spine of the cover showed an ND catalogue number prefix (as used on mid-priced CDs), where the correct one, NL, was shown on the back cover and on the label. The round RCA logo appeared on the cover twice, along with the BMG logo. The release carried a YY price code (indicating a mid-price release). But to illustrate how seriously the release was taken in the UK, a display pack for in-store advertising was also produced, and it was given a 'catalogue' number - ELVIS D1. This pack became available on 2 November 1990, just prior to the official release date of the album on 10 November.

As had become standard since mid-1990, the album cover bore an 'Elvis In The 90's' sticker. However, only the back of the sleeve showed any reference to the mode of the album - stereo - there being no mention of it on the label, front cover or spine.

In conclusion, it seems worth noting that this album was not issued in the USA until November 1991, when it was revised for the US market and released on CD only (07863 61024-2). The cover design was completely different - the new one simulated a brown paper parcel! - hence the use of **The Lost Album** as its main title. Additionally, and unnecessarily we feel, new sleeve notes were written. However, rumours that the tracks would be issued in their original mix form, proved to be false. The delay in issuing this album in the USA was thought to be because the US division felt its release was unnecessary.

(It's a) Long Lonely Highway was shown without the words in brackets on both label and sleeve. Don Robertson had his name spelt Robinson on side 1, track 5; the words in brackets were omitted on **(You're the) Devil In Disguise**, again on both label and sleeve. The comma was missing in **Finders Keepers, Losers Weepers**, but on the label only, whereas it was omitted entirely in **Memphis, Tennessee**.

Label Variations

GERMAN BLACK LABEL

1	1990 PRESSING: STEREO Round RCA logo at top of label

Sleeve Variations

1	Gloss

LP 310 — The Legend Lives On

Reader's Digest V86002 VB1 GELG-A-209

Album 1 The First Hits

Side 1

1 **That's All Right** (Crudup)
2 **Heartbreak Hotel** (Axton, Durden, Presley)
3 **Blue Suede Shoes** (Perkins)
4 **Money Honey** (Stone)
5 **I Want You, I Need You, I Love You** (Mysels, Kosloff)
6 **My Baby Left Me** (Crudup)
7 **Don't Be Cruel** (Blackwell, Presley)

Side 2

1   **Hound Dog** (Leiber, Stoller)
2   **Blue Moon** (Rodgers, Hart)
3   **I Don't Care If The Sun Don't Shine** (David)
4   **Love Me Tender** (Presley, Matson)
5   **Any Way You Want Me (that's how I will be)** (Schroeder, Owens)
6   **When My Blue Moon Turns To Gold Again** (Walker, Sullivan)
7   **Love Me** (Leiber, Stoller)

Album 2 *The Hits Of 1957*

Side 1

1   **Too Much** (Rosenberg, Weinman)
2   **Paralyzed** (Blackwell, Presley)
3   **Poor Boy** (Presley, Matson)
4   **Old Shep** (Foley, Arthur)
5   **Playin' For Keeps** (Kesler)
6   **All Shook Up** (Blackwell, Presley)
7   **That's When Your Heartaches Begin** (Raskin, Brown, Fisher)

Side 2

1   **Mystery Train** (Parker, Phillips)
2   **Rip It Up** (Blackwell, Marascalco)
3   **(Let me be your) Teddy Bear** (Mann, Lowe)
4   **(There'll be) Peace In The Valley (for me)** (Dorsey)
5   **Party** (Robinson)
6   **Got A Lot O Livin' To Do!** (Schroeder, Weisman)
7   **Loving You** (Leiber, Stoller)

Album 3 *The Hits Of 1958*

Side 1

1   **Jailhouse Rock** (Leiber, Stoller)
2   **Trying To Get To You** (Singleton, McCoy)
3   **Lawdy, Miss Clawdy** (Price)
4   **Santa Bring My Baby Back (to me)** (Schroeder, DeMetrius)
5   **I'm Left, You're Right, She's Gone** (Kesler, Taylor)
6   **Treat Me Nice** (Leiber, Stoller)
7   **Don't** (Leiber, Stoller)

Side 2

1   **Hard Headed Woman** (DeMetrius)
2   **I Beg Of You** (McCoy, Owens)
3   **Wear My Ring Around Your Neck** (Carroll, Moody)
4   **Doncha' Think It's Time** (Otis, Dixon)
5   **Trouble** (Leiber, Stoller)
6   **I Got Stung** (Schroeder, Hill)
7   **One Night** (Bartholomew King)

Album 4 *The Army Years (1958-1960)*

Side 1

1   **King Creole** (Leiber, Stoller)
2   **(Now and then there's) A Fool Such As I** (Trader)
3   **I Need Your Love Tonight** (Wayne, Reichner)
4   **A Big Hunk O' Love** (Schroeder, Wyche)
5   **My Wish Came True** (Hunter)
6   **Fame And Fortune** (Wise, Weisman)
7   **Stuck On You** (Schroeder, McFarland)

Side 2

1   **It's Now Or Never** (DiCapua, Schroeder, Gold)
2   **A Mess Of Blues** (Pomus, Shuman)
3   **Are You Lonesome Tonight?** (Turk Handman)
4   **I Gotta Know** (Evans, Williams)
5   **Wooden Heart** (Wise, Weisman, Twomey, Kaempfert)
6   **Lonely Man** (Benjamin, Marcus)
7   **Surrender** (DeCurtis, Pomus, Shuman)

Album 5 *The Movie Years (1961-1962)*

Side 1

1   **Flaming Star** (Wayne, Edwards)
2   **I Feel So Bad** (Willis)
3   **Wild In The Country** (Peretti, Creatore, Weiss)
4   **(Marie's the name) His Latest Flame** (Pomus, Shuman)
5   **Little Sister** (Pomus, Shuman)
6   **Rock-A-Hula Baby** (Wise, Weisman, Fuller)
7   **Can't Help Falling In Love** (Peretti, Creatore, Weiss)

Side 2

1   **Good Luck Charm** (Schroeder, Gold)
2   **Anything That's Part Of You** (Robertson)
3   **Follow That Dream** (Wise, Weisman)
4   **She's Not You** (Pomus, Leiber, Stoller)
5   **Just Tell Her Jim Said Hello** (Leiber, Stoller)
6   **King Of The Whole Wide World** (Batchelor, Roberts)
7   **Return To Sender** (Blackwell, Scott)

Album 6 *More Hits From The Movie Years (1963-1965)*

Side 1

1   **(You're the) Devil In Disguise** (Giant, Baum, Kaye)
2   **One Broken Heart For Sale** (Blackwell, Scott)
3   **Bossa Nova Baby** (Leiber, Stoller)
4   **Witchcraft** (Bartholomew, King)
5   **They Remind Me Too Much Of You** (Robertson)
6   **Kiss Me Quick** (Pomus, Shuman)
7   **Viva Las Vegas** (Pomus, Shuman)

Side 2

1   **Kissin' Cousins** (Wise, Starr)
2   **What'd I Say** (Charles)
3   **Such A Night** (Chase)
4   **Ain't That Loving You Baby** (Otis, Hunter)
5   **Blue Christmas** (Hayes, Johnson)
6   **Do The Clam** (Wayne, Weisman, Fuller)
7   **Crying In The Chapel** (Glenn)

Album 7 *Big Boss Man (1965-1968)*
            The Concert years (1968-1972)

Side 1

1   **Big Boss Man** (Smith, Dixon)
2   **(Such an) Easy Question** (Blackwell, Scott)
3   **Frankie And Johnny** (Gottlieb, Karger, Weisman)
4   **Love Letters** (Young, Heyman)
5   **Guitar Man** (Hubbard)
6   **U.S. Male** (Hubbard)
7   **You'll Never Walk Alone** (Rodgers, Hammerstein II)

Side 2

1   **If I Can Dream** (Brown)
2   **In The Ghetto** (Davis)
3   **Suspicious Minds** (James)
4   **The Wonder Of You** (Knight)
5   **You Don't Have To Say You Love Me** (Pallavicini, Donaggio, Wickham, Napier-Bell)
6   **I Just Can't Help Believin'** (Mann, Weil)
7   **I'm Leavin'** (Jarrett, Charles)

Album 8 *Elvis' Last Hits (1972-1977)*

Side 1

1   **Until It's Time For You To Go** (Sainte-Marie)
2   **An American Trilogy** (Arr. Newbury)
3   **Burning Love** (Linde)
4   **Always On My Mind** (James, Carson, Christopher)
5   **Fool** (Sigman, Last)
6   **Promised Land** (Berry)
7   **My Boy** (Francois, Bourtayre, Martin, Coulter)

Side 2

1   **T.R.O.U.B.L.E** (Chesnut)
2   **Hurt** (Craine, Jacobs)
3   **The Girl Of My Best Friend** (Ross, Bobrick)
4   **Moody Blue** (James)
5   **She Thinks I Still Care** (Lipscomb)
6   **Way Down** (Martine Jnr.)
7   **My Way** (Thibault, Francois, Revaux, Anka)

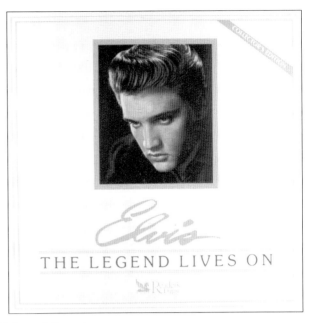

THE LEGEND LIVES ON

Released November 1990

The earlier Reader's Digest Elvis boxed set, ***Elvis Presley's Greatest Hits***, GELV 6-A (*LP 82*), first issued in October 1975, had been very successful. Indeed, by the early nineties, the set had sold in excess of 300,000 units (vinyl and cassette formats only), a remarkable achievement given its cost, despite the number of years it was available. Part of its success was undoubtedly due to the fact that, at the time, it was the largest collection of Elvis material available in the UK, and appealed to both collectors and the general public alike. But, by early 1990, the set had become something of a problem for Reader's Digest UK, in that no CD version had been produced at a time when record buyers had begun to demand more product in this format than on vinyl. Reader's Digest thus considered issuing the set on CD to bring it more up-to-date and, presumably, to capitalise on the 'back issue' boom, which would have given the package a new lease of life and a further extended run. However, these plans were shortlived for, in 1987, Reader's Digest in Belgium had prepared a new eight album Elvis boxed set which had been issued throughout continental Europe, in all three formats. Consequently, Reader's Digest UK abandoned their own plans to 'upgrade' ***Elvis Presley's Greatest Hits*** to CD, in favour of the European ***The Legend Lives On*** set. Clearly, this was not only a lower cost option, but a sensible and more practical decision, given that CDs already existed, and the likelihood was that a new compilation would generate additional sales to the collectors' market. Further, the UK division would incur no production costs, as the set was simply imported from Europe.

The new set was compiled by Henri Heymans, Director of Reader's Digest's International Music Development in Brussels, whose intention it was to produce a selection of Elvis's greatest hits, not just in terms of hits in America and the UK, but also in Continental Europe. Reference to the track listing shows that there were several examples of songs which had never appeared on singles in the UK, and we could only assume that selections like ***(Such an) Easy Question*** and ***Money Honey*** had made some impact as singles in selected European outlets.

The set, then, was a revised greatest hits package and, actually, contained more hits than its illustrious predecessor - a fact which will become more apparent when we consider the specific differences between the two collections later in the text. Noticeably, whilst ***Elvis Presley's Greatest Hits*** covered the period up to, and including, 1972, the new set covered Elvis's complete recording career, including material released in 1977.

The Legend Lives On had been issued in Europe to coincide with the 10th anniversary of Elvis's death, and Reader's Digest reported that sales were 'excellent'. When issued in the UK (without being 'wet tested' incidentally), sales were also good with the percentage mix for the three formats showing that vinyl (at 17%) was still holding its own against cassettes (40%) and CDs (43%). Reader's Digest believed that collectors' editions, such as this, as opposed to various artists' compilations, sold rather better on vinyl, and the reported sales figures would seem to bear this out.

Yet, while **The Legend Lives On** was, effectively, a replacement for the earlier collection, **Elvis Presley's Greatest Hits** was still available for some years after 1990, despite not being advertised as such. Copies could still be ordered, and the set was on display in Reader's Digest shops.

The eight albums (which amounted to almost five hours of material) were rather conveniently divided into chronological periods covering aspects of Elvis's career, with each album being sub-titled to 'describe' and represent each period. These were: -

Album 1	**The First Years** - from 1954 through to 1956.	
Album 2	**The Hits Of 1957**.	
Album 3	**The Hits Of 1958**.	
Album 4	**The Army Years (1958-1960)**.	
Album 5	**The Movie Years (1961-1962)** - half of the 14 tracks were not film songs, however.	
Album 6	**More Hits From The Movie Years (1963-1965)** - only six of the tracks were from films.	
Album 7	Two titles: - side 1 **Big Boss Man (1965-1968)** - side 2 **The Concert Years (1968-1972)**.	
Album 8	**Elvis' Last Hits (1972-1977)**.	

Some changes were made for the CD format version, as the tracks were combined to produce 5 CDs so that, for example, one CD was entitled **The Hits Of 1957 and 1958**.

The albums, then, followed a broadly chronological sequence, but the tracks themselves were not strictly chronological, even accepting that the recording date and eventual single release often followed no pattern. **Big Boss Man**, for example, recorded and released as a single in 1967, preceded tracks released before that date. The design of the box was simple enough - a plain white front with a small picture of Elvis from 1956, which had been used several times previously, for example, on the 1980 single **It's Only Love**, RCA 4 (*S 122*); on the sleeve of album 1 of **Elvis Aron Presley**, CLP8 3699 (*LP 126*); and on **Romantic Elvis**, RCALP 1000 (*LP 192*). Also featured was the title, Elvis's name and a 'flash' across the top right hand corner proclaiming 'Collectors Edition'. The back of the box listed the tracks, which were printed with a very distracting and inconsistent use of upper and lower case characters.

Note that the front of the box and labels used a different catalogue number to the normal Reader's Digest UK system, although this was shown as GELG-A-209 in the bottom right hand corner on the back of the box.

We would like to turn our attention now to the contents of this set. Because there were so many tracks included, what we have done is list the ones which deserve comment, and note anything of interest to the reader. However, before we do so, two songs deserve special mention - **Anything That's Part Of You** and **(Such an) Easy Question** - as these were uncredited, alternative takes. Apparently, when Henri Heymans received the tapes from BMG he was aware that several of the tracks were not the original single versions, but he chose not to take the matter up with BMG. Consequently, the use of the term 'Collectors Edition' took on a greater significance.

Song Title	Comments/Notes
Mystery Train	Not proper mono. On using headphones you can hear separation.
Got A Lot Of Livin' To Do!	Electronic stereo.
Doncha' Think It's Time	Take 40, as used on **Elvis' Golden Records Vol. 2** (*LP 10*).

Trouble	Incorrectly listed as **T.R.O.U.B.L.E.**
I Gotta Know	In mono.
Lonely Man	In mono.
Wild In The Country	An outtake (take 16) - in stereo - as featured on **Elvis Aron Presley** (*LP 126*).
Anything That's Part Of You	An unlisted alternative take (take 8).
Little Sister	In mono.
Follow That Dream	In mono.
King Of The Whole Wide World	In mono.
Viva Las Vegas	In mono.
Kissin' Cousins	In mono (single version).
What'd I Say	In mono (from **Viva Las Vegas**).
Do The Clam	Poor editing. Loss of sound on one channel during break.
(Such an) Easy Question	An unlisted alternative take (take 4).
Frankie And Johnny	In mono.
Big Boss Man	In mono.
If I Can Dream	Stereo. Alternative take - take 4 - as featured on the **He Walks Beside Me: Favourite Songs Of Faith And Inspiration** album (*LP 101*).
I'm Leavin	Stereo.
An American Trilogy	Stereo. Single version from February 1972 (*S 83*).
Always On My Mind	Original single version in stereo (S 85).
Fool	Version from **Elvis Aron Presley** (*LP 126*) - with stringed accompaniment.
Promised Land	The edited version (just under two minutes) as used in **This Is Elvis** (*LP 150*). Poor sound quality.
She Thinks I Still Care	The overdubbed version as released on the 1981 **Guitar Man** album (*LP 146*).
My Way	From **Aloha From Hawaii** (*LP 66*) 1973.

However, in fairness to Reader's Digest, any 'errors' or 'wrong' versions used were the responsibility of BMG who supplied the tapes. Nonetheless, it was not unreasonable to have expected the people at Reader's Digest in charge of compiling the set to have listened carefully to the tapes and, in the case of poor audio quality, bad edits or mono tracks from the post-1960 era, to have checked their sources again with BMG and, perhaps, have requested better quality tapes.

The Legend Lives On featured 112 tracks, 33 of which had not been featured on **Elvis Presley's Greatest Hits**. Conversely, 32 of the tracks on the earlier album were not included on **The Legend Lives On**. What follows is a list of tracks excluded from this set.

> **All That I Am**
> **(You're so square) Baby I Don't Care**
> **Blueberry Hill**

Bridge Over Troubled Water

Don't Cry Daddy

Double Trouble

Fever

Good Rockin' Tonight

I Love You Because

I Was The One

I'm Gonna Sit Right Down And Cry (over you)

It Feels So Right

It's A Wonderful World

I've Lost You

Kentucky Rain

Lonesome Cowboy

Long Legged Girl (with the short dress on)

Long Tall Sally

Mean Woman Blues

Milkcow Blues Boogie

Patch It Up

Proud Mary

Rags To Riches

Ready Teddy

Shake, Rattle And Roll

Soldier Boy

Tell Me Why

The Next Step Is Love

There Goes My Everything

Tutti Frutti

Your Cheatin' Heart

You've Lost That Lovin' Feelin'

Obviously the tracks used reflected a) those Reader's Digest wanted to use, and/or b) those which BMG would agree to license. However, it was a little surprising to note that the following were omitted, especially as they were reasonably successful A side singles. Their highest chart position in the UK is given in brackets:-

All That I Am (18)

Don't Cry Daddy (8)

I've Lost You (9)

Kentucky Rain (21)

Rags To Riches (9)

Tell Me Why (15)

There Goes My Everything (8)

On the other hand, the following tracks were added to **The Legend Lives On**:-

Big Boss Man A side single, 1967 (*S 61*).

Blue Christmas A side single, 1964 (*S 48*).

Doncha' Think It's Time B side of **Wear My Ring Around Your Neck**, though not this version.

(Such an) Easy Question A single in the USA in 1965.

Fame And Fortune B side of **Stuck On You** in 1960 (*S 28*).

Follow That Dream from an EP of the same name (*EP 15*).

Fool A side hit in 1973 (*S 87*).

Hurt a minor hit in 1976 (*S 96*).

I Beg Of You B side of **Don't**, 1958 (*S 19*).

I Don't Care If The Sun Don't Shine B side of **Blue Moon** in 1956 (*S 5*).

King Of The Whole Wide World the lead track on the **Kid Galahad** EP (*EP 16*).

Little Sister B side of **(Marie's the name) His Latest Flame** in 1961 (*S 35*).

Lonely Man B side of **Surrender** in 1961 (*S 33*).

Love Me B side of **Mystery Train** in 1957 (*S 7*).

Moody Blue A side hit in 1977 (*S 99*).

My Boy A side from 1974 (*S 91*).

My Way A side hit from 1977, though not this version.

My Wish Came True B Side of **A Big Hunk O' Love** in 1959 (*S 27*).

Mystery Train A side in 1957 (*S 7*).

Poor Boy never released on a single in the USA or UK.

Promised Land A side hit from 1974, though not this version.

Santa Bring My Baby Back (to me) A side single in 1957 (*S 16*).

She Thinks I Still Care B Side of **Moody Blue** in 1977, though not this version.

That's All Right not issued on a single in the UK prior to 1981 (*S 130*).

They Remind Me Too Much Of You B side of **One Broken Heart For Sale**, 1963 (*S 40*).

Treat Me Nice B side of **Jailhouse Rock** in 1958 (*S 18*).

Trouble only issued in UK as an EP and LP track.

T.R.O.U.B.L.E. A side hit from 1975 (*S 93*).

Way Down A side number 1 in 1977 (*S 116*).

What'd I Say B side of **Viva Las Vegas** in 1964 (*S 44*).

When My Blue Moon Turns To Gold Again B side of **Paralyzed** in 1957 (*S 13*).

Witchcraft B side of **Bossa Nova Baby**, 1963 (*S 42*).

You'll Never Walk Alone A side from 1968 (*S 65*).

As you will see from the notes, not all of these were, as the set claimed, 'hits' - throwing into question the legitimacy of their inclusion. However, we hasten to add, this was all academic, as we were not privy to all of the reasons why certain tracks were, or were not, included. Obviously, the notes referred to the UK only, and we acknowledge that some songs may have been more successful in the charts in other countries.

Sadly, there were errors - of all descriptions - on labels, the box, and in the accompanying booklet, many of which seemed so unnecessary and reflected badly on the set as a whole. Perhaps some of the errors in song titles and writing credits could be forgiven, but many could not - especially as the set was promoted as a collectors' edition! There were glaring errors which indicated a lack of care and basic knowledge about Elvis and, in view of the number concerned, we felt the need to list these individually and to consider the booklet errors separately.

Album 1, side B, track 5. *Any Way You Want Me (that's how I will be)* included the old error of using *Anyway....*

Album 2, side A, track 3. *Poor Boy* was credited to someone called Lietz, when normally Presley, Matson were given. Also, there was no reference to the fact that the song was featured in the film *Love Me Tender*.

Album 2, side A, track 4. Co-writer Arthur was not mentioned for *Old Shep*.

Album 2, side A, track 7. As with BMG releases, Fisher, Hill, Raskin were given as the writers of *That's When Your Heartaches Begin*.

Album 2, side B, track 1. The writers of *Mystery Train*, Phillips and Parker, were shown in the wrong order.

Album 2, side B, track 2. Co-writer of *Rip It Up*, Marascalco, had his name spelt Marascaleo.

Album 2, side B, track 5. *Party* was featured in the film *Loving You*, though no mention was made of this.

Album 2, side B, track 6. There was no exclamation mark at the end of *Got A Lot O' Livin' To Do!*, nor was there a reference to the film *Loving You*.

Album 3, side B, track 5. This was most certainly not **T.R.O.U.B.L.E.**, but **Trouble**, an entirely different song.

Album 4, side A, track 2. The words in brackets were omitted from **(Now and then there's) A Fool Such As I**.

Album 4, side B, track 1. The normal order of the writers of **It's Now Or Never** was DiCapua, Schroeder, Gold.

Album 4, side B, track 7. The normal order for the writers of **Surrender** was DeCurtis, Pomus, Shuman.

Album 5, side A, track 1. The writers of **Flaming Star** were normally shown as Wayne and Edwards, not the other way around.

Album 5, side A, track 4. The words in brackets were omitted from **(Marie's the name) His Latest Flame**.

Album 5, side B, track 5. The writers of **Just Tell Her Jim Said Hello**, Leiber and Stoller, were shown in the wrong order.

Album 6, side A, track 4. **Witchcraft** was credited to Coleman and Leigh, which would have been correct if this had been the Frank Sinatra song of the same name. As it wasn't, credit should have been given to Bartholomew and King.

Album 6, side A, track 7. It may be obvious, but no reference was made to the fact that **Viva Las Vegas** came from the film of the same name.

Album 7, side A, track 4. **Love Letters** should have been credited to Young, Heyman - not the other way around.

Album 7, side B, track 5. **You Don't Have To Say You Love Me** was written by Pallavicini, Donaggio, Wickham, Napier-Bell.

Album 8, side A, track 2. There was no mention that Newbury arranged **An American Trilogy**.

Album 8, side A, track 4. **Always On My Mind** was credited to Thompson, James, Christopher instead of James, Carson, Christopher.

Album 8, side A, track 7. **My Boy** placed the order of writers incorrectly. They should have read Francois, Bourtayre, Martin, Coulter.

Album 8, side B, track 5. The writers of **She Thinks I Still Care** were shown as Duffy and Lipscomb. In fact the sole writer was Lipscomb.

Album 8, side B, track 7. The writers of **My Way**, Thibault, Francois, Revaux, Anka, were placed in the wrong order.

Accompanying this set was a booklet containing programme notes - a brief biography (key dates) followed by a track by track discussion and an index, all written, we believe, by Henri Heyman. As with the discussion of contents earlier, we decided to deal with issues raised by errors in the booklet separately. We have not repeated the errors found on the labels and box. To assist in locating the errors in the notes, we have shown the booklet page numbers.

Page 3. **(to a heart that's true)** was incorrectly added to **Don't Be Cruel**.

Page 5. Incorrectly stated that 11 July 1955 was Elvis's final Sun session. It wasn't. Elvis recorded **When It Rains, It Really Pours** in November 1955, though the version was not issued until November 1983 on **Elvis - A Legendary Performer Vol. 4**, PL 84848 (LP 204).

Page 5. Claude Demetrius' name was mis-spelt as DeMetruis, yet it was spelt correctly on the label and back of the box.

Page 5. **Trouble**, from **King Creole**, wrongly listed as **T.R.O.U.B.L.E.**.

Page 6. **A Mess Of Blues** was the B side of **It's Now Or Never** in the USA, though it was a UK A side in 1960, pending the sorting out of copyright problems with **It's Now Or Never**. No credit was given to the Italian composers of **It's Now Or Never**, and to claim that the song only sold 2 million copies worldwide was a staggering understatement.

Page 6. The Italian writer of **Surrender** was not credited.

Page 7. On **Little Sister** the lead guitar was provided by Hank Garland and not Scotty Moore as stated.

Page 8. On **Witchcraft**, the writer wrongly implied that this was the song Elvis sang part of on the 1960 Frank Sinatra Special and subsequently recorded in May 1963 in Nashville. It wasn't.

Page 8. **Kiss Me Quick** was released as a single in April 1964 (US), but it had also been issued on the 1962 **Pot Luck** album (LP 16).

Page 8. **(Such an) Easy Question** did not, as the script said, 'remain unreleased for several years after Elvis recorded it on 18 March 1962, in Nashville'... as it was included on the **Pot Luck** album (LP 16) issued in the UK in July 1962. This was, in fact, an unlisted outtake (take 4).

Page 9. Although **The Wonder Of You** was a popular inclusion in Elvis's stage act during 1970, it is misleading and inaccurate to say 'Elvis included the song in virtually every show during that decade', as he only performed it sporadically after that year.

Page 10. The writer of **T.R.O.U.B.L.E.** was Jerry Chesnut not Chestnut.

Page 10. This version of **She Thinks I Still Care** was not the B side of **Moody Blue**, but an overdubbed version cut in 1980, using a different vocal track, different arrangement and a newly recorded backing track.

Label Variations

WHITE LABEL

1   1990 PRESSING: MONO/STEREO
ELECTRONIC STEREO

Box Variations

1   None known

Label Design Change

The appearance in November 1990 of the album *Elvis Sings The Wonderful World Of Christmas*, NL 81936 (**LP 311**), heralded the last major amendment to the design of RCA labels. The computer style RCA logo had been replaced by the round RCA logo, situated, not at the top of the label - as on those albums which had copied the design of the old fifties' and early sixties' labels - but on the left of the label. The computer style design had, however, served RCA well (it had been introduced with the orange labels in 1969) and had survived for 21 years!

The basic layout of track details and so on, remained much the same, but LC 0316 was moved underneath the logo and the 33 speed symbol moved to the bottom of the label.

This change in design should be used in dating a re-pressing of earlier albums as, it seems, that virtually the whole of RCA's Elvis catalogue at the time was re-pressed using this label design. And this also included albums not available in the UK.

However, very few of the albums released from 1986 onwards were re-pressed, as the number of variations in labels design will testify. Those that were, used the new label design.

We should, however, point out that this label design was not used on most of the new albums released after November 1990. Several continued to use copies of the old label design; others had special labels, and it was not until almost a year later, in October 1991, that a new album used the design - *Elvis In Person At The International Hotel Las Vegas, Nevada*, NL 83892 (**LP 316**). This album was, of course, new to the UK only, as it had been released in Europe previously.

LP 311	**Elvis Sings The Wonderful World Of Christmas**

RCA NL 81936

Side 1
1 **O Come, All Ye Faithful** (Trad. Arr. Presley)
2 **The First Noel** (Trad. Arr. Presley)
3 **On A Snowy Christmas Night** (Gelber)
4 **Winter Wonderland** (Smith, Bernard)
5 **The Wonderful World Of Christmas** (Tobias, Frisch)
6 **It Won't Seem Like Christmas (without you)** (Balthrop)

Side 2
1 **I'll Be Home On Christmas Day** (Jarrett)
2 **If I Get Home On Christmas Day** (McCaulay)
3 **Holly Leaves And Christmas Trees** (West, Spreen)
4 **Merry Christmas Baby** (Baxter, Moore)
5 **Silver Bells** (Evans, Livingston)

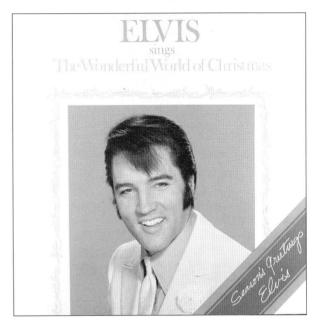

Released November 1990   Deleted April 1991
Original Issue November 1971. RCA SF 8221 (LP 56)
Previous Re-issue November 1979. RCA PL 42371 (LP 117)

This album never achieved the same level of popular acclaim given to the 1957 *Elvis' Christmas Album*, RD 27052 (*LP 5*), but, nevertheless, this issue represented the third time that the album had been released in the UK. The original from November 1971, was a candidate for the worst ever Elvis sleeve design; while the November 1979 version featured a re-designed sleeve which was re-presented here. As it was, neither issue attracted large sales and their overall availability was short-lived. The same was true of this album, for it was deleted at the beginning of April 1991, less than six months after it was issued in late November 1990. Perhaps the real claim to fame of this album was that it was on catalogue for such a short time. The problem this time around was that a CD version was also issued, which drew most of the interested customers. And part of the attraction of the CD was that it included material not found on the vinyl format. There was the rhythm version of *I'll Be Home On Christmas Day*, *If Every Day Was Like Christmas*, and a seven minute version of *Merry Christmas Baby*. Also there was both direct and indirect competition from *Elvis' Christmas Album*, NL 90300 (**LP 312**), released shortly after this album, and from assorted compilation CDs, including the 1987 issue of *I Wish You A Merry*

Christmas, ND 89474 (a CD only issue), which was still available at the time when *Elvis Sings The Wonderful World Of Christmas* was released. Throughout 1991, copies of the vinyl album were to be found in large quantities in certain discount shops as reduced items.

This was a mid-price issue and, typical of many other original seventies' releases, had not previously been available in the UK on the German black label. As we have said, the last UK appearance dated back to 1979. However, the catalogue number - 81936 - provided confirmation that the album existed as a European release long before its UK issue. Indeed, the matrix number indicated mastering dates of January and February 1984.

Despite this, the label featured the round RCA logo situated on the left, showing that this was a new pressing and not old stock being sold off. Similarly, the round RCA logo was to be found on the back of the sleeve.

With the exception of the RCA logo, the front of the sleeve was identical to that of the 1979 issue, and the back too was very similar, but with minor modifications, including the addition of a bar code and the round RCA logo. The most important (and useful) addition was the inclusion of song timings for all the tracks (on the previous issue - *LP 117* - only *Winter Wonderland* had a time shown on the sleeve). No UK price code was shown on the back of the sleeve; and while the CD symbol was shown, no CD catalogue number was quoted, despite there being a simultaneous CD release. The BMG logo was not printed on the back of the sleeve.

As with many of the German black label releases, there was no track numbering shown, a strange, and annoying omission, given that the details relating to vocal accompaniment showed which tracks The Imperials Quartet were featured on.

The only errors appeared on the label and concerned tracks 1 and 2 on side 1, which showed the writer as (Presley) - implying that Elvis wrote the songs which, of course, he didn't. This ought to have read (Arranged Presley), or better still, (Traditional. Arranged Presley) in the same way as the 1979 album had done.

Label Variations

GERMAN BLACK LABEL

 1   1990 PRESSING: STEREO
         Round RCA logo at side of label

Sleeve Variations
 1   Gloss

LP 312	**Elvis' Christmas Album**

RCA NL 90300

Side 1

1   **Santa Claus Is Back In Town** (Leiber, Stoller)
2   **White Christmas** (Berlin)
3   **Here Comes Santa Claus (right down Santa Claus lane)** (Autry, Haldeman, Melka)
4   **I'll Be Home For Christmas (if only in my dreams)** (Kent, Gannon, Ram)
5   **Blue Christmas** (Hayes, Johnson)
6   **Santa Bring My Baby Back (to me)** (Schroeder, DeMetrius)

Side 2

1   **O Little Town Of Bethlehem** (Redner, Brooks)
2   **Silent Night** (Mohr, Gruber)
3   **(There'll be) Peace In The Valley (for me)** (Dorsey)
4   **I Believe** (Drake, Graham, Shirl, Stillman)
5   **Take My Hand, Precious Lord** (Dorsey)
6   **It Is No Secret (what God can do)** (Hamblen)

Released December 1990   **Deleted April 1991**

Original Issue November 1957. RCA RD 27052 (*LP 5*)

Previous Re-issue November 1980. RCA International INTS 5060 (*LP 140*)

Previous Re-issue April 1984. RCA International NL 89116 (*LP 218*)

Previous Re-issue October 1985. RCA PL 85486 (*LP 275*)

An album with this title but with some different tracks was released in October 1970: RCA International (Camden), INT 1126 (*LP 42*). This album was later re-released in October 1975: RCA Camden CDS 1155 (*LP 81*).

Outlined above are details of the previous issues of this album, and from this it is possible to see that the saga of *Elvis' Christmas Album* had been long and complex, and one which dated back to November 1957, when it was issued in the UK. And, although it was the fifth UK album to be issued, it was the first to have a track content identical to its American counterpart. Despite containing mainly seasonal recordings, the album sold well and survived in its original form until early 1970, when it was replaced by an album with the same title on the RCA International label, INT 1126 (*LP 42*), but with a different track listing. In this form - or rather a 1975 electronic stereo re-issue on Camden, CDS 1155 (*LP 81*) - the album was continuously available until late 1988, when RCA decided to issue the original version, again on the International series, INTS 5060 (*LP 140*). The point was that both this and the Camden version were available at the same time but, whereas the RCA issue used the original UK sleeve artwork from 1957, the Camden sleeve featured a new design.

The transfer by RCA to central European production had little effect on the 1984 re-issue, NL 89116 (*LP 218*). In October 1985, the album was again re-issued, but this time with the original American artwork, including a gatefold sleeve, complete with photographs, PL 85486 (*LP 275*). In addition, the record was pressed in green vinyl, and, importantly, it became a full-priced album again, a status last achieved with the original issue (the Camden release was budget-priced; the International albums, mid-priced).

This album, then, was a revised re-issue of the October 1985 release, issued with an NL prefix to the catalogue number indicating mid-price. The sleeve, on the other hand, showed a PL (full price) down the side and on the top, although the correct NL prefix was shown on the back. A mid-price CD was issued a month earlier, in November 1990 (ND 90300).

This time the album was in a single pocket sleeve, and consequently there were no photographs from the *Jailhouse Rock* publicity sessions which had graced the previous issue.

The front of the sleeve, which carried an 'Elvis in the 90s' sticker, showed some signs of having been tampered with, although most of the image was crystal clear. In the top right hand corner, for example, was a clearly visible patch where the RCA Victor box had appeared on the 1985 issue, and towards the top left hand corner was a smudge and what appeared to be a fingerprint.

Unfortunately, the back of the sleeve retained the poor quality photograph, diminishing the quality feel of the album. It seemed a pity that RCA, who by now had rejected re-processed stereo and were displaying a new will to use original masters instead of several generation copies, were unable to divert some of their energies to finding, or at least re-creating, original photographic artwork. Perhaps the original no longer existed and the quality of this particular photograph could not be improved, but nevertheless having gone to the trouble of producing a copy of the 1957 American original, fans and collectors may have been more interested in buying another copy of the album had it been made available in a newly designed sleeve.

Whilst the 1985 issue displayed the tracks on the back of the sleeve, there were no writers' names, track timings or publishers detailed. These were included this time, along with reference to The Jordanaires being featured on a couple of tracks, a detail only previously shown on the original UK issue of the album sleeve. This was a welcome addition, but unfortunately hopelessly inaccurate, for The Jordanaires actually appeared on other songs featured on the album for which they received no credit. The labels were equally inaccurate; there was no mention whatsoever of The Jordanaires on side 1. The back of the sleeve also carried both the RCA and BMG logos; and note also that the labels had side 1 and side 2, whereas the sleeve referred to side A and side B.

The label design was modelled on the old RCA black label design, by this time adopted as official, but, because of the length of some of the song titles, the label had become very cluttered and difficult to read.

The album was deleted on 8 April, 1991, a mere five months after it was issued.

Two errors persisted from previous issues: the words in brackets were omitted from *I'll Be Home For Christmas (if only in my dreams)*, and *O Little Town Of Bethlehem* commenced with the word *Oh*.

Label Variations

GERMAN BLACK LABEL

1   **1990 PRESSING: MONO**
             Round RCA logo at top of label

Sleeve Variations

1   Gloss

Time-Life Spirit Of The 60s

In February 1991 advertisements began to appear in magazines for a new Time-Life series of records entitled *Spirit Of The 60s* and two separate advertisements were used, so that, depending on which magazine was purchased, the information available was different. Probably the best example to refer to concerns the television magazines *TV Times* and *Radio Times* which, for the same week, carried completely different advertisements for the first album in the series covering the year 1964.

Spirit Of The 60s was a series of albums each devoted to specific years during the sixties, but what was interesting was that the advert in the *TV Times* referred to albums 'devoted to such superstars as the Beach Boys and more' - meaning that in addition to an album for each year, there would be special releases similar to those of the *Rock 'N' Roll Era* series, whereby the most popular artists and groups would be given a release of their own. The *Radio Times* advert went further and revealed that albums would be 'devoted to such superstars as The Beach Boys and Elvis Presley'.

Each double album cost £11.99, plus £2.25 postage and handling, contained 24 tracks, and was also available in CD and cassette formats. As an incentive, subscribers were offered a free watch.

Both advertisements were clearly geared to getting people to sign up for the whole series, although, as with similar campaigns, there was no indication of how many records would be involved in the series, and even less information as to when the Elvis record would become available. This kind of advert made it very difficult for potential customers to be selective in the product they actually wished to purchase. Of course it would have been feasible to take each record in turn and take advantage of the ten day free trial, returning the record without cost, but Time-Life, like all other companies involved in this kind of marketing, knew that customers either forgot or could not be bothered to return goods, and therefore would elect to pay.

We tried a more direct approach and wrote to Time-Life ordering the Elvis record by name, stating that we did not require other albums in the series. In return Time-Life sent, not the *Spirit Of The 60s* album referred to in the advert, but the Elvis release from *The Rock 'N' Roll Era* series. When we checked with them, they told us that an Elvis album had not been planned for the *Spirit Of The 60s* series, contrary to the advert. Further, the lady we spoke to had no idea why such misleading information should have been given or, indeed, why there were two different adverts for the same product.

Obviously, some people would have seen the advert and 'signed up', with the sole intention of obtaining the Elvis record. They would either be completely disappointed, receiving no such record, or have been sent The *Rock 'N' Roll Era* record, which they may already have had. This was an absurd situation. Fortunately Time-Life are a responsible company and, in our case, we got a refund, but we had paid for only the one record. Our questions remained unanswered, and it is still unclear as to whether Time-Life had ever planned an Elvis release in this series. Certainly, it was possible, for Time-Life planned such releases well into the future. For example, *The Rock 'N' Roll Era* series had titles planned in March 1991 to be issued up to and including December 1992, with other volumes to be announced at a later date. As it turned out, no such LP was issued.

| **LP 313** | ***From Elvis In Memphis*** |
| | ***RCA NL 90548*** |

Side 1

1 **Wearin' That Loved On Look** (Frazier, Owens)
2 **Only The Strong Survive** (Gamble, Huff, Butler)
3 **I'll Hold You In My Heart (till I can hold you in my arms)** (Arnold, Horton, Dilbeck)
4 **Long Black Limousine** (Stovall, George)
5 **It Keeps Right On A-Hurtin'** (Tillotson)
6 **I'm Movin' On** (Snow)

Side 2

1 **Power Of My Love** (Giant, Baum, Kaye)
2 **Gentle On My Mind** (Hartford)
3 **After Loving You** (Miller, Lantz)
4 **True Love Travels On A Gravel Road** (Owens, Frazier)
5 **Any Day Now** (Hilliard, Bacharach)
6 **In The Ghetto** (Davis)

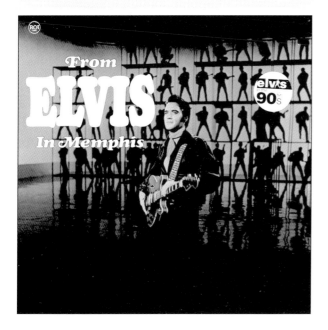

Released February 1991   **Deleted March 1992**
Original Issue August 1969. RCA RD/SF 8029 (LP 38)

The original vinyl album of *From Elvis In Memphis* (*LP 38*) had been deleted as long ago as January 1982, and some would argue that a classic album had been treated rather unfairly because of this. Yet here it was being restored to catalogue as part of a co-ordinated drive to release product covering a wide perspective of different periods - in this case studio work from 1969 - on CD. Two other CDs were also released in February 1991, *On Stage - February 1970* and *NBC TV Special*, and all three releases were also available in vinyl, the last time that such an automatic all-format pattern was made for back catalogue material.

Priced at £4.99, this album - a particular favourite with many fans - was well received, although, as one of the few original albums never to have been re-issued up to this point, most people probably opted for the CD version, also making its first appearance in the UK. Unfortunately, it did not survive on vinyl for very long - it was deleted on 24 March 1992.

The front of the sleeve was identical to the original, with the exception that RCA and VICTOR had been replaced by a round RCA logo in the top left hand corner. On the back, a number of minor modifications had taken place, as expected, given the many changes which had occurred over the years. Obviously the note regarding stereo records - found on the original - was no longer necessary and was omitted. The track listing had the timings added. Other necessary changes had been made to include the price code, bar code, and so on but, in the main, the artwork remained unchanged, and this included the photograph of the *Elvis* (NBC TV Special) album which, perhaps fortuitously, was available again to accompany the CD version.

One disappointing feature of the sleeve was that the letters RE were printed on both the front and the back. This was an American method of showing that the album was a re-issue, but its inclusion here seemed rather pointless, because this feature was not normally used on European releases, and could so easily have been removed.

On a more positive note, it was refreshing to see that the back of the sleeve displayed *I'll Hold You In My Heart (till I can hold you in my arms)* in full, which the original sleeve had failed to do. Similarly, *I'm Movin' On* was correctly shown with the apostrophe and not the 'g' in *Movin'*. The label also showed both titles correctly.

In keeping with our policy to review all errors relating to song titles and writers' names, it has been necessary to make some amendments to the order in which the names of the writers were shown. The original UK issue of this album listed the writers of *Only The Strong Survive* as being Gamble, Huffs, Butler. We know that the spelling of Huff was incorrect, adding an 's', but this was the correct order. For some reason we converted this to read Butler, Gamble, Huff, which we now concede was an error. The song index has been amended accordingly. Strangely though, BMG had amended the order of Arnold, Horton, Dilbeck (the writers of *I'll Hold You In My Heart (till I can hold you in my arms)*), to read Dilbeck, Horton, Arnold on the label of this album. This, therefore, became a new error.

A further error on our part was changing the order Owens, Frazier, the writers of *True Love Travels On A Gravel Road*, to Frazier, Owens, the way it was correctly shown on the label of this release. We were obviously influenced by the fact that *Wearin' That Loved On Look* (written by the same team) had always been shown as being written by Frazier, Owens. Again, the song index has been amended.

Label Variations

GERMAN BLACK LABEL

1   1991 PRESSING: STEREO
         Round RCA logo at top of label

Sleeve Variations

1   Gloss

Vinyl Re-issues

From 1977 onwards album re-issues became commonplace and eventually outnumbered 'new' product several times over. The reason for this was simple and all too easy to understand: Elvis's death meant no new recordings but, at the same time, the public demand for any material, old or new, was all that RCA needed to produce as much product as possible to satisfy a resurgence of interest in back catalogue material. Of course, re-issues appealed to collectors as well, although not everyone was tempted by such moves - far from it - and, in fact, re-issues became a lesson in diminishing returns, with each subsequent appearance faring less well than its predecessor. Some albums, such as *Kissin' Cousins* and *Girls! Girls! Girls!*, were re-issued no less than four times from 1977, despite their obvious shortcomings. On the other hand, several albums from the mid-seventies were never re-issued, no doubt due - in part at least - to their poor sales record at the time.

From 1986 onwards the number of re-issues slowed dramatically following the huge number of albums produced in 1984 and 1985, as a result of centralisation of record production in Europe by RCA. Even so, RCA UK exerted some influence over re-issues (and reference here to the list of albums never re-issued in vinyl in the UK - found in the Introductory Section - will demonstrate to what extent they were successful). Albums like *Good Times* and *Elvis As Recorded Live On Stage In Memphis* (*LPs 71* and *72*), were not re-issued in the UK, despite being available in Europe, although many fans may have bought imported copies.

What occurred from 1986 was the rapid transition to compact disc from vinyl, which resulted in a gradual decline in the numbers of vinyl albums being produced and, in the case of back catalogue material, an end to it all together.

The last re-issued vinyl albums were *From Elvis In Memphis* (**LP 313**) and *On Stage - February, 1970* (**LP 314**) issued in February 1991, although the October 1991 release of *Elvis In Person At The International Hotel Las Vegas, Nevada* (**LP 316**) should be

mentioned, despite the fact that it had never appeared as a single album previously in the UK. Other back catalogue albums appeared on CD after this, but none were produced on vinyl by BMG.

Price Of Records

The Budget of March 1991 increased the rate of Value Added Tax (VAT) from 15% to 17.5%, which meant higher prices for all consumer goods, including records, CDs, cassettes etc., but what was interesting was the difficulty experienced by those responsible for applying the new rate to existing prices.

Taking £4.99 as being the recommended retail price for the majority of Elvis LPs, then the change in the rate of VAT should have increased the price to £5.10. Happily, some stores got their sums right, but the same record could be found in other stores at £5.11, £5.12 and £5.20 - when most of the stores had charged £4.99 previously. Was this merely a case of faulty calculators, or a deliberate ploy to increase profits?

LP 314	On Stage - February, 1970
	RCA NL 90549

Side 1

1   **See See Rider** (Broonzy)
2   **Release Me (and let me love again)** (Miller, Williams, Yount, Harris)
3   **Sweet Caroline** (Diamond)
4   **Runaway** (Crook, Shannon)
5   **The Wonder Of You** (Knight)

Side 2

1   **Polk Salad Annie** (White)
2   **Yesterday** (Lennon, McCartney)
3   **Proud Mary** (Fogerty)
4   **Walk A Mile In My Shoes** (South)
5   **Let It Be Me (Je T'Appartiens)** (Curtis, Delanoe, Becaud)

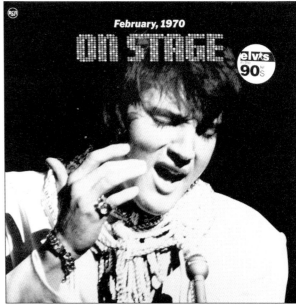

Released February 1991   **Deleted March 1992**
Original Issue July 1970. RCA SF 8128 (LP 41)

As with the previous album, *From Elvis In Memphis* (**LP 313**), this was only the second time that this collection of live recordings had been released. Indeed, this album had been deleted in the UK for almost six years (in May 1985), although many European countries seemed to have retained it on catalogue. A CD version was issued around the same time and outlived the vinyl format which was deleted on 24 March 1992.

There had always been some confusion over the exact title of this album. Popularly and simply known as *On Stage*, the correct title was *On Stage - February, 1970*, the hyphen and comma being added for the first time on the label of this release. The original sleeve had no reference to the date, but this was now added above the words *On Stage*, but the top and side spine only referred to the abbreviated title.

The photograph of Elvis was much lighter than on the original sleeve front, so much so that in fact it was now possible to see the outline of his hair against the black background, spoiling the effect which the original conveyed. The round RCA logo was to be found in the top left hand corner on the front of the sleeve, but only the BMG logo appeared on the back.

Some tidying up had been carried out to the back of the sleeve, with the song timings being added. The most notable change being that the February 1970 date had been removed from the note as to when the recordings were made. Presumably this was due to the fact that not all of the songs had actually been recorded during the February 1970 season at the International Hotel. Both *Yesterday* and *Runaway* were from the August 1969 season at the same venue. If this was so, then why had someone gone to trouble of adding the date to the title on both label and sleeve? If RCA were concerned that the recording information was likely to lead to some kind of misrepresentation, then surely this would most likely have been noticed in the title.

Another noticeable change from the original issue occurred on the back of the sleeve with the addition of three red boxes around 'Side 1', 'Side 2', and the note regarding where the recordings were made.

The label design was based on LPs from the fifties, complete with the two parallel lines across the middle of the label design. The last original Elvis LP with this particular characteristic was *Elvis Is Back!* (*LP 11*), first released in July 1960. Note though that neither the label nor the sleeve referred to the mode.

There were also some interesting changes in track details, giving rise to new errors. Firstly, the song *See See Rider* (a song which in itself was subject to some controversy as to its actual title) was now quoted as being a traditional (no known writer) song and credited Elvis as the arranger. No doubt Elvis did do the arrangements, but we're sticking with the title *See See Rider* and Bill Broonzy as the writer.

Release Me (and let me love again) presented a bit of a puzzle. The 1970 issue of the album quoted Miller, Williams, Yount and Hamis (the 1982 black label issue reading Harris), but on this issue, however, the writers were shown as Miller, Stevenson. This may be technically correct, as Stevenson was the correct name of Dub Williams (who co-wrote the song with Eddie Miller), but normally the name given was Williams.

Even stranger than the alteration to the writer's name for *Release Me (and let me love again)* was the one for *Runaway* where, for some unknown reason, Del Shannon was referred to by his real name (Charles) Westover, whereas previously his stage name had always been used.

Label Variations

GERMAN BLACK LABEL
1   **1991 PRESSING: STEREO**
Round RCA logo at top of label

Sleeve Variations
1   Gloss

Album Deletions - April 1991

A number of albums were deleted in April 1991, including the first four *Golden Records*, and both of the religious albums first released in the sixties, *His Hand In Mine* and *How Great Thou Art* (*LPs 214* and *235*). Even the two Christmas albums, *Elvis Sings The Wonderful World Of Christmas* and *Elvis' Christmas Album* (**LPs 311** and **312**), released towards the end of 1990, were also deleted. The full list of these deletions, including release date and release number, are as follows:

NL 81382	*Elvis*	Apr 1984	*LP 211*
NL 81707	*Elvis' Golden Records*	Jul 1984	*LP 232*
NL 81936	*Elvis Sings The Wonderful World Of Christmas*	Nov 1990	**LP 311**
NL 82765	*Elvis' Golden Records Vol. 3*	Nov 1984	*LP 256*
NL 83758	*How Great Thou Art*	Jul 1984	*LP 235*
NL 83921	*Elvis' Golden Records Vol. 4*	Apr 1984	*LP 213*
NL 83935	*His Hand In Mine*	Apr 1984	*LP 214*
NL 84114	*That's The Way It Is*	May 1984	*LP 224*
NL 84116	*Something For Everybody*	Aug 1984	*LP 243*
NL 89429	*Elvis' Golden Records, Volume 2*	Nov 1984	*LP 253*
NL 90300	*Elvis' Christmas Album*	Dec 1990	**LP 312**

Album Deletions - May 1991

On 24 May 1991, a further four albums were deleted, following the eleven in April. *The Alternate Aloha*, PL 86985 (**LP 294**), was deleted by BMG almost three years to the day after its release. *Rare Elvis*, PL 89003 (*LP 263*), from January 1985, outlived the two subsequent volumes in the series by two years.

One of the first UK inspired/German produced black label albums, *I Can Help And Other Great Hits*, PL 89287 (*LP 207*), first issued in March 1984, was also deleted, as was *Always On My Mind*, PL 85430 (*LP 272*), first released in July 1985.

Sleeve Detail Change

The BMG logo, which had first appeared on an album sleeve in May 1988, **The Alternate Aloha** (**LP 294**), initially had the word 'Music' underneath. Later, this was replaced by 'A Bertelsmann Music Group Company' on some albums, while others dispensed with the logo completely.

The back of the box of **Collectors Gold**, PL 90574(3) (**LP 315**), the next BMG album to be released, introduced the word 'International'.

Price Code

Collectors Gold featured a new UK price code - JC.

LP 315	Collectors Gold
	RCA PL 90574(3)

Album 1 *Hollywood*

Side 1

1. **G.I. Blues** (Tepper, Bennett)
2. **Pocketful Of Rainbows** (Wise, Weisman)
3. **Big Boots** (Wayne, Edwards)
4. **Black Star** (Wayne, Edwards)
5. **Summer Kisses, Winter Tears** (Wise, Weisman, Lloyd)
6. **I Slipped, I Stumbled, I Fell** (Wise, Weisman)
7. **Lonely Man** (Benjamin, Marcus)
8. **What A Wonderful Life** (Wayne, Livingston)
9. **A Whistling Tune** (Edwards, David)

Side 2

1. **Beyond The Bend** (Weisman, Wise, Fuller)
2. **One Broken Heart For Sale** (Blackwell, Scott)
3. **You're The Boss** (Leiber, Stoller)
4. **Roustabout** (Giant, Baum, Kaye)
5. **Girl Happy** (Pomus, Meade)
6. **So Close, Yet So Far** (Byers)
7. **Stop, Look And Listen** (Byers)
8. **Am I Ready** (Tepper, Bennett)
9. **How Can You Lose What You Never Had** (Weisman, Wayne)

Album 2 *Nashville*

Side 1

1. **Like A Baby** (Stone)
2. **There's Always Me** (Robertson)
3. **I Want You With Me** (Harris)
4. **Gently** (Wizell, Lisbona)
5. **Give Me The Right** (Wise, Blagman)
6. **I Met Her Today** (Robertson, Blair)
7. **Night Rider** (Pomus, Shuman)
8. **Just Tell Her Jim Said Hello** (Leiber, Stoller)

Side 2

1. **Ask Me** (Modugno, Giant, Baum, Kaye)
2. **Memphis, Tennessee** (Berry)
3. **Love Me Tonight** (Robertson)
4. **Witchcraft** (Bartholomew, King)
5. **Come What May** (Tableporter)
6. **Love Letters** (Young, Heyman)
7. **Goin' Home** (Byers)

Album 3 *Live In Las Vegas*

Side 1

1. **Blue Suede Shoes** (Perkins)
2. **I Got A Woman** (Charles)
3. **Heartbreak Hotel** (Axton, Durden, Presley)
4. **Love Me Tender** (Presley, Matson)
5. **Baby, What You Want Me To Do** (Reed)
6. **Runaway** (Crook, Shannon)
7. **Surrender** (DeCurtis, Pomus, Shuman)
   Are You Lonesome Tonight? (Turk, Handman)
8. **Rubberneckin'** (Jones, Warren)
9. **Memories** (Strange, Davis)
10. **Introductions by Elvis Presley**

Side 2

1. **Jailhouse Rock** (Leiber, Stoller)
   Don't Be Cruel (Blackwell, Presley)
2. **Inherit The Wind** (Rabbitt)
3. **This Is The Story** (Arnold, Morrow, Martin)
4. **Mystery Train** (Parker, Phillips)
   Tiger Man (Lewis, Burns)
5. **Funny How Time Slips Away** (Nelson)
6. **Loving You** (Leiber, Stoller)
   Reconsider Baby (Fulson)
7. **What'd I Say** (Charles)

Released August 1991   Deleted October 1993

200

On its release in August 1991, **Collectors Gold** became the third official BMG/RCA boxed set to be issued since Elvis's death in 1977, excluding mail order and restricted release product, such as **Elvis Forever - 96 Hits Of The King**, NL 89830(6) (**LP 285**), and **Special Edition**, CL 90249(3) (*LP 297*). In 1980, there had been **Elvis Aron Presley**, CPL8 3699 (*LP 126*), an eight album boxed set; then, in 1985, came **A Golden Celebration**, PL 85172(6) (*LP 251*), a six LP collection.

This time, however, there were some significant differences from previous boxed sets. The first two had originated in the USA under the guidance of Joan Deary (for the 1980 release), and Deary and Geller for the 1985 set. **Collectors Gold** was the product of Roger Semon and Ernst Mikael Jorgensen's combined efforts, and attempted to offer fans what they had been clamouring for: a release comprising almost entirely unreleased material: outtakes - or unreleased performances, as they were now known. The set focused on Elvis's sixties' material, probably because work was under way on the projected definitive '50s set; and, secondly, because it was known that there was a wealth of outtakes available from the sixties' era. Sensibly then, the producers elected for three albums, each dealing with the major aspects of Elvis's sixties' output: his film soundtrack work; his non-film studio work and, finally, his live performances made at the end of the decade in Las Vegas. The vast bulk of the studio outtakes were located in late 1989, when the producers searched RCA's vaults in the US.

As had become almost inevitable, the release of this three album set met with delays, despite having been mastered in New York in December 1990. (Incidentally January 1991 had been mentioned for the release of **Collectors Gold**.) In fact, this release saw the debut of Roger Semon as an engineer on the project - a role he shared with Dick Baxter. The overall job of compiling and producing the set was handled by Semon, Jorgensen and Erik Rasmussen (a co-author of the book **Recording Sessions**). Part of the delay was due to problems with the packaging, so we were told.

Equally inevitably, there were many rumours concerning how many tracks were to be included. At one point a figure of 25 tracks per album was mentioned but, of course, there was no way a vinyl album could have accommodated that number of tracks anyway. So, for whatever reasons - be they artistic and/or commercial - the producers finally settled on 18 tracks for the 'Hollywood' album, 15 from the Nashville sessions, and 16 from the August 1969 Las Vegas appearances. And while it was no secret that there exists a wealth of studio outtakes from the sixties (film soundtrack and original studio material), what was less commonly known was that there was not too much live material from 1969 to warrant release. Certainly there were innumerable versions of songs, but not all were sufficiently different to make their release worthwhile. This was stated clearly to us by Ernst Mikael Jorgensen. Similarly, the producers found no other live versions of songs as yet not issued in one form or another. Another rumour circulating was that the producers had hoped to include the full recording of Elvis's opening show in Las Vegas (31 July 1969) for this release. For whatever reason that idea was scrapped in favour of culling tracks from several dates during that season. There was an unsubstantiated rumour that the master tapes of the opening night show had gone missing en route from Nashville to New York!

Remarkably, only one track - the 'laughing' version of **Are You Lonesome Tonight?** - had been issued previously, officially that is. All other tracks were either unreleased performances (outtakes) or, as in the case of **You're The Boss**, an unreleased song. Interestingly - and perhaps very strangely - the US division pre-empted the release of this song by including it in a slightly revised version of the Leiber and Stoller collection which, ironically, had started life as a UK inspired release in June 1980 (*LP 125*). Now whether or not this was a deliberate move on the part of the US division to assert itself is hard to say. One consequence of this was that fans in the UK and Europe bought imported copies of the US CD in order to obtain the hitherto unreleased song. Another oddity was the inclusion of **Black Star**. In fact, this was said to be the original title track for **Flaming Star**, but

was dropped in favour of the latter title. Essentially, the songs - apart from minor lyric changes - were the same. However, many fans had already heard **Black Star**, as it had appeared on a bootleg release a few years previously.

The set was unashamedly aimed at the collectors' market - hence the title, of course. Nonetheless, although generally well-received by fans (notwithstanding the standard cries for more), the release was criticised by a lot of the music press. Basically the fault may have lain in its marketing - something which the producers have since acknowledged. It raised the whole question of how valid it was to market material which, by its very nature, was directed at hard-core collectors. It seemed safe to assume that the general record/CD buying public were not interested in alternative versions of well-known songs - especially if they were patently not as good as the 'standard' releases. Therefore, apart from anything else, perhaps the music press misunderstood the philosophy behind such a release at the time, although the concept became much more acceptable as the nineties progressed, and other artists issued similar sorts of releases.

On the other hand, the set could never have been accused of being lavish. Its packaging and its limited contents fixed it firmly in the mid-price range. But leaving aside the packaging and its presentation for a while, the release did not exude a quality anything like that of the fifties' set released a year later. Then again, its recommended selling price of £24.99 represented very good value. A good number of dealers actually retailed it for a lot less - some as low as £19.99, which applied to the CD and vinyl versions. In fact, for a good while there was uncertainty as to whether there would be a vinyl version.

The first album was **Hollywood** and featured outtakes from the movie years. In general, the principle was good though, in fact, some of the songs were actually recorded elsewhere - Nashville, for instance. However, this was a small point - and certainly not an error - as the title obviously referred to outtakes from the Hollywood years. Interestingly, the company had already issued outtakes of the following songs: **G.I. Blues**, **Big Boots** and **Pocketful Of Rainbows**. As for the rest though, none had been issued officially before. The films represented were as follows (with dates made in brackets).

G.I. Blues (1960) -	**G.I. Blues - Big Boots - Pocketful Of Rainbows**
Flaming Star (1960) -	**Black Star - Summer Kisses, Winter Tears**
Wild In The Country (1960) -	**I Slipped, I Stumbled, I Fell - Lonely Man**
Follow That Dream (1961) -	**What A Wonderful Life - A Whistling Tune**
It Happened At The World's Fair (1962)	**Beyond The Bend - One Broken Heart For Sale**
Love In Las Vegas (1963) -	**You're The Boss**
Roustabout (1964) -	**Roustabout**
Girl Happy (1964) -	**Girl Happy**
Harem Holiday (1965) -	**So Close, Yet So Far**
California Holiday (1966) -	**Stop, Look And Listen - Am I Ready**
Clambake (1967) -	**How Can You Lose What You Never Had**

Of special interest to fans was the 'fast' version of **Big Boots**; the alternative title song to **Flaming Star - Black Star**; a solo version of **Lonely Man**; an earlier version of **A Whistling Tune**, cut for **Follow That Dream** and later re-recorded for **Kid Galahad**; the film version of **One Broken Heart For Sale**; the hitherto unissued (in Europe at least) duet with Ann-Margret, **You're The Boss**; and an alternative take of **Girl Happy** - which ran at the correct tape speed. Disappointment awaited those fans who were led to believe that the song **I Apologise** was to be included - as it had been listed in an **Elvis Monthly** advert. Elvis did sing a few lines whilst waiting for the recording of **Beyond The Bend** to start, but this was nothing more than Elvis passing the time and exercising his voice on a song he clearly knew in part and enjoyed. The song was not referred to on the label or box, but was mentioned in the accompanying booklet.

The album of Nashville outtakes dated, in the main, from the early 1960s. None of the songs had been issued in outtake form before (officially, that is).

The sources of the tracks are listed below with their first UK issue.

Title	Recording Date	First UK Appearance	Release Number
Like A Baby	3 Apr 1960	Elvis Is Back!	LP 11
There's Always Me	12 Mar 1961	Something For Everybody	LP 14
I Want You With Me	12 Mar 1961	Something For Everybody	LP 14
Gently	12 Mar 1961	Something For Everybody	LP 14
Give Me The Right	12 Mar 1961	Something For Everybody	LP 14
I Met Her Today	16 Oct 1961	Elvis For Everyone	LP 26
Night Rider	16 Oct 1961	Pot Luck	LP 16
Just Tell Her Jim Said Hello	19 Mar 1962	B side of She's Not You	S 38
Ask Me	12 Jan 1964	B side of Ain't That Loving You Baby	S 47
Memphis, Tennessee	12 Jan 1964	Elvis For Everyone	LP 26
Love Me Tonight	26 May 1963	Fun In Acapulco	LP 20
Witchcraft	26 May 1963	B side of Bossa Nova Baby	S 42
Come What May	28 May 1966	B side of Love Letters	S 54
Love Letters	26 May 1966	Single release	S 54
Goin' Home	15 Jan 1968	Speedway	LP 35

The tracks, therefore, were issued more or less chronologically. A quirk concerned **Ask Me** and **Memphis, Tennessee**. Although both songs were cut at the May 1963 session, the standard released versions dated from the January 1964 sessions. Bootleg collectors had possessed copies of the earlier cuts for many years, available on the **Memphis Tennessee** bootleg. The versions on **Collectors Gold** dated from 27 May 1963. The producers deliberately chose less well-known material for the set.

Now, although both of the two albums already discussed comprised a lot of unreleased versions - thus helping to meet the demands of fans who had pestered RCA for many years to take a leaf out of the bootleggers' books - and in extremely high quality, they failed to provide fans with the other aspect they also liked: studio chat. This was kept to a minimum, which was a pity, as the playing time could have been quite easily extended to accommodate this. Incidentally though, it is worth mentioning that while bootleg releases have included what some would regard as obscene or unsavoury language

on the part of Elvis, it seems highly unlikely that official mainline releases will ever feature such language. This was certainly the view expressed by Roger Semon in 1992 who felt that releases widely available to the record-buying public ought to have regard for people's sensitivity, not to mention the artist's own reputation.

The final album concentrated on Elvis's return to live appearances in 1969, featuring material cut at the International Hotel, Las Vegas, during August 1969. Only one of the tracks had been issued in the same form previously - notably the ever-popular 'laughing' version of **Are You Lonesome Tonight?**. Previously RCA had issued live versions of **Blue Suede Shoes**, **I Got A Woman**, **Reconsider Baby**, **Love Me Tender**, **Runaway**, **Are You Lonesome Tonight?**, **Mystery Train/Tiger Man**, **Funny How Time Slips Away**, **Jailhouse Rock**, **Don't Be Cruel**, **Baby, What You Want Me To Do**, **Heartbreak Hotel**, **Memories** and **What'd I Say** - although not all from the 1969 season. Entirely new to fans were 1969 stage versions of **Baby, What You Want Me To Do**, **I Got A Woman**, snatches of **Surrender** and **Loving You**, **Funny How Time Slips Away** and a hitherto unknown version of **Reconsider Baby**. Two other songs, **Inherit The Wind** and **This Is The Story** (cut earlier in the year in Memphis), were featured in a live form for the first and last time. And although some fans criticised the inclusion of **Are You Lonesome Tonight?** again, the producers maintained that in some ways it was forced upon them a) because of its popularity and, b) because there was little else of any real value worth using from this time. It is also worth noting that the live version of **Funny How Time Slips Away** preceded the studio version, which was cut in June 1970.

The actual packaging of the three album set gave rise to some other criticism. The cover photograph (a picture from the Colonel's collection, circa the filming of **Girl Happy** - judging by his hairstyle) was used no less than five times: on the cover of the box, on each of the albums, and on the front cover of the booklet. It was believed to have been used previously on a calendar, although for many fans it would be entirely new to them. Equally, the back cover shot (a common enough publicity pose from **Flaming Star**) appeared six times. Hence the effect of each shot was entirely lost by repeated use. Indeed, the CD version featured the **Flaming Star** picture on the inlay sheet too - making nine appearances! The only things to discriminate the covers of each album, in addition to the background colour, were the legends **Hollywood**, **Nashville** and **Live In Las Vegas** in the bottom right hand side corner of each album. The back covers listed the tracks, but gave no writing credits or running times. The actual labels showed the titles and running times only. Writing credits only appeared in the booklet along with recording data - session men used and take numbers (where known) in addition to recording dates and publishers' information. The original producers and engineers were listed on the album sleeves (apart from the Hollywood set where the original producers were not quoted), while the 'new' producers - Roger Semon, Erik Rasmussen and Ernst Mikael Jorgensen - were credited in the booklet and album covers, alongside Don Wardell (Digital Series Coordinator), Dick Baxter (Digital Mix and Engineering), and Chick Crumpacker (Digital A&R).

On the actual box itself, the 'Elvis in the 90's' legend was printed along the spine, instead of on a sticker. Each of the record labels were colour coded: pale blue for **Hollywood**, orange for **Nashville**, and pink for **Live In Las Vegas**. The same colour coding was also used for the track listing on the back of the box. The inner bags (made of very thin and flimsy paper) were also colour matched. And the LPs were also poorly packed in the box - in effect they flopped about - whereas at least the CDs were packed neatly into a moulded tray. Each of the labels featured both the BMG International and small round RCA logos, as did the back of the box. The albums had side A and side B (instead of side 1 and side 2).

In-store promotional browser cards were produced - in thick card - both in LP and CD sizes to fit into the appropriate racks. The front picture was the same as the one used on the cover design of the box, but it was a closer image of Elvis and the printing was larger. It said '49 Previously unreleased tracks in an exclusive 3 volume box set'. The back of the card listed all the tracks featured, but had the

Hollywood album first, the **Live In Las Vegas** album second, and the **Nashville** material last. The promotional cards were even given 'catalogue' numbers (although they were not shown on the cards themselves) for ordering purposes. The 12 inch vinyl LP card was allocated ELVIS 1, and the 5 inch CD card ELVIS 2. Both cards became available on 1 August in time for the official album release date of 10 August.

Theoretically, the sets were not to be sold individually, though some dealers (including some major high street chain stores) did spilt the CD boxes and sold the CDs separately (usually for around £8 - the mid-price range). To be best of our knowledge though, this did not happen with the vinyl LP sets.

The price code was a new one: JC. As mentioned previously, the top price charged was slightly under £25, while certain dealers did retail the sets anywhere from £19.99 upwards to £25. And, while this is purely a value judgement, we believe the price charged was not exorbitant when compared with other releases. For, bearing in mind that this included an eight page booklet with quite detailed notes, it made each LP or CD slightly cheaper than the average mid-priced release.

As for the booklet itself, this came in a standard 12 inch by 12 inch size for all formats. The cover was the same as the individual album covers, but simply stated 'Elvis' and then, down the right hand side, **Collectors Gold**. The back featured a blown-up version of the **Flaming Star** pose. The same shot was used yet again on page three of the booklet. On page four and five were a few other photos: one of the Colonel (and others) beside a cut-out of Elvis from **G.I. Blues**; a pose of Elvis and Ann-Margret; and an off-set candid of Elvis, Juliet Prowse and Pat Boone. On page six was a shot of Elvis and Frank Sinatra taken at the International Hotel, Las Vegas, in 1969; while page seven showed a newspaper cutting from August 1969 and a live on stage shot from the same time.

The notes, by Christopher Niccoli, gave some background to the release of this material and went on to discuss each of the phases individually, noting things for fans to listen out for.

Page two gave details of each track: running times, writers, publishers, some take numbers (where known), and recording dates. In general, they were accurate, though one or two errors slipped through. **Summer Kisses, Winter Tears** listed takes 1 and 14 but only one take was heard. **Beyond The Bend** was incorrectly listed as being recorded on 22 September 1963: it was, in fact, 22 September 1962. Similarly, on **So Close, Yet So Far** the recording date was given as 25 February 1962, when it should have read 25 February 1965.

We noted previously that the record labels carried only the song titles, and made no reference to writers. Writing credit errors shown below referred to the booklet - this being the only source of this information.

There were no errors of any kind on album 1. We must, however, acknowledge that we have made three amendments to the index as a result of this album. We have:

Dropped reference to the subtitle *(from paradise)* at the end of **So Close, Yet So Far**.

Amended the order of the writers' names of **Beyond The Bend** from Wise, Weisman, Fuller to Weisman, Wise, Fuller; and for **How Can You Lose What You Never Had** from Wayne, Weisman to Weisman, Wayne.

Album 2 provided some interesting discussion points regarding both song titles and writers' names. We know that the basis for **Ask Me** was the Italian folk song **Io**, written by Domenico Modugno and that Giant, Baum, Kaye wrote the English lyrics and music, but the name Migliacci had been added on this occasion. Presumably this was Franco Migliacci, who worked with Modugno on songs such as **Volare**, a hit for several artists, including Dean Martin in 1958, but

his name had never been credited on **Ask Me** previously, and nor was it mentioned on the song's last appearance on **For The Asking (The Lost Album)**, NL 90513 (**LP 309**). Whatever, the normal convention of showing the original writer first was breached.

Another interesting feature was that **Come What May** was sub-titled *(you are mine)*, the first time that this had occurred on an Elvis release.

The writers of **Love Letters**, Young and Heyman, were placed in the wrong order.

On album 3, an error occurred when DeCurtis was not credited for **Surrender** along with Pomus, Shuman. There was no question mark at the end of Are **You Lonesome Tonight?**, and **Rubberneckin'** was shown as two separate words - **Rubber Neckin'**. On side 2, the normal order of Blackwell, Presley was reversed on **Don't Be Cruel**, and the same was true for the writers of **Mystery Train**. Finally, the writer of **Reconsider Baby** was Lowell Fulson, not two people Lowell, Fulsom as shown (Fulson was also mis-spelt).

The set, of course, spawned a single release in the UK, in three formats: 7 inch (**S 177**), 12 inch (**S 178**), and a CD single. The 7 inch version had **Are You Lonesome Tonight?** as the A side and **Reconsider Baby** as the B side. The 12 inch and CD versions featured two extra tracks: **Runaway** and **Baby, What You Want Me To Do**. Interestingly, for single release, the tape of **Are You Lonesome Tonight?** (sent to Bob Jones for mastering purposes) had been edited slightly: there was no opening guitar chord and no talk on the end, thus making it ten seconds shorter than the album version.

An odd situation occurred regarding this release in the USA. At its original point of release in August 1991, the US market was not offered a vinyl version of the set. Ironically though, a vinyl set was produced belatedly in 1992, and although the precise details are no longer important, it is believed that 10,000 sets were manufactured. However, prior to its release, someone at BMG in the USA ordered the project to be cancelled and the sets to be destroyed. Fortunately, some sets survived (a figure of 300 was mentioned), with the result that they became extremely valuable and collectable. The artwork for the set was virtually identical to the UK release. The catalogue number of the set was 3114-1-R, and on the back of the box and the record labels the copyright date of 1992 was shown.

Finally, we thought it would be useful to list the master take and take numbers of the songs featured on albums 1 and 2, along with the recording dates for the live recordings on album 3.

Title	Master Take Number	Take Number On Collectors Gold
Album 1 *Hollywood*		
G.I. Blues	7/10 splice	1
Pocketful Of Rainbows	2 *	22, 17
Big Boots	2/4 splice	10
Black Star	splice	not known
Black Star (end title version)	6	6
Summer Kisses, Winter Tears	20	1, 14
I Slipped, I Stumbled, I Fell	13	18
Lonely Man	13	4
What A Wonderful Life	7	2, 1
A Whistling Tune	1/8 splice	4
Beyond The Bend	4	1, 2
One Broken Heart For Sale	5	1
You're The Boss	-	16/3 (ending)**
Roustabout	17	6
Girl Happy	13	4
So Close, Yet So Far	3/4 splice	splice

Stop, Look And Listen	6	3
Am I Ready	7	1
How Can You Lose What You Never Had	6	1, 3

* The master take issued on **G.I. Blues** (*LP 12*) was recorded on 6 May 1960, whereas the takes (22 and 17) featured on **Collectors Gold** date from an earlier session held on 28 April 1960.

** The full unspliced take on the Double Features CD **Viva Las Vegas**/**Roustabout** (74321 13432 2) was take 16.

Album 2 *Nashville*

Like A Baby	6	1, 2
There's Always Me	10	4
I Want You With Me	2	1
Gently	5	3
Give Me The Right	4	1
I Met Her Today	18	1
Night Rider	3	1, 2
Just Tell Her Jim Said Hello	6	1
Ask Me	2	2
Memphis, Tennessee	2	2
Love Me Tonight	8	1
Witchcraft	3	1
Come What May	8	6
Love Letters	9	4, 7
Goin' Home	30	24, 21

Album 3 *Live In Las Vegas*

	Recording Date
Blue Suede Shoes	25 August 1969 Dinner show
I Got A Woman	25 August 1969 Dinner show
Heartbreak Hotel	24 August 1969 Dinner show
Love Me Tender	22 August 1969 Midnight show
Baby, What You Want Me To Do	26 August 1969 Midnight show
Runaway	26 August 1969 Midnight show
Surrender	21 August 1969 Midnight show
Are You Lonesome Tonight?	26 August 1969 Midnight show
Rubberneckin'	26 August 1969 Midnight show
Memories	25 August 1969 Dinner show
Introductions by Elvis Presley	21 August 1969 Midnight show
Jailhouse Rock	22 August 1969 Midnight show
Don't Be Cruel	22 August 1969 Midnight show
Inherit The Wind	26 August 1969 Dinner show
This Is The Story	26 August 1969 Midnight show
Mystery Train	22 August 1969 Midnight show
Tiger Man	22 August 1969 Midnight show
Funny How Time Slips Away	25 August 1969 Dinner show
Loving You	22 August 1969 Midnight show
Reconsider Baby	22 August 1969 Midnight show
What'd I Say	23 August 1969 Midnight show

Label Variations

PINK/BLUE/ORANGE LABEL
1   **1991 PRESSING: STEREO**

Box Variations
1   None known

Cassette Only Release

EMC 003 *Elvis*

October 1991

The short notes in the introductory section relating to cassette releases pointed out that we rarely mentioned cassettes when discussing Elvis's UK output, principally because the collectors' market has had little interest in them. Indeed, by the mid-nineties, the music industry as a whole had begun to see cassette releases as dispensable and, without actually saying so publicly, BMG had determined not to issue any further Elvis cassettes.

A further reason for deliberately omitting reference to cassettes lay in the fact that, with some notable exceptions, they contained identical material to that found on the vinyl and/or CD version. This cassette was, however, an exception, in that there was no vinyl or CD equivalent and, because of this, we felt it deserved some comment.

The cassette contained a particularly strong collection of tracks covering the period 1956-73 (**My Way** being the **Aloha From Hawaii** single version). It contained the following:

> *Heartbreak Hotel*
> *In The Ghetto*
> *Suspicious Minds*
> *I Just Can't Help Believin'*
> *The Wonder Of You*
> *My Way*
> *Hound Dog*
> *Blue Suede Shoes*
> *(Marie's the name) His Latest Flame*
> *All Shook Up*
> *Jailhouse Rock*
> *Guitar Man*

This particular set was produced for Avon (the cosmetics company) by BMG, who classed the product as 'non-commercial', as it was not available in the shops or from BMG themselves, but could only be purchased through the Avon catalogue.

The BMG/Avon partnership had its origins in America, where a fourteen track compilation, entitled *Elvis At His Romantic Best*, was released on CD in July 1991. As the title readily suggested, the content of the American CD was love song orientated, whereas the UK cassette was unashamedly a 'greatest hits' package. This kind of 'switch' was not uncommon - each market was different, and releases were often tailored to meet specific needs. The idea to market a 'love songs' collection in the UK at the time - October 1991 - may have caused some concern, as BMG's own collection *From The Heart* (**LP 317**) was probably in early stages of development, and to release similar material, albeit via another company, could have been seen as counterproductive. In fact, there was a noticeable difference between the contents of the American Avon cassette and *From The Heart*, released in February 1992. Whereas the cassette included some lesser known Elvis tracks (to the general public), such as *And I Love You So*, *Help Me Make It Through The Night*, and *Let It Be Me*, BMG's *From The Heart* concentrated almost exclusively on instantly recognisable hit singles. Nevertheless, four tracks were common to both releases: *Love Letters*, *The Wonder Of You*, *Always On My Mind* and *Until It's Time For You To Go*.

For your information, the full track listing of the American CD was as follows:

> *One Night*
> *Fever*
> *Love Letters*
> *You Don't Know Me*
> *The Wonder Of You*
> *And I Love You So*
> *Always On My Mind*
> *Love Me*
> *Help Me Make It Through The Night*
> *Unchained Melody*
> *Let It Be Me*
> *I Really Don't Want To Know*
> *Until It's Time For You To Go*
> *Any Way You Want Me*

The only track featured on both the original US CD and subsequent UK cassette release was *The Wonder Of You*, although the CD did contain fourteen tracks as opposed to twelve on the UK cassette.

In all, 12,500 cassettes were produced and these must have sold well, as the cassette could not be obtained by 1993.

LP 316	**Elvis In Person At The International Hotel Las Vegas, Nevada**
	RCA NL 83892

Side 1

1   **Blue Suede Shoes** (Perkins)
2   **Johnny B. Goode** (Berry)
3   **All Shook Up** (Blackwell, Presley)
4   **Are You Lonesome Tonight?** (Turk, Handman)
5   **Hound Dog** (Leiber, Stoller)
6   **I Can't Stop Loving You** (Gibson)
7   **My Babe** (Dixon)

Side 2

1   **Mystery Train** (Parker, Phillips)
    Tiger Man (Lewis, Burns)
2   **Words** (B., R. & M Gibb)
3   **In The Ghetto** (Davis)
4   **Suspicious Minds** (James)
5   **Can't Help Falling In Love** (Peretti, Creatore, Weiss)

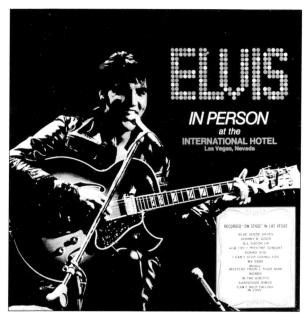

Released October 1991   Deleted December 1992

This was the live half of the *From Memphis To Vegas From Vegas To Memphis*, NL 89068(2) (*LP 231*), album which was still available at the time this single album appeared. We say 'appeared' rather than issued, for there was a great deal of confusion as to whether the album was actually intended as a UK vinyl release.

Fans in both America and Europe had been able to buy the two albums comprising *From Memphis To Vegas From Vegas To Memphis* as separate single albums for many years, but in the UK the release had always been as a double album. To all intents and purposes, this was the German issue of *Elvis In Person*. Indeed, the back of the sleeve showed a copyright date of 1983, and no-one had bothered to change the distribution details, which still insisted that UK distribution was by RCA Ltd., not BMG. Of course, this detail had never been accurate in the first place, for this album had not previously been issued in the UK.

The front of the sleeve was identical to that of the double album, minus the RCA logo and *From Memphis To Vegas* title, while the three shots of Elvis which formed the right-hand side of the inner gatefold sleeve, now appeared on the back with the track listing being a modified version of the original. There was a price code box, but no code was shown for the UK. Then again, neither had *From Memphis To Vegas From Vegas To Memphis*. Despite this omission, and the confusion surrounding its origin, the album was a UK issue, and it was a new pressing because it featured the round RCA logo situated on the left of the label. Reference to the matrix number in between the run-out grooves showed that old stampers were used, as the date 2/83 could clearly be seen.

There was yet more confusion regarding the actual title of the album. The original album, and subsequent German black label issue, used the sub-title *Elvis In Person At The International Hotel Las Vegas, Nevada*, but the removal of the main title of this part of the album, *From Memphis To Vegas*, effectively promoted the sub-title to be the main one, when the simpler *Elvis In Person* would have sufficed.

Annoyingly, and unlike the original double album, the tracks were unnumbered on the label, yet reference was made at the bottom of the label to which tracks featured vocal accompaniment, making it unnecessarily difficult to locate the tracks concerned.

It will be no surprise to learn that the label and sleeve errors found on *From Memphis To Vegas From Vegas To Memphis* were repeated here. The 'e' was missing from *Johnny B. Goode*, as was the question mark in *Are You Lonesome Tonight?*. The writers of *Mystery Train* were in the wrong order, and the Gibb Brothers were listed in the order R., B. & M., when normally they appear as B., R. & M. The writers' names did not appear on the sleeve.

Elvis In Person At The International Hotel Las Vegas, Nevada was deleted on 23 December 1992.

Label Variations

GERMAN BLACK LABEL

1   1991 PRESSING: STEREO
          Round RCA logo at side of label

Sleeve Variations

1   Gloss

Albums Released Prior To 1986

Checking through listings of vinyl albums still available at this point in time in the RCA catalogue, revealed the startling impact compact discs had had on the record market over the previous six years. Of course, whilst compact discs offered an alternative medium to buyers, there had also been a steady decline in general interest in Elvis product, and this too had had an effect on availability. The simple truth of the matter, irrespective of the reason, was that at the end of December 1991 a total of thirty-seven vinyl albums were still available, and of those only 19 (or 20, if the *Romantic Elvis/Rockin' Elvis - The Sixties* were counted as two albums) were released prior to 1986. Most of those still available had a CD equivalent, suggesting that once vinyl stocks fell, these too would also be deleted. Even some of the CDs released during the same period had been deleted.

Below is a complete list of vinyl albums released prior to 1986 which were still available at the end of December 1991. They are shown in catalogue number order for ease of reference, and the date the album was released, and its release number are also shown.

	Catalogue Number	Title	Release Date	
1	NL 81515	*Loving You*	Apr 1984	*LP 210*
2	PL 82587(2)	*Elvis In Concert*	Aug 1985	*LP 273*
3	NL 83683	*Blue Hawaii*	Aug 1984	*LP 238*
4	NL 83733	*King Creole*	Apr 1984	*LP 212*

5	NL 83735	*G.I. Blues*	Jan 1984	*LP 206*
6	NL 83894	*Elvis* *	Sep 1984	*LP 245*
7	BL 84031(2)	*This Is Elvis*	May 1984	*LP 226*
8	NL 84232	*Elvis For Everyone*	May 1984	*LP 225*
9	PL 85172(6)	*A Golden Celebration*	Oct 1984	*LP 251*
10	NL 89011	*Love Letters From Elvis* **	Sep 1984	*LP 250*
11	NL 89013	*Elvis Is Back!*	Jun 1984	*LP 230*
12	NL 89024	*20 Greatest Hits Vol. 1*	Apr 1984	*LP 216*
13	NL 89046	*Elvis Presley*	Jan 1985	*LP 267*
14	NL 89068(2)	*From Memphis To Vegas, From Vegas To Memphis*	Jun 1984	*LP 231*
15	NL 89098	*Pot Luck*	Jul 1984	*LP 233*
16	NL 89107	*The Elvis Presley Sun Collection*	Oct 1983	*LP 201*
17	PL 89124	*Romantic Elvis* ***	Apr 1984	*LP 220*
18	NL 89125	*Rock 'N' Roll*	Jul 1984	*LP 236*
19	PL 89132	*Rockin' Elvis - The Sixties* ***	Apr 1984	*LP 221*
20	NL 89168	*20 Greatest Hits Vol. 2*	Apr 1984	*LP 219*

*   This album, the NBC TV Special, had practically vanished from the stores, although it had not actually been deleted. Ironically, additional vinyl copies became available to accompany the compact disc version when it was released in March 1991.

**   *Love Letters From Elvis* also disappeared from the shelves, although it too had not been officially deleted. Further copies were circulated when the album was issued on CD.

***   These albums were actually a 'buy one, get one free' collection, and whilst we have shown them separately, one could not be officially obtained without the other.

Album Deletions - January 1992

Throughout 1992, BMG undertook an on-going review of the vinyl album catalogue, the result of which was the deletion of many Elvis albums. The first album to be deleted, in January 1992, was one of the four remaining film soundtrack albums, *King Creole*, NL 83733 (*LP 212*), first released in April 1984.

The other three film soundtrack albums - *Loving You*, NL 81515 (*LP 210*), *Blue Hawaii*, NL 83683 (*LP 238*), and *G.I. Blues*, NL 83735 (*LP 206*) - survived a little longer, until they too were deleted in March 1992.

Price Codes

The next RCA album, *From The Heart*, PL 90642 (**LP 317**), used a new price code - TV - a move clearly linked to the fact that the album was extensively advertised on television.

Sleeve Detail Change

The sleeve of *From The Heart*, PL 90642 (**LP 317**), released in February 1992, showed, in addition to the round RCA logo, two variations of the BMG logo. The first mentioned that the album was marketed by BMG Enterprises, and the second logo had underneath it 'BMG Records (UK) Limited'.

Label Design

From The Heart was also the first totally new release to use the round RCA logo on the left of the label.

Side 1

1 **The Wonder Of You** (Knight)
2 **I Just Can't Help Believin'** (Mann, Weil)
3 **Always On My Mind** (James, Carson, Christopher)
4 **You Don't Have To Say You Love Me** (Pallavinci, Donaggio, Wickham, Napier-Bell)
5 **Until It's Time For You To Go** (Sainte-Marie)
6 **Suspicious Minds** (James)
7 **There Goes My Everything** (Frazier)
8 **The Girl Of My Best Friend** (Ross, Bobrick)
9 **It's Now Or Never** (DiCapua, Schroeder, Gold)

Side 2

1 **Good Luck Charm** (Schroeder, Gold)
2 **Love Letters** (Young, Heyman)
3 **Can't Help Falling In Love** (Peretti, Creatore, Weiss)
4 **Suspicion** (Pomus, Shuman)
5 **She's Not You** (Pomus, Leiber, Stoller)
6 **Are You Lonesome Tonight?** (Turk, Handman)
7 **Wooden Heart** (Wise, Weisman, Twomey, Kaempfert)
8 **Love Me Tender** (Presley, Matson)
9 **Don't** (Leiber, Stoller)
10 **Loving You** (Leiber, Stoller)

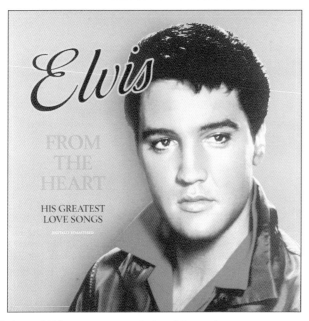

Released February 1992   Deleted December 1993

The idea of releasing an album of Elvis love songs was not a new one but, with the exception of *A Valentine Gift For You*, PL 85353 (*LP 270*), issued in January 1985, it had not been undertaken by RCA themselves. Several other labels though - Camden and K-tel - had compiled such releases before:

Love Songs (K-tel) NE 1062 (*LP 116*), October 1979.
Love Songs (Camden) CDS 1211 (*LP 199*), August 1983.

Truthfully, when this release was being planned - by Lee Simmonds, an ex-RCA employee, with the assistance of Roger Semon, who was still employed by BMG at the time - it aroused little interest among the fans. In fact, not long after Simmonds had issued the CD only

release of *16 Top Ten Tracks - The Diamond Collection* - a hotch-potch of film songs, plus one original item, *Tomorrow Is A Long Time* - it had been announced that the next budget release (budget as opposed to mid-priced release) was to be a collection of love songs. This never materialised, although a track listing was formulated.

However, early in 1992, it became obvious that BMG were going to promote the *From The Heart* album quite extensively, including a television advertisement. Clearly the release was perceived as being for the wider market, way beyond that of loyal fans. This, in fact, was reflected in the track listing: there was very little included for collectors, and certainly nothing as interesting as regards an outtake. The release was unashamedly aimed at the middle-of-the-road buyer. The only item of minor interest for die-hard collectors was the inclusion of a 'clean' stereo version of *There Goes My Everything*, without the *I Was Born About 10,000 Years Ago* link.

At the time of its release - 10 February 1992 (it had been intended for release on 3 February) - rumours abounded that it was to be the last vinyl release in the UK, although Roger Semon expressed doubts about this, as he and others were presenting a very strong case for issuing the proposed fifties' set in vinyl form too in the UK and Europe - as indeed happened. In fact *From The Heart* was issued in all three formats, although the vinyl version had five tracks fewer than the CD and cassette versions. Not included were *(Now and then there's) A Fool Such As I*, *Love Me*, *I Want You, I Need you, I Love You*, *It's Only Love* and *Unchained Melody*. Nonetheless, the release generated a lot of media interest, with the result that it was placed at number two in the BBC Radio 2 Easy Listening Chart, week beginning February 17 1992. W.H. Smith also featured it at number seven in their album chart prior to its release! It was heavily featured on Radio 2 generally and was, at one point, their album of the week, even though there was no current single culled from the set. It peaked at number one in the BBC chart, week beginning March 9, but remained there for one week only. Nonetheless, it sold well, more than justifying the money spent on advertising it.

Some may wonder why the album was so successful - to the chagrin of many devoted fans, it has to be said, if only because the set did not cater for their needs as collectors. On a basic level the answer was simple: past experience for all companies had shown that there was a healthy interest in 'hits' packages - meaning that every four or five years it was profitable for companies to recycle old product at minimum cost to themselves, to cater for an ever growing user group who like 'Best Of..' type releases. If, as was the case here, the company determined to promote a product vigorously throughout its normal outlets, and then add to that fairly extensive TV advertising, then the returns could be most impressive. And while TV advertising is expensive, it was normally understood that a company could more than justify its expenditure in sales' returns. So, while collectors may scorn such releases, they do fulfil some useful purposes:

- earn revenue for the company (and the artist or his company);
- keep an artist's name in the public eye; and,
- lay the ground-work for more serious artistic undertakings - in this case the fifties' boxed set.

To illustrate how seriously BMG regarded this release, the company went to considerable trouble to issue an advisory marketing sheet for its sales department. The marketing points brought to the dealers' attention were as follows:

- 'A meticulously researched collection of Elvis' greatest love songs. Track listing, sleeve and TV commercial have all been researched to create the most appealing album.

- The first Elvis love songs album for many years and a long awaited sequel to *All Time Greatest Hits*, which sold in excess of 600,000 units (at that point).

- Research has shown a very positive consumer reaction to a 'themed' Elvis compilation to follow *All Time Greatest Hits* (sic). Love songs emerged as the unanimous choice of theme.

- Extremely good value for money with 24 tracks on the tape and CD, 21 tracks on vinyl.' (In fact the advertised listing identified the five songs not on the vinyl format - the LP included 19 songs only).

- Included *The Wonder Of You*, as featured in the £1,000,000 Bovril campaign, which continues until the spring.

- Also included *Good Luck Charm*, as featured in the Pentax camera campaign currently on air.'

Now before looking more closely at some of the claims made, it had to be said that it was obvious the company had determined to 'push' this release. However, the TV campaign was not fully networked for much of the time; indeed we know many fans who did not see the advert at all, and were puzzled by its non-appearance on TV following its initial release. The reason for this was that BMG had spread the campaign over several weeks, and concentrated on the various regions at different times. The marketing leaflet informed dealers when TV and radio advertising would appear in a particular area.

'Weeks commencing February 3 and 10 - Central TV, HTV and London Capital Gold.
Week commencing February 17 - National TV.
Weeks commencing February 24 and March 2 - London TV, Scottish TV and Yorkshire TV.
Weeks beginning March 9 and 16 - Granada TV, TVS and Anglia TV.'

Also mentioned was a press and promotion campaign, including competitions and on-air promotions with all the major 'gold' radio stations.

As you might expect, some of the points raised in the advertising promotion were questionable. Chiefly though, the oddest claim was that the release was in any way a 'sequel' to *Presley - The All Time Greatest Hits* (**LP 287**). It most certainly could not be described thus, as there was a significant level of duplication of tracks on both releases. In fact, only seven of those featured on *From The Heart* were unique to that collection: *You Don't Have To Say You Love Me*; *Until It's Time For You To Go*; *There Goes My Everything*; *Loving You*; *Love Me*; *I Want You, I Need You, I Love You*, and *Unchained Melody* (remember the last three were only on the CD version which had a running time of 69 minutes 49 seconds).

Looking at the track listing revealed what a strong set it was: all tracks on the vinyl album had been used as single releases. And, of the 19 tracks featured, only three were pre-army songs. Oddly, the publishing dates quoted on a number of the tracks were wrong. While *I Just Can't Help Believin'* was recorded in 1970, it was not published in the UK until January 1971 on the album *That's The Way It Is* (*LP 47*). The same was true of *You Don't Have To Say You Love Me* and *There Goes My Everything*, both shown as 1970, but not released in the UK until 1971 on *LPs 47* and *49* respectively. *Are You Lonesome Tonight?* was recorded in 1960, but not issued in the UK until January 1961 (*S 31*). *Don't* was cut in 1957 but, again, not issued in the UK until February 1958 (*S 19*). None of these versions was different from previous issues. For example, *Always On My Mind* was the original 1972 single version (*S 85*), as was *Suspicious Minds* (*S 70*). *Unchained Melody* was the overdubbed version, as featured on the *Moody Blue* album (*LP 93*).

The cover photograph was a publicity still circa 1963/4, possibly around the time of *Kissin' Cousins* (judging by his hairstyle). The back cover featured a colour shot (posed) from the *Jailhouse Rock* era. There were no liner notes at all, simply a track listing and a note saying 'Compiled by Lee Simmonds'.

Incidentally, a mere three months after its release, the album was said to have sold in excess of 200,000 units (65% CD; 8% vinyl, the rest in cassette form). Needless to say this more than justified the estimated £100,000 figure spent in promoting the album.

In mid-1993, over a year after its original release, the album was re-promoted by BMG, with the result that a high volume of copies were to be found in the large high street stores, retailing at less than £10 - over £3 cheaper than its original selling price. In addition, a promo-only CD single featuring *Love Letter*s was made available, although it was a very restricted release.

There were a few errors regarding the song writers, which were confined to the labels only. Cynthia Weil had her surname misspelt Weill on *I Just Can't Help Believin'*, while the writers of *You Don't Have To Say You Love Me*, *Can't Help Falling In Love* and *Love Me Tender* were all shown in the wrong order.

Label Variations

GERMAN BLACK LABEL
1	1992 PRESSING: STEREO/MONO
	Round RCA logo at side of label

Sleeve Variations
1	Gloss

Album Deletions - February 1992

Two old favourites were deleted in February 1992:

PL 85172(6) *A Golden Celebration* (*LP 251*), first released in October 1984; and, NL 89068(2) *From Memphis To Vegas, From Vegas To Memphis* (*LP 231*), from June 1984.

From Memphis To Vegas, From Vegas To Memphis (*LP 231*) was interesting in that it was deleted after the release of *Elvis In Person At The International Hotel Las Vegas, Nevada*, the re-titled live half of the former double album. BMG released *Elvis In Person At The International Hotel Las Vegas, Nevada*, NL 83892 (**LP 316**) in October 1991, when the two albums (this one and *Back In Memphis*) appeared separately in CD format.

Album Deletions - March 1992

BMG undertook a massive deletion programme in March 1992, when a total of seventeen albums were deleted, including some relatively recent releases. These are listed below, in catalogue number order, and their respective release date and release number is also shown.

NL 81515	*Loving You*	Apr 1984	*LP 210*
NL 83683	*Blue Hawaii*	Aug 1984	*LP 238*
NL 83735	*G.I. Blues*	Jan 1984	*LP 206*
NL 83894	*Elvis*	Sep 1984	*LP 245*
NL 84232	*Elvis For Everyone*	May 1984	*LP 225*
NL 89011	*Love Letters From Elvis*	Sep 1984	*LP 250*
NL 89013	*Elvis Is Back!*	Jun 1984	*LP 230*
NL 89024	*20 Greatest Hits Vol. 1*	Apr 1984	*LP 216*
NL 89046	*Elvis Presley*	Jan 1985	*LP 267*
NL 89098	*Pot Luck*	Jul 1984	*LP 233*
NL 89125	*Rock 'N' Roll*	Jul 1984	*LP 236*
NL 89168	*20 Greatest Hits Vol. 2*	Apr 1984	*LP 219*
NL 90252	*Moody Blue*	Oct 1988	**LP 296**
NL 90359	*For LP Fans Only*	Sep 1989	**LP 303**
NL 90360	*A Date With Elvis*	Sep 1989	**LP 304**
NL 90548	*From Elvis In Memphis*	Feb 1991	**LP 313**
NL 90549	*On Stage - February, 1970*	Feb 1991	**LP 314**

Many of these albums had formed the backbone of the RCA/BMG catalogue for many years, and several had never effectively been deleted since their original release, despite several changes in label design and catalogue numbers. The final three remaining film soundtrack albums (**King Creole**, NL 83733, *LP 212*, had been deleted in January 1992), fell by the wayside, as did classic albums like **Elvis Is Back!**, NL 89013 (*LP 230*).

While the bulk of the deletions were albums released prior to 1986, five were released after 1986, with the final two on the list, **From Elvis In Memphis**, NL 90548 (**LP 313**), and **On Stage - February, 1970**, NL 90549 (**LP 314**), being just over a year old.

Label And Sleeve Variations

From this point onwards we have not made any references to label and sleeve variations at the end of the script of each vinyl album. The reason for this is quite simple: to the best of our knowledge there weren't any. It appears that all of the BMG releases from mid-1992 onwards had an initial print run only, and were never re-pressed. It is possible that **The Essential Collection** (**LP 320**) may have been an exception to this, given the number of copies sold. But if there were any label and/or sleeve variations produced as a result, we are not aware of them.

Starting with **The King Of Rock 'N' Roll The Complete 50's Masters** (**LP 318**), BMG dispensed with their traditional label design in favour of picture labels (although **Elvis 56**, **LP 321**, used a design based on the RCA Victor labels of the sixties), in much the same way as they had with CDs. This has allowed us to include additional details about the label design in the script itself.

Disc 1

Side 1

1. **My Happiness** (Peterson, Bergantine)
2. **That's All Right** (Crudup)
3. **I Love You Because** (Payne)
4. **Harbour Lights** (Kennedy, Williams)
5. **Blue Moon Of Kentucky** (Monroe)
6. **Blue Moon** (Rodgers, Hart)
7. **Tomorrow Night** (Coslow, Grosz)
8. **I'll Never Let You Go (little darlin')** (Wakely)
9. **I Don't Care If The Sun Don't Shine** (David)
10. **Just Because** (B. & J. Shelton, Robin)
11. **Good Rockin' Tonight** (Brown)
12. **Milkcow Blue Boogie** (Arnold)

Side 2

1. **You're A Heartbreaker** (Sallee)
2. **Baby Let's Play House** (Gunter)
3. **I'm Left, You're Right, She's Gone** (Kesler, Taylor)
4. **Mystery Train** (Parker, Phillips)
5. **I Forgot To Remember To Forget** (Kesler, Feathers)
6. **Trying To Get To You** (Singleton, McCoy)
7. **When It Rains, It Really Pours** (Emerson)
8. **I Got A Woman** (Charles)
9. **Heartbreak Hotel** (Axton, Durden, Presley)
10. **Money Honey** (Stone)
11. **I'm Counting On You** (Robertson)
12. **I Was The One** (Schroeder, DeMetrius, Blair, Peppers)

Disc 2

Side 1

1. **Blue Suede Shoes** (Perkins)
2. **My Baby Left Me** (Crudup)
3. **One-Sided Love Affair** (Campbell)
4. **So Glad You're Mine** (Crudup)
5. **I'm Gonna Sit Right Down And Cry (over you)** (Thomas, Biggs)
6. **Tutti Frutti** (LaBostrie, Penniman)
7. **Lawdy, Miss Clawdy** (Price)
8. **Shake, Rattle And Roll** (Calhoun)
9. **I Want You, I Need You, I Love You** (Mysels, Kosloff)
10. **Hound Dog** (Leiber, Stoller)
11. **Don't Be Cruel** (Blackwell, Presley)
12. **Any Way You Want Me (that's how I will be)** (Schroeder, Owens)

Side 2

1 **We're Gonna Move** (Presley, Matson)
2 **Love Me Tender** (Presley, Matson)
3 **Poor Boy** (Presley, Matson)
4 **Let Me** (Presley, Matson)
5 **Playin' For Keeps** (Kesler)
6 **Love Me** (Leiber, Stoller)
7 **Paralyzed** (Blackwell, Presley)
8 **How Do You Think I Feel** (Walker, Pierce)
9 **How's The World Treating You** (Atkins, Bryant)
10 **When My Blue Moon Turns To Gold Again** (Walker, Sullivan)
11 **Long Tall Sally** (Johnson, Blackwell, Penniman)
12 **Old Shep** (Foley, Arthur)

Disc 3

Side 1

1 **Too Much** (Rosenberg, Weinman)
2 **Anyplace Is Paradise** (Thomas)
3 **Ready Teddy** (Blackwell, Marascalco)
4 **First In Line** (Schroeder, Weisman)
5 **Rip It Up** (Blackwell, Marascalco)
6 **I Believe** (Drake, Graham, Shirl, Stillman)
7 **Tell Me Why** (Turner)
8 **Got A Lot O' Livin' To Do!** (Schroeder, Weisman)
9 **All Shook Up** (Blackwell, Presley)
10 **Mean Woman Blues** (DeMetrius)
11 **(There'll be) Peace In The Valley (for me)** (Dorsey)

Side 2

1 **That's When Your Heartaches Begin** (Raskin, Brown, Fisher)
2 **Take My Hand, Precious Lord** (Dorsey)
3 **It Is No Secret (what God can do)** (Hamblen)
4 **Blueberry Hill** (Lewis, Stock, Rose)
5 **Have I Told You Lately That I Love You** (Wiseman)
6 **Is It So Strange** (Young)
7 **Party** (Robinson)
8 **Lonesome Cowboy** (Tepper, Bennett)
9 **Hot Dog** (Leiber, Stoller)
10 **One Night Of Sin** (Bartholomew, King)
11 **(Let me be your) Teddy Bear** (Mann, Lowe)

Disc 4

Side 1

1 **Don't Leave Me Now** (Schroeder, Weisman)
2 **I Beg Of You** (McCoy, Owens)
3 **One Night** (Bartholomew, King)
4 **True Love** (Porter)
5 **I Need You So** (Hunter)
6 **Loving You** (Leiber, Stoller)
7 **When It Rains, It Really Pours** (Emerson)
8 **Jailhouse Rock** (Leiber, Stoller)
9 **Young And Beautiful** (Silver, Schroeder)
10 **I Want To Be Free** (Leiber, Stoller)
11 **(You're so square) Baby I Don't Care** (Leiber, Stoller)
12 **Don't Leave Me Now** (Schroeder, Weisman)

Side 2

1 **Treat Me Nice** (Leiber, Stoller)
2 **My Wish Came True** (Hunter)
3 **Don't** (Leiber, Stoller)
4 **Blue Christmas** (Hayes, Johnson)
5 **White Christmas** (Berlin)
6 **Here Comes Santa Claus (right down Santa Claus lane)** (Autry, Haldeman, Melka)
7 **Silent Night** (Mohr, Gruber)
8 **O Little Town Of Bethlehem** (Redner, Brooks)
9 **Santa Bring My Baby Back (to me)** (Schroeder, DeMetrius)
10 **Santa Claus Is Back In Town** (Leiber, Stoller)
11 **I'll Be Home For Christmas (if only in my dreams)** (Kent, Gannon, Ram)

Disc 5

Side 1

1 **Danny** (Wise, Weisman)
2 **Hard Headed Woman** (DeMetrius)
3 **Trouble** (Leiber, Stoller)
4 **New Orleans** (Tepper, Bennett)
5 **Crawfish** (Wise, Weisman)
6 **Dixieland Rock** (Schroeder, Frank)
7 **Lover Doll** (Wayne, Silver)
8 **Don't Ask Me Why** (Wise, Weisman)
9 **As Long As I Have You** (Wise, Weisman)
10 **King Creole** (Leiber, Stoller)
11 **Young Dreams** (Kalmanoff, Schroeder)
12 **Steadfast, Loyal And True** (Leiber, Stoller)
13 **Doncha' Think It's Time** (Otis, Dixon)
14 **Your Cheatin' Heart** (Williams)

Side 2

1 **Wear My Ring Around Your Neck** (Carroll, Moody)
2 **I Need Your Love Tonight** (Wayne, Reichner)
3 **A Big Hunk O' Love** (Schroeder, Wyche)
4 **Ain't That Loving You Baby** (Otis, Hunter)
5 **(Now and then there's) A Fool Such As I** (Trader)
6 **I Got Stung** (Schroeder, Hill)
7 **Interview with Elvis.** Press Conference, Brooklyn, New York, 22 September 1958

Disc 6

Side 1

1 **That's When Your Heartaches Begin** (Raskin, Brown, Fisher)
2 **Fool, Fool, Fool** (Nugetre)
3 **Tweedle Dee** (Scott)
4 **Maybellene** (Berry)
5 **Shake, Rattle And Roll** (Calhoun)
6 **Blue Moon Of Kentucky** (Monroe)
7 **Blue Moon** (Rodgers, Hart)
8 **I'm Left, You're Right, She's Gone** (Kesler, Taylor)
9 **Reconsider Baby** (Fulson)
10 **Lawdy, Miss Clawdy** (Price)
11 **Shake, Rattle And Roll** (Calhoun)
12 **I Want You, I Need You, I Love You** (Mysels, Kosloff)
13 **Heartbreak Hotel** (Axton, Durden, Presley)

Side 2

1 **Long Tall Sally** (Johnson, Blackwell, Penniman)
2 **Blue Suede Shoes** (Perkins)
3 **Money Honey** (Stone)
4 **We're Gonna Move** (Presley, Matson)
5 **Old Shep** (Foley, Arthur)
6 **I Beg Of You** (McCoy, Owens)
7 **Loving You** (Leiber, Stoller)
8 **Loving You** (Leiber, Stoller)
9 **Young And Beautiful** (Silver, Schroeder)
10 **I Want To Be Free** (Leiber, Stoller)
11 **King Creole** (Leiber, Stoller)
12 **As Long As I Have You** (Wise, Weisman)
13 **Ain't That Loving You Baby** (Otis, Hunter)

Released July 1992   Deleted July 1994

Indisputably, the release of *The King Of Rock 'N' Roll The Complete 50's Masters* was RCA/BMG's most important and prestigious Elvis Presley package to date. Acclaimed on all fronts: the media, the music industry and, of course, by the fans themselves, the release was, in all likelihood, the pinnacle of success for those who had worked long and hard - chief among them Roger Semon and Ernst Mikael Jorgensen - to make this concept (mooted as early as 1987) a reality.

Indeed, all that had gone before - including the imaginative and well-received *Essential Elvis* series - was eclipsed by the scale, scope and quality (in all respects) of this new release. Needless to say, of course, the transition from what was most likely regarded as a wild and uncommercial idea: to release all of Elvis's fifties' material on one collection - to its realisation in the summer of 1992 - was not an easy one. And while we are not privy to all the background detail, it seems reasonable to assume that the likes of Semon and Jorgensen had a major selling job on their hands in order to convince all those sceptics who believed that the days of Elvis Presley material selling in huge quantities were over. Whatever arguments they used - and no doubt their proven track record with Elvis material over a four to five year period must have carried considerable weight - clearly they were ultimately successful in convincing the company of the need for such a release, but more, of its commercial viability.

Of course, they did have some potent factors on their side. To a great extent, Elvis as an artist had been largely ignored by the US market for a long time. There was no clear leadership, no vision, no imagination, and little to fire the interest of either fans or the general

public. Moreover, RCA's foray into the back-catalogue market via compact discs had been poorly handled: not only had there been a distinct lack of quality in terms of audio fidelity, but the releases had been ill-conceived with a dreadful mix of superfluous compilations, alongside seemingly random selections from the back catalogue. In short, Elvis's material had been shoddily presented and his fans cheated in a sense. However, with the inception of *Essential Elvis*, the ground was laid for a release which would boast the highest possible audio quality (tapes from master sources - common among most other artists but not Elvis!) alongside such things as serious documentation of the era and detailed discographical information. Indeed, many key figures associated with Presley product acknowledged publicly what a mess the catalogue was in, and gave sincere undertakings that the catalogue would be restored to the highest possible standards in terms of sound quality. At the time of its release, Senior Vice President of Marketing at RCA, Randy Goodman, was quoted as saying that the boxed set allowed RCA '... a real opportunity to make a statement to the trade and to consumers about how we intend to handle Elvis in the future. I'll be honest with you: we've not been known in the past couple of decades for the commitment we've given to this artist. We've cried wolf a lot of times on Elvis, but this package is different.'

Interestingly, the actual release of the set had been mentioned as early as the summer of 1990, with a provisional release date of September 1991 which, of course, ultimately stretched to July 1992. The final track listing and the sequencing were done towards the end of February 1992, and the mastering overseen by Semon and Jorgensen. And around the same time, the decision to market a vinyl collection in Europe (a limited edition of 15,000 numbered copies) was taken. Similarly, in April 1992, the company agreed to market a single comprising material from the release - although, as it turned out, the four track single (**S 179**) contained a previously unissued performance of *I Need Your Love Tonight* - take 9 - left over from *Hits Like Never Before - (Essential Elvis Vol. 3)* (**LP 306**), presumably to entice collectors to buy it.

Back-tracking slightly though, at the end of March 1992 Semon had to fly out to Los Angeles to co-ordinate the text and photographs for the booklet - demonstrating the scale of the operation on all aspects of the release, bearing in mind that the "experts" lived outside the USA and had to be kept informed of goings on and help supervise all the disparate parts of the process. The time and effort expended by all concerned clearly paid dividends, as the booklet proved to be a first class job, comprising authoritative notes by Peter Guralnick (who was at the time writing what many believed would be the ultimate biography of Elvis). The package included many previously unseen photographs, some provided by long-time Elvis fan and collector Ger Rijff from Holland (whose own photographic chronicles of Elvis were highly regarded and respected by most fans), and a detailed discography compiled by Jorgensen and Eric Rasmussen. Incidentally, Guralnick's first Elvis sleeve notes had appeared on *Reconsider Baby* (*LP 271*) in May 1985.

Of course, errors occurred, no matter how much care was taken, and sometimes they were so glaringly obvious - after publication. Take, for example, the photograph of Elvis and the Jordanaires featured in the 1956 discography. Taken in September 1956, it showed Ray Walker on the extreme right. Walker, however, did not join the Jordanaires until 1958 when he replaced Hugh Jarrett! The original photograph had been tampered with - supposedly as a joke - and, presumably, had not been intended for use.

On Thursday 27 May 1992 both producers - Semon and Jorgensen - took the hitherto unprecedented step of arranging one-to-one interviews with members of the music press, in order to answer specific points about the fifties' set, and to discuss the company's policy regarding Presley material in general. Extracts from the set were played to the journalists who were provided with tape cassette copies of the set and the booklet. (In fact, the tape copies of the set contained the outtake of *Your Cheatin' Heart* - something which was corrected by the time the albums were manufactured.) These interview sessions, held at BMG's London headquarters, were held at the express suggestion of the two producers.

Not surprisingly, the release generated a very high interest within the industry, in the media, and among fans in general. Radio promotion and publicity in the daily and music press exceeded that of any other Elvis release. And the responses were uniformly favourable; there was not a dissenting voice to be heard. Once again, not surprisingly, import copies of the set (from America) were available slightly ahead of the European release. The cost to fans not willing to wait for a domestic release, was anywhere from £75 to £83. *Elvis Monthly* advertised the European set for £62.99 plus P+P (and suggested that the set would consist of seven albums). However, when the set was actually released in early July 1992, its recommended retail price was £49.95. Some fans were able to purchase copies of the CD set for as low as £39.95. By the week beginning 13 July 1992, the set was presented as the Album of the Week on Radio 2. Yet, despite the high level of publicity and general interest, some major UK outlets failed to stock the album initially (notably Our Price, who later acknowledged this to be a mistake).

The US set (which only came in CD and cassette formats), came with a booklet measuring 12 inches by 6 inches, whereas European fans not only had the choice of a vinyl record version, but had an LP (12 inch x 12 inch) sized booklet. Considerable thought had been given as to whether or not a vinyl version would be made available at all. However, a persuasive case was presented for producing vinyl LPs (six of them, in this case), particularly as there was a sizeable core of fans dedicated to vinyl. It was decided that 15,000 individually numbered units would be pressed for consumption in Europe and the UK. However, 3,000 copies were exported to the USA to meet demands from collectors there. It was always made very clear though that no further pressings would be made; and that once supplies were exhausted, then that was it. Clearly, while the decision to press was not a foregone conclusion, it was heavily influenced by the extra sales revenue the set would generate, for no doubt a number of collectors would have purchased both a vinyl and CD version. Incidentally, the set was one of the last vinyl releases pressed by BMG at their own factory. By mid-1994 all 15,000 copies of the vinyl format had been sold, and in excess of a half million copies (all formats) had been sold worldwide! Not bad considering the initial press run for CD sets was a mere 30,000 copies!

Sequencing

While the set did include every master take recording known to have been cut in the '50s, the sequencing was not strictly chronological, as some might believe. Of course, in broad terms the tracks did run reasonably close to the order in which they were recorded (certainly as far as anyone knows), but the producers did feel the need to make some slight adjustments from time to time for reasons of pacing - something which it would be churlish to contest.

For example, there was good reason to suppose that Elvis cut *I Love You Because* prior to *That's All Right* (in July 1954), yet this was not observed in the running order. Similarly, it was always understood that *I Forgot To Remember To Forget* came before *Mystery Train*. Once again though, the two were reversed on the set. Now, interested readers can compare the running order on the albums with the discographical session information inside the booklet where close inspection reveals some adjustments to the 1 September 1956 session; the 21-22 January sessions; and the 5-7 September 1957 sessions - the latter done, presumably, to separate the secular and Christmas songs. Of course, there is no criticism implicit in this: simply that we believed the readers' attention ought to be drawn to this.

The album covers and labels

The cover shot of the set was a black and white photograph, almost certainly from June 1956. This shot had, in fact, been featured in the photo booklet which had accompanied the bootleg album *The Rockin' Rebel Vol. II*, first issued in 1979, although the photographs were wrongly dated to 1955.

On the right of the box front was a sticker advertising that this was part of a special limited vinyl edition (15,000 copies) which included three rare bonus photographs (in black and white) for framing. However, the photographs were not included with the CD set. Each set was also numbered and included a signed certificate of authenticity, signed by the President of RCA Records, Jo Galante, and the Senior Vice President, BMG International, Heinz Henn. The stickers for the LP and CD versions varied slightly. Common to both was the announcement that the set contained 'a sheet of RCA Records label four-color stamps..' (note the spelling of colour), which turned out to be inaccurate. The final page of the booklet also referred to these but, because there were no perforations just pictures, they could hardly be classed as stamps. Incidentally, the 1993 sixties' boxed set (**LP 319**) included actual stamps.

The wording on the back of the box read 'Contains every original master take released during the 1950's and many additional performances', was, of course, quite accurate. Yet, the same words failed to make it clear that all of the fifties' masters were included, including those released afterwards. Perhaps, it would have been better to have said 'every master take recorded in the fifties....'.

The three 10 inch x 8 inch photographs featured Elvis live on stage, playing his guitar; another of him playing piano on stage; and, finally a publicity pose, taken, it seems, in July 1955 as part of a photo session for Hungerford Furniture. All three were featured in the booklet. The shot of him playing the piano was from October 1957, taken in the Pan-Pacific Auditorium, Los Angeles. This photo was also used on the back cover of the *Rare And Rockin'* vinyl LP. The other photo of him playing guitar was from July 1955, and was featured in Ger Rijff's book *Long Lonely Highway*.

A minor criticism voiced by some (and acknowledged by the producers) was the use of flimsy paper to hold the vinyl albums. The paper was so thin that there appeared to be a constant threat of the edges of the vinyl poking through, just as there had been with the *Collectors Gold* (**LP 315**) set.

The back cover of the box listed the 140 tracks featured on the six vinyl albums. The script for album one (24 tracks) was in yellow; album two (24 tracks) was in pink; album three (22 tracks) was in green; album four (23 tracks) in a beige colour; album five (21 tracks) in blue; and, album six (26 tracks) in lilac. For both the vinyl LP and CD versions (6 albums and 5 albums respectively), *Rare And Rockin'* had exactly the same material, whereas the material on the remaining five vinyl albums were included on four CDs. The only previously unreleased material on the set not included in the *Rare And Rockin'* album was the unreleased portion of interviews from the *Elvis Sails* recordings, done in Brooklyn, New York, in September 1958, as Elvis was about to leave for Germany as part of his service in the US army. There were no production credits shown on the back of the box, unlike the sixties' boxed set (**LP 319**).

All of the labels featured the same simple layout, with side A displaying the '*Elvis The King Of Rock 'N' Roll*' logo above the centre hole, while '*The Complete Fifties Masters*' was at the bottom of the label, in a curve following the label contour. To the right of the label were the various company logos along with the date of publication. No titles were listed, and below the catalogue number on the right of the label it said 'Disc 1'. The label on the other side featured the front cover photograph of each album. All the lettering and photographs were coloured in the same shade (more or less) as the track listing on the back of the box itself.

The front cover shot of album one was from 1955, while the rear cover photo was from Louisville, Kentucky, 1955.

The front cover shot of album two was from the June 1956, West Coast tour, while the back shot was from Houston, Texas and dated from April 1956. This photo had appeared in Ger Riff and Jan van Gestel's 1991 publication, *Fire In The Sun*.

The front cover shot of album three featured a publicity head and shoulders pose from *Jailhouse Rock*. The back cover shot was taken during a press conference at the Sports Arena, Philadelphia, on 6 April 1957. This shot had also been featured in the book *Fire In The Sun*.

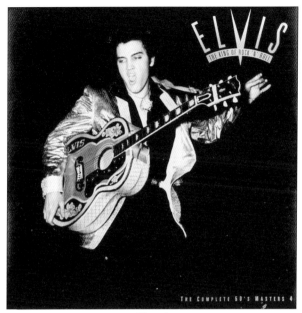

Album 4.

The photographs used on album four were unique to the covers of the vinyl albums - remember there were six vinyl albums compared to five CD albums, and this was where the extra photographs were used. The front cover featured another live on stage photo, this time said to be Spokane in Washington which, according to *All Shook Up - Elvis Day By Day* would make it 30 August 1957, the day before his performance in Vancouver, Canada. The back cover shot was taken in the recording studio during the *Jailhouse Rock* sessions in April/May 1957.

The cover of album five featured a vary rare shot of Elvis in his army uniform, playing Hank Garland's six-stringed Danelectro bass - the same one featured so prominently on *I Got Stung*. This was taken during the June 1958 Nashville sessions, held a few months after Elvis enlisted in the army. The back cover featured Elvis lying down on the steps outside his army barracks at Fort Hood, Texas, probably in March 1958.

The shot on the front of album six was probably taken in Houston, Texas in April 1956, while the rear cover shot (also one of the 10 inch x 8 inch photos included in the vinyl set) was from October 1957, taken in the Pan-Pacific Auditorium, Los Angeles.

Promotional material

A wealth of promotional material was produced in support of the set, including a special six track CD. There were also three individually numbered, framed posters (showing three album covers), produced as a limited - and very exclusive - edition. More readily visible were in-store LP and CD browser cards, but only the LP card carried the photograph of Elvis as featured on the front of the box. A poster showed all five CD front covers and featured the *Rare And Rockin'* photograph.

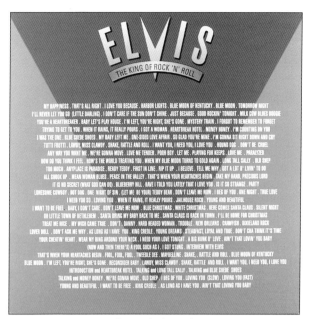

In-store display card.

The music

While few have criticised the set, it was inevitable that a project of such enormous scope involved some creative licence on the part of the producers. In particular, a relatively small number of fans voiced complaints at the small number of outtakes and/or unreleased songs included on the set, arguing that having to buy a six LP or five CD set to obtain previously unissued tracks, was unfair. This was, of course, a matter of personal judgement. However, those voicing such reservations missed the main point of the release: to re-issue in the best quality sound available the complete fifties' master tracks. Strictly speaking, the appearance of unreleased material, however much expected and gratefully received, was a bonus and, it must be said, a powerful motivator to buy the complete set. On the other hand, those who clamoured for more unreleased material missed two other key points. Firstly, that the company had no other unissued songs to include and, secondly, that there were no other suitable alternative versions which warranted release at that time. Remember, the three *Essential Elvis* series included many unreleased alternatives. The only other obvious possibilities concerned more outtakes of *Lawdy, Miss Clawdy* and *Shake, Rattle And Roll* (the only other fifties' 'finds' at the time), more from the likes of the *Essential Elvis* tapes and, finally, the song *Hearts Of Stone* which had been offered to RCA by a private individual. But, by all accounts, the price asked was too high and the sound quality too poor to warrant buying it at the time. However, it was finally included on the *Sunrise* CD, 07863 67675 2, issued in February 1999.

All argument aside: the fact was that around ten percent of the album comprised unreleased material - a significant proportion, given the project's main aim.

Clearly then, once the producers and the company had decided on a six LP/five CD configuration for the set, the running time assumed a critical importance in terms of what could or could not be added. And so, although the following tracks were not actually released during the fifties, they had to be included. (And here we are referring to material issued subsequently to the fifties, not the likes of the 1953 recording of *That's When Your Heartaches Begin*, which was premiered on this release.)

My Happiness. This was a private recording from 1953 and first issued in 1990 on *The Great Performances* (**LP 308**).

Harbour Lights. This song dated from July 1954, and was finally released in January 1976 on *Elvis - A Legendary Performer Vol. 2* (*LP 87*).

Tomorrow Night. This was, to all intents and purposes, the original undubbed version (thought to be in its original, unedited form), which was included on the May 1985 release, **Reconsider Baby** (*LP 271*) though it had been re-edited by engineer Rick Rowe on that occasion.

When It Rains, It Really Pours. This was the version Elvis cut at Sun in late 1955, but not actually known about or released until November 1983 on **Elvis - A Legendary Performer Vol. 4** (*LP 204*). Ironically, of course, even Elvis's February 1957 version, cut for RCA, was not issued until late 1965 on the album **Elvis For Everyone** (*LP 26*).

One Night Of Sin. This alternative and more lyrically risque version, recorded on 24 January 1957, was not issued until November 1983 when it appeared on **Elvis - A Legendary Performer Vol. 4** (*LP 204*).

Danny. This, the original 'theme' song from the film **King Creole**, made its debut in January 1979 on **Elvis - A Legendary Performer Vol. 3** (*LP 106*).

Your Cheatin' Heart. As with the February 1957 version of **When It Rains, It Really Pours**, this track made its debut on the 1965 album **Elvis For Everyone** (*LP 26*). This recording dated from the 1 February 1957 Radio Recorders session.

Tell Me Why. This track was recorded on 12 January 1957, also at Radio Recorders, but was not issued until November 1965 when it was the A side of **Puppet On A String** (*S 51*).

Ain't That Loving You Baby. This song had been released earlier, in October 1964, as a single (*S 47*). This song was one of the final tracks Elvis recorded in the 1950s (at least officially), cut in Nashville in June 1958, along with the likes of **(Now and then there's) A Fool Such As I**, **I Got Stung** and **A Big Hunk O' Love**.

On the other hand, for a variety of reasons - chief of which was probably space - the following fifties' tracks were not included on the set. Of course, in recent years, many outtakes had been issued and there was no sense in repeating all of them, but the key omissions are discussed briefly below. We must, however, make it clear that these observations are made for completeness and should not be construed as criticism.

I Love You Because. The 'original' version was a splice of takes 2 and 4. Takes 1-5 of the song were included in the July 1987 release **The Complete Sun Sessions** (**LP 283**).

That's All Right. In October 1984, as part of the six LP set **A Golden Celebration** (*LP 251*), RCA released an outtake (plus false starts) of Elvis's first commercial recording for Sun Records. Of course, this was later made available on CD as part of **The Sun Sessions** album - note that the CD version dropped the word 'Complete' because there were more tracks on the double vinyl album than on the CD.

I'll Never Let You Go (little darlin'). The same situation pertained to this outtake, also first issued officially in October 1984 as part of **A Golden Celebration** (*LP 251*).

I Don't Care If The Sun Don't Shine. As **I'll Never Let You Go (little darlin')**.

I'm Left You're Right, She's Gone (My Baby's Gone). Several takes of this song - takes 7-13 - were included on **The Complete Sun Sessions** (**LP 283**) vinyl album in 1987. Only take 11 of the song was included on the fifties' set, mainly because it was the only take not available thus far on CD (it had been omitted from the CD version of the Sun material). However, the first official appearance of this slower version appeared, once again, on **A Golden Celebration** (*LP 251*).

Tomorrow Night. Of course the 1965 over-dubbed version of the song (as featured on **Elvis For Everyone** (*LP 26*), was not a valid inclusion on the fifties' set. Indeed, as it turned out, for equally good reason, it was not included on the sixties' set **From Nashville To Memphis The Essential 60's Masters 1** (**LP 319**) either.

I Want You, I Need You, I Love You. The alternative version included on **Rare And Rockin'** was take 16. Not included though, was the previously issued outtake (wrongly thought to have been take 3), which had appeared as early as 1976 on **Elvis - A Legendary Performer Vol. 2** (*LP 87*).

Jailhouse Rock. RCA had issued an outtake (take 5) of this song on **Essential Elvis** (**LP 280**) in late 1986.

Young And Beautiful. Although take 3, from the soundtrack recording, was used on **Rare And Rockin'**, another outtake (take 12) was not used, as it had been on **Essential Elvis** (**LP 280**) also.

Treat Me Nice. The movie version of this song (recorded almost five months before the better known single version - cut in September 1957 and featured on the B side of the single **Jailhouse Rock** (*S 18*)), had been included on **Essential Elvis** (**LP 280**) in 1986. Nonetheless, because this was a legitimate alternative recording of the song (as opposed to an outtake recorded at the same session) - much the same as **One Night Of Sin** - then there were probably powerful reasons why it should have been included for the sake of completeness.

Doncha' Think It's Time. Arguably the take which had been the version accidentally included on **Elvis' Golden Records Vol. 2** (*LP 10*) in 1960 should also have been featured on the fifties' collection. However, as it had been included fairly recently on **Hits Like Never Before (Essential Elvis Vol. 3)** (**LP 306**), a decision was taken not to include it.

Your Cheatin' Heart. The alternative (and longer version) included on **Hits Like Never Before (Essential Elvis Vol. 3)** (**LP 306**) was also not featured.

Lover Doll. The same was true of the undubbed version of this song, which had also been on **Hits Like Never Before (Essential Elvis Vol. 3)** (**LP 306**).

Obviously there were other omissions too, especially from the soundtrack recordings **Loving You**, **Jailhouse Rock** and **King Creole** - all of which had been featured on one of the **Essential Elvis** series. Not surprisingly though, the producers saw no point in repeating all of the outtakes previously issued in this series, particularly as they were still on catalogue and, more pertinently, as there was simply not enough room to include them all.

Other alternative versions of fifties' songs not featured on the fifties' set included the following:

> **Got A Lot O' Livin' To Do!**
> **Loving You**
> both from **Essential Elvis** (**LP 280**)
>
> **I Believe**
> **(There'll be) Peace In The Valley (for me)**
> **I Beg Of You**
> **That's When Your Heartaches Begin**
> **It Is No Secret (what God can do)**
> **Blueberry Hill**
> **Have I Told You Lately That I Love You**
> **Is It So Strange**
> all from **Stereo '57 (Essential Elvis Volume 2)** (**LP 298**)

King Creole
I Need Your Love Tonight
A Big Hunk O' Love
Ain't That Loving You Baby
(Now and then there's) A Fool Such As I
I Got Stung

all from *Hits Like Never Before (Essential Elvis Vol. 3)* (**LP 306**)

Rare And Rockin'

Of special interest to serious fans and collectors was the LP record which featured the rare and previously unissued material. Of course, the unissued portion of the ***Elvis Sails*** interview material was tagged on to the end of album 5.

LP 6 contained 26 tracks, though 14 of them had not been issued officially before. We say 'officially' because, obviously to die-hard fans, some of the material had been available unofficially (i.e. on bootleg recordings) for some while. However, because of the rarity value of these tracks, we have elected to discuss each one separately.

That's When Your Heartaches Begin. This was on the other side of ***My Happiness***, Elvis's first private recording in 1953. It was entirely new to fans and was supplied to RCA by Ed Leek in 1989. The company used the latter side as a lead track of ***The Great Performances*** album (**LP 308**).

Fool, Fool, Fool. This was another previously unreleased track for the fans. Recorded in Lubbock, Texas in early 1955, it was done at a radio station, probably for promotional purposes. The producers obtained this track from an acetate source.

Tweedle Dee. A rare, though not unknown track to fans. This was an early performance from the Louisiana Hayride (thought to be Gladewater, Texas, 30 April 1955). It was first made available by RCA in July 1984 on ***The First Live Recordings*** (*LP 234*), though a number of fans had heard it on bootleg releases previously.

Maybellene. As with the above track, this was not new to fans, having been on ***The First Live Recordings*** (*LP 234*) also. This track was also cut for the Louisiana Hayride, in Shreveport, in August 1955.

Shake, Rattle And Roll. This too was an acetate recording also cut in Lubbock, Texas, at the same time as ***Fool, Fool, Fool***. Once again, this version was entirely new to fans.

Blue Moon Of Kentucky. This slow, country version had been issued previously on ***A Golden Celebration*** (*LP 251*) in October 1984, though it had appeared on bootleg records long before that.

Blue Moon. This was said to be take 1 of the July 1954 recording; this version was previously unissued.

I'm Left, You're Right, She's Gone. This was the slow version of the song, often referred to as ***My Baby's Gone***. Issued originally on ***A Golden Celebration*** (*LP 251*) in October 1984, this track (though not necessarily this take) had been available on bootleg recordings for some years. Later, in 1987, when RCA issued the erroneously titled ***The Complete Sun Sessions*** album (**LP 283**), the vinyl version featured takes 7, 8, 9, 10, 11, 12 and 13 of the song. Oddly though, the CD version of ***The Sun Sessions*** did not include take 11 which, for completeness, was included on the fifties' set, thus making its first appearance on CD. Only takes 7, 9 and 12 appeared on the CD ***The Sun Sessions*** (PD 86414).

Reconsider Baby. This was an entirely new find. This version was recorded at Sun studios on 4 December 1956 as part of the session which became known as The Million Dollar Quartet, not only was it previously unreleased, but was also never even rumoured to have been recorded. For some inexplicable reason, this song was separated from the rest of the informal jam session tape.

Lawdy, Miss Clawdy. This was a previously unreleased outtake (take 3) from Elvis's 2 February 1956 recording session. This find, along with outtakes of the studio version of ***Shake, Rattle And Roll***, was located in New York in November/December 1989.

Shake, Rattle And Roll. This outtake (take 8) was also found at the same time as the outtake of ***Lawdy, Miss Clawdy***. It was included because of the unusual piano break and the fact that Elvis sang some of the more risque lyrics on this version.

I Want You, I Need You, I Love You. This was take 16 of the song. Once again, it was a previously unissued performance. Remember there had been a version of the song included on ***Elvis - A Legendary Performer Vol. 2*** (*LP 87*) in 1976, which was thought to have been take 3. However, fans in possession of the bootleg CD ***When All Was Kool*** will know that the outtakes of this song, including take 3, were different again from the version on ***Elvis - A Legendary Performer Vol. 2***.

Heartbreak Hotel, ***Long Tall Sally***, ***Blue Suede Shoes*** and ***Money Honey***. These were four live versions of the songs recorded on 6 May 1956 at the New Frontier Hotel, Las Vegas. They were first made available on ***Elvis Aron Presley*** (*LP 126*) in August 1980.

We're Gonna Move. This was a previously unreleased performance - take 4 - from the ***Love Me Tender*** film sessions, held on 24 August 1956 at 20th Century Fox, Stage 1, Hollywood.

Old Shep. This was the previously unreleased version of the song - take 5 - recorded on 26 September 1956, at Radio Recorders, Hollywood. Rumours that this version had been issued inadvertently on ***Rock 'N' Roll (No. 2)*** (*LP 2*) have never been substantiated. Instead, we believe it far more likely that it was included on a batch of US albums (LPM 1282) which were available from the UK fan club in 1960.

I Beg Of You. This version, said to be take 12, cut on 13 January 1957, had been available in a binaural form on ***Stereo '57 (Essential Elvis Volume 2)*** (**LP 298**) in January 1989. This time, however, BMG released the original mono mix of the track.

Loving You. (Slow version). This version, take 12, was from the 14 February 1957 soundtrack recording session, and was previously unreleased. Take 10 of the slow version had been included on ***Essential Elvis*** (**LP 280**), released in December 1986.

Loving You. (Fast version). This was also an unreleased performance (take 13) from 14 February 1957. Previously, take 1 of this fast version had been on ***Essential Elvis*** (**LP 280**).

Young And Beautiful. This was a previously unreleased alternative recording of the song - take 3 - recorded on 30 April 1957 at Radio Recorders, Hollywood, as part of the ***Jailhouse Rock*** sessions. Elvis played guitar on this track. This was the film version.

I Want To Be Free. This too was previously unreleased officially. It was take 10 from the 3 May 1957 session, and was the 'straight' version as used in the film soundtrack.

King Creole. This was take 3 from the 15 January 1958 recording session (an alternative master recording). And although this take (and take 18) had been released in 1990 on ***Hits Like Never Before (Essential Elvis Vol. 3)*** (**LP 306**), the sound quality on this was improved, as the previously released version had been from a lacquer source.

As Long As I Have You. The same applies to this song too. This version - take 8 - had also been on ***Hits Like Never Before (Essential Elvis Vol. 3)*** (**LP 306**), but only from a lacquer source. This was a better quality version.

Ain't That Loving You Baby. (Fast version). This was take 11, as included on ***Hits Like Never Before (Essential Elvis Vol. 3)*** (**LP 306**), notable because it was shorter than the version originally included on *Reconsider Baby* (*LP 271*) - which was, in fact, a spliced version - and had only two guitar breaks in the song.

Tape Sources

One of the most exciting and interesting aspects of the fifties' set was that, for the first time for more than 35 years, the producers (Semon and Jorgensen) were able to search out and use original tape sources for almost all of the material featured on the set. And, while making aural comparisons is subjective and beyond our brief in this book, there are few who would dissent from the view that, overall, the sound quality bettered anything we had had before.

However, sadly, not all the tracks were from first generation masters, and where they were not available, the producers had then to use the next best sources available. Not surprisingly, the Sun material presented the most problems in this respect. And, according to Ernst Mikael Jorgensen in June 1994, only the following Sun tracks were direct from masters:

> *Mystery Train*
> *I Forgot To Remember To Forget*
> *Blue Moon*
> *Just Because*
> *Tomorrow Night*
> *I'll Never Let You Go (little darlin')*

All the rest were copies.

More surprisingly though, was the revelation that four tracks from 1956 were not from masters either:

> *I Want You, I Need You, I Love You*
> *Hound Dog*
> *Don't Be Cruel*
> *Any Way You Want Me (that's how I will be)*

Further, *Treat Me Nice* had to be repaired, while the long lost *Danny* had to be dubbed from a film soundtrack source - 35mm tape - which was a common way of storing information. However, Jorgensen acknowledged that the sound quality on this track was poor, but as it was the only available copy, it had to be used.

As regards some of the unreleased performances, Jorgensen elaborated on how and where they were found. The outtake of *Blue Moon* (one of a number found) was filed under its correct number but in a separate room in the vault at New York. The version of *Reconsider Baby* from The Million Dollar Quartet was found on a tape bought from Colonel Parker. Don Wardell had negotiated the purchase of the tape from another source not realising that the company had it already! Jorgensen says that essentially the tape was the same as the one issued by BMG; there were a few more minutes of it, that's all.

The outtakes of *Shake, Rattle And Roll* and *Lawdy, Miss Clawdy* were also located in the vaults in New York. The outtake of *I Want You, I Need You, I Love You* had been found on a Hank Snow tape; while the alternative version of *We're Gonna Move* had been provided by Ernst Mikael Jorgensen from one of his own sources.

Label and sleeve errors

There should be no doubt in anyone's mind that a great deal of care and attention had gone into the production of this collection. Therefore, when we approached the point of looking for label and sleeve errors, we did so with some trepidation. After all, we only had one minor quibble with the rest of the package - the paper quality of the inner sleeves. What about label and sleeve errors? Quite simply, the same thought and effort that obviously went in to produce this quality package had been applied to the area of song titles and their writers. To achieve standardisation, considerable revision of writers' names and song titles had been carried out at the highest level within BMG, reversing the previous practice of simply carrying forward

sloppy errors. We can modestly report that our own efforts in *Elvis UK 1956-86* contributed to this change of policy, and we know that BMG referred to original US label information in arriving at their final decisions.

And, what a refreshing change it was to report that there were no, repeat no, glaringly obvious and annoying errors as there had been in the past. There was no *I'm All Shook Up* to criticise, no *One Night With You*, no *Don't Be Cruel To A Heart That's True*. Yes, we do have some points to draw to your attention, but these are very minor, and, perhaps, we should consider these more differences of opinion than errors. In fact, this release more than any other, caused us to reconsider our stance with regard to some song titles and writers' names. We have always said that we had reservations about certain titles, and in *Elvis UK 1956-86* we stuck our necks out on several occasions. The point we made then, and will make again here, was that we tried to achieve a consistency that had rarely been applied elsewhere. All of us will have different views about what is right and what is wrong, and sometimes there are no hard and fast rules to follow, and this is what we have tried to establish. Our logic was that the song's title and the writers given on the song's first UK record appearance was correct, unless we knew for certain that an error had been made. Taking an extreme example: if the writer of *Yesterday* was given as Roger Semon, we would straight away say that was wrong! But, if it was the writer of an Elvis track which had been recorded by no-one else, we would have little option to accept that name as being accurate. However, we are not saying that we have to automatically accept the information given on the label, or sleeve, of a song's first UK appearance. Indeed, during the early stages of our work we endeavoured to cross-check these details, wherever this was possible.

What had occurred with the release of *The King Of Rock 'N' Roll The Complete 50's Masters* was twofold; firstly, many of the annoying errors had been correctly sorted out. Secondly, the discrepancies between what first appeared on American releases and on UK releases were highlighted. In addition, inspired by what we saw, we looked again at our files and readily admit that we too were guilty of perpetuating errors - often our own. In short, we made some mistakes. Therefore, in a departure from our normal method of reporting errors, we have listed below the differences we have noted, action we have taken (with the reason), and where we still believe an error has been made.

That's All Right. We previously considered the full title to be *That's All Right (Mama)*, but now accept that the word in brackets should not be shown. *(Mama)* did not appear on the label of *Rock 'N' Roll*, HMV CLP 1093 (*LP 1*), the song's first UK appearance, nor did it on the Sun original. Even more importantly, Crudup's own version, recorded in 1946, excluded the word *(Mama)*.

Harbour Lights. When this song first appeared in the UK in 1976 on *Elvis - A Legendary Performer Vol. 2* (*LP 87*), the American spelling of *Harbor* had been anglicised. Technically both are correct, but we have decided to retain the normal English spelling, although we do acknowledge that this is not an error.

Blue Moon. The writing team of Rodgers and Hart has always appeared in that order. We believe, therefore, to show Hart, Rodgers is an error, irrespective of how they were shown on the original American label.

Baby Let's Play House. We now believe that showing a comma after the word *Baby* is not correct. This was not shown on the March 1957 single, HMV POP 305 (*S 9*) (the song's first UK appearance), nor on the original Sun single.

Tutti Frutti. The name Lubin was added to those of LaBostrie and Penniman on the original UK single, HMV 7M 405 (*S 2*), as did many other references, except for Little Richard's original! With that in mind, we believe that to include the name Lubin is incorrect.

We're Gonna Move, *Love Me Tender*, *Poor Boy* and *Let Me*. We have always shown the 'writers' - Matson, Presley - in that order, but now accept that they should be the other way around. Presley,

Matson is the order in which they appeared on UK originals - **Love Me Tender** on an HMV single, POP 253 (*S 6*), in December 1956, and all four songs on the **Love Me Tender** EP, 7EG 8199 (*EP 1*), in February 1957. We cannot be certain now, but we think our original decision was influenced by the normal practice of placing Elvis's name after people like Axton, Durden, and on other songs where Elvis's name was added in order to warrant a part share of writers' royalties.

Long Tall Sally. A minor point, we agree, but the order of Johnson, Blackwell, Penniman should be Johnson, Penniman, Blackwell. At least this is how they appeared on the first RCA release in the UK to include the track - RD/SF 7528, **Rock 'N' Roll (No.2)** (*LP 17*), in December 1962. But, the song's first appearance in the UK was on the HMV album of the same name, CLP 1105 (*LP 2*), in April 1957, when the writer was shown as Johnson only!

Old Shep. This is another tricky one. The song's appearance on the HMV **Rock 'N' Roll (No. 2)**, CLP 1105 (*LP 2*), credited Foley, Arthur, whereas all RCA listings show Red Foley only. Yet other sources referred to Willis Arthur as being co-writer, the most important of which being Foley's own recording, from 1946 (the song dated back to 1933).

That's When Your Heartaches Begin. When this song was first issued in the UK as the B side of **All Shook Up** (*S 11*), the writers were shown as Raskin, Brown, Fisher. However, on **Elvis' Golden Records**, RB 16069 (*LP 7*), released in October 1958, the writers referred to on the label were Fisher, Hill, Raskin, whereas the sleeve notes referred to Raskin, Brown, Fisher. And to confuse matters further, subsequent re-issues have referred to Fisher and Hill only. By 1999 BMG were using Raskin, Brown, Fisher on **Sunrise**, 07863 67675 2, a CD only release. We have also opted to use Raskin, Brown, Fisher.

One Night Of Sin/One Night. We know that the Smiley Lewis original was entitled **One Night**, so **One Night Of Sin** cannot be the correct title, but we acknowledge the usefulness of separating this version from the later hit, and so, we have decided to adopt this title also, but placing the words **Of Sin** in brackets would have been preferable. In addition to the title, RCA spell the co-writers name Bartholemew, the way the name was shown on the very first pressing of the UK original single **One Night**, RCA 1100 (*S 25*), in January 1959. Later pressings correctly, we believe, changed the 'e' to an 'o', reading Bartholomew. We think, therefore, that the sleeve contains an error.

(You're so square) Baby I Don't Care. It was pleasing to see the official adoption of the words in brackets, but the question regarding whether there should be a comma after the word **Baby** remains. As there was no comma included on the UK original - the **Jailhouse Rock** EP, RCX 106 (*EP 5*) - we decided to ignore it. However, we should point out though that the words in brackets were not shown either!

Here Comes Santa Claus (right down Santa Claus lane). The name Melka has always been associated with those of Autry and Haldeman, right from the first appearance of the song on **Elvis' Christmas Album**, RD 27052 (*LP 5*), in November 1957. Why the name should not appear here remains uncertain but, presumably, the writing team featured were referred to on the US original. We see no reason to change and consider this omission an error.

Silent Night. The origins of this song date back to the early 1800s and a Austrian poem entitled **Stille Nacht, Heilige Nacht**, and on many early recordings the full English title was used. Later the abbreviated title was substituted, and because this was how the title appeared on Elvis's records, this is the title we use.

O Little Town Of Bethlehem. According to the story, pastor Phillips Brooks wrote a poem with this title and asked church organist Lewis Redner to write the music for it. RCA's order seems to follow the convention of placing the writer of the music first followed by the lyricist, and we accept this to be correct.

I'll Be Home For Christmas (if only in my dreams). The words in brackets were included when the song first appeared on **Elvis' Christmas Album**, RD 27052 (*LP 5*), in November 1957, but were not featured on the US original. Why this should be the case is something we cannot answer, but it does seem strange that the UK division thought the additional words necessary. Then again, the same source inexplicably changed **I Got A Woman** to **I Got A Sweetie**! Rightly or wrongly, we have retained the words in brackets. Also, the original (and consistent) order in which the writers have been shown is Kent, Gannon, Ram - not Ram, Kent, Gannon. We have retained the original order.

Ain't That Loving You Baby. The order Otis, Hunter has normally been applied, not the other way around, and we consider Hunter, Otis to be an error.

Claude DeMetrius. Readers of our original book **Elvis UK 1956-86** will know that we frequently referred to Claude as being the chief victim when it came to incorrect spelling of surnames. We have always believed the correct spelling to be DeMetrius, and here we have RCA again using the incorrect, or so we believe, De Metruis. We are sticking with our interpretation. The songs written (or co-written) by Claude on this set were as follows:

> **I Was The One**
> **Mean Woman Blues**
> **Santa Bring My Baby Back (to me)**
> **Hard Headed Woman**

Summary

By now you will have realised that we have been considering very minor details, and, we have to agree, issues that have no bearing on the quality of the recordings. But, in terms of accuracy (a basis of all our work), we have tried to explain our logic, however bizarre this might seem. Where does this then leave us in terms of errors? As we reported at the outset, there are few, irrespective of whether we made any amendments to our listings. Yet, we believe the following errors remain:

The writers of **Blue Moon** should appear as Rodgers, Hart and not the other way around.

The writers of **Long Tall Sally** ought to be Johnson, Penniman, Blackwell.

Foley and Arthur wrote **Old Shep**.

One Night/One Night Of Sin was written by Dave Bartholomew.

The writers of **Here Comes Santa Claus (right down Santa Claus lane)** were Autry, Haldeman, Melka.

I'll Be Home For Christmas (if only in my dreams) includes the words in brackets.

Ain't That Loving You Baby - the writers should appear as Otis, Hunter.

Claude DeMetrius!

Where we have agreed that our previously published listings contained an error, an amendment has been made to the song index at the back of the book. In addition, all references to the songs/writers affected throughout the book have been amended accordingly.

Postscript To The King Of Rock 'N' Roll The Complete 50's Masters

One obvious consequence of BMG issuing the complete fifties' boxed set was that it rendered a number of albums - both vinyl and CD - redundant. Of course, avid collectors/completists may well have retained their copies 'for old times' sake'. Out of interest though, we would like to list the albums which could have been dispensed with, and those which needed to be retained to have all the outtakes/alternative performances from the fifties' period. There was no problem with sound quality as the fifties' set surpassed all previous releases. Note that we have shown the last issue of the albums in question.

Albums Not Needed

> *The Elvis Presley Sun Collection*, NL 89107 (*LP 201*)
>
> *Elvis Presley Rock 'N' Roll No. 1*, NL 89046 (*LP 267*)
>
> *Elvis Rock 'N' Roll No. 2*, NL 81382 (*LP 211*)
>
> *Loving You*, NL 81515 (*LP 210*)
>
> *Elvis' Christmas Album*, NL 90300 (**LP 312**) *
>
> *King Creole*, NL 83733 (*LP 212*)
>
> *Elvis' Golden Records*, NL 81707 (*LP 232*)
>
> *Elvis' Golden Records Volume 2*, NL 89429 (*LP 253*)
>
> *A Date With Elvis*, NL 90360 (**LP 304**)
>
> *For LP Fans Only*, NL 90359 (**LP 303**)

* Note: there was the 20 seconds studio chat before **White Christmas** to be considered on the 1985 re-release of this album.

Albums To Be Retained

Please note: the following list refers to albums needed at the point the fifties' set was released - it may be that subsequent CD releases included some of the tracks in question.

> 1. **The Complete Sun Sessions**, PL 86414(2) (**LP 283**)

To have all of the available out-takes of *I'm Left, You're Right, She's Gone (My Baby's Gone)* - takes 7-13 (LP only); and of *I Love You Because* - takes 3-5.

Additionally, there was the alternative *That's All Right*, *When It Rains It Really Pours*, *Blue Moon Of Kentucky*, *I Don't Care If The Sun Don't Shine*, and *I'll Never Let You Go (little darlin')*. However, *When It Rains It Really Pours* and take 11 of *I'm Left, You're Right, She's Gone* were included on the fifties' set.

> 2. **Essential Elvis**, PL 89979 (**LP 280**)

This was necessary for the following outtakes: take 5 of *Jailhouse Rock*; take 12 of *Young And Beautiful*; take 10 of *Treat Me Nice* (original mono mix); take 10 of *Loving You* (slow version); takes 1, 20 and 21 of *Loving You* (fast version); as well as the film version of *Jailhouse Rock* (i.e. the standard version, take 6, with overdubs). On the CD version (PD 89980), there were another two versions of *Loving You* - one fast, one slow, takes 8 and 1 respectively. This was the only album to also include the end title version of *Love Me Tender*.

> 3. **Stereo '57 (Essential Elvis Volume 2)**, PL 90250 (**LP 298**)

This was essential for the binaural versions of the following: *(There'll be) Peace In The Valley (for me)* (takes 2, 3, 7); *I Beg Of You* (takes 1, 6, 8, 12); *That's When Your Heartaches Begin* (takes 4, 5, 6); *It Is No Secret (what God can do)* (takes 1, 2, 3); *Blueberry Hill* (takes 2, 7); *Have I Told You Lately That I Love You* (takes 2, 6, 12, 13); *Is It So Strange* (takes 1, 7, 11); *I Believe* (take 4). Note: take 12 of *I Beg Of You* (mono mix) was also included on the fifties' set.

The version of *Mean Woman Blues* (take 14) was the standard issue, though it was issued in binaural for the first time on this album. And, unlike the fifties' set version, although the track faded towards the end it did actually stop. Further, the 'dub' version of this song - where part of Elvis's vocal had been edited from the track to simulate a partial instrumental version - could only be found on either the CD or 12 inch version of the single issued a short while after the album.

> 4. **Hits Like Never Before (Essential Elvis Vol. 3)**, PL 90486 (**LP 306**)

This vinyl album and/or CD was needed for the following tracks: *King Creole* (take 18); *I Got Stung* (takes 1, 13, 14); *(Now and then there's) A Fool Such As I* (take 3); *Wear My Ring Around Your Neck* (take 22 - undubbed version); *Your Cheatin' Heart* (take 9); *Ain't That Loving You Baby* (takes 1, 5); *I Need Your Love Tonight* (takes 2, 5, 10); *Lover Doll* (take 7 - undubbed version); *Crawfish* (take 7 - which included Kitty White's vocal); *A Big Hunk O' Love* (take 1); *Steadfast, Loyal And True* (take 6); and the LP version of *Doncha' Think It's Time* (take 40), first issued on *Elvis' Golden Records Vol 2.* (*LP 10*).

The CD (PD 90486) version had, in addition to the above, *I Got Stung* (take 12); *As Long As I Have You* (take 4), and an instrumental version of *King Creole* (take 8).

Please note: take 3 of *King Creole* (also on this album) was in much better quality on the fifties' set, as was take 8 of *As Long As I Have You*. Take 11 of *Ain't That Loving You Baby* was also included. And to have another outtake of *I Need Your Love Tonight* (take 9), the single *Don't Be Cruel*, 74321 11077 7 (**S 179**), issued in August 1992, was also required.

The details above covered all of the official fifties' releases i.e. studio and film recordings. However, this list does not include live recordings from this era, made on stage (e.g. Louisiana Hayride), or TV shows.

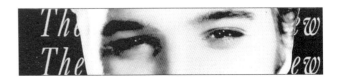

Fifties' Material Issued Subsequent To The King Of Rock 'N' Roll The Complete 50's Masters

Inevitably, despite the best efforts of the producers of the fifties' set, other material pertinent to this era surfaced following its release in July 1992. Indeed, no-one was surprised that this happened, as the search for previously unissued material was an on-going task.

A particularly interesting find was the discovery of some outtakes (unreleased performances) from Elvis's first RCA session in January 1956. In April 1996, the album **Elvis 56** (**LP 321**) included an unreleased performance of **Heartbreak Hotel** (take 5), while in May 1996, a four track single (**S 181**) was released (in vinyl and CD form) which also included take 5 of **Heartbreak Hotel**, in addition to what was said to be take 2 of **I Was The One**. Strictly speaking, this probably ought to have been referred to as take 3, as in late 1998, Time-Life, in conjunction with BMG in the USA, included the same version but with two false starts - hence the belief that the full run-through was, in fact, take 3.

Then, in April 1997, as a continuing part of their restoration and revision of back catalogue items, BMG reissued the **Loving You** and **King Creole** albums, with additional tracks (in CD form only), using for the first time the first generation master tapes as used on the fifties' set. However, of much greater interest to collectors was the **Jailhouse Rock** CD (07863 67453 2) which included some previously unheard versions of fifties' songs. They were as follows:

Don't Leave Me Now (track 11) - alternative master
Love Me Tender (track 16) - stereo version*
Let Me (track 17) - 'solo' - no backing track
We're Gonna Move (track 18) - take 9 (the master, but in stereo)
Poor Boy (track 19) - an edited (shortened) version of the master in stereo

* The stereo version of **Love Me Tender** had been originally released on a compilation album called **Heart And Soul**, a US only release from February 1995.

Please note, in early 2002 Castle Music issued a vinyl version of **Jailhouse Rock** (**LP 343**).

However, in July 1997, BMG released the 4 CD set **Platinum A Life In Music** (07863 67469 2) which comprised almost all unreleased performances. Devotees of fifties' material were pleased to note the inclusion of yet more previously unissued versions from the era. They were as follows:

I'll Never Stand In Your Way - private recording from January 1954
Blue Moon - another previously unreleased version
I Got A Woman - alternative take from the first RCA session
Heartbreak Hotel - take 6
I'm Counting On You - take 13
Lawdy, Miss Clawdy - take 1
I Want You, I Need You, I Love You - take 4
Rip It Up - take 15
When The Saints Go Marching In - informal recording from December 1956
(There'll be) Peace In The Valley (for me) - take 3. This take was listed as being on **Stereo '57 (Essential Elvis Volume 2)** (**LP 298**), but it was not the same one. Jorgensen's book **A Life In Music** quotes this as take 4
Blueberry Hill - acetate from early 1957
I Need Your Love Tonight - take 7

A Big Hunk O' Love - take 4

Bad Nauheim Medley - I'll Take You Home Again Kathleen, **I Will Be True**, **It's Been So Long Darling**, **Apron Strings**, and **There's No Tomorrow** - home recordings, circa 1958/59.

Further unreleased performances were included on the CD only release **Sunrise** (07863 67675 2) in February 1999. These were:

It Wouldn't Be The Same Without You - private recording from January 1954
I'm Left, You're Right, She's Gone
That's All Right
Money Honey
Tweedle Dee
I Don't Care If The Sun Don't Shine
Hearts Of Stone

- all live recordings from 1955

Yet more unreleased performances were issued, again on CD only, in March 1999 when **The Home Recordings**, 07863 67676 2, was released. As the title clearly showed, these were private recordings, not intended for commercial use. The unissued '50s recordings were as follows:

When The Saints Go Marching In - private recording, said to be from 1956.

I Understand How You Feel - private recording from 1958.

I Asked The Lord - private recording from 1959. This version is different from the one that appeared on **A Golden Celebration** (**LP 251**), when the song was listed as **He's Only A Prayer Away**. (Incidentally, BMG listed the song's title as **I Asked The Lord (He's only a prayer away)** on the 1998 CD issue of **A Golden Celebration**, 07863 67456 2.

The emergence of the Collector's Label CD releases in July 1999 opened new possibilities for previously unreleased performances to be issued. The second release in the series, **Out In Hollywood** (October 1999), included the vocal overdub track for **(You're so square) Baby I Don't Care**, recorded on 9 May 1957.

In A Private Moment (January 2000). the third release in the same series, included private recordings made in 1959 when Elvis was stationed in Germany: a very short version of **Loving You**, **Danny Boy** and another version of **I'm Beginning To Forget You**.

The **Easter Special** CD released in 2001 included a binaural version of **It Is No Secret (what God can do)** (take 12), while **Silver Screen Stereo**, issued in late 2001, included binaural versions of **Loving You** (fast version - take 14), **Jailhouse Rock** (take 5) and **Don't Leave Me Now** (takes 16, 17, & 18).

Tape Sources For Future Releases

Apart from the obvious artistic merit of the fifties' boxed set, one key issue not to be overlooked was that, wherever possible, the producers of the set located and used the master tapes of songs or, alternatively, the best quality copies available at the time. Undoubtedly, the time and trouble expended to do this paid off handsomely, in that the set could legitimately boast having the fifties' material presented in a better quality of sound than ever before.

Of course, there was a further advantage too, in that all future releases bearing any of the tracks re-mastered for this set would probably use these newly established masters, and not the third rate (or worse) copies from which other previous compilations were compiled. Thankfully, this quite scandalous situation ought not to happen again, as those responsible for releases had taken all steps to ensure that inferior and now redundant copy tapes had been disposed of. And, as the early 1990s saw an increasing degree of cooperation and co-ordination among the company divisions throughout the world - there were far fewer 'local' releases, peculiar to one area, than before - hopefully there would be less chance of any sub-standard copies being used. On the other hand, existing items on catalogue and back catalogue re-issues had not normally been remastered from the master tapes. It was expected that as BMG issued the definitive sixties' and seventies' collections though, including all the film soundtrack items, then within a few years - perhaps by the mid-nineties - the whole back catalogue would have been restored in the highest possible sound quality. On the other hand, as Roger Semon did point out, if any division - or representative of the company - was to by-pass the agreed system for releases i.e. via the Committee, then errors would be likely to occur. Hopefully though, this ought not to happen, particularly in the US, UK and European regions.

In 1997, there was a long overdue sorting out of back catalogue titles which comprised fifties' material. Up to this point, the film albums *Loving You* and *King Creole*, along with the first two volumes in the *Elvis' Golden Records* series, had still been available to buy (on CD at least) though not in the sound quality evident on the fifties' set. However, in 1997, true to his word, Roger Semon announced that the albums mentioned above would be remastered and revised to include extra tracks. There were other albums from this era not part of this restoration plan at that point in time, although as part of the 'Artist Of The Century' programme for 1999, the original two album releases were scheduled to receive the same sort of treatment, both in terms of sound quality and contents. Essentially, the only fifties' album not to receive this special treatment then was *Elvis' Christmas Album*, although it had been 're-launched' in October 1985 (*LP 275*); and then in 1994 all the Christmas material (from the whole of Elvis's career) had been compiled on one CD release *If Every Day Was Like Christmas* (07863 66482 2). The remastered fifties' tracks were, of course, included. However, the eight original christmas songs from 1957 appeared on the 10inch *I'll Be Home For Christmas* (**LP 399**).

The Lost Performances

The concept of a planned, co-ordinated series of video and audio releases had taken a step forward in August 1990 when *The Great Performances*, PL 82227 (**LP 308**), was issued. This was a new and potentially very exciting concept for the fans, even though other artists and their companies had realised the sales potential of such a marketing plan years before.

Unfortunately, in August 1992, when outtakes from the films *That's The Way It Is* and *Elvis On Tour* were released on video under the title *The Lost Performances*, BMG elected not to issue a complementary audio package, although they had talked about doing so. Thus, it was left to the bootleggers, who simply copied the video soundtrack and mastered a CD for release. A number of fans were saddened by this apparently wasted opportunity. On the other hand, it had to be remembered that at this time BMG's release schedule was set. Unlike the bootleggers, who could respond to a perceived need in the market very quickly - probably because they are, in the main, low volume and do not need to observe the niceties of a balanced, carefully rationalised and agreed release programme - the company chose not to rush into a release when all the attention was on the highly prestigious boxed set *The King Of Rock 'N' Roll The Complete 50's Masters*. One view expressed by Roger Semon was that, as an album, *The Lost Performances* would not have had a great deal of impact, as most of the songs were in a similar vein. Ernst Mikael Jorgensen agreed, saying that when the company did decide to release an audio set, it would probably include material not used in the video, which would have the effect of strengthening the set.

Later, in August 2000 Castle Music issued the five LP set *"That's The Way It Is"* (LP 328) which included many unissued tracks from 1970.

Album Deletion - November 1992

NL 89004, *Elvis Forever* (**LP 277**), was deleted in November 1992, having survived, almost unnoticed, for over six years.

Album Deletions - December 1992

A further four Elvis albums were deleted in December 1992, all of which had been released after 1986. Sadly, *Essential Elvis* (**LP 280**) was one of them - confirmation, if it was needed, that the vinyl format could no longer compete with the overwhelming popularity of compact discs. The four albums were:

NL 83892	*Elvis In Person At The International Hotel Las Vegas, Nevada*	Oct 1991	**LP 316**
PL 86221(2)	*The Memphis Record*	Aug 1987	**LP 284**
PL 86414(2)	*The Complete Sun Sessions*	Jul 1987	**LP 283**
PL 89979	*Essential Elvis*	Dec 1986	**LP 280**

The Elvis Album Catalogue - January 1993

At the beginning of January 1993, following the major deletion programme of 1992, the number of Elvis albums still available had been reduced to a mere fourteen (or thirteen if you counted the *Romantic Elvis/Rockin' Elvis - The Sixties* package as one album).

Only two other albums, both doubles, had survived from the pre-1986 era - *Elvis In Concert* and *This Is Elvis* (*LPs 273* and *226*).

Below is a complete listing of Elvis albums held on catalogue by BMG as at 1 January 1993.

Catalogue Number	Title	Release Date	
PL 82227	*The Great Performances*	Aug 1990	**LP 308**
PL 82587(2)	*Elvis In Concert*	Aug 1985	*LP 273*
BL 84031(2)	*This Is Elvis*	May 1984	*LP 226*
PL 89124	*Romantic Elvis**	Apr 1984	*LP 220*
PL 89132	*Rockin' Elvis - The Sixties**	Apr 1984	*LP 221*
NL 89830(6)	*Elvis Forever - 96 Hits Of The King*	Aug 1987	**LP 285**
PL 90100(2	*Presley - The All Time Greatest Hits*	Aug 1987	**LP 287**
CL 90249(3)	*Special Edition*	Oct 1988	**LP 297**
PL 90250	*Stereo '57 (Essential Elvis Volume 2)*	Jan 1989	**LP 298**
PL 90486	*Hits Like Never Before (Essential Elvis Vol. 3)*	Jul 1990	**LP 306**
NL 90513	*For The Asking (The Lost Album)*	Nov 1990	**LP 309**
PL 90574(3)	*Collectors Gold*	Aug 1991	**LP 315**
PL 90642	*From The Heart*	Feb 1992	**LP 317**
PL 90689(6)	*The King Of Rock 'N' Roll The Complete 50's Masters*	Jul 1992	**LP 318**

* To be sold together as 'a buy one, get one free'.

The most significant album releases since 1986, with the exception of *Essential Elvis* (**LP 280**) (deleted in December 1992), had survived, including the flagship, *Presley - The All Time Greatest Hits* (**LP 287**), but so too had some of the least successful releases. The rather specialised boxed sets - *Elvis Forever - 96 Hits Of The King* (**LP 285**), and *Special Edition* (**LP 297**) were also still available, not because of their success, rather the lack of it. These were the original copies and were available because they had sold poorly compared to *Presley - The All Time Greatest Hits*.

During 1993 the deletion programme continued, and most of the albums on the above list failed to survive.

Album Deletion - March 1993

One of the great dinosaurs in BMG's Elvis catalogue was the six LP boxed set ***Elvis Forever - 96 Hits Of The King***, NL 89830(6), (**LP 285**), which had been released in August 1987. The set had not sold particularly well, and had remained on BMG's catalogue as a consequence of this.

Album Deletions - April 1993

A further three (or four, depending on how you class them) vinyl albums were deleted in April 1993, including the longest surviving LPs on RCA's Elvis catalogue. The two record collection ***Romantic Elvis/Rockin' Elvis - The Sixties***, (*LPs 220* and *221*), sold together as a 'Buy one, get one free' set, had been issued in April 1984, and had, therefore, survived for exactly nine years at the time they were deleted.

The two other deletions were much more recent. Both ***Hits Like Never Before (Essential Elvis Vol. 3)*** (**LP 306**), and ***For The Asking (The Lost Album)*** (**LP 309**), had been released in 1990.

Catalogue Numbers

The new format - whereby the catalogue number took on dual identity with the bar code - first appeared on the RCA single of ***Don't Be Cruel*** (**S 179**), issued in August 1992. The change did not appear on a vinyl LP until September 1993 when ***From Nashville To Memphis The Essential 60's Masters 1*** (**LP 319**) was released, although the new system was used when four Double Feature CDs were issued in March 1993. For further information regarding the new catalogue numbering system see the notes in the introduction.

221

LP 319 From Nashville To Memphis The Essential 60's Masters 1

RCA 74321 15430 1

Record 1

Side 1

1. **Make Me Know It** (Blackwell)
2. **Soldier Boy** (Jones, Williams Jnr.)
3. **Stuck On You** (Schroeder, McFarland)
4. **Fame And Fortune** (Wise, Weisman)
5. **A Mess Of Blues** (Pomus, Shuman)
6. **It Feels So Right** (Wise, Wiseman)
7. **Fever** (Davenport, Cooley)
8. **Like A Baby** (Stone)
9. **It's Now Or Never** (DiCapua, Schroeder, Gold)
10. **The Girl Of My Best Friend** (Ross, Bobrick)
11. **Dirty, Dirty Feeling** (Leiber, Stoller)

Side 2

1. **Thrill Of Your Love** (Kesler)
2. **I Gotta Know** (Evans, Williams)
3. **Such A Night** (Chase)
4. **Are You Lonesome Tonight?** (Turk, Handman)
5. **Girl Next Door Went A'Walking** (Rice, Wayne)
6. **I Will Be Home Again** (Benjamin, Leveen, Singer)
7. **Reconsider Baby** (Fulson)
8. **Surrender** (DeCurtis, Pomus, Shuman)
9. **I'm Comin' Home** (Rich)
10. **Gently** (Wizell, Lisbona)
11. **In Your Arms** (Schroeder, Gold)

Record 2

Side 1

1. **Give Me The Right** (Wise, Blagman)
2. **I Feel So Bad** (Willis)
3. **It's A Sin** (Rose, Turner)
4. **I Want You With Me** (Harris)
5. **There's Always Me** (Robertson)
6. **Starting Today** (Robertson)
7. **Sentimental Me** (Cassin, Morehead)
8. **Judy** (Redell)
9. **Put The Blame On Me** (Twomey, Wise, Blagman)
10. **Kiss Me Quick** (Pomus, Shuman)
11. **That's Someone You Never Forget** (West, Presley)
12. **I'm Yours** (Robertson, Blair)

Side 2

1. **(Marie's the name) His Latest Flame** (Pomus, Shuman)
2. **Little Sister** (Pomus, Shuman)
3. **For The Millionth And The Last Time** (Tepper, Bennett)
4. **Good Luck Charm** (Schroeder, Gold)
5. **Anything That's Part Of You** (Robertson)
6. **I Met Her Today** (Robertson, Blair)
7. **Night Rider** (Pomus, Shuman)
8. **Something Blue** (Evans, Byron)
9. **Gonna Get Back Home Somehow** (Pomus, Shuman)
10. **(Such an) Easy Question** (Blackwell, Scott)
11. **Fountain Of Love** (Giant, Lewis)
12. **Just For Old Time's Sake** (Tepper, Bennett)

Record 3

Side 1

1. **You'll Be Gone** (West, Presley, Hodge)
2. **I Feel That I've Known You Forever** (Pomus, Jeffreys)
3. **Just Tell Her Jim Said Hello** (Leiber, Stoller)
4. **Suspicion** (Pomus, Shuman)
5. **She's Not You** (Pomus, Leiber, Stoller)
6. **Echoes Of Love** (Roberts, McMains)
7. **Please Don't Drag That String Around** (Blackwell, Scott)
8. **(You're the) Devil In Disguise** (Giant, Baum, Kaye)
9. **Never Ending** (Kaye, Springer)
10. **What Now, What Next, Where To** (Robertson, Blair)
11. **Witchcraft** (Bartholomew, King)
12. **Finders Keepers, Losers Weepers** (D. & O. Jones)
13. **Love Me Tonight** (Robertson)
14. **(It's a) Long Lonely Highway** (Pomus, Shuman)

Side 2

1. **Western Union** (Tepper, Bennett)
2. **Slowly But Surely** (Wayne, Weisman)
3. **Blue River** (Evans, Tobias)
4. **Memphis, Tennessee** (Berry)
5. **Ask Me** (Modugno, Giant, Baum, Kaye)
6. **It Hurts Me** (Byers, Daniels)
7. **Down In The Alley** (Jesse Stone and The Clovers)
8. **Tomorrow Is A Long Time** (Dylan)
9. **Love Letters** (Young, Heyman)
10. **Beyond The Reef** (Pitman)
11. **Come What May** (Tableporter)

Record 4

Side 1

1. **Fools Fall In Love** (Leiber, Stoller)
2. **Indescribably Blue** (Glenn)
3. **I'll Remember You** (Lee)
4. **If Every Day Was Like Christmas** (West)
5. **Suppose** (Dee, Goehring)
6. **Guitar Man** (Hubbard)
   What'd I Say (Charles)
7. **Big Boss Man** (Smith, Dixon)
8. **Mine** (Tepper, Bennett)
9. **Just Call Me Lonesome** (Griffin)
10. **Hi Heel Sneakers** (Higgenbotham)

Side 2

1. **You Don't Know Me** (Walker, Arnold)
2. **Singing Tree** (Owens, Solberg)
3. **Too Much Monkey Business** (Berry)
4. **U.S. Male** (Hubbard)
5. **Long Black Limousine** (Stovall, George)
6. **This Is The Story** (Arnold, Morrow, Martin)
7. **Wearin' That Loved On Look** (Frazier, Owens)
8. **You'll Think Of Me** (Shuman)
9. **A Little Bit Of Green** (Arnold, Morrow, Martin)
10. **Gentle On My Mind** (Hartford)

Record 5

Side 1

1. **I'm Movin' On** (Snow)
2. **Don't Cry Daddy** (Davis)
3. **Inherit The Wind** (Rabbitt)
4. **Mama Liked The Roses** (Christopher)
5. **My Little Friend** (Milete)
6. **In The Ghetto** (Davis)
7. **Rubberneckin'** (Jones, Warren)
8. **From A Jack To A King** (Miller)
9. **Hey Jude** (Lennon, McCartney)
10. **Without Love (there is nothing)** (Small)

Side 2

1. **I'll Hold You In My Heart (till I can hold you in my arms)** (Arnold, Horton, Dilbeck)
2. **I'll Be There (if ever you want me)** (Darin)
3. **Suspicious Minds** (James)
4. **True Love Travels On A Gravel Road** (Owens, Frazier)
5. **Stranger In My Own Home Town** (Mayfield)
6. **And The Grass Won't Pay No Mind** (Diamond)
7. **Power Of My Love** (Giant, Baum, Kaye)
8. **After Loving You** (Miller, Lantz)

Record 6

Side 1

1. **Do You Know Who I Am** (Russell)
2. **Kentucky Rain** (Rabbitt, Heard)
3. **Only The Strong Survive** (Gamble, Huff, Butler)
4. **It Keeps Right On A-Hurtin'** (Tillotson)
5. **Any Day Now** (Hilliard, Bacharach)
6. **If I'm A Fool (for loving you)** (Kesler)
7. **The Fair's Moving On** (Fletcher, Flett)
8. **Who Am I?** (Goodman)
9. **This Time** (Moman)
   I Can't Stop Loving You (Gibson)
10. **In The Ghetto** (Davis)

Side 2

1. **Suspicious Minds** (James)
2. **Kentucky Rain** (Rabbitt, Heard)
3. **Big Boss Man** (Smith, Dixon)
4. **Down In The Alley** (Jesse Stone and The Clovers)
5. **Memphis, Tennessee** (Berry)
6. **I'm Yours** (Robertson, Blair)
7. **(Marie's the name) His Latest Flame** (Pomus, Shuman)
8. **That's Someone You Never Forget** (West, Presley)
9. **Surrender** (DeCurtis, Pomus, Shuman)
10. **It's Now Or Never** (DiCapua, Schroeder, Gold)
11. **Love Me Tender** (Presley, Matson)
    Witchcraft (Coleman, Leigh)

Released September 1993   Deleted late 1996

Barely a year after the release of the universally acclaimed fifties' boxed set, BMG released its next major project as part of the restoration of Elvis Presley material to catalogue in the best possible sound quality: *From Nashville To Memphis The Essential 60's Masters 1*.

Once again, as with the '50s boxed set, all those involved in the planning and production of the '60s set agreed on a 6 LP/5 CD configuration, presumably in response to some consumer/dealer research, which suggested that adding more LPs/CDs to the set jeopardised its sales potential. Of course, that then presented its compilers with a problem: given the constraint of 6 LP/5 CDs there was the issue of what to include and what to leave out. Remember the '50s set had boasted 140 tracks but there was no way that all of Elvis's sixties' output - in excess of 360 studio and film songs alone (see additional notes later) - would have fitted into the agreed parameters. It is reasonably well understood that the producers did experiment with a variety of options whereby some gospel tracks may have been included, along with the 'best' of the movie songs, though quite what would have happened to the '68 TV Special material is anyone's guess. Clearly, it was a test of the producers' creative judgement, for what was finally opted for was to concentrate on Elvis's secular recordings cut at sixteen recording sessions between March 1960 and February 1969, the bulk of which were recorded in Nashville. Gospel/religious items, film songs, live or TV material was not included. Naturally enough, this did lead to one or two confusing situations e.g. including the seasonal *If Every Day Was Like Christmas* and the obviously religious *Who Am I?* (from the Memphis sessions), yet omitting *You'll Never Walk Alone*. On the other hand, as we will discuss later, this was precisely the sort of creative decision the producers were called upon to make. And as

223

regards the film material, although it may have made some sense to include the likes of **Wooden Heart**, **Can't Help Falling In Love**, **Return To Sender**, as they were big hits, the producers felt the sound quality of these tracks not compatible with the Nashville sound. Besides, BMG had already undertaken a major re-issue programme of Elvis's sixties' film soundtracks as part of their Double Feature series. Thus, it could be argued, the film soundtracks were being marketed elsewhere and there were plans in the making to release a gospel/religious set in 1994. Equally, there was probably good reason for supposing the NBC TV Special material would be marketed separately also. (Indeed this happened in autumn 1998 when BMG issued **Tiger Man** and **Memories** - a single and double CD set - comprising much of the NBC material.) Whatever, the decision to concentrate on non-film studio material was generally agreed to be a sound and rational one. BMG finally released volume 2 in July 1995, a CD only release entitled **Command Performances The Essential 60's Masters II** (07863 66601 2), a double CD comprising 62 songs from the sixties' movies.

Of course another issue facing the producers concerned that of remixing the 2, 3, 4 and 8 track masters they were using. This was not a problem when re-mastering the '50s set, as all the tracks were in mono and, to that end, had essentially been mixed at source i.e. during the original recording sessions. However, the '60s material posed a dilemma: where the original multi-track tapes were found (as opposed to the stereo master tape mixed from the original tape - see the introductory section for more information on this), how far was it felt desirable for the producers to go in remixing the tracks, thus producing a different sound from that found on the original recordings which, it may be assumed, had the general support of Elvis, his management and the people at RCA? As a result, the producers worked on a number of different mixes, with varying degrees of success until, finally, it was decided to try to achieve a balance between the best clarity while replicating the original mix as far as possible - not least of which because to have done otherwise may have caused considerable dissent amongst the fans. And so, although there were some discernible differences in sound on some tracks, in essence the remixing was fairly faithful to the originals.

Certainly, in the case of the **Elvis Is Back!** material, produced at the March/April 1960 sessions, the only tapes the producers had to work from were the two-track stereo masters, as the original 3-track tapes could not be located at the time. Fortunately, however, the mix on these tracks was never regarded as a problem - indeed the clarity of the recordings and their mix was highly regarded.

The total number of vinyl sets manufactured was 10,000, of which 3,000 were said to have been exported to the USA. This overall figure was lower than the number of vinyl sets made for the '50s set reflecting, we believe, an anticipated lower level of interest in the '60s material generally - and vinyl in particular - as well as indicating the steady move away from vinyl to CD. On the other hand, there was good reason to believe that the bulk of vinyl sales were to people who also bought the CD version. The belief was that collectors bought (and probably kept sealed) copies of the vinyl set, but bought CDs to play. Each vinyl set was numbered and came with a certificate of authenticity.

As with the '50s set, there seemed a wide gulf in terms of what the dealers charged for the set. At an independent dealer in Newcastle the first 20 sets sold retailed for £39.98. Equally though, many high street chain stores sold theirs anywhere from £50 to almost £65. Perhaps the most common price focused around £50 at the time of its release. But, in April 1994, for example, the LP set would have cost you £64.99 in an HMV shop.

Although all boxed sets (in all formats) included a fly-sheet advertising the '50s set and the **Elvis In Hollywood** video, only 25,000 sets (all formats) contained the first day cover stamps and envelope. Apparently the initial batches, including the stamps, were sent to the Official Elvis Presley Fan Club of Great Britain and the Our Price shops. Thereafter, remaining stocks were sent out to the rest of the trade.

The LP sized booklet, running to 48 pages, was, like its '50s predecessor, excellent. The text was by Peter Guralnick once again, and each session was listed in detail by Ernst Mikael Jorgensen. And, even though the material comprised non-film songs, many of the photographs in the booklet were from films or the '68 TV Special. There was also a mistake on one of the 1961 sessions. The booklet referred to a session in May 1961, whereas it ought to have read June 1961. Fellow fans may be interested to know that originally an outtake of **A Mess Of Blues** was to have been included on the set. At the last moment, however, it was dropped because the sound quality was said to be not as good as the other material included. Ironically though, this take was later included on **Platinum A Life In Music**, 07863 67469 2, a 4 CD set issued in July 1997.

Material Used

With the exception of the **Love Me Tender/Witchcraft** item from the Frank Sinatra Show in 1960, all of the material included was recorded either in Nashville, or Memphis. The set covered sixteen recording sessions throughout the 1960s:

1960	20-21 March ; 3-4 April; 30-31 October
1961	12-13 March; 25-26 June; 15-16 October
1962	18-19 March
1963	26-27 May
1964	12 January
1965	No original (non-film) material recorded
1966	25-28 May; 10 June
1967	20 March; 10-12 September
1968	15-17 January
1969	13-23 January; 17-22 February

Unlike the '50s set, there were no interviews included this time. The reason for this was two-fold: firstly, there was the time factor to consider - the total running time was almost five and a half hours; secondly, interviews were not considered to be that important, especially as the obvious ones - the March 1960 Graceland interview, or the Memphis interview from 1961 had been widely available before, whereas some of the interview material used on the '50s set had not been issued.

Unreleased Performances/Outtakes

While no-one would deny that most ardent fans/collectors relish the thought of outtakes and/or unreleased performances, it has to be made clear that the boxed sets such as the '50s and '60s collections were not the primary vehicles for such tracks. Of course, no-one, least of all the producers, would argue that to include such material made the releases that much more attractive, but they wished to re-state that the main purpose was to restore original tracks to catalogue in the best available sound quality at the time. Any extra tracks (26 on the '50s, and 19 on the '60s set) were included as a bonus - though, no doubt, a marketing strategy too.

Central to this lay some awkward issues for the producers. How far could, or should, they go in including incomplete, technically or artistically flawed tracks on such prestigious sets when the intended market lay beyond the die-hard fans? There was the question of Elvis's image, and that of the company's to consider too. Consequently, while a bootleg recording may reveal all sorts of things an artist such as Elvis said or did during recordings - such as swearing, blaspheming etc. - the likelihood remains that such personal and private things will not appear on albums made for mass consumption.

BMG were persuaded by the producers as to the worth of the **Essential Elvis** series on the general market. However, the poor critical reception of **Collectors Gold** (**LP 315**) in August 1991 (apart from the fans, that is), focused attention on whether or not such releases were, a) financially viable in terms of world sales and, b) whether or not the concept of three albums of outtakes/unreleased performances (many of which were inferior to the original released versions) was not at variance with the dealer/general public's expectations.

Certainly, the Essential Elvis series (vols 1-3) had several things going for them which **Collectors Gold** did not: they had clearly discernible themes; were patently well produced and marketed; and, concentrated on an era (the fifties) which many still regarded as his best in critical terms. To that end, **Collectors Gold**, featuring some likeable but hardly great Nashville songs, some plainly suspect Hollywood film songs and, finally, some exciting though repetitious live tracks from Las Vegas 1969, simply could not compete.

Now, whether or not the hard-core Elvis fans approved, theirs were not the only needs the company had to satisfy. Increasingly, large companies have a limited amount of money to devote to their releases - whether it is to stimulate new talent or to finance re-issues of old material or expensive boxed sets. Companies such as BMG have to be convinced that their products will sell in large enough quantities to justify things like expensive tape vault searches, transcription of finds, remixing and remastering costs, not to mention the research needed for photographs and memorabilia in the now obligatory booklets. And, while there had been some concession made to collectors in a small way - starting with the first **Elvis - A Legendary Performer Vol. 1** (*LP 70*) in February 1974, and developing through the two EP Collections (1982), Essential Elvis series and culminating in 1991 with the three album set of **Collectors Gold** (**LP 315**), achieving the correct balance and targeting an audience had become more and more critical - especially during times of economic caution or, worse, recession.

Finally then, it has to be mentioned that while releases such as **From The Heart** (**LP 317**) may have been scorned and derided by collectors, it must be remembered that a) the target audience was much wider than that of ordinary fans; and, b) the enormous sales it generated would go a long way towards persuading the company to finance less attractive and smaller volume sales' releases, such as **Essential Elvis**.

Sequencing/Versions

And, just as the entire contents, of the '50s set had been in mono, all tracks on the '60s set (with the exception of the **Love Me Tender**/**Witchcraft** sequence, recorded not in Nashville or Memphis, but in a TV studio in Miami in March 1960) were in stereo. The set was also sequenced in almost complete chronological order. The only slight discrepancy noted between the actual running order and the sessionography order concerned **Hey Jude** and **From A Jack To A King**. Following the matrix numbering system, **Hey Jude** (XPA5 1157) ought to have been positioned after **Rubberneckin'**, whereas on the set **From A Jack To A King** (XPA5 1158) followed it. This was, however, a small deviation, though one which we could discern no obvious reason for in this instance.

As for the 'rarities', the idea here was to sequence them in reverse chronological order; thus the last studio recorded track for 1969, **Who Am I?**, was followed by an unreleased performance, also from 1969. The sequence here was more or less correct, but the first four tracks in particular, were not in reverse date or recorded order.

This Time/I Can't Stop Loving You	17.2.69
In The Ghetto	20.1.69
Suspicious Minds	22.1.69
Kentucky Rain	19.2.69

The only other minor change was that according to the session logs **I'm Yours** (M2WW 0859) preceded **(Marie's the name) His Latest Flame** (M2WW 0860), which suggested that on the album they ought to have been reversed. We can only assume that this switch was made in the interests of pacing, so as to avoid two fast tracks being followed by two slow songs.

The main body of the set threw up a few oddities though, and raised the issue whether or not the tracks in question ought not to have been more legitimately placed on the final LP/CD among other alternative performances. This was, of course, a good example of the judgement required by the producers compiling the set and did not,

we hasten to add, come down to the question of being right or wrong. But that still left some unusual matters to explain, which we will discuss track by track.

Come What May (28.5.66). The odd thing about this cut was that it was an alternative version - take 7, in fact - from the original released recording (take 8) - albeit an extremely similar performance in most respects. The reason for this switch was simple: the original master tape with the stereo version on it could not be found. Happily, the alternative used was very close to the original released track. However, the stereo master (take 8) was located later on, and finally released on the CD **Long Lonely Highway Nashville 1960-1968**, 07863 76749 2, in June 2000.

I'll Remember You (10.6.66 - 12.6.66). The version best known to fans was the one featured as a bonus track on **California Holiday** (*LP 30*) in November 1966. However, the version featured on the '60s set, (a splice of takes 1 and 3) was over a minute longer, and mixed differently.

Suppose (20.3.67). This was a previously unreleased version of the song cut in Nashville. The version fans were more familiar with was recorded a couple of months later in June 1967 at United Recorders, Hollywood, as part of the **Speedway** soundtrack (*LP 35*), and later included on the album of the same name in August 1968. Ironically, a lot of fans probably believed that the song had never been intended for the film soundtrack, as it had a distinctly 'original song' feel to it.

Guitar Man/**What'd I Say** (10.9.67). The first time the two songs were linked together was in February 1981 with the release of the **Guitar Man** album (*LP 146*). This was the overdubbed version produced by Felton Jarvis in 1980. For some considerable time it was unclear as to whether or not the **What'd I Say** piece had been artificially added to the run-out of **Guitar Man**. Even Ernst Mikael Jorgensen in early 1991 felt that Jarvis had, in his words, '... did a number on it'. It wasn't until a year or so later, while researching the tape vaults for the '60s masters and outtakes, that the original version of the song with the **What'd I Say** tag turned up, much to everyone's surprise.

Hi Heel Sneakers (11.9.67). As with **I'll Remember You**, the version of **Hi Heel Sneakers** best known to fans was the original one issued as the B side to **Guitar Man** (**S 62**) in February 1969. Here though, the set included the full version of the song (the single version had been edited) which included some 'chat' and fooling around at the beginning of the track on which Elvis sang a one-line parody of **Ode To Billy Joe**.

Blue River (27.5.63). The thing to note about this track was that it was the original 1.32 version of the song, not the artificially extended single version which had featured the guitar break twice. The correct length version had first been used in 1990 on the album **For The Asking (The Lost Album)** (**LP 309**).

Singles From The '60s Set

Unlike the '50s set which spawned a single in the UK - **Don't Be Cruel**, **All Shook Up**, **Jailhouse Rock** and **I Need Your Love Tonight** (**S 179**) - there was no single release issued in conjunction with the '60s set. On the other hand, it was interesting to note how many of the tracks featured on the '60s set had been used as A or B sides of singles over the years (by RCA/BMG).

1960s	23 titles were A sides	
	24 titles were B sides	
1970	2 titles were A sides	
	8 titles were B sides	
1980	1 title was an A side (**Stuck On You**)	
	2 titles were B sides	

In the '70s, only one of the sixties' couplings *A Mess Of Blues/The Girl Of My Best Friend* (*S 29*) was reversed, and was released with *The Girl OF My Best Friend* as the A side (*S 97*) in August 1976. We have not considered straight reissues in these figures.

In the sixties, six singles had film titles as their A sides and non-film '60s recordings on the B sides. They were as follows:

Release
Number

S 34	*Wild In The Country/I Feel So Bad*	Aug 1961
S 42	*Bossa Nova Baby/Witchcraft*	Oct 1963
S 45	*Kissin' Cousins/It Hurts Me*	Jun 1964
S 49	*Do The Clam/You'll Be Gone*	Feb 1965
S 59	*Long Legged Girl (with the short dress on)/ That's Someone You Never Forget*	Jul 1967
S 69	*Clean Up Your Own Backyard/The Fair's Moving On*	Aug 1969

Far less commonly, an original studio recording would be an A side and have a film track as its B side.

Release
Number

S 51	*Tell Me Why* (a '50s track)/*Puppet On A String*	Nov 1965
S 63	*U.S. Male/Stay Away*	May 1968

On one occasion an original fifties' track, previously unissued, was an A side, coupled with a '60s original song as a B side.

Release
Number

S 47	*Ain't That Loving You Baby/Ask Me*	Oct 1964

Promotional Material

The most obvious and collectable promotional material for any album release would normally be the vinyl promotional disc or CD. And, of course, for the '60s set the European division did produce a fourteen track CD sampler for promotional purposes. Immediately it became highly collectable, especially as only 750 copies were made.

However, additionally, BMG also produced a series of mobiles and posters for in-store display. And, while there was no specific promotional package for the '60s set (as there had been for the '50s), there were some 'tasty' items available to the press and media generally. In particular, there was a series of postcards - *From Memphis to Bad Nauheim*, *From Bad Nauheim to New Jersey*, and *From Nashville To Memphis* (thought to be about 1,500 issued), plus black and orange rugby shirts and a sports umbrella!

Only browser cards for CDs were produced. They showed a picture of the box cover and stated that the set comprised 130 tracks, of which eighteen were unreleased performances, though there were, in fact, nineteen.

Label and sleeve errors

In reporting label and sleeve errors found on *The King Of Rock 'N' Roll The Complete 50's Masters* (**LP 318**), we adopted a summary approach which allowed us the flexibility of including more detailed reasoning which would otherwise have been impossible given the number of tracks involved. It seems appropriate, therefore, to continue with this format for *From Nashville To Memphis The Essential 60's Masters 1*.

As with the fifties' set, there were no track details whatsoever on the label. This was entirely due to the number of tracks featured, and nothing to do with avoiding errors. References to song titles and writers' names are, therefore, confined to the back of each album sleeve only.

It was inevitable, given the number of songs involved, that there were bound to be some discrepancies between our interpretation and what was printed. And, just as we did with the fifties' set, we took this opportunity to re-assess some of our earlier decisions in the same way that BMG had looked at their files in a fresh light. Consequently, we have made some amendments to titles and to writers' names where we believe we had made an error in the past, or where some new information has become available. In doing so, we have amended the song index at the back of the book to reflect these changes. And, wherever a change has occurred, we have endeavoured to explain our reasoning.

Once again, we can report that despite the length of this section the number of actual errors was relatively small, and the majority appeared to be regarding writers' names. However, a small number of what would appear to be typographical errors did, annoyingly, creep in to the production process.

It's Now Or Never. In the UK, the name Eduardo Di Capua, one of the Italian composers of *O Sole Mio* (on which *It's Now Or Never* was based), was normally included. We consider its omission here to be an error.

The Girl Of My Best Friend. The sleeve showed the writers to be B. Ross Butler/S. Bobrick. As the song was written by Beverley Ross and Sam Bobrick (a psuedonym for Bunny Lewis), there should have been no reference to 'Butler'.

Girl Next Door Went A'Walking. This was one of those song titles which have appeared in a variety of guises: *The Girl Next Door Went A'Walking*; *The Girl Next Door (went-a-walking)* and other variations. However, the writers had always been shown as Rice, Wayne, whereas the sleeve on this occasion showed Ri̲se, Wayne.

Reconsider Baby. Another spelling error - Lowell Fulson appeared as Fulsom.

Surrender. As with *It's Now Or Never*, one of the original Italian writers, DeCurtis, was omitted. The sleeve read Pomus, Shuman only.

Sentimental Me. Co-writer Jimmy Cassin had his surname spelt Casin.

(Marie's the name) His Latest Flame. The words in brackets were omitted.

For The Millionth And The Last Time. The team of Tepper, Bennett had written many songs recorded by Elvis and, as a rule, their names were usually shown in that order. When *For The Millionth And The Last Time* made its debut in the UK in November 1965 on *Elvis For Everyone* (*LP 26*), their names were reversed for some reason, as they were on all subsequent re-issues of that album. The August 1982 compilation *Romantic Elvis* (*LP 192*) corrected the error which, unfortunately, re-occurred here.

Just For Old Time's Sake. Tepper, Bennett were shown in the correct order, but the song title had been incorrectly changed to *Just For Old Time Sake*, omitting the '*s*'. This error was another throwback to the original UK *Pot Luck* album (*LP 16*) from 1962, although later pressings - red dot and orange labels - used the correct title. Later International label re-issues perpetuated the error.

You'll Be Gone. The song first appeared in the UK as the B side of *Do The Clam*, RCA 1443 (*S 49*), in February 1965, and the label listed the writers as being West, Presley, Hodge (although Hodge had his name misspelt Hoage). Shortly afterwards, in April 1965, *You'll Be Gone* was released as the final track on *Girl Happy* (*LP 24*), only this time the writers appeared as Presley, West, Hodge. The order given on the sleeve of the '60s set is in keeping with that of the original single and, therefore, no error occurred. The reason we have mentioned this is twofold: to illustrate how variations can so easily appear, and to acknowledge that in *Elvis UK 1956-86*, we made the mistake of using both sequence of names.

Just Tell Her Jim Said Hello. For some inexplicable reason, the established order of Leiber, Stoller was reversed - as it was when the song first appeared as the B side of *She's Not You* (*S 38*) in August 1962. Our logic in considering that to be an error was that it broke the normal convention of how the writers were usually shown - Leiber, Stoller.

She's Not You. Having concluded that the correct order is Leiber, Stoller for *Just Tell Her Jim Said Hello*, a collaboration with Doc Pomus to write *She's Not You* presented a difficulty. The writers were listed as Pomus, Stoller, Leiber as they had been previously. We believe the correct order to be Pomus, Leiber, Stoller.

Echoes Of Love. The correct writers were Roberts, McMains not Roberts, Batchelor.

Memphis, Tennessee. The comma was omitted.

It Hurts Me. Throughout *Elvis UK 1956-86* we reported that *It Hurts Me* was written by Joy Byers alone and that RCA's reference to Byers, Daniels was incorrect. Further checking shows that we were wrong, and we have amended the song title index accordingly. In fact, there was no-one called Joy Byers: this was a pseudonym used by the writer/producer Bob Johnson.

Down In The Alley. Another error on our part previously was the omission of Jesse Stone's band The Clovers when considering writing credits. The song title index has been amended.

Love Letters. This track first appeared in the UK on a single, RCA 1526 (*S 54*), in June 1966, and showed the writers as Young, Heyman. In later years, the order was reversed and this was how it was shown on the sleeve here. We see no reason for this and still consider Young, Heyman to be the correct order.

Guitar Man. The sleeve credited Hubbard and not the usual Reed. Of course, this referred to the same person - Jerry Reed Hubbard - but *Guitar Man* normally credited Reed whereas *U.S. Male* usually referred to Hubbard. Perhaps re-crediting *Guitar Man* was an attempt to be consistent. Unfortunately, we had opted for Reed in the past, but are now happy to concur with BMG and use Hubbard.

Hi Heel Sneakers. The song's first appearance - as the B Side of *Guitar Man* (*S 62*) in February 1968 - did not include the hyphen between *Hi* and *Heel* that is shown on the sleeve here.

U.S. Male. As previously stated, we have amended Reed to Hubbard.

I'll Hold You In My Heart (till I can hold you in my arms). This song should have been credited to Arnold, Horton, Dilbeck, and not Dilback, Arnold as the sleeve claimed.

I'll Be There (if ever you want me). This song first appeared in the UK on the album *Let's Be Friends* (*LP 40*) in May 1970. The first pressing credited Gabbard, Price, although later pressings referred to Bobby Darin. Later issues on albums like *Easy Come Easy Go*, CDS 1146 (*LP 76*), reverted to Gabbard, Price. The sleeve here shows Darin, and we now consider this to be correct. There had also been an inconsistent use of the words in brackets which was not shown this time, whereas they were on *Let's Be Friends*. We have retained them as part of the title.

The precise deletion date for this set is not shown on BMG's files and, consequently, we have been forced to include an estimation of when this took place. We know for certain that the set was still available in October 1996 (although very few copies were in stock). Around this time, BMG introduced a new computer system, and it is assumed that details of some older releases were not transferred from the old system.

Postscript To *From Nashville To Memphis The Essential 60's Masters 1*

Albums No Longer Required

With the release of *From Nashville To Memphis The Essential 60's Masters 1* (**LP 319**) some fans - though probably not the serious collectors - probably entertained the idea of selling off or trading albums (both vinyl and CD) no longer required to have a complete collection of sixties' studio material, once they had bought the boxed set. Surprisingly though, there were not too many, at this stage.

However, strictly speaking, there was no need to retain the following albums:

> *Elvis Is Back!*, NL 89013 (*LP 230*)
> *Something For Everybody*, NL 84116 (*LP 243*)
> *Elvis' Golden Records Vol. 3*, NL 82765 (*LP 256*)
> *From Elvis In Memphis*, NL 90548 (**LP 313**)

simply because all of the tracks were included on the boxed set, and in better sound quality. However, completists would keep the following LPs/CDs because they included tracks not otherwise available on an up-dated boxed set (or CD collection - such as the Double Features releases, started in 1993).

Finally, the boxed set rendered the 1990 release *For The Asking (The Lost Album)*, NL 90513 (**LP 309**), (comprising tracks Elvis recorded in Nashville in May 1963 and January 1964) redundant also.

Albums To Be Retained

Please note: the following list refers to albums needed at the point the sixties' set was released. It may be that subsequent CD releases included some of the tracks in question.

1. *Pot Luck*, NL 89098 (*LP 233*)

This would need to be retained for one track: *Steppin' Out Of Line*, an unused track from the soundtrack recording for *Blue Hawaii* in March 1961.

2. *Elvis For Everyone*, NL 84232 (*LP 225*)

Once again, completists would keep this album (vinyl or CD) to have the overdubbed version of *Tomorrow Night* (a left-over Sun track not released until 1965).

3. *Elvis' Gold Records Volume 4*, NL 83921 *(LP 213)*.

The need for retaining this album was because it included the full-version of **Lonely Man** (cut from **Wild In The Country**), and for vinyl-only collectors because it also included **What'd I Say** (from the film **Love In Las Vegas**). Of course, CD buyers had the chance to obtain this track as it was included on one of the four Double Feature film soundtrack albums issued in 1993.

Completists would also wish to retain the following two singles: **Blue River**, RCA 1504, released in February 1966 *(S 52)*, and **Love Letters**, RCA 1526, released in June 1966 *(S 54)*. The former because it was the spliced version (extended for single release), and the latter to retain its B side, the original mono master of **Come What May**, not included in the '60s set because no stereo master could be located at that time.

'60s Outtakes Issued On Collectors Gold

Of special interest to fans of Elvis's '60s Nashville recordings (all done in RCA's Studio B, off Music Row), was the fact that a number of outtakes (unreleased performances) had been issued in August 1991 as part of the **Collectors Gold** release (**LP 315**). The following songs were included in that set:

	Take Number	Recorded
Like A Baby	1, 2	3 Apr 1960
There's Always Me	4	12 Mar 1961
I Want You With Me	1	12 Mar 1961
Gently	3	13 Mar 1961
Give Me The Right	1	12 Mar 1961
I Met Her Today	1	16 Oct 1961
Night Rider	1, 2	16 Oct 1961
Just Tell Her Jim Said Hello	1	19 Mar 1962
Ask Me	2	12 Jan 1964
Memphis, Tennessee	2	12 Jan 1964
Love Me Tonight	1	26 May 1963
Witchcraft	1	26 May 1963
Come What May	6	28 May 1966
Love Letters	4, 7	26 May 1966
Goin' Home	24, 21	15 Jan 1968

Since the release of the '60's set a considerable number of other outtakes from the sixties' have been issued on various CDs.

Proposed Releases

It seems worth pointing out - obvious though it may seem - that the responsibility for determining which tracks are included on an Elvis release lies with the producers. They are the ones who select the tracks, decide their running order and, indeed, anything else to do with the material. This is their role; one of their chief responsibilities. Of course, it would be naive to assume that there is no reference to anyone else when they are doing this - clearly they are required to submit listings to higher authority - but, in the main, their creative judgement usually prevails. Provided all else is acceptable - concept, marketing etc., it will probably go ahead.

However, two things producers cannot nor should not be held responsible for are:

a) delays in items being released, as often they occur for reasons beyond their control and influence e.g. overcrowded schedules/production problems or delays; and,

b) long term delays to proposed releases. For example, in early 1994 it was announced that there would probably be a new volume of the Essential Elvis series, comprising either fifties' outtakes (unreleased performances, as well as the recently found acetate recording

I'll Never Stand In Your Way - circa January 1954), or seventies' material, which would be released in the autumn. Roger Semon discussed his and Ernst Mikael Jorgensen's thoughts on the subject in March 1994 with the authors of this book. He expressed the wish to keep the series alive and, further, regretted that so long had passed between **Hits Like Never Before (Essential Elvis Vol. 3)** (**LP 306**) and the proposed volume 4. At the same time, they had an alternative volume of **Essential Elvis**, a sort of contingency release, comprising outtakes from the June and September 1970 sessions, available too, in the event that the rights to **I'll Never Stand In Your Way** could not be secured. In the event though, following a meeting in the USA in May 1994, neither release was sanctioned at that stage. Initially, this was because the acetate from 1954 was not, at that point, in the possession of BMG; and, secondly, because there was felt to be some internal disagreement about the validity or appropriateness of using the **Essential Elvis** series for the seventies' material, which few would regard as essential by any stretch of the imagination. Both projects were, as a result, shelved.

However, in July 1996 the fourth volume of **Essential Elvis - A Hundred Years From Now** was issued on CD (07863 66866 2), comprising the '70/71 material referred to above. As for **I'll Never Stand In Your Way**, it was eventually issued in 1997 on the 4 CD set **Platinum A Life In Music** (07863 67469 2).

The key point here is simple: fans/collectors must understand that proposals for releases are just that: proposals. In any company there will be an untold number of people whose say so and sanction has to be given before a release can go ahead. If releases do not materialise, or are delayed, then it is neither right nor fair to blame the producers. The likelihood is they may feel equally disheartened or disappointed that their creative projects have been delayed or shelved indefinitely.

Full Priced Albums

In the period between December 1986 and September 1993, BMG released at least one full-priced vinyl album a year comprising some unreleased performances.

Dec 1986	*Essential Elvis*	PL 89979	**LP 280**
Jul 1987	*The Complete Sun Sessions*	PL 86414(2)	**LP 283**
May 1988	*The Alternate Aloha*	PL 86985	**LP 294**
Jan 1989	*Stereo '57 (Essential Elvis Volume 2)*	PL 90250	**LP 298**
Jul 1990	*Hits Like Never Before (Essential Elvis Vol. 3)*	PL 90486	**LP 306**
Aug 1990	*The Great Performances*	PL 82227	**LP 308**
Aug 1991	*Collectors Gold*	PL 90574(3)	**LP 315**
Jul 1992	*The King Of Rock 'N' Roll The Complete 50's Masters*	PL 90689(6)	**LP 318**
Sep 1993	*From Nashville To Memphis The Essential 60's Masters 1*	74321 15430 1	**LP 319**

When you compare this with releases between 1977-1985 this was a very good record on the part of the company, and clearly indicative of their desire to cater for the needs of serious fans/collectors.

Album Deletions - October 1993

In October 1993 three of the remaining vinyl albums were deleted from the catalogue. The double album **This Is Elvis**, BL 84031(2) *(LP 226)*, had first been released in May 1984 and was the oldest of the albums still on catalogue. **Stereo '57 (Essential Elvis Volume 2)** (**LP 298**), first released in January 1989, was the last of the Essential Elvis series to be deleted.

The other LP to be deleted in October 1993 was the much more recent three LP set **Collectors Gold** (**LP 315**) which had only been released in August 1991.

Album Deletion - December 1993

A relatively recent issue was deleted in December 1993. *From The Heart*, PL 90642 (**LP 317**), had only been released in February 1992 and, although it had done extremely well (as a TV promoted album it generated a lot of interest from casual buyers), the album was not re-pressed. This was very much a sign of the times: once a product had sold out, stocks were not replaced, as the company concentrated on other projects. In this particular case, *From The Heart* was superceded by *The Essential Collection*, 74321 22871 1 (**LP 320**), another album promoted on TV and which contained a number of tracks common to both albums.

Even the CD version of *From The Heart* had a relatively short life span. It was deleted on 31 March 1995 as BMG rationalised their catalogue.

The Elvis Album Catalogue - January 1994

Throughout 1993 more albums had been deleted from BMG's Elvis catalogue. At the beginning of January 1994 the complete list of vinyl albums still available was:

Catalogue Number	Title	Release Date	
PL 82227	*The Great Performances*	Aug 1990	LP 308
PL 82587(2)	*Elvis In Concert*	Aug 1985	*LP 273*
PL 90100(2)	*Presley - The All Time Greatest Hits*	Aug 1987	LP 287
CL 90249(3)	*Special Edition*	Oct 1988	LP 297
PL 90250	*Stereo '57 (Essential Elvis Volume 2)*	Jan 1989	LP 298
PL 90689(6)	*The King Of Rock 'N' Roll The Complete 50's Masters*	Jul 1992	LP318
74321 15430 1	*From Nashville To Memphis The Essential 60's Masters 1*	Sep 1993	LP 319

Album Deletion - July 1994

The King Of Rock 'N' Roll The Complete 50's Masters (**LP 318**), the six album boxed set, was deleted on 22 July 1994. Although it had only been issued two years previously, in July 1992 (it was a genuine limited edition release), no further pressings were made by BMG after the initial run.

LP 320 — The Essential Collection
RCA 74321 22871 1

Side 1

1. **Heartbreak Hotel** (Axton, Durden, Presley)
2. **Hound Dog** (Leiber, Stoller)
3. **Don't Be Cruel** (Blackwell, Presley)
4. **Love Me Tender** (Presley, Matson)
5. **All Shook Up** (Blackwell, Presley)
6. **(Let me be your) Teddy Bear** (Mann, Lowe)
7. **Jailhouse Rock** (Leiber, Stoller)
8. **The Girl Of My Best Friend** (Ross, Bobrick)
9. **It's Now Or Never** (DiCapua, Schroeder, Gold)
10. **Are You Lonesome Tonight?** (Turk, Handman)
11. **Wooden Heart** (Wise, Weisman, Twomey, Kaempfert)
12. **(Marie's the name) His Latest Flame** (Pomus, Shuman)
13. **Can't Help Falling In Love** (Peretti, Creatore, Weiss)

Side 2

1. **Good Luck Charm** (Schroeder, Gold)
2. **Return To Sender** (Blackwell, Scott)
3. **(You're the) Devil In Disguise** (Giant, Baum, Kaye)
4. **In The Ghetto** (Davis)
5. **Suspicious Minds** (James)
6. **The Wonder Of You** (Knight)
7. **I Just Can't Help Believin'** (Mann, Weil)
8. **An American Trilogy** (Arranged Newbury)
9. **Always On My Mind** (James, Carson, Christopher)
10. **Moody Blue** (James)

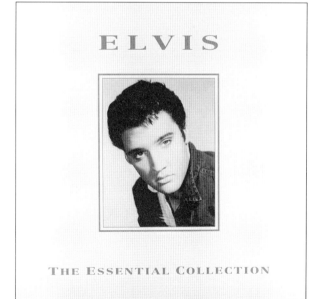

Released August 1994   Deleted Not known

This was the first UK only album release since *From The Heart* (**LP 317**) in February 1992. And, although perhaps not apparent at the time, the release of this vinyl album was thought to be the last Elvis vinyl album issued by BMG in the UK. (A general belief that the '70s set released in September 1995 would spawn a vinyl release proved false.) However, the distinction of being the last BMG vinyl album actually went to *Elvis 56* (**LP 321**), issued in April 1996.

Of course the reason for this was easy to understand: the release was TV advertised, and out of deference to the audience it was designed to appeal to, all formats were offered. And, although few collectors saw anything to get excited about, the release did remarkably well sales-wise. In fact, within a year of its release the set had sold well in excess of 350,000 copies (all formats) in the UK, thus vindicating entirely the decision to have yet another 'hits' collection. Note: at the time *The Essential Collection* was released *Presley - The All Time Greatest Hits* (**LP 287**) was still available, as was the 'love songs' collection *From The Heart* (**LP 317**). *The Essential Collection* was advertised on television, the first Elvis album to be TV advertised since *From The Heart* in 1992.

The idea for the project emerged from a market research document which clearly indicated there was a real public demand for a single album of hits. To that end, according to Roger Semon, the public determined which tracks would be included, simply by being asked which Elvis tracks they knew and would like to see on an album (probably a sample of 2,000 people were interviewed). Not surprisingly then, eleven of the tracks had been featured on *From The Heart* (**LP 317**) vinyl album, and of all the other tracks only *Don't Be Cruel* had not been on *Presley - The All Time Greatest Hits* (**LP 287**). All tracks had been A side singles at some time or other, and they were in chronological release order.

Remarkably, the album consisted of 23 tracks - one of the greatest number of tracks ever assembled onto a single Elvis album. And, with a running time of around 64 minutes, it represented excellent value for money. The CD counterpart went further, adding five extra tracks - *Blue Suede Shoes*, *King Creole*, *She's Not You*, *Crying In The Chapel*, and *Burning Love*. Perhaps a surprising omission on this set was *Way Down* - a posthumous number one record in 1977. Incidentally, both the LP and CD were released on 29 August, a UK bank holiday!

The set was compiled by Roger Semon and Ernst Mikael Jorgensen, based on information presented to them by RPM (the market research company). The tracks, therefore, were not chosen by the two producers.

The market research also influenced the cover design. In keeping with several other artists' collections, the watchword was simplicity. Hence the use of minimal writing on the front and back cover - confined to Elvis's name, the title, and, on the back, the track listing. The choice of a white cover with gold lettering was deliberate also, and much thought was given to using an inset shot of Elvis - in black and white too - to complete the effect. The simple listing of tracks and showing six small photographs on the back cover continued this stark, minimalist impression. The photographs used on the back cover, working from left to right, dated from:

1. Live on stage in 1956.
2. A publicity still from *Jailhouse Rock.*
3. A live shot from the 'stand-up' portion of the 1968 NBC TV Special.
4. A publicity still from 1960/61.
5. Live on stage in August 1970.
6. Live on stage in February 1970.

And, while collectors usually expected informative sleeve notes and session details, it was argued that the general record buying public were not really interested in such detail, and so it could be dispensed with for, after all, the target audience was not collectors but the general public. Indeed, the advertising campaign was based around the catchphrase 'Every home should have at least one Elvis album'. This, the massive in-store publicity programme - especially in shops like WH Smiths and Our Price - and the ten second TV advert, ensured that the album sold phenomenally well. Most Our Price and Smiths outlets featured window displays of the album. This was done by Aspen Window Dressers but paid for by BMG. Normally such displays lasted for about two weeks.

The inner sleeve of the album featured a 'key points' biography in date order from June 1933 through to August 1992. On one side were two shots from the *Jailhouse Rock* recording session, while the third photo was a publicity shot from his signing for RCA in November 1955. On the other side was a live stage shot from the early 1970s, and a publicity still from late 1960 (circa *Wild In The Country*). The central cover shot was a publicity shot from *Jailhouse Rock* - in black and white, of course! - though slightly tinted.

The record itself was pressed in Holland (BMG themselves had, by this time, no vinyl production capability) and, indeed, it said so on the label. No track details were given on the label, nor were the modes, but there was an image of Elvis (the front cover shot) to the left of the centre hole. The legend 'See sleeve for details' appeared across the top part of the label, along with a note saying that this was a UK compilation, published in 1994. The cover was printed in Holland, though designed by Mainartery in London.

On the track listing only the publishing date for *Jailhouse Rock* - given as 1957 - was incorrect. It was not published in the UK until January 1958. Technically, the date given on *Always On My Mind* was wrong, as it was the 'stringed' version, not issued until 1985.

As regards the versions used, as mentioned above, *Always On My Mind* was not the original single mix from 1972, but the so-called 'stringed' version - basically a remix - first used in 1985. And, the only other track used where the versions were sometimes confused was *An American Trilogy*, which was not the February 1972 single version, but the 9 April 1972 recording from Hampton Roads done while on tour, and subsequently used on *This Is Elvis* in April 1981 (*LP 150*), and then on collections such as *Presley - The All Time Greatest Hits*, PL 90100(2) (**LP 287**).

Full track details were confined to the inner bag and revealed only two minor errors. There was no comma between Matson and Presley under *Love Me Tender* (and their names should have been reversed), and Thompson, not Christopher, was shown as co-writer of *Always On My Mind*.

As with *From Nashville To Memphis The Essential 60's Masters 1* (**LP 319**), we have not been able to determine exactly when this LP was deleted. We know that both the CD and cassette versions were deleted on 1 October 1996, before the LP. In all probability the LP survived until the end of the year, but, as we have, said, we cannot be certain about this, as no date is shown in BMG's files.

Album Deletion - August 1994

One more of the remaining vinyl albums was deleted on 24 August 1994, **Elvis In Concert**, PL 82586(2) (*LP 273*). At the time it was the longest surviving vinyl album, this version having been issued in August 1985.

Album Deletion - December 1994

The last of three albums to be deleted during 1994 was **Presley - The All Time Greatest Hits** (**LP 287**), which was undoubtedly the flagship of BMG's Elvis catalogue until the release of the '50s and '60s boxed sets in 1992 and 1993 respectively.

The Elvis Album Catalogue - January 1995

Of particular interest to vinyl collectors was the realisation that while the US division may have decided to stop pressing vinyl copies of releases (the last full-price one was **The Great Performances**, 2227-1-R in August 1990), there were still five vinyl LPs on catalogue in January 1995.

ANL1 1936	*Elvis Sings The Wonderful World Of Christmas*
AQL1 2274	*Welcome To My World*
AFL1 2765	*Elvis' Golden Records Vol. 3*
AYL1 3683	*Blue Hawaii*
AQL1 3758	*How Great Thou Art*

This contrasted with the UK division where the only vinyl releases available were as follows:

PL 82227	*The Great Performances*	**LP 308**
CL 90249(3)	*Special Edition*	**LP 297**
74321 15430 1	*From Nashville To Memphis The Essential 60's Masters 1*	**LP 319**
74321 22871 1	*The Essential Collection*	**LP 320**

Indeed, at this point in time, December 1994, BMG's own stock control system revealed that there were only 2,000 copies of **The Essential Collection** left and a mere 280 copies of the sixties' set. The computer showed that there were three copies of the '50s set (vinyl) left in stock but, to all intents and purposes, it was officially no longer available, although some specialist dealers may have had copies in stock. In fact, BMG had officially deleted the album in July 1994.

Album Deletion - February 1995

The Great Performances (**LP 308**), first released in August 1990, was deleted on 10 February 1995.

Album Deletion - March 1995

What can only be described as a rather specialised product, the three album set **Special Edition** (**LP 297**), was deleted on 13 March 1995. It was the last of the old vinyl albums to have remained on catalogue, and had survived for so long (it was released in October 1988) presumably because no-one wanted to buy the stocks!

At this point, therefore, only two albums remained on BMG's catalogue, both relatively recent issues - **From Nashville To Memphis The Essential 60's Masters 1** (**LP 319**) (released in September 1993), and **The Essential Collection** (**LP 320**) (released August 1994). Both of these were destined to remain available for a considerable time as BMG failed to clear remaining stocks.

US Vinyl Albums

Astonishingly at the end of 1995 there were still five vinyl albums left on catalogue in the USA - indeed representing no change from the previous year. They were:

ANL1 1936	*Elvis Sings The Wonderful World Of Christmas*
AQL1 2274	*Welcome To My World*
AFL1 2765	*Elvis' Golden Records Vol. 3*
AYL1 3683	*Blue Hawaii*
AQL1 3758	*How Great Thou Art*

Yet in the UK the only vinyl albums left on catalogue were as follows:

| 74321 15430 1 | *From Nashville To Memphis The Essential 60's Masters 1* | **LP 319** |
| 74321 22871 1 | *The Essential Collection* | **LP 320** |

The US situation was hard to understand, especially as the last vinyl release was in August 1990, **The Great Performances**, 2227-1-R. Perhaps the explanation lay in the fact that very few copies were being sold. And, if stock levels were reasonably substantial, then the company would be reluctant to take them off catalogue. Remember, most deletions occur when stock levels of slow selling items, or those superfluous to the catalogue requirements, fall to inconsequential levels. In short, they are not re-ordered.

| **LP 321** | **Elvis 56** |
| **RCA 07863 66817 1** | |

Side 1

1 **Heartbreak Hotel** (Axton, Durden, Presley)
2 **My Baby Left Me** (Crudup)
3 **Blue Suede Shoes** (Perkins)
4 **So Glad You're Mine** (Crudup)
5 **Tutti Frutti** (LaBostrie, Penniman)
6 **One-Sided Love Affair** (Campbell)
7 **Love Me** (Leiber, Stoller)
8 **Anyplace Is Paradise** (Thomas)
9 **Paralyzed** (Blackwell, Presley)
10 **Ready Teddy** (Blackwell, Marascalco)
11 **Too Much** (Rosenburg, Weinman)
12 **Hound Dog** (Leiber, Stoller)

Side 2

1 **Any Way You Want Me (that's how I will be)**
(Schroeder, Owens)
2 **Don't Be Cruel** (Blackwell, Presley)
3 **Lawdy, Miss Clawdy** (Price)
4 **Shake, Rattle And Roll** (Calhoun)
5 **I Want You, I Need You, I Love You** (Mysels, Kosloff)
6 **Rip It Up** (Blackwell, Marascalco)
7 **Heartbreak Hotel** (Axton, Durden, Presley)
8 **I Got A Woman** (Charles)
9 **I Was The One** (Schroeder, DeMetrius, Blair, Peppers)
10 **Money Honey** (Stone)

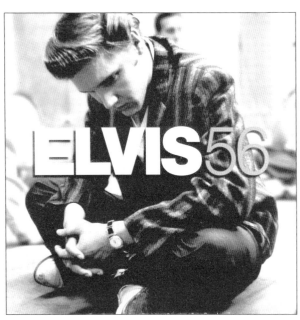

Released April 1996   **Deleted May 1996**

Vinyl, it seems, refused to die, as this release indicated! The previous vinyl LP was issued in August 1994 when BMG released *The Essential Collection* (**LP 320**) in all three formats, though it was subject to a TV advertised campaign and aimed at a wider audience profile than the serious collector. So, too, with *Elvis 56*, though there was no TV advertising to support this release. Clearly by now BMG were considering the release of vinyl versions of product very carefully and weighing up whether or not a vinyl version would be viable. However, in the case of *Elvis 56*, it was not just a question of

viability but appropriateness too. If ever a release deserved a vinyl equivalent then it was this album, though many collectors regretted not having a '70s boxed set in vinyl.

Obviously BMG, having issued the complete '50s set in 1992, wanted to celebrate Elvis's 40 years on the RCA label, and chose to do so by compiling a 22 track album, initially set for a January 1996 release. Sadly, that anniversary was missed (as described in the Singles section - **S 181** - *Heartbreak Hotel*), for reasons thought to be connected with copyright problems over the use of Wertheimer's photos from July 1956. However, BMG also chose to issue a single, *Heartbreak Hotel/I Was The One*, which included the master take of each song and an unreleased performance of each one too. Additionally, the video *Elvis 56*, originally issued in 1987, was relaunched by BMG Video Enterprises. Not surprisingly, the releases attracted a lot of media attention, most of it extremely positive and favourable. Indeed, by the autumn of 1996, *Q* magazine had nominated the album as the best compilation of the year.

Both the vinyl and CD versions of this album were delayed considerably, though for some odd reason copies of the CD were available in parts of Europe several weeks prior to its English release date of 29 April. However, BMG had issued cassette copies of the album quite a few weeks before the CD or LP were released, to act as promotional copies. These were not available to buy at this stage.

The vinyl album was pressed by Sony in Germany and/or Holland, though few territories other than the UK ordered the vinyl version. It was yet another limited edition, and within a few days - on 8 May - was deleted from catalogue. Obviously demand was such that the available copies sold very quickly. The average price of this album seemed to be around £10.50. Lots of major record shops displayed promotional posters - both small and large - of this release - basically using the same artwork as the album cover. As with *The Essential Collection* (**LP 320**), the emphasis was on simplicity regarding its design.

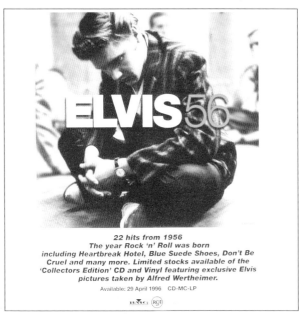

In-store poster.

Indeed, the LP cover, front and back, was virtually identical to the CD covers in terms of the major artwork, though the background detail varied slightly. As with the Collector's Edition CD, the LP cover had the same legend printed along the bottom of the cover. The back cover used the same photograph as featured on the CD cover (Elvis sitting on a chair, his back to the camera), though the tracks were listed under Side One and Side Two. Compilation and production credits were shown under the track listing (not shown on CD versions) though unlike the CD covers the photographer, Alfred Wertheimer, was not acknowledged. The bar code appeared in the top right corner; the BMG, RCA logos in the bottom left; publishing and copyright date and country of manufacture detail was situated bottom centre; while the LC 0316 number was in the bottom right hand corner under the distribution and copyright details. Along the edge of the gatefold sleeve was the catalogue number, title (**Elvis** in bold black print; **56** in red); and the words 'Collectors Edition', also in black.

This album was, in fact, the first gatefold cover since the release of **Hits Like Never Before (Essential Elvis Vol. 3)** (**LP 306**) issued in July 1990. Inside the gatefold was another Wertheimer shot from 2 July 1956, while the opposite photograph was from earlier in the year (17 March) when Elvis appeared on the Dorsey Brothers TV show.

The LP itself was jacketed in a black and white picture sleeve using two more photographs from Wertheimer's collection. Accompanying the LP (but in the other gatefold holder) was a 24 page booklet. And, although the cover of this booklet used the same photographs that were featured on the album cover, there was no **Elvis 56** emblazoned across the front. Inside, there were 27 more Wertheimer shots, some of which were different from those used in the Collector's Edition CD package. Major biographical detail between November 1955 and December 1956 was printed, as was the recording data and photo legend information.

The album was shrink-wrapped and attached to it was a sticker which read:

'The definitive Rock 'N' Roll Album! Includes **Heartbreak Hotel - Don't Be Cruel - Hound Dog - Blue Suede Shoes** - and many others. DIGITALLY REMASTERED Exclusive 24-page booklet includes many rare photos - 56 calendar - Full recording data - Strictly limited Vinyl Deluxe Edition **Heartbreak Hotel** 40th Anniversary Commemorative 07863 66817 1'

Sadly, if you unsealed the wrapper then you were likely to lose this sticker.

As for the LP itself, it used the old RCA Victor black label logo (see photograph for detail). All tracks were listed beneath the title which was in small white print beneath the centre hole. Each track was listed as Band 1, 2 etc, followed by the title and writers. No vocal credits were shown. The mode, mono, was shown to the right of the centre hole, just above 'Made in the EC'. To the left of the centre hole was the BMG logo, Side 1 and below it a small RCA logo. The take numbers were also given for the two outtakes featured: **Shake, Rattle And Roll** (take 8) and **Heartbreak Hotel** (take 5).

Collectors will, of course, remember that in 1978-79 RCA issued a two volume set entitled **The '56 Sessions** (**LPs 102** and **113**), which included all studio material recorded during 1956.

During 1956 Elvis recorded in the studio on six occasions. They were as follows:

10-11 January RCA Studios, Nashville - 5 songs

30-31 January and 3 February RCA Studios, New York - 8 songs

14 April RCA Studios, Nashville - 1 song

2 July RCA Studios, New York - 3 songs

August/September 20th Century Fox, Hollywood - 4 songs

1-3 September Radio Recorders, Hollywood - 13 songs

Precise details of each session could be found in the booklet accompanying the '50s masters boxed set issued in 1992. Of minor note was that for many years it was believed that Elvis recorded **I Want You, I Need You, I Love You** on 11 April in Nashville; it was, in fact, 14 April 1956.

Of the 34 tracks recorded that year (four of which were film songs - from **Love Me Tender**) only 21 were included on **Elvis 56**: the 22nd one was the alternative version of **Heartbreak Hotel** (take 5). And, of course BMG chose to include the previously issued outtake of **Shake, Rattle And Roll** (take 8), first released on the '50s masters set in 1992, in preference to the master take version.

The tracks omitted from **Elvis 56** were as follows:

I'm Counting On You

I'm Gonna Sit Right Down And Cry (over you)

Playin' For Keeps

How Do You Think I Feel

How's The World Treating You

When My Blue Moon Turns To Gold Again

Long Tall Sally

Old Shep

First In Line

Of these perhaps it was surprising that **I'm Gonna Sit Right Down And Cry (over you)** and **Long Tall Sally** were omitted, as these were uptempo songs.

The only label and sleeve error to report was the continued use of **Anyway** in **Any Way You Want Me (that's how I will be)** being shown as one word.

LP 322	**The Louisiana Hayride/ Little Rock, Arkansas**

Stomper Time Records STEN 3

Side 1

1   **That's All Right** (Crudup)

2   **Blue Moon Of Kentucky** (Monroe)

3   **Tweedle Dee** (Scott)

4   **Baby Let's Play House** (Gunter)

5   **Maybellene** (Berry)

6   **That's All Right** (Crudup)

233

Side 2

1 **Heartbreak Hotel** (Axton, Durden, Presley)
2 **Long Tall Sally** (Johnson, Blackwell, Penniman)
3 **I Was The One** (Schroeder, DeMetrius, Blair, Peppers)
4 **Money Honey** (Stone)
5 **I Got A Woman** (Charles)
6 **Blue Suede Shoes** (Perkins)
7 **Hound Dog** (Leiber, Stoller)

Released October 1997

This 10 inch album had a number of distinctions - leaving aside its extremely attractive packaging. First of all it was only the third 10 inch Elvis album release in the UK - the other two being *Loving You* (*LP 3*) and *The Best Of Elvis* (*LP 4*), released in August and October 1957 respectively. Secondly, although featuring previously issued material, it was presented on a label which had not issued Presley material before - in itself an unusual occurrence - but, what is more, it was entirely legitimate. And, finally, it resurrected a format (10 inch vinyl) which many fans probably believed had expired forever. Indeed, the last BMG vinyl release had been the 12 inch LP *Elvis 56* (**LP 321**), issued in April 1996.

Clearly the main virtue of this release on Stomper Time Records lay in its format and presentation which, not surprisingly, appealed to collectors. As mentioned previously, the material itself was common enough (in fact it was available on a bewildering array of cheap CD releases), though it had been edited and properly mastered for release. This had been done by Mike Brown at CTS (who had, along with the legendary Bob Jones, mastered lots of Presley material in the eighties) and the album had been pressed in late August, early September, at Adrenalin in Slough, England.

Incidentally, BMG had cleared the material for both sides of the album - side one comprising recordings made on the Louisiana Hayride prior to Elvis signing to RCA in November 1955, and side two featuring the seven songs Elvis performed at Little Rock, Arkansas, on 16 May 1956, which had first appeared on bootlegs, and then been used liberally on a host of budget line CDs. Ironically, BMG had never released this material themselves. Whatever though, they raised no objection to the material being used, and it was then licensed from The Magnum Music Group who had themselves featured it on CD. On this release though, the tracks had been banded and the performances edited to remove introductions and incidental chat. Some evidence of reverb could also be detected on the tracks too.

Apparently there had been a production error on the first batch pressed, whereby the labels had been off-centre. Therefore, the second batch of 1,000 had been the standard run. And, just to tease

collectors, Dave Travis, the owner of Stomper Time Records, revealed that 25 red vinyl copies had been pressed at the end of the run. These were being held back, presumably a move which would serve to enhance the collectability of such pressings. Travis confirmed in mid-2000 that there were no plans to delete this album. Indeed, since its inception, it had sold steadily (about 3,500 copies), and had been re-pressed several times (usually a minimum of 500 copies at a time).

Unfortunately, the original company which had manufactured this and other Stomper Time releases had gone into liquidation, and the metalwork needed to re-press the albums had been lost. However, Travis confimred that the Elvis release would be re-pressed in the autumn of 2000, using new metalwork and at a different location. This would then make it a genuine variation, although the expectation was that label and sleeve details would remain identical, as Stomper Time had the artwork for these.

The album itself was not available through conventional outlets, but was handled by specialist dealers, or sold directly from Stomper Time Records. Its selling price of £8 seemed fair considering its rarity value, and obviously much care had been taken with its production.

The cover shot - a black and white pose from 1954 (supplied by Trevor Cajiao, the editor of **Now Dig This** and **Elvis The Man And His Music** magazines) had been 'doctored' to produce a wide stage effect. Ironically, this was the same photograph BMG had used on CD 1 of **Platinum - A Life In Music**, 07863 67469 2. The company name and catalogue number, artist and title information, appeared above the picture, while the picture itself was flanked by five titles either side. *That's All Right* (shown as *That's All Right Mama*) was listed once only, though side 1 featured two versions; missing from side 2 was *I Got A Woman* and *Hound Dog*, though on the back cover and labels all tracks were listed. Along the bottom edge of the front cover was 'King Of Western Bop' in white lettering against a red background.

The back cover featured another on stage 'pose' in black and white. Underneath the tracks the musicians were listed, and a clear reference (though no dates) to where the tracks were recorded. Beneath the photograph were credits and thanks to all who helped produce the album, along with the Stomper Time Records logo.

While the cover showed the full title, the side 1 label read *The Louisiana Hayride*, alongside the 'living mono' legend. Using a yellow Sun-type label the credits listed Elvis Presley, Scotty and Bill (as the Sun singles had done). And, in keeping with the era, to the left of the centre hole was 'Vocalist with Hot Group Accompaniment'. All tracks and writers were listed though, once again, *Mama* was added to *That's All Right*, and *Tweedle Dee* was listed as *Tweedlee Dee*. Correctly the 'Recording First Published' read 1997. Side 2 read *Little Rock, Arkansas* and, once again, all tracks were listed below the centre hole.

Record 1

Side 1

1   **That's All Right** (Crudup)
2   **Good Rockin' Tonight** (Brown)
3   **Baby Let's Play House** (Gunter)
4   **Mystery Train** (Parker, Phillips)
5   **Trying To Get To You** (Singleton, McCoy)
6   **Heartbreak Hotel** (Axton, Durden, Presley)
7   **Blue Suede Shoes** (Perkins)
8   **My Baby Left Me** (Crudup)
9   **Lawdy, Miss Clawdy** (Price)
10   **Hound Dog** (Leiber, Stoller)

Side 2

1   **Any Way You Want Me (that's how I will be)** (Schroeder, Owens)
2   **Don't Be Cruel** (Blackwell, Presley)
3   **Love Me Tender** (Presley, Matson)
4   **Love Me** (Leiber, Stoller)
5   **Anyplace Is Paradise** (Thomas)
6   **All Shook Up** (Blackwell, Presley)
7   **Got A Lot O' Livin' To Do!** (Schroeder, Weisman)
8   **(Let me be your) Teddy Bear** (Mann, Lowe)
9   **One Night** (Bartholomew, King)
10   **Jailhouse Rock** (Leiber, Stoller)

Record 2

Side 1

1   **(You're so square) Baby I Don't Care** (Leiber, Stoller)
2   **Treat Me Nice** (Leiber, Stoller)
3   **Don't** (Leiber, Stoller)
4   **Santa Claus Is Back In Town** (Leiber, Stoller)
5   **Trouble** (Leiber, Stoller)
6   **Hard Headed Woman** (DeMetrius)
7   **Wear My Ring Around Your Neck** (Carroll, Moody)
8   **A Big Hunk O' Love** (Schroeder, Wyche)
9   **(Now and then there's) A Fool Such As I** (Trader)
10   **Stuck On You** (Schroeder, McFarland)

Side 2

1   **It's Now Or Never** (DiCapua, Schroeder, Gold)
2   **Are You Lonesome Tonight?** (Turk, Handman)
3   **A Mess Of Blues** (Pomus, Shuman)
4   **Like A Baby** (Stone)
5   **The Girl Of My Best Friend** (Ross, Bobrick)
6   **Such A Night** (Chase)
7   **Reconsider Baby** (Fulson)
8   **Surrender** (DeCurtis, Pomus, Shuman)

Record 3

Side 1

1   **Can't Help Falling In Love** (Peretti, Creatore, Weiss)
2   **That's Someone You Never Forget** (West, Presley)
3   **Little Sister** (Pomus, Shuman)
4   **(Marie's the name) His Latest Flame** (Pomus, Shuman)
5   **Anything That's Part Of You** (Robertson)
6   **Good Luck Charm** (Schroeder, Gold)
7   **She's Not You** (Pomus, Leiber, Stoller)
8   **Return To Sender** (Blackwell, Scott)
9   **(You're the) Devil In Disguise** (Giant, Baum, Kaye)
10   **Memphis, Tennessee** (Berry)

Side 2

1   **It Hurts Me** (Byers, Daniels)
2   **Down In The Alley** (Jesse Stone and The Clovers)
3   **Run On** (Arranged and adapted Presley)
4   **Tomorrow Is A Long Time** (Dylan)
5   **Big Boss Man** (Smith, Dixon)
6   **Guitar Man** (Hubbard)
7   **Tiger Man** (Lewis, Burns)

Record 4

Side 1

1   **If I Can Dream** (Brown)
2   **In The Ghetto** (Davis)
3   **Suspicious Minds** (James)
4   **Don't Cry Daddy** (Davis)
5   **I'll Hold You In My Heart (till I can hold you in my arms)** (Arnold, Horton, Dilbeck)
6   **Stranger In My Own Home Town** (Mayfield)

Side 2

1   **After Loving You** (Miller, Lantz)
2   **Only The Strong Survive** (Gamble, Huff, Butler)
3   **The Wonder Of You** (Knight)
4   **Polk Salad Annie** (White)
5   **I've Lost You** (Howard, Blaikley)
6   **You Don't Have To Say You Love Me** (Pallavicini, Donaggio, Wickham, Napier-Bell)

Record 5

Side 1

1   **I Just Can't Help Believin'** (Mann, Weil)
2   **Merry Christmas Baby** (Baxter, Moore)
3   **I'm Leavin'** (Jarrett, Charles)
4   **An American Trilogy** (Arranged Newbury)

Side 2

1   **Burning Love** (Linde)
2   **Always On My Mind** (James, Carson, Christopher)
3   **Promised Land** (Berry)
4   **For The Heart** (Linde)

Released August 1999

The idea of promoting Elvis as 'Artist of the Century' was heard long before the actual product itself was compiled and finalised for release in the summer of 1999. Thus, the announcement of a 75 track, 3 CD set, came as no surprise to fans. However, what did shock even seasoned collectors was the news that, in addition to the CD set, there was to be a 5 LP limited edition set, marketed not by BMG, but by Castle Music, in conjunction with BMG. What was even more shocking was the announcement that, in addition to the 10,000 limited edition black vinyl sets, there was also a very limited edition (500) blue vinyl set sold exclusively through HMV stores. And, in view of the fact that BMG had released their last Elvis vinyl album in April 1996 (*Elvis 56* - **LP 321**), this apparent shift in policy deserved some investigation and explanation.

Throughout the early nineties, it was evident that standard vinyl releases were becoming a thing of the past. Indeed, as each major release was being mooted, the question of whether or not there would be a vinyl equivalent was raised. However, as it turned out, BMG were persuaded to produce vinyl boxed sets for the fifties' and sixties' sets (**LPs 318** and **319**), in 1992 and 1993 respectively. Sadly though, by the time the seventies' set was compiled and released (in October 1995), a vinyl set was not manufactured, presumably because it was not thought to be viable in financial terms. At this point, many thought that vinyl had finally 'died'. However, in April 1996, another surprise awaited fans: the release of *Elvis 56* (**LP 321**), also on vinyl. And, perhaps, it was then that the seed of what would follow three years later was laid. Quite obviously, although a defunct medium for the majority of album buyers, vinyl began to enjoy a quasi-cult status with serious collectors; and, correspondingly, a number of companies saw the commercial advantage in producing high quality, limited edition sets for those who refused to embrace the latest technology - CDs - with any great vigour.

Ironically though, it was not BMG (using the RCA Records label) who chose to capitalise on this marketing opportunity, but Roger Semon, co-producer of Elvis product throughout the world, who by this time was also working for Castle Music. Presumably it was he who pushed the idea of having a vinyl equivalent for what was to be BMG's last major Elvis release of the century and millennium. Now, while we were not privy to the behind-the-scenes negotiations, clearly Semon perceived a marketing opportunity for his idea, and was able to see this through to its logical conclusion because of his unique position vis-a-vis BMG, and his highly impressive track record as co-producer. The actual deal between Castle and BMG had been negotiated in New York, over a year prior to the release of the album set. In a way, no more needs to be said. Whether or not BMG actually gave serious consideration to marketing such a set themselves became irrelevant: for the first time ever a third party company -

Castle Music - marketed a major Elvis release alongside BMG. The tracks were licensed to Castle Music who, using the RCA Records label, arranged for the vinyl sets to be pressed on 180 gms finest quality vinyl. Whichever way you looked at it, it was a coup and, moreover, one which proved so successful that, by December 1999, yet another special edition boxed set - this time picture discs - was produced (**LP 324**). Some people - perhaps even BMG! - must have wondered why BMG could not have marketed the set themselves. In some ways it was reminiscent of the situation when, in 1974, RCA licensed Arcade to release *Elvis's 40 Greatest* (*LP 73*) who then, to use industry jargon, 'cleaned up in a big way' - outselling RCA releases of the time many times over. A strange paradox.

Unquestionably though - leaving aside any consideration of its contents - what resulted was a product of the highest quality. For not only was the vinyl of the highest standard, but the packaging too exceeded all that had gone before it - even the prestigious fifties' and sixties' sets - in terms of quality materials. For example, the quality of the card used for each of the LP sleeves was of a high standard, quite unlike anything which had gone before; and, moreover, each album was, in turn, housed within yet another inner cardboard sleeve. Each was royal blue in colour, and each had a cut out so that the label was visible. Incidentally, each label was a different colour and on the A side gave minimal detail (there were no tracks listed) simply quoting which record and side it was i.e. Record 1 Side A, the artist's name, the album title, followed by copyright details. The only detail on each B side was which record it related to, and a part of Elvis's signature incorporated into the design.

As regards the design of the outer box containing the LPs, this replicated that of the CD set, except that in this case the increased size of the box (12 inch x 12 inch) meant that the full effect of its design was apparent, whereas its effect on the CD box was all but lost. The image of Elvis (a shot from 1956) was, like the background, made up of minute images of album or single covers. Sharp-eyed fans would notice the inclusion of the likes of Elvis's second HMV album! A neat touch.

The design of the back of the box was much the same, although there was no large image of Elvis. Instead, the main feature was the track listing (in five columns) below the artist and title. In the top left corner - in very small print - was the legend 'Marketed and distributed by Castle Music Ltd. in conjunction with BMG Special Products'. Just above this legend was the bar code. Please note that, although the HMV blue vinyl version bore a revised bar code number, 5 038456 410017, this was actually stuck over the original bar code number. Obviously this was done to discriminate between the two sets, although HMV had the sole rights to the blue vinyl set (limited to 500 copies), therefore it was for their stock control purposes only. Incidentally, according to Roger Semon, there was no significance in the ELVIS 100 catalogue number. We had thought it may have been intended as a 100 track album. Not so, we were assured.

Beneath the track listing were three logos: RCA, BMG and Castle Music, alongside the various production credits, while to the right of these details were more copyright details and a statement 'Made in the EU'. Further right again, was the small 'ELVIS 100' catalogue number. Along each edge of the box were the following details: the RCA and BMG logos, artist's name and title of the set, the 'ELVIS 100' catalogue number (just above the '5 Disc Set' script), and then Castle Music's logo. Attached to the front cover was a black sticker (approximately 13 x 4 cms) on which was printed the following:

'Elvis Presley / Artist Of The Century
Limited Edition 5-Disc Vinyl Set/180gms
75 Digitally Remastered Tracks
Featuring His Greatest Hits and Performances/1954-1976
Includes 24 Page Full Colour Booklet'

As mentioned previously, each album was housed in an outer album cover. Record 1 used the same photograph (from mid-1956) as used on the *Rare Elvis* album (*LP 263*). Record 2 used a colour shot from

Jailhouse Rock, while record 3 featured a sixties' shot circa 1963/64. Record 4 used a photograph from Elvis's summer 1969 press conference, while record 5 displayed a profile shot from the Aloha special in 1973. Behind all of these shots were faded images of Elvis as seen on album and singles' covers from all over the world.

On the reverse side of the first album cover was a colour shot of Elvis in Hollywood in August 1956. Below this picture was the track listing, featuring the song title, timing, writers, recording date (using the American way of putting the month, day and year), and publishers. The various logos and copyright information were featured in the bottom left hand corner. Departing from this pattern, the back cover of the second sleeve featured a photograph of the UK single *A Big Hunk O' Love*, RCA 1136 (*S 27*), though sharp-eyed observers would, perhaps, notice that it was the label copy which featured the wrong writers - Schroeder, Jaxon - when it ought to have been Schroeder, Wyche!

Each of the other sleeves used the same sort of layout, with only the small photograph changing. Album 3 was a colour photograph from *Blue Hawaii* (1961); album 4, a black and white shot from his summer 1969 press conference; while album 5 featured a black and white image of Elvis holding a microphone behind his back. This was from the Aloha concert in 1973.

As befitted such a set, there was a 24 page, full colour booklet to accompany it. The front and back cover used the same design as the outer box, minus the titles, of course, although the logos and publishing information were still to be found on the back cover. Within the booklet were comments made about Elvis by some famous people, music journalists and fans; a track by track commentary; production and musicians' credits, all neatly interspersed with photos of album, EP and singles' covers from all over the world. Perhaps the worst aspect of an otherwise very well-produced booklet was the illustration on pages 10 and 11, where there were three identical images of Elvis in his boxing gear from the film *Kid Galahad*. This, incidentally was the image on the 'Full Colour Poster' included with the HMV blue vinyl set. It was not very impressive.

Of course the blue vinyl set (which to some looked purple), was restricted to 500 copies, and sold through larger HMV outlets. Apparently there had been some discussion about using a different coloured vinyl, but eventually 'blue' was decided upon. However, in all other respects, the sets were identical to the black vinyl ones. The 'HMV' set bore a couple of additional stickers on the front and back of the box. A white sticker (4 x 4 cm) carried the HMV logo and read, 'HMV Exclusive Limited Edition Includes Blue Vinyl/180 gms and Full Colour Poster', followed by the individual number of the set of 500. In the top right hand corner was an HMV bar code, detailing price (£44.99), artist and title details. Note the use of 'ELVIS 100X'. And, as referred to previously, HMV also overstuck their bar code on the back of the box.

Incidentally, all of these sets were manufactured in the UK by EMI, and distributed throughout the world, although, according to Roger Semon, the only other territory to manufacture their own was North America. Ironically, in December 1999, a further 3,000 red vinyl sets were manufactured in the UK, this time solely for export to the USA.

Supposedly, this album was compiled not by the producers, but by fans, critics, fellow artists and other interested parties, who were sufficiently motivated to select their three favourite Elvis tracks and respond to BMG's request for this information. Additionally, the respondents were also invited to comment on Elvis, his influences, and so on. These comments were, in turn, included in the booklet and the people in question credited for their contributions.

The 75 tracks were then, we were told, selected on the basis of how many 'votes' were cast for them, although some fans expressed some scepticism as to whether or not this actually happened - particularly as there were some unusual inclusions and some strange omissions. However, this is not the place to discuss these theories, though we felt bound to report on what was said by other observers.

The track selection was more or less in chronological order, from 1954 through to 1976, though the years 1965, 1974 and 1975 were

not represented. Not surprisingly, the fifties and sixties were most heavily represented (29 and 34 tracks respectively), while only 12 tracks from the seventies were included, four of them live performances. Only two tracks from the post-1972 period were used: *Promised Land* (1973) and *From The Heart* (1976). Ten of the songs were from films, and the writers Leiber and Stoller had seven inclusions in the set, six of them consecutively.

As regards the versions used, there were no surprises here - and nor were there any alternative versions. *Love Me Tender* was the mono version, while *A Big Hunk O' Love* was the take as used on the fifties' set - remember the original single master had been a splice of takes 3 and 4. *Down In The Alley* had the full drum introduction (clipped on the sixties' set), while *Guitar Man* was presented without the *What'd I Say* ending. *Suspicious Minds* was the normal single version with its extended fade out; *I've Lost You* the studio version; *Merry Christmas Baby* a five minute plus version (one of several previously released edits), while *An American Trilogy* and *Always On My Mind* were the original single versions.

Incidentally, while there was no vinyl promo, there was a CD promo release, featuring 10 tracks.

There were no track details on the record labels - this information was confined to the back of the album covers and the outer box itself. The errors on the album covers were as follows:

Album 2. There was no reference to DiCapua on *It's Now Or Never*, and DeCurtis was not credited for *Surrender*. Lowell Fulson had his name mis-spelt Fulsom.

Album 3. The writers of *Tiger Man*, Louis and Burns, had their names reversed.

Album 4. The subtitle *(till I hold you in my arms)* was not shown after *I'll Hold You In My Heart*, and Dilback was credited, instead of Dilbeck. The writers of *You Don't Have To Say You Love Me* were shown in the wrong order.

Album 5. The writers of *I Just Can't Help Believin'* were shown as Weil and Mann, instead of the other way around. The writers of *Always On My Mind* were also in the wrong order. Mickey Newbury was wrongly credited as the writer of *An American Trilogy*, not the arranger.

Label Variations

BLACK VINYL

1	1999 PRESSING: MONO/STEREO

BLUE VINYL

2	1999 PRESSING: MONO/STEREO

LP 324 · Artist Of The Century

RCA/Castle Music ELVIS 100P

Record 1

Side 1

1. **That's All Right** (Crudup)
2. **Good Rockin' Tonight** (Brown)
3. **Baby Let's Play House** (Gunter)
4. **Mystery Train** (Parker, Phillips)
5. **Trying To Get To You** (Singleton, McCoy)
6. **Heartbreak Hotel** (Axton, Durden, Presley)
7. **Blue Suede Shoes** (Perkins)
8. **My Baby Left Me** (Crudup)
9. **Lawdy, Miss Clawdy** (Price)
10. **Hound Dog** (Leiber, Stoller)

Side 2

1. **Any Way You Want Me (that's how I will be)** (Schroeder, Owens)
2. **Don't Be Cruel** (Blackwell, Presley)
3. **Love Me Tender** (Presley, Matson)
4. **Love Me** (Leiber, Stoller)
5. **Anyplace Is Paradise** (Thomas)
6. **All Shook Up** (Blackwell, Presley)
7. **Got A Lot O' Livin' To Do!** (Schroeder, Weisman)
8. **(Let me be your) Teddy Bear** (Mann, Lowe)
9. **One Night** (Bartholomew, King)
10. **Jailhouse Rock** (Leiber, Stoller)

Record 2

Side 1

1. **(You're so square) Baby I Don't Care** (Leiber, Stoller)
2. **Treat Me Nice** (Leiber, Stoller)
3. **Don't** (Leiber, Stoller)
4. **Santa Claus Is Back In Town** (Leiber, Stoller)
5. **Trouble** (Leiber, Stoller)
6. **Hard Headed Woman** (DeMetrius)
7. **Wear My Ring Around Your Neck** (Carroll, Moody)
8. **A Big Hunk O' Love** (Schroeder, Wyche)
9. **(Now and then there's) A Fool Such As I** (Trader)
10. **Stuck On You** (Schroeder, McFarland)

Side 2

1. **It's Now Or Never** (DiCapua, Schroeder, Gold)
2. **Are You Lonesome Tonight?** (Turk, Handman)
3. **A Mess Of Blues** (Pomus, Shuman)
4. **Like A Baby** (Stone)
5. **The Girl Of My Best Friend** (Ross, Bobrick)
6. **Such A Night** (Chase)
7. **Reconsider Baby** (Fulson)
8. **Surrender** (DeCurtis, Pomus, Shuman)

Record 3

Side 1

1. **Can't Help Falling In Love** (Peretti, Creatore, Weiss)
2. **That's Someone You Never Forget** (West, Presley)
3. **Little Sister** (Pomus, Shuman)
4. **(Marie's the name) His Latest Flame** (Pomus, Shuman)
5. **Anything That's Part Of You** (Robertson)
6. **Good Luck Charm** (Schroeder, Gold)
7. **She's Not You** (Pomus, Leiber, Stoller)
8. **Return To Sender** (Blackwell, Scott)
9. **(You're the) Devil In Disguise** (Giant, Baum, Kaye)
10. **Memphis, Tennessee** (Berry)

Side 2

1. **It Hurts Me** (Byers, Daniels)
2. **Down In The Alley** (Jesse Stone and The Clovers)
3. **Run On** (Arranged and adapted Presley)
4. **Tomorrow Is A Long Time** (Dylan)
5. **Big Boss Man** (Smith, Dixon)
6. **Guitar Man** (Hubbard)
7. **Tiger Man** (Lewis, Burns)

Record 4

Side 1

1. **If I Can Dream** (Brown)
2. **In The Ghetto** (Davis)
3. **Suspicious Minds** (James)
4. **Don't Cry Daddy** (Davis)
5. **I'll Hold You In My Heart (till I can hold you in my arms)** (Arnold, Horton, Dilbeck)
6. **Stranger In My Own Home Town** (Mayfield)

Side 2

1. **After Loving You** (Miller, Lantz)
2. **Only The Strong Survive** (Gamble, Huff, Butler)
3. **The Wonder Of You** (Knight)
4. **Polk Salad Annie** (White)
5. **I've Lost You** (Howard, Blaikley)
6. **You Don't Have To Say You Love Me** (Pallavicini, Donaggio, Wickham, Napier-Bell)

Record 5

Side 1

1. **I Just Can't Help Believin'** (Mann, Weil)
2. **Merry Christmas Baby** (Baxter, Moore)
3. **I'm Leavin'** (Jarrett, Charles)
4. **An American Trilogy** (Arranged Newbury)

Side 2

1. **Burning Love** (Linde)
2. **Always On My Mind** (James, Carson, Christopher)
3. **Promised Land** (Berry)
4. **For The Heart** (Linde)

238

Released December 1999

In terms of track contents, this 5 LP boxed set was, of course, identical to both the black and blue vinyl versions of *Artist Of The Century* (**LP 324**), issued in August 1999. Indeed, other than having different stickers describing the set and giving it a slightly modified catalogue number, outwardly the packaging was identical to that of the earlier release. The major difference between this and the earlier sets was that this one comprised five picture discs.

Although, as we have said, the musical contents were the same, we have classed this set as a different product, and assigned a new LP release number to it, principally because it was issued in picture disc form. However, unlike the blue vinyl version which was sold exclusively in HMV stores, this set was given a revised catalogue number (a 'P', for picture disc, was added to ELVIS 100) on a small white sticker applied to the back of the box. The HMV set used an 'X', but this was only shown on the HMV sticker on the front of the box, and its purpose was to assist HMV staff distinguish between the normal black and their blue vinyl version. A confusing situation, we agree.

Many collectors greeted news of the release of this boxed set with dismay. Perhaps understandably, there was a view that this was exploitation at its very worst, and those who felt this way were quick to quote the cost, not just of this 'version', but of the different CD and LP packages released prior to this. And it was easy to see why, as both CD and LP formats in different versions would have cost around £200. Of course, there was also a contrary viewpoint: other collectors expressed their delight at receiving a picture disc collection. Perhaps this was because LP picture discs had rarely been used in the UK by RCA/BMG. Indeed, only *Elvis - A Legendary Performer Vol. 3* (*LP 109*) had been issued by RCA (in January 1979), although in 1987 a double picture disc set, *Tribute To Elvis* (**LP 286**), was licensed from RCA by another company. Quite possibly, vinyl picture discs had retained some kind of novelty value, heightened by the general decline in vinyl. Then again, it was clear that products such as this - and all high cost releases - were aimed at the collectors' market. And whatever your particular stance, there was no doubt that this was supreme marketing, and proof - if proof was needed - was clearly evident in terms of the quantities sold. A total of 3,000 copies were made.

Attached to the top left corner on the front of the box was a black sticker similar to the one found on the black vinyl version set, although this one read 'Limited Edition 5-Picture Disc Vinyl Set', and 'Limited Edition Number', in addition to the modified catalogue number ELVIS 100P. There were also small colour pictures of the front of each disc along the bottom of the sticker.

Each of the records themselves used the same photographs and basic artwork as that featured on the outer album cover of each disc. In the case of the various photographs of Elvis, the size and amount of visible detail had been altered to facilitate reproduction on a round disc as opposed to a square cover. Side 2 contained only the song titles and timings, whereas the back of the outer sleeve also included full writing and publishing credits. The various small photographs of Elvis (and, in the case of record 2, the UK single *A Big Hunk O' Love*), along with his name and title of the collection had been re-positioned in the top half of the disc, above the centre hole, and, in the case of the photograph, made slightly larger. The layout of the copyright warning and the logos was also different, as was the position of the word 'Elvis'.

All of the song title and writing credit errors found on the black and blue vinyl versions were to be found on this set.

Castle Music

While the precise details of the deal between BMG and Castle Music were not known, apparently it was based on a non-exclusive agreement whereby Castle would issue certain product on vinyl. In simple terms, BMG could have, if they wished, issued vinyl releases also. Castle Music were simply filling a niche in the market, based on a contract which would last for three years. The two companies worked in conjunction with one another.

The origin of the blue vinyl version of *Artist Of The Century* was that HMV approached Castle Music and requested exclusive rights on a coloured vinyl version of the set. The industry jargon for this is a 'bespoke pressing'. In this instance, HMV wanted a gold vinyl version, but when this did not work out (presumably its appearance was not pleasing to the eye), a blue version was decided upon. Incidentally, although all Elvis releases (in whatever format) have to be approved by the Committee, the issue of how many variations there are - in terms of coloured vinyl etc. - was overseen by Roger Semon.

Simply Vinyl

In March 2000 yet another 'player' emerged in the continuing saga of vinyl releases in the UK. Simply Vinyl, a UK company formed in 1997 and dedicated to meeting the small but hardcore demand for quality vinyl releases, issued their first Elvis Presley album in the UK. At that point, their roster of releases was just under 200 strong, comprising, in the main, artists from the 1960s through to the 1980s. Elvis was the first artist from the 1950s to be featured.

As with other trends in the music industry, it had become obvious that, while compact discs were the pre-eminent medium for releasing music, there was still a demand for vinyl releases which major record companies were not generally prepared to cater for. Hence the development of a company such as Simply Vinyl, which focused on the small collectors' market and, furthermore, undertook to produce a very high quality product in all respects - but at a price, of course.

Simply Vinyl had what is referred to as a 'finished product' deal with BMG, organised between themselves and Ray Jencks at BMG's Commercial division in London. The LPs were mastered from BMG CDs at Abbey Road studios in London, but actually pressed at the Record Industry (the old Sony factory) in Holland.

The albums were made from 180gm vinyl, which not only gave them a substantial feel, but which made for high quality sound reproduction also. Initially, 2,000 copies of each album were pressed (the licensing agreement with BMG was for a minimum of 2,000 units), and the belief was that any re-pressing would not exceed

4,000 copies in total. Distribution was handled by Vital Distribution who used the traditional outlets, though customers could order directly from Simply Vinyl. Incidentally, although a UK company, there was general acknowledgement by Simply Vinyl that the bulk of its sales were concentrated in the European market. Direct sales in the UK were thought to be relatively few.

Strangely, the Elvis LPs featured an orange label. This colour had long been superceded by different colours and designs. Indeed, the last Elvis album to use this colouring in the UK had been 21 years prior to this when RCA issued *Elvis Presley*, NL 43054 (*LP 119*), in December 1979. And even that release was something of an oddity, as the blue 'Elvis' label had been introduced some months previously. However, the label carried the round RCA logo, not the 'computer style' design. Ironically, but co-incidentally, Simply Vinyl's first Elvis release was also entitled *Elvis Presley* (**LP 325**), although the two albums were not the same.

As regards the sleeve artwork, it was taken from BMG's originals, re-scanned and touched up, where necessary. Somewhat incongruously, original sleeve notes were reproduced, although the inserts featured new notes by Colin Escott. Although made from high quality card, the sleeves themselves had a matt finish.

Sensibly, we believe, Simply Vinyl opted for a simple catalogue numbering system which used SV (Simply Vinyl), followed by the LP-- number which ran in ascending order. Out of interest, their first release was *Toys In The Attic* by Aerosmith (SVLP 001). But, because Simply Vinyl were basically obtaining finished stock from BMG (in the case of the Elvis albums), the Simply Vinyl catalogue number was not shown on either the label or sleeve (nor on the stickers attached to the outer plastic wallet). We have shown both catalogue numbers in the header block for each Simply Vinyl release.

Incidentally, there were a very small number of white label promo copies of each album made. They were, in a sense, test pressings and were housed in a generic promo sleeve.

Finally, it is worth noting that, although the titles of the Elvis albums issued by Simply Vinyl were familiar ones - *Elvis Presley*, *Elvis*, and so on - these were not re-issues of earlier RCA/BMG product. Instead, these albums were based on the latest BMG CDs which had been re-mastered to include additional tracks. In that sense, they were not the original 'classic albums' to which Simply Vinyl referred to, but newer compilations. That said, the improved sound and the fact that they included more tracks made them an even better proposition for vinyl collectors.

LP 325	**Elvis Presley**
	RCA/Simply Vinyl **07863 67735 1 SVLP 185**

Side 1

1. **Heartbreak Hotel** (Axton, Durden, Presley)
2. **I Was The One** (Schroeder, DeMetrius, Blair, Peppers)
3. **Blue Suede Shoes** (Perkins)
4. **I'm Counting On You** (Robertson)
5. **I Got A Woman** (Charles)
6. **One-Sided Love Affair** (Campbell)
7. **I Love You Because** (Payne)
8. **Just Because** (B. & J. Shelton, Robin)
9. **Tutti Frutti** (LaBostrie, Penniman)

Side 2

1. **Trying To Get To You** (Singleton, McCoy)
2. **I'm Gonna Sit Right Down And Cry (over you)** (Thomas, Biggs)
3. **I'll Never Let You Go (little darlin')** (Wakely)
4. **Blue Moon** (Rodgers, Hart)
5. **Money Honey** (Stone)
6. **Shake, Rattle And Roll** (Calhoun)
7. **My Baby Left Me** (Crudup)
8. **Lawdy, Miss Clawdy** (Price)
9. **I Want You, I Need You, I Love You** (Mysels, Kosloff)

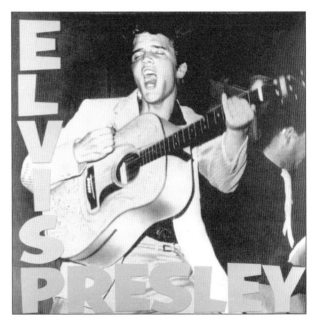

Released March 2000
Re-issued December 2001 Simply Vinyl S125010 (LP 340)

Simply Vinyl's first Elvis release was, appropriately enough, an album based on Elvis's first LP release in 1956. However, it was based on the original US album (LPM 1254), issued in March 1956, not the HMV release (*LP 1*) from October 1956.

Essentially, this release (based on the 18 track CD issued by BMG in July 1999), topped and tailed the original US album, starting off with Elvis's first US number one hit, *Heartbreak Hotel* and its B side, *I Was The One*, before moving into the twelve tracks which comprised the 1956 release. The last four tracks, *Shake, Rattle And*

240

Roll, *My Baby Left Me*, *Lawdy, Miss Clawdy* and *I Want You, I Need You, I Love You*, (all from early 1956) rounded off the album.

This release used the original US title - *Elvis Presley*. Originally, of course, the album had been entitled *Rock 'N' Roll* when issued in the UK. And although the advertising sheet for this new album claimed that there were updated liner notes, in fact this was not the case: the notes were as they appeared on the original US album in 1956. However, included as an insert for the album was a sheet which included several photographs from the era, alongside new sleeve notes (written for the upgraded CD version) by Colin Escott. Strangely, in paragraph five, Escott made reference to *I Forgot To Remember To Forget* being included on this revised album. Of course, it wasn't; but *I Want You, I Need You, I Love You* was. On the other side of the insert were the track details (writers, publishers and timings), along with credits for the musicians and to those involved in the production of this album. Nowhere on this sheet was any reference made to Simply Vinyl. However, there was a separate sheet advertising their products generally and listing the first 191 releases available.

The orange RCA label (with RCA's logo to the left of the centre hole) listed all the tracks, gave the writers and publishers but, very unusually, gave the recording date of each track also - shown in the American manner - 1/10/56 (10 January 1956). The label also displayed the BIEM/GEMA legends, as well as the LC 0316 number. And, although its catalogue number was SVLP 185, the label gave the 07863 67735 1 number, and quoted a publishing date of 2000 BMG Entertainment. Grievously though, the label read 'Stereo' when all tracks were in mono. Both label and sleeve read 'Made in the EU (UK)' - odd when the album was pressed in Holland.

The only reference to Simply Vinyl on the actual album cover was the hologram in the top left corner, which read 'Simply Vinyl' and, in very small lettering, 'Simply Vinyl Genuine LP'. However, the album was housed in a clear plastic wallet which had a closing flap, and attached to it was a Simply Vinyl circular sticker which read 'Limited Edition Vinyl LP'. Also etched into the flap were the words 'Simply Vinyl' and its logo.

On front of the plastic wallet was a silver sticker which bore the logo 'Simply Vinyl', and read:

> 'Limited Edition Vinyl LP
> Classic Albums
> 180g Virgin Vinyl Pressings
> Heavy Quality Sleeves'

In all major respects the album artwork replicated that of the original album cover, apart from catalogue number differences, and compilation credits. The company (RCA), artist, title, and catalogue number all appeared along the spine of the cover.

The only errors concerned writing credits, and were limited to the 's' missing from Peppers, co-writer of *I Was The One*, and an unusual format for the writers of *Just Because* - shown as Shelton, Shelton, Robin - instead on the more common B. & J. Shelton, Robin.

LP 326	Elvis

RCA/Simply Vinyl
07863 67736 1 SVLP 212

Side 1

1 **Hound Dog** (Leiber, Stoller)
2 **Don't Be Cruel** (Blackwell, Presley)
3 **Any Way You Want Me (that's how I will be)** (Schroeder, Owens)
4 **Rip It Up** (Blackwell, Marascalco)
5 **Love Me** (Leiber, Stoller)
6 **When My Blue Moon Turns To Gold Again** (Walker, Sullivan)
7 **Long Tall Sally** (Johnson, Blackwell, Penniman)
8 **First In Line** (Schroeder, Weisman)
9 **Paralyzed** (Blackwell, Presley)

Side 2

1 **So Glad You're Mine** (Crudup)
2 **Old Shep** (Foley, Arthur)
3 **Ready Teddy** (Blackwell, Marascalco)
4 **Anyplace Is Paradise** (Thomas)
5 **How's The World Treating You** (Atkins, Bryant)
6 **How Do You Think I Feel** (Walker, Pierce)
7 **Too Much** (Rosenberg, Weinman)
8 **Playin' For Keeps** (Kesler)
9 **Love Me Tender** (Presley, Matson)

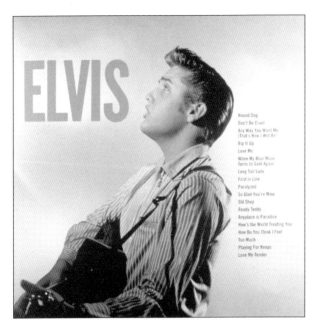

Released May 2000
Re-issued December 2001 Simply Vinyl S125029 (LP 341)

As with its first Elvis release in March 2000 (*Elvis Presley*, SVLP 185, **LP 325**), Simply Vinyl used the original US title for this their second Elvis album. In the UK, of course, the album had been known as *Rock 'N' Roll (No. 2)*, even though the front cover of the HMV release (*LP 2*) had read *Elvis Presley No. 2*. And, of course, the HMV album had sported an entirely different cover design.

Once again, this Simply Vinyl album had no direct RCA or HMV equivalent, but was, in fact, a vinyl version of BMG's upgraded CD version from July 1999. The front cover design and back sleeve notes copied those of the original US album (which were, of course, used by RCA in the UK when they chose to issue the album in December 1962 - *LP 17*).

Eleven of the original twelve tracks on this album had been recorded in September 1956 in Hollywood - thus making it Elvis's first dedicated album release. Similarly, the additional tracks - *Hound Dog*, *Don't Be Cruel* and *Any Way You Want Me (that's how I will be)* - tagged on the beginning of the album had been cut in New York in early July 1956. *Too Much* and *Playin' For Keeps* also dated from the early September 1956 sessions, while *Love Me Tender* was cut a month earlier. Only *So Glad You're Mine* pre-dated any of these tracks, having been recorded on 30 January 1956 in New York.

As was common with all Simply Vinyl releases, this album appeared on 180gm vinyl, which offered a greatly improved sound quality on standard vinyl pressings. Naturally, all tracks had been re-mastered anyway by BMG, so the source for mastering this album was of the highest quality. The pressings were carried out at the Record Industry plant in Holland. And as with *Elvis Presley* (**LP 325**), Simply Vinyl had been provided with the artwork by BMG, but had then re-scanned it.

The album had an orange RCA label - indeed the small RCA logo was situated to the left of the centre hole. And as with *Elvis Presley* (**LP 325**), the label read 'Stereo' - a mistake, of course, as all tracks were mono cuts. Beneath this legend was the bar code number and a publishing date of 2000 credited to BMG Entertainment. The mechanical rights details were situated to the right of the centre hole. The catalogue number was almost identical to that of the CD version, apart from the last digit - a 1 instead of a 2.

The nine tracks on each side were listed three above the centre hole and six below. This time, however, only the title and timings were shown - no writers, publishers or recording date details were displayed, as they had been on *Elvis Presley* (**LP 325**).

The front artwork copied that of the original album, but showed the revised track details as they appeared on the upgraded CD version when it had been released in July 1999. Similarly, too, the back cover artwork, except that the bar code appeared top left instead of bottom right and the Simply Vinyl hologram was situated below this, but above the track listings. The compilation, engineering and production credits followed, and the RCA and BMG logos were placed in the bottom left hand corner. Unlike the CD, there was no reference to the tracks being digitally re-mastered. The details along the spine included the RCA legend, catalogue number, artist and title.

Inside the album sleeve were two inserts. One was the Simply Vinyl leaflet advertising their other product (the same sheet that had been included with *Elvis Presley*, **LP 325**), plus another sheet which reproduced the original sleeve notes for the album on one side, and then on the other Colin Escott's revised notes as featured in the 1999 CD version. Below these notes, the tracks were listed in two columns. The song timings were given, followed by the writer credits, publishers and then recording dates. At the foot of the page were the general credits.

As with all Simply Vinyl albums, this album was housed in a heavy polythene sleeve with a fold over flap stuck down by a Simply Vinyl sticker. Slightly above this was the logo and the words 'Simply Vinyl' embossed into the cover itself. On the front cover was another silver sticker, rectangular in shape, on which was printed 'Simply Vinyl Limited Edition LP Classic Albums 180g Virgin Vinyl Pressing Heavy Quality Sleeves'. Incidentally, nowhere on the record label or sleeve was there a reference to the Simply Vinyl catalogue number. The record retailed for around £16 - reflecting its high quality finish, but also the production costs of specialised vinyl releases.

The track details printed on the insert contained three errors: Arthur's name had been omitted from *Old Shep*, *Playin' For Keeps* was shown with a '**g**' instead of the apostrophe, and the 'writers' of *Love Me Tender*, Presley, Matson, were in the wrong order.

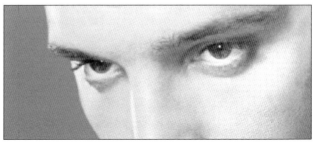

LP 327 — Elvis' Golden Records

RCA/Simply Vinyl
07863 67462 1 SVLP 231

Side 1

1. **Hound Dog** (Leiber, Stoller)
2. **Loving You** (Leiber, Stoller)
3. **All Shook Up** (Blackwell, Presley)
4. **Heartbreak Hotel** (Axton, Durden, Presley)
5. **Jailhouse Rock** (Leiber, Stoller)
6. **Love Me** (Leiber, Stoller)
7. **Too Much** (Rosenberg, Weinman)
8. **Don't Be Cruel** (Blackwell, Presley)
9. **That's When Your Heartaches Begin** (Raskin, Brown, Fisher)
10. **(Let me be your) Teddy Bear** (Mann, Lowe)

Side 2

1. **Love Me Tender** (Presley, Matson)
2. **Treat Me Nice** (Leiber, Stoller)
3. **Any Way You Want Me (that's how I will be)** (Schroeder, Owens)
4. **I Want You, I Need You, I Love You** (Mysels, Kosloff)
5. **My Baby Left Me** (Crudup)
6. **I Was The One** (Schroeder, DeMetrius, Blair, Peppers)
7. **That's All Right** (Crudup)
8. **Baby Let's Play House** (Gunter)
9. **Mystery Train** (Parker, Phillips)
10. **Blue Suede Shoes** (Perkins)

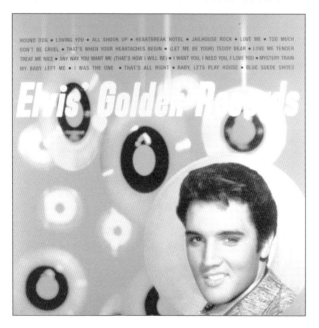

Released July 2000

Simply Vinyl's own advertising for this album listed it as *Elvis' Golden Records Vol. 1*, although its correct title was *Elvis' Golden Records*. However, as with *Elvis Presley* (**LP 325**) and *Elvis* (**LP 326**), there had never been a vinyl release of this album on any UK label bearing this exact track listing. Instead, this album was a vinyl version of BMG's upgraded CD version issued in July 1997, including the extra six tracks. Apart from the last digit (identifying the format), the catalogue number was identical to the CD version.

Of course, when the original *Elvis' Golden Records* (*LP 7*) was first issued in October 1958 in the UK, it was a modified album from that of the US original. And, while there is no time or space to revisit the differences and reasons for the changes in these albums, suffice it to say that the core of this latest album i.e. the first 14 tracks, represented the original US track listing. This 'version' had first been made available to UK collectors in July 1984 when it appeared on the German black label (*LP 232*). Thus, when BMG issued an upgraded version of the album on CD in July 1997, the following tracks were added: *My Baby Left Me*, *I Was The One*, *That's All Right*, *Baby Let's Play House*, *Mystery Train*, and *Blue Suede Shoes* - a mixture of three Sun recordings and three early RCA cuts. And, although big sellers in their own right, it was stretching a point to include some of these tracks on such an album. Obviously, their inclusion represented, in part at least, a tidying up exercise.

This was not the first time that a vinyl version of this particular compilation had been released. Shortly after the CD was released (in July 1997), BMG America issued a special white label vinyl version, along with *50,000,000 Elvis Fans Can't Be Wrong - Elvis' Gold Records Volume 2*. However, these LPs were not widely distributed and were thought to be exclusive to Tower Records.

In keeping with Simply Vinyl's philosophy and practice, this 180gm vinyl LP was pressed to the highest standard in Holland and housed in a top quality sleeve, replicating the artwork as featured on the July 1997 CD version - with some minor differences, of course, as is explained later.

The orange label LP - with the RCA logo shown to the left of the centre hole - gave a publishing date of 1997, the year the CD appeared. However, as with the previous two Elvis LPs on Simply Vinyl, the label read 'Stereo' - a grave error, as all tracks were in mono. The artist and title were shown followed by a numbered list of tracks on each side, three above the centre hole, and the rest below. The mechanical rights details were positioned to the right of the centre hole.

The front cover artwork copied that of the original LP version, apart from the addition of extra tracks, while the back cover was similar to the CD version. The Simply Vinyl hologram appeared above the track listing, and below this was a brief publishing note. In the top right hand corner was the catalogue number, bar code and compilation and production credits. The RCA logo, album title (but no artist's name) and catalogue number was shown along the spine.

Inside the album cover was a revised and updated list of other Simply Vinyl product - by this time 249 albums, though some were shown as 'Temporarily Deleted' or 'Temporarily Delayed'. One such album was *Elvis' Golden Records Vol. 2* (LP 329), originally intended for release in late August, but delayed until September 2000.

The other 12 inch x 12 inch insert displayed the track listing, and the original LP sleeve notes by Anne Fulchino on one side. The other side reprinted the CD sleeve notes written by Colin Escott, a couple of photos from 1956 (one showing him receiving a gold record for *Heartbreak Hotel* at the session in April 1956 when he recorded *I Want You, I Need You, I Love You*), then the full track listing down the left hand side. This gave the title, timing, writers, publishers and recording dates for each track.

The album was housed in a clear polythene cover, embossed with the Simply Vinyl logo, and had the usual rectangular label on the front cover (which obscured some of the song titles), announcing it as a 'Limited Edition Vinyl LP', and a circular silver label on the rear, used to stick the flap down.

A comma was used in *Baby Let's Play House*.

Side 1 Stereo

0786367462 1 A   ©1997 BMG Entertainment

ELVIS PRESLEY
ELVIS' GOLDEN RECORDS

1	HOUND DOG 2.15
2	LOVING YOU 2.12
3	ALL SHOOK UP 1.57

BIEM/GEMA
33 RPM
LC 00316

4	HEARTBREAK HOTEL 2.09
5	JAILHOUSE ROCK 2.27
6	LOVE ME 2.43
7	TOO MUCH 2.31
8	DON'T BE CRUEL 2.02
9	THAT'S WHEN YOUR HEARTACHES BEGIN 2.23
10	(LET ME BE YOUR) TEDDY BEAR 1.45

See insert for full credits

LP 328 | "That's The Way It Is"

RCA/Castle Music ELVIS 102

Record 1

Side A

1 **I Just Can't Help Believin'** (Mann, Weil)
2 **Twenty Days And Twenty Nights** (Weisman, Westlake)
3 **How The Web Was Woven** (Westlake, Most)
4 **Patch It Up** (Rabbitt, Bourke)
5 **Mary In The Morning** (Cymbal, Rashkow)
6 **You Don't Have To Say You Love Me** (Pallavicini, Donaggio, Wickham, Napier-Bell)

Side B

1 **You've Lost That Lovin' Feelin'** (Spector, Mann, Weil)
2 **I've Lost You** (Howard, Blaikley)
3 **Just Pretend** (Flett, Fletcher)
4 **Stranger In The Crowd** (Scott)
5 **The Next Step Is Love** (Evans, Parnes)
6 **Bridge Over Troubled Water** (Simon)

Record 2

Side A

1 **Love Letters** (Young, Heyman)
2 **When I'm Over You** (Milete)
3 **Something** (Harrison)
4 **I'll Never Know** (Karger, Wayne, Weisman)
5 **Sylvia** (Stephens, Reed)
6 **Cindy, Cindy** (Kaye, Weisman, Fuller)
7 **Rags To Riches** (Adler, Ross)

Side B

1 **That's All Right** (Crudup)
2 **Mystery Train** (Parker, Phillips)
    Tiger Man (Lewis, Burns)
3 **Hound Dog** (Leiber, Stoller)
4 **Love Me Tender** (Presley, Matson)
5 **Just Pretend** (Flett, Fletcher)

Record 3

Side A

1 **Walk A Mile In My Shoes** (South)
2 **There Goes My Everything** (Frazier)
3 **Words** (B., R., & M. Gibb)
4 **Sweet Caroline** (Diamond)
5 **You've Lost That Lovin' Feelin'** (Spector, Mann, Weil)
6 **Polk Salad Annie** (White)

Side B

1 **Heartbreak Hotel** (Axton, Durden, Presley)
2 **One Night** (Bartholomew, King)
3 **Blue Suede Shoes** (Perkins)
4 **All Shook Up** (Blackwell, Presley)
5 **Little Sister** (Pomus, Shuman)
    Get Back (Lennon, McCartney)
6 **I Was The One** (Schroeder, DeMetrius, Blair, Peppers)
7 **Love Me** (Leiber, Stoller)
8 **Are You Lonesome Tonight?** (Turk, Handman)

Record 4

Side A

1 **Bridge Over Troubled Water** (Simon)
2 **Suspicious Minds** (James)
3 **Can't Help Falling In Love** (Peretti, Creatore, Weiss)
4 **I Got A Woman** (Charles)
5 **I Can't Stop Loving You** (Gibson)
6 **Twenty Days And Twenty Nights** (Weisman, Westlake)

Side B

1 **The Next Step Is Love** (Evans, Parnes)
2 **You Don't Have To Say You Love Me** (Pallavicini, Donaggio, Wickham, Napier-Bell)
3 **Stranger In The Crowd** (Scott)
4 **Make The World Go Away** (Cochran)
5 **Don't Cry Daddy** (Davis)
6 **In The Ghetto** (Davis)
7 **Peter Gunn Theme** (Instrumental) (Mancini)

Record 5

Side A

1 **That's All Right** (Crudup)
2 **Cottonfields** (Ledbetter)
3 **Yesterday** (Lennon, McCartney)
4 **I Can't Stop Loving You** (Gibson)
5 **Such A Night** (Chase)
6 **It's Now Or Never** (DiCapua, Schroeder, Gold)
7 **(Now and then there's) A Fool Such As I** (Trader)
8 **Little Sister** (Pomus, Shuman)
Get Back (Lennon, McCartney)

Side B

1 **I Washed My Hands In Muddy Water** (Babcock)
2 **Johnny B. Goode** (Berry)
3 **Mary In The Morning** (Cymbal, Rashkow)
4 **The Wonder Of You** (Knight)
5 **Santa Claus Is Back In Town** (Leiber, Stoller)
6 **Farther Along** (Arranged and adapted Presley)
7 **Oh Happy Day** (Hawkins)

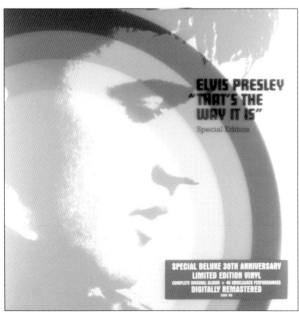

Released August 2000

An album with this title (minus the inverted commas), comprising the 12 tracks which make up record 1 of this set, was released in January 1971, RCA SF 8162 (*LP 47*). This album was subsequently re-issued in September 1981, RCA International INTS 5137 (*LP 167*), and again in May 1984, RCA International NL 84114 (*LP 224*).

Having established a winning formula with the vinyl versions of **Artist Of The Century** (LP 323) in 1999, Castle Music negotiated another joint release with BMG with the 5 LP vinyl set offered as a deluxe 30th anniversary limited edition - thought to be no more than 5,000 copies.

BMG themselves had released a 3 CD set comprising the same material in July 2000, and presumably had given no serious consideration to issuing a vinyl version themselves. Of course, as with the sets mentioned above, the release of the **Sun Singles** boxed set (**S 182**), as well as the release of **The UK No. 1 Singles Collection** (**S 183**), a joint Castle Music, BMG venture in association with QVC, the role of Roger Semon was thought to be crucial to this happening at all. And while no-one was privy to the precise details of such an

arrangement, what seems certain was that only someone of Semon's stature and repute - not to mention his unique relationship to BMG and the Presley Estate - could have carried off such a marketing coup.

As with other key events in Elvis's career, the real significance of the film **That's The Way It Is** assumed an even greater importance as the years went on. Certainly, it was welcomed and admired back in 1971 when it was first released in cinemas, coming as it did in the wake of the '68 TV Special for NBC and the majestic recording sessions held in Memphis in early 1969. In the eyes of a number of fans and critics, **That's The Way It Is** represented Elvis's last major peak period. Yes, he went on to tour extensively throughout the rest of his life and, of course, presented the first major satellite TV show in January 1973 (**Aloha From Hawaii**), but the drive and raw energy captured in **That's The Way It Is** was, for many, never surpassed. Thus the announcement that there would be a completely revised film version - preceded by a 3 CD set comprising a lot of previously unreleased material - was greeted with great anticipation and excitement. Hardly surprising then that a collectors' vinyl set was considered such a good prospect.

It is worth remembering that the title of the original **That's The Way It Is** album (*LP 47*), released in January 1971, was, to some extent, misleading. For while it purported to be a movie soundtrack album, only four of the songs featured were live version from the August 1970 season in Las Vegas. Further, of the four songs - **I Just Can't Help Believin'**, **Patch It Up**, **You've Lost That Lovin' Feelin'** and **I've Lost You** - only the first two were the versions as used in the film itself. **Bridge Over Troubled Water** was not a live version, but was a studio cut with an audience reaction overdubbed to simulate a live cut. All of the other tracks had been cut in Nashville during his June 1970 recording sessions. However, the revised version of the set added many more genuine live cuts as well as some rehearsal material.

Record 1, in fact, was exactly the same as the original album, using the same mixes, although the set sounded better as it was digitally remastered.

Record 2 offered a mixture of studio tracks recorded in June and September 1970, and live material from the 12 August show in Las Vegas. Only track 3, **Something**, was a live cut on side A, though this had first appeared on the '70s CD set **Walk A Mile In My Shoes The Essential 70's Masters** (74321 30331 2). Side B included a live version of **Just Pretend**, a song which had featured on record 1 as a studio recording. In fact, a number of the songs - or rather versions - on records 2, record 3 and record 4 had been seen or heard before (either in the original film or on albums such as the '70s boxed set), but this did not detract from the appeal of having a full show from August 1970 available for the first time officially. The material from 12 August concluded at track 3 on record 4. From **I Got A Woman** onwards, this material included more live versions of songs, plus some rehearsal items from July 1970. In short, there was something for everybody on the set including, as it did, 45 unreleased performances.

Now, while the material included on the set was generally greeted very positively, there was less enthusiasm for the sleeve design. The same kind of clear PVC box used for the 3 CD set was used to house the 5 LPs and, of course, the outer design was the same. Equally, each album cover featured a monochromatic image against a stark white background.

On the front of the box Elvis's name was printed above the title - and note the use of inverted commas. Underneath these were the words 'Special Edition'. These details were repeated along the top, bottom and side of the box, along with the catalogue number and the three company logos. Also on the front was a dark red/brown rectangular sticker with yellow printing, which read:

'Special Deluxe 30th Anniversary
Limited Edition Vinyl
Complete Original Album + 45 Unreleased Performances
Digitally Remastered
Elvis 102'

Printed in five columns across the back of the PVC box were the track details, restricted to song titles, but with an asterisk denoting the unreleased performances. Printed underneath were the bar code, logo, credits, and copyright details. As we have previously stated, the design of the box attracted some criticism. In addition, concerns were also voiced because the box appeared to be too small - certainly the LPs could not be removed easily.

As with earlier multi-LP and singles' sets, we have discussed each LP individually. However, all the LPs were pressed in 180gm vinyl and, in addition to having a top opening outer sleeve, each LP was housed in a substantial inner sleeve. In each case, the outer sleeve contained full track details - song titles, writers, publishers, and recording dates. The move from a 3 CD to a 5 LP format necessitated modifications to the artwork, and these are noted. The major difference was that there was no booklet included with the vinyl LP set. Instead, the sleeve notes and many of the photographs were incorporated into the LP sleeve.

Common to all five LPs was the use of a picture label which used the same photograph found on the front of the outer sleeve on side A, while side B contained no track details, but instead showed the artist's name, the title of the set, copyright details, catalogue number, and logos. Side B labels were, however, printed in different colours. The five photographs (printed to read 'ELVIS') from pages 2 and 3 of the CD booklet, were reproduced as a poster measuring 24 inches x 12 inches.

Incidentally, because there are more than one version of some songs, we have only mentioned any error in song titles and writers's names once.

Record 1

The outer sleeve for record 1 featured a close-up image of Elvis's face, and it was this that showed through the clear PVC box to complete the 'front cover' design. The back used the photograph of Elvis (complete with yellow background) found inside the cover of CD 1. It was this photograph that was used on the front of the original *That's The Way It Is* album (*LP 47*).

The inner sleeve was printed in light grey and reproduced the sleeve notes from pages 4 and 5 of the CD booklet on one side, while on the other side was a series of circular patterns, taken from pages 8 and 9 of the CD booklet. Through the cut-outs in the inner sleeve it was possible to see the same close-up image of Elvis used on the front of the outer sleeve on one side, while on the other (side B), the green label contained the basic details described above.

There were several errors on record 1. The names of the writers of *I Just Can't Help Believin'* - Mann, Weil - had their names reversed. The writers of *You Don't Have To Say You Love Me* were in the wrong order, as they were on *You've Lost That Lovin' Feelin'* which was shown with a '*g*', instead of apostrophes.

Record 2

The outer sleeve of record 2 featured the same photograph of Elvis as page 1 of the CD booklet, but the photograph on the back (taken at the rehearsals) was unique to the LP version. The inner sleeve showed the montage of record covers, letters, photographs, and session details from pages 7 and 8 of the CD booklet. Just to the right of this was what appeared to be a poster featuring a colour photograph. The same image had been used in the CD booklet, but in black and white. The other side featured the full version of the striking yellow and orange design from the front of the CD booklet. Side B featured an orange label.

The errors on record 2 included showing the names of the writers of *Love Letters*, *I'll Never Know*, *Mystery Train*, *Love Me Tender*, and *Just Pretend* in the wrong order.

Record 3

This used the same photograph found on the front of CD 3, while the back featured the one from the inside of the cover. Printed in light green, the inner sleeve showed three picture sleeve singles from Japan and America, none of which had been used for the CD format. The green floral design from the middle pages of the CD booklet was used on the back, and this time the side B label was red in colour.

The writers of *Words* appeared in the unusual format of Gibb/Gibb/Gibb, instead of the more common B. M. & R. Gibb. In addition, the writers were shown in the wrong order on *I Was The One*, and co-writer DeMetrius was shown as De Metrius.

Record 4

The photograph on the front was from the inside of the CD booklet - the same one found on the inner sleeve of record 2, but in poster form. The back of the outer sleeve reproduced the photograph of Elvis in rehearsal reading from either a lyric sheet or music score. What appear to be foreign posters for the film were included on the inner sleeve, again unique to the LP format version. The label colour of side B was purple.

Record 5

The front and back of the sleeve re-used the photographs from the front and inside of CD 2, while the yellow inner sleeve featured five of the nine colour photographs found on page 15 of the CD booklet. The back of the inner sleeve used the yellow and orange design found on page 14. The B side label was pink in colour.

There was no reference to DiCapua on *It's Now Or Never*.

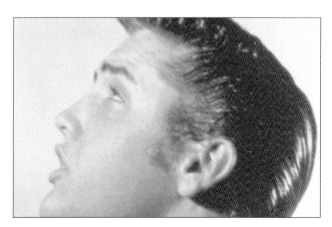

50,000,000 Elvis Fans Can't Be Wrong Elvis' Gold Records - Volume 2

RCA/Simply Vinyl 07863 67463 1 SVLP 241

Side 1

1 **A Big Hunk O' Love** (Schroeder, Wyche)
2 **My Wish Came True** (Hunter)
3 **(Now and then there's) A Fool Such As I** (Trader)
4 **I Need Your Love Tonight** (Wayne, Reichner)
5 **Don't** (Leiber, Stoller)
6 **I Beg Of You** (McCoy, Owens)
7 **Santa Bring My Baby Back (to me)** (Schroeder, DeMetrius)
8 **Santa Claus Is Back In Town** (Leiber, Stoller)
9 **Party** (Robinson)
10 **Paralyzed** (Blackwell, Presley)

Side 2

1 **One Night** (Bartholomew, King)
2 **I Got Stung** (Schroeder, Hill)
3 **King Creole** (Leiber, Stoller)
4 **Wear My Ring Around Your Neck** (Carroll, Moody)
5 **Doncha' Think It's Time** (Otis, Dixon)
6 **Mean Woman Blues** (DeMetrius)
7 **Playin' For Keeps** (Kesler)
8 **Hard Headed Woman** (DeMetrius)
9 **Got A Lot O' Livin' To Do!** (Schroeder, Weisman)
10 **(There'll be) Peace In The Valley (for me)** (Dorsey)

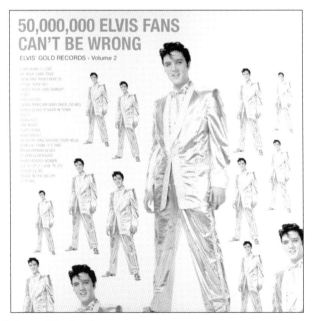

Released September 2000

For some reason the release of this album was delayed by a month. All Simply Vinyl would say was that there had been a hold up in some part of the production process.

As with **Elvis' Golden Records** (**LP 327**), this latest Simply Vinyl album - their fourth Elvis release - was a vinyl version of BMG's 1997 CD release. In other words, although the title had been used before, there had never been an original UK vinyl album bearing this precise track listing. What there had been was a white label album issued as a limited edition in the USA in 1997, after the CD version was released.

Once again, as we mentioned in the notes to **LP 327**, the history of this album was complicated and convoluted because the original 10 track 1959 US album was modified for release in the UK in 1960 and featured 14 tracks. It wasn't until November 1983 that a copy of the US album was issued in the UK (*LP 203*). But to complicate matters further, in November 1984, yet another album, using much the same title, was released in the UK (*LP 253*), but containing a revised track listing.

This latest LP version included the ten original titles as featured on the 1959 US album, but added ten more:

> *Santa Bring My Baby Back (to me)*
> *Santa Claus Is Back In Town*
> *Mean Woman Blues*
> *Party*
> *Paralyzed*
> *King Creole*
> *Playin' For Keeps*
> *Hard Headed Woman*
> *Got A Lot O' Livin' To Do!*
> *(There'll be) Peace In The Valley (for me)*

Of these titles neither **Mean Woman Blues** nor (**There'll be**) **Peace In The Valley (for me)** were released as singles during the fifties in either the US or the UK. Incidentally, **King Creole** was never issued as a single in the USA.

The artwork used the same images as featured on the original LP cover, but the back cover shot used the same photograph that had been used on the US single release of **Wear My Ring Around Your Neck** when issued in April 1958. In the top left was the Simply Vinyl impress, while the track details (song titles only) were listed below. In the top right hand corner was the catalogue number and bar code. Beneath the track listing were the RCA and BMG logos. The full title of the album (but no separate artist name) was featured along the spine of the cover, followed by the catalogue number.

Inside the album cover was the now familiar colour leaflet listing other Simply Vinyl LPs and their numbers. Additionally though there was another insert detailing the track information (titles, writers, publishers, recording dates, and song timings), production credits, and updated liner notes by Colin Escott. Adjacent to these notes were two black and white photos: one from the back cover of the original album, and the other from the rehearsal for the Frank Sinatra TV Show in March 1960. On the other side was a photo of Elvis and pianist Dudley Brooks at the **Loving You** recording session in early 1957. Please note that beneath the RCA and BMG logos (bottom left) was the 1997 publishing and copyright date - a clear indication that the artwork and details had been copied from the 1997 CD version.

In keeping with the other Elvis releases, the orange RCA label stated 'Stereo' (another error), gave the 1997 publishing date, the full title of the album, and listed all tracks plus their running times. There were three tracks listed above the spindle hole; the rest appeared below. To the left of the hole was the RCA logo. Beneath the track listing was the legend 'See insert for full credits'.

Once again the album was pressed on 180gm vinyl in Holland, and the quality of the packaging was of the highest standard. Each album was housed in the now familiar thick plastic sleeve which carried the Simply Vinyl logo and was stuck down by the silver sticker.

There were only two errors. The surname of the co-writer of **One Night**, Dave Bartholomew, was spelt Batholemew, and **Playin' For Keeps** was shown as **Playing For Keeps**, just has it had been on **Elvis** (**LP 326**), an earlier Simply Vinyl release.

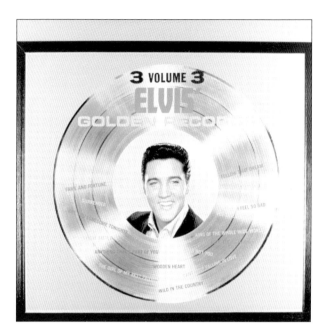

Released November 2000

LP 330	*Elvis' Golden Records - Vol. 3*
	RCA/Simply Vinyl
	07863 67464 1 SVLP 273

Side 1

1 **It's Now Or Never** (DiCapua, Schroeder, Gold)
2 **Stuck On You** (Schroeder, McFarland)
3 **Fame And Fortune** (Wise, Weisman)
4 **I Gotta Know** (Evans, Williams)
5 **Surrender** (DeCurtis, Pomus, Shuman)
6 **I Feel So Bad** (Willis)
7 **Are You Lonesome Tonight?** (Turk, Handman)
8 **(Marie's the name) His Latest Flame** (Pomus, Shuman)
9 **Little Sister** (Pomus, Shuman)

Side 2

1 **Good Luck Charm** (Schroeder, Gold)
2 **Anything That's Part Of You** (Robertson)
3 **She's Not You** (Pomus, Leiber, Stoller)
4 **Wild In The Country** (Peretti, Creatore, Weiss)
5 **Wooden Heart** (Wise, Weisman, Twomey, Kaempfert)
6 **The Girl Of My Best Friend** (Ross, Bobrick)
7 **Follow That Dream** (Wise, Weisman)
8 **King Of The Whole Wide World** (Batchelor, Roberts)
9 **Can't Help Falling In Love** (Peretti, Ceatore, Weiss)

Continuing the theme, Simply Vinyl released the third volume in the Golden Records series in November 2000 although, as with previous volumes (**LPs 327** and **329**), this particular set was based upon BMG's updated CD release from 1997 (07863 67464 2), and not an original vinyl compilation.

This time the album comprised 18 tracks, six more than the original 1964 album had (*LP 21*). The additional tracks were *Wild In The Country*, *Wooden Heart*, *The Girl Of My Best Friend*, *Follow That Dream*, *King Of The Whole Wide World*, and *Can't Help Falling In Love*, although two of them - *Follow That Dream* and *King Of The Whole Wide World* were never issued as singles in the USA or UK. Ironically, the B side of *Wild In The Country* had been on the original LP, though for some odd reason *A Mess Of Blues* (the A side of *The Girl Of My Best Friend* in the UK) was held over for volume 4 in this series, though this was probably because it had been the B side of *It's Now Or Never* in the USA in 1960.

Interestingly, none of the Golden Records series featured *Rock-A-Hula Baby*, originally issued in the UK as the A side of *Can't Help Falling In Love*. Furthermore, the belated inclusion of *Wooden Heart* was probably due to the fact that although it had been a number one in the UK in 1961, its release as a single in the USA had not happened until late 1965 - and even then as the B side of *Puppet On A String*.

Of course, these apparent anomalies had originated from the period when the release pattern of singles had varied between the US market and the UK, a situation which was clearly evident from the original *Elvis' Golden Records* and, of course, volume 2 also. Another anomaly occurred in that the version used of *Follow That Dream* was a stereo outtake (previously issued) as at that time the stereo master could not be located.

The major artwork was similar to that of the original album cover though, as on the CD cover, the extra tracks were listed on the 'golden record' image. The back cover, however, boasted a colour shot of Elvis from *It Happened At The World's Fair* with the catalogue number, bar code, Simply Vinyl hologram, track listing, brief production credits and company logos down to the left. Down the spine of the sleeve was the RCA logo, title and catalogue number.

Inside the album cover was a coloured leaflet listing other Simply Vinyl product, although this particular album was not listed. However, as with other LPs in the series, there was a separate leaflet with sleeve notes by Colin Escott (as used on the CD version) on one side, while just below these were pictures of the relevant picture covers in black and white. However, there was no picture for **Stuck On You**, **Follow That Dream** or **The Girl Of My Best Friend**, yet **Wooden Heart** was featured twice: the picture cover from the 1965 US release and the label copy of the UK hit in 1961 - RCA 1226 (*S 32*).

On the other side were two black and white photos, both from the early sixties. To their left, the tracks were listed, showing their writers, publishers, recording dates and timings. Beneath these details were some production credits and a publishing and copyright date of 1997 (when the CD was released).

As with the other Simply Vinyl Elvis releases the orange labelled album was pressed in Holland, using 180gm vinyl. For the first time the Stereo legend on the album label was correct. The label listed the tracks and their timings. And, finally, the LP was housed in the thick plastic sleeve bearing the Simply Vinyl logo, and featuring the silver logo which acted as a seal on the flap.

DiCapua was not credited for **It's Now Or Never**, nor was DeCurtis on **Surrender**.

Only the back of the booklet showed the correct title *(Marie's the name) His Latest Flame*. All other references omitted the words in brackets.

The writers of **She's Not You** were in the wrong order.

The Girl Of My Best Friend was credited to Ross Butler/Bobrick, but there should be no reference to Butler.

RCA/Simply Vinyl
74321 81102 1   SVLP 296

Side 1

1. **That's All Right** (Crudup)
2. **Mystery Train** (Parker, Phillips)
3. **Heartbreak Hotel** (Axton, Durden, Presley)
4. **Blue Suede Shoes** (Perkins)
5. **Lawdy, Miss Clawdy** (Price)
6. **Hound Dog** (Leiber, Stoller)
7. **Don't Be Cruel** (Blackwell, Presley)
8. **Love Me Tender** (Presley, Matson)
9. **Too Much** (Rosenberg, Weinman)

Side 2

1. **All Shook Up** (Blackwell, Presley)
2. **(Let me be your) Teddy Bear** (Mann, Lowe)
3. **Party** (Robinson)
4. **Loving You** (Leiber, Stoller)
5. **Jailhouse Rock** (Leiber, Stoller)
6. **Don't** (Leiber, Stoller)
7. **Trouble** (Leiber, Stoller)
8. **Wear My Ring Around Your Neck** (Carroll, Moody)
9. **King Creole** (Leiber, Stoller)

Side 3

1. **Hard Headed Woman** (DeMetrius)
2. **One Night** (Bartholomew, King)
3. **(Now and then there's) A Fool Such As I** (Trader)
4. **A Big Hunk O' Love** (Schroeder, Wyche)
5. **Stuck On You** (Schroeder, McFarland)
6. **The Girl Of My Best Friend** (Ross, Bobrick)
7. **It's Now Or Never** (DiCapua, Schroeder, Gold)
8. **Are You Lonesome Tonight?** (Turk, Handman)

Side 4

1. **Wooden Heart** (Wise, Weisman, Twomey, Kaempfert)
2. **Surrender** (DeCurtis, Pomus, Shuman)
3. **(Marie's the name) His Latest Flame** (Pomus, Shuman)
4. **Can't Help Falling In Love** (Peretti, Creatore, Weiss)
5. **Good Luck Charm** (Schroeder, Gold)
6. **She's Not You** (Pomus, Leiber, Stoller)
7. **Return To Sender** (Blackwell, Scott)
8. **(You're the) Devil In Disguise** (Giant, Baum, Kaye)

Side 5

1. **Viva Las Vegas** (Pomus, Shuman)
2. **Crying In The Chapel** (Glenn)
3. **Love Letters** (Young, Heyman)
4. **Guitar Man** (Hubbard)
5. **If I Can Dream** (Brown)
6. **In The Ghetto** (Davis)
7. **Suspicious Minds** (James)
8. **Don't Cry Daddy** Davis)

Side 6

1 **The Wonder Of You** (Knight)
2 **I Just Can't Help Believin'** (Mann, Weil)
3 **An American Trilogy** (Arranged Newbury)
4 **Burning Love** (Linde)
5 **Always On My Mind** (James, Carson, Christopher)
6 **Suspicion** (Pomus, Shuman)
7 **Moody Blue** (James)
8 **Way Down** (Martine Jnr.)

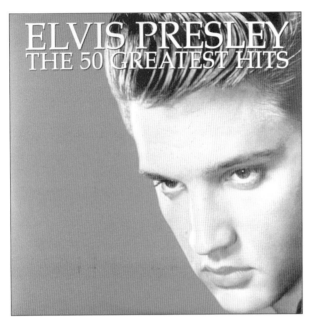

Released November 2000

On 20 November 2000 BMG released a double CD **The 50 Greatest Hits** (74321 81102 2), the latest in a long line of such releases. Clearly, unlike previous sets, this collection was devised and marketed specifically for the Christmas market and had the added benefit of being part of a £400,000 TV advertising campaign, in addition to a press campaign in daily newspapers.

Somewhat surprisingly, Simply Vinyl secured the rights to market a 3 LP vinyl set of this release, though this may well have been because Castle Music (perhaps the logical choice to market such a package) had released a 5 LP set of **Peace In The Valley The Complete Gospel Recordings** (**LP 332**), around the same time.

Once again, Simply Vinyl were replicating in vinyl form a package which started life as a CD release, only this time it was a triple album package (all previous Elvis releases issued by Simply Vinyl had been single albums) and, indeed, a contemporary release, unlike the others which had been from the back catalogue, albeit in an upgraded form.

Not surprisingly, the set ran chronologically, starting out with Elvis's first commercial recording, **That's All Right** from 1954, through to **Way Down** his posthumous number one hit in 1977, although in the case of the former song it was never a 'greatest hit' in either the USA or the UK. Its inclusion, we assume, was for historical purposes. Equally, other titles which had gone high in the UK charts (certainly top ten entries) were omitted (songs such as **A Mess Of Blues**, 1960, **Promised Land**, 1975, and **It's Only Love**, 1980).

Very unusually, this 3 LP set was housed in a single LP jacket, though it was understandably thicker than a conventional LP sleeve.

The front cover design was a partial close-up featuring a shot from 1956, indeed a trimmed down version of the one used on the cover of **Romantic Elvis** (*LP 192*) in August 1982. This time though, the blue velour shirt he was wearing had been airbrushed out of the shot

and you could not see all of his hair. Set against a dark red background, the words 'Elvis Presley The 50 Greatest Hits' were printed in white. On the back cover were two live shots, one above the other: the top one from his September 1957 tour, and the one beneath it from mid-1956. Alongside each were two famous quotations: 'Before Elvis there was nothing' (John Lennon), and 'I don't sing like nobody', attributed to Elvis himself in 1954 when asked by Marion Keisker who he sounded like.

To the right of these black and white shots was the track listing of each album (shown as Side One, Side Two etc.). Unusually, the numbering of each track adopted the 01, 02 format. At the top was the bar code, while at the bottom, beneath the track listing, were the copyright details, followed by the BMG and RCA logos. Down the spine of the cover was the small RCA logo, artist's name, title and catalogue number.

Inside the album cover was a 12 inch square glossy sheet. On one side were the track details (title, writer(s) and publication date), followed by copyright information, photo credits, an advert for the Official Elvis Presley Fan Club of Great Britain, and thanks to various named individuals. Incidentally, the publication details pertained to the US release dates, not the UK ones as several of them were different. For example:

	USA date	UK Release Date
That's All Right	1954	1956
Mystery Train	1955	1956
Jailhouse Rock	1957	1958
Are You Lonesome Tonight?	1960	1961
Guitar Man	1967	1968
I Just Can't Help Believin'	1970	1971
Moody Blue	1976	1977

On the other side were black and white photos from the fifties, and a quotation from Bruce Springsteen. Also included in the sleeve was a full-colour sheet advertising other product available on Simply Vinyl. Their catalogue now extended to almost 300 titles, six of which were Elvis albums.

As usual the albums were manufactured in Holland using the highest grade vinyl (180gms). The label format was much the same as previous Elvis releases. Using an orange RCA label (the logo was to the left of centre), each label gave the artist's name and full album title, followed by the track listing and their timings. The copyright date was shown as 2000 BMG Entertainment. Sadly, though, all labels read 'Stereo' when, in fact, all tracks on side 1 and side 2 were in mono, as were the first four on side 3. All subsequent tracks were in stereo. Needless to say, none of the versions of the songs were different. **An American Trilogy** was the single version (*S 83*) from 16 February 1972, whereas the last two major hits collections, **Presley - The All Time Greatest Hits** (**LP 287**) and **The Essential Collection** (**LP 320**) - 1987 and 1994 respectively - used the 9 April 1972 version which had first appeared on **This Is Elvis** (*LP 150*) in April 1981. Similarly with **Always On My Mind** which was the original version (*S 85*), whereas on the above mentioned collections the 'stringed' version had been used.

In keeping with other Simply Vinyl albums, the LP was housed in a thick PVC wallet with a closing flap. This time though, the sticker on the front of the wallet and the seal used on the flap were gold in colour, instead of silver as the others had been.

There were only a few errors. The words in brackets were missing from both **(Let me be your) Teddy Bear** and **(Now and then there's) A Fool Such As I**.

The writers of **I Just Can't Help Believin'** were in the wrong order. The old error of adding the name Kennedy to the writing credits for **Way Down** re-appeared, and Martine omitted the 'e', reading Martin.

Side 1 Stereo

74321 811021 A   ⓒ 2000 BMG Entertainment

ELVIS PRESLEY
THE FIFTY GREATEST HITS

1   THAT'S ALL RIGHT 1.56
2   MYSTERY TRAIN 2.24
3   HEARTBREAK HOTEL 2.08

BIEM/GEMA
33 RPM
LC 00316

4   BLUE SUEDE SHOES 1.59
5   LAWDY MISS CLAWDY 2.08
6   HOUND DOG 2.15
7   DON'T BE CRUEL 2.01
8   LOVE ME TENDER 2.41
9   TOO MUCH 2.30

See insert for full credits

LP 332 — Peace In The Valley The Complete Gospel Recordings

RCA/Castle Music ELVIS 104X

Vinyl One

Side 1

1   **His Hand In Mine** (Lister)
2   **I'm Gonna Walk Dem Golden Stairs** (Holt)
3   **In My Father's House** (Hanks)
4   **Milky White Way** (Arranged and adapted Presley)
5   **Known Only To Him** (Hamblen)
6   **I Believe In The Man In The Sky** (Howard)
7   **Joshua Fit The Battle** (Arranged and adapted Presley)
8   **He Knows Just What I Need** (Lister)
9   **Swing Down, Sweet Chariot** (Arranged and adapted Presley)

Side 2

1   **Mansion Over The Hilltop** (Stamphill)
2   **If We Never Meet Again** (Brumley)
3   **Working On The Building** (Hoyle, Bowles)
4   **Crying In The Chapel** (Glenn)
5   **How Great Thou Art** (Hine)
6   **In The Garden** (Miles)
7   **Somebody Bigger Than You And I** (Lange, Heath, Burke)
8   **Farther Along** (Arranged and adapted Presley)

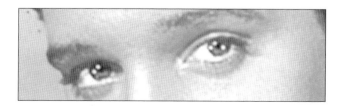

Vinyl Two

Side 1

1   **Stand By Me** (Tindley)
2   **Without Him** (LeFevre)
3   **So High** (Arranged and adapted Presley)
4   **Where Could I Go But To The Lord** (Coats)
5   **By And By** (Arranged and adapted Presley)
6   **If The Lord Wasn't Walking By My Side** (Slaughter)
7   **Run On** (Arranged and adapted Presley)
8   **Where No One Stands Alone** (Lister)
9   **We Call On Him** (Karger, Wayne, Weisman)

Side 2

1   **You'll Never Walk Alone** (Rodgers, Hammerstein II)
2   **Who Am I?** (Goodman)
3   **Life** (Milete)
4   **Only Believe** (Rader)
5   **He Touched Me** (Gaither)
6   **I've Got Confidence** (Crouch)
7   **Amazing Grace** (Newton)

Vinyl Three

Side 1

1   **Seeing Is Believing** (West, Spreen)
2   **He Is My Everything** (Frazier)
3   **Bosom Of Abraham** (Johnson, McFadden, Brooks)
4   **An Evening Prayer** (Battersby, Gabriel)
5   **Lead Me, Guide Me** (Akers)
6   **There Is No God But God** (Kenny)
7   **A Thing Called Love** (Hubbard)
8   **I, John** (Johnson, McFadden, Brooks)
9   **Reach Out To Jesus** (Carmichael)

Side 2

1   **Miracle Of The Rosary** (Denson)
2   **Put Your Hand In The Hand** (MacLellan)
3   **I Got A Feelin' In My Body** (Linde)
4   **Help Me** (Gatlin)
5   **If That Isn't Love** (Rambo)
6   **Help Me** (Gatlin)
7   **Why Me Lord** (Kristofferson)

Vinyl Four

Side 1

1   **How Great Thou Art** (Hine)
2   **Farther Along** (Traditional)
3   **Oh Happy Day** (Hawkins)
4   **I, John** (Johnson, McFadden, Brooks)
5   **Bosom Of Abraham** (Johnson, McFadden, Brooks)
6   **You Better Run** (Traditional)
7   **Lead Me, Guide Me** (Akers)
8   **Turn Your Eyes Upon Jesus** (Lemmel, Clarke)
     Nearer My God To Thee (Adams, Mason)
9   **When The Saints Go Marching In** (Traditional)

Side 2

1   Just A Little Talk With Jesus (Derricks)
2   Jesus Walked That Lonesome Valley (Traditional)
3   I Shall Not Be Moved (Morris)
4   (There'll Be) Peace In The Valley (for me) (Dorsey)
5   Down By The Riverside (Traditional)
6   Farther Along (Traditional)
7   Blessed Jesus (hold my hand) (Traditional)
8   On The Jericho Road (Traditional)
9   I Just Can't Make It By Myself (Brewster)
10 I Hear A Sweet Voice Calling (Monroe)
11 When The Saints Go Marching In (Traditional)
12 Softly And Tenderly (Traditional)

Vinyl Five

Side 1

1   (There'll be) Peace In The Valley (for me) (Dorsey)
2   It Is No Secret (what God can do) (Hamblen)
3   I Believe (Drake, Graham, Shirl, Stillman)
4   Take My Hand, Precious Lord, (Dorsey)
5   I Asked The Lord (Lange, Duncan)
6   He (Richards, Mullen)
7   Oh How I Love Jesus (Traditional)
8   Show Me Thy Ways, O Lord (Shade)
9   Hide Thou Me (Lowry, Crosby)

Side 2

1   Down By The Riverside
    When The Saints Go Marching In (Arranged Giant, Baum, Kaye)
2   Sing You Children (Nelson, Burch)
3   Swing Down, Sweet Chariot (Arranged and adapted Presley)
4   Let Us Pray (Weisman, Kaye)
5   Sometimes I Feel Like A Motherless Child (Traditional)
    Where Could I Go But To The Lord (Coats)
    Up Above My Head (Brown)
    Saved (Leiber, Stoller)
6   The Lord's Prayer (Traditional)
7   How Great Thou Art (Hine)
8   (There'll be) Peace In The Valley (for me) (Dorsey)

Bonus 10 Inch   *I'll Be Home For Christmas*

Side 1

1   Santa Claus Is Back In Town (Leiber, Stoller)
2   White Christmas (Berlin)
3   Here Comes Santa Claus (right down Santa Claus lane) (Autry, Haldeman, Melka)
4   I'll Be Home For Christmas (if only in my dreams) (Kent, Gannon, Ram)

Side 2

1   Blue Christmas (Hayes, Johnson)
2   Santa Bring My Baby Back (to me) (Schroeder, DeMetrius)
3   O Little Town Of Bethlehem (Redner, Brooks)
4   Silent Night (Mohr, Gruber)

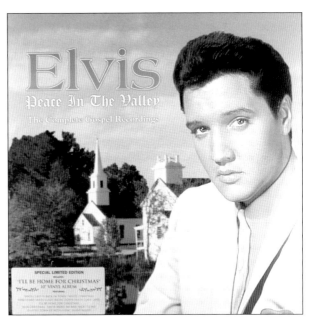

Released December 2000

The release of this 5 LP set came somewhat as a surprise when it was announced in late autumn 2000. BMG had compiled a 3 CD set (07863 67991 2) and issued this in November 2000, claiming it included 88 'gospel classics' dating from late 1956 (The Million Dollar Quartet Session) through to 1977, and embracing all known gospel/religious and quasi-religious items recorded formally or informally. There was some scepticism about this release generally as the audio quality on some tracks was not very good and, furthermore, BMG still retained the *Amazing Grace His Greatest Sacred Performances* double CD set from 1994 on catalogue. However, in fairness, this set did offer more tracks for completists, though the outtakes included on *Amazing Grace* were not used here.

The decision by Castle Music to release a vinyl boxed set ought to have come as no surprise, for their previous efforts featuring vinyl versions of CD sets had done very well for the company over the last year or so. On this occasion, the contents of three CDs had been spread over five vinyl albums. However, as a bonus, there was an eight track, 10 inch album included which featured the original Christmas recordings cut in September 1957 at Radio Recorders. These tracks, plus four religious cuts, went on to form *Elvis' Christmas Album* (*LP 5*) in November 1957.

The contents of the set, as mentioned earlier, spanned most of Elvis's career and included studio recordings (both formal and informal), some live recordings, as well as rehearsals and some home recordings. Inevitably, there was some duplication of material and the tracks in question are listed below with their recording dates (where known) and source.

Bosom Of Abraham

✱   Vinyl Three, side 1, track 3
    Studio recording, 9 June 1971, Nashville.

✱   Vinyl Four, side 1, track 5
    Informal session, 31 March 1972, RCA Hollywood.

Down By The Riverside

✱   Vinyl Four, side 2, track 5
    Informal session, 4 December 1956, Sun Studios, Memphis.

✱   Vinyl Five, side 2, track 1
    Soundtrack recording (*Frankie And Johnny*), 12 May 1965, Hollywood.

252

Farther Along

* Vinyl One, side 2, track 8
  Studio recording, 27 May 1966, Nashville.

* Vinyl Four, side 1, track 2
  Rehearsal, 4 August 1970, Las Vegas.

* Vinyl Four, side 2, track 6
  Informal session, 4 December 1956, Sun Studios, Memphis

Help Me

* Vinyl Three, side 2, track 4
  Studio recording, 12 December 1973, Stax Studios, Memphis.

* Vinyl Three, side 2, track 6
  Live recording, 30 March 1974, Memphis.

How Great Thou Art

* Vinyl One, side 2, track 5
  Studio recording 25 May 1966, Nashville.

* Vinyl Four, side 1, track 1
  Live recording, 20 March 1974, Memphis.

* Vinyl Five, side 2, track 7
  Live recording, 19 June 1977, Omaha, Nebraska.

I, John

* Vinyl Three, side 1, track 8
  Studio recording, 9 June 1971, Nashville.

* Vinyl Four, side 1, track 4
  Informal session, 31 March 1972, RCA Hollywood.

Lead Me, Guide Me

* Vinyl Three, side 1, track 5
  Studio recording, 17 May 1971, Nashville.

* Vinyl Four, side 1, track 7
  Informal session, 31 March 1972, RCA Hollywood.

(There'll be) Peace In The Valley (for me)

* Vinyl Four, side 2, track 4
  Informal session, 4 December 1956, Sun Studios, Memphis.

* Vinyl Five, side 1, track 1
  Studio recording, 13 January 1957, Hollywood.

* Vinyl Five, side 2, track 8
  Television recording (*The Ed Sullivan Show*) 6 January 1957, CBS Studios, New York.

Swing Down, Sweet Chariot

* Vinyl One, side 1, track 9
  Studio recording, 31 October 1960, Nashville

* Vinyl Five, side 2, track 3
  Soundtrack recording (*The Trouble With Girls*), 23 October 1968, Hollywood.

When The Saints Go Marchin' In

* Vinyl Four, side 1, track 9
  Informal home recording, December 1956, Memphis.

* Vinyl Four, side 2, track 11
  Informal session, 4 December 1956, Sun Studios, Memphis.

* Vinyl Five, Side 2, track 1
  Soundtrack recording (*Frankie And Johnny*), 12 May 1965, Hollywood

Where Could I Go But To The Lord

* Vinyl Two, side 1, track 4
  Studio recording, 27 May 1966, Nashville.

* Vinyl Five, side 2, track 5
  Television recording (NBC TV Special), 21 June 1968, NBC Studios, Burbank, Hollywood.

While the running order of the tracks was not strictly chronological (the earliest dated from 1956, and the last from June 1977), nor was it random either. Instead, the set opened with the **His Hand In Mine** sessions from late October 1960, and then onto the **How Great Thou Art** material from May 1966 (using the running order of each album, with the exception of **Crying In The Chapel** - a 1960 recording - which had originally closed the **How Great Thou Art** album). This material was followed by a few quasi-religious songs before moving on to the **He Touched Me** album from 1971. Thereafter followed more gospel influenced songs (studio cuts), some live performances, extracts from 'The Million Dollar Quartet' session, studio cuts from early 1957, more informal recordings, a few film songs, a segment from the 1968 NBC TV Special before concluding with a final version of **(There'll be) Peace In The Valley (for me)** from Elvis's January 1957 TV appearance on The Ed Sullivan Show.

Of course, the title of the set re-used the title of Elvis's first religious extended player release (*EP 2*), issued in July 1957 in the UK. However, the cover shot was different. It used an early sixties' image of Elvis's face superimposed over what appears to be a shot taken probably in 1969, circa **The Trouble with Girls (and how to get into it)**. Affixed to the front of the box was a blue sticker advertising the fact that this was a 'Special Limited Edition' - including the 10 inch vinyl album **I'll Be Home For Christmas**. The full title of the set, along with the RCA, BMG and Castle Music logos, appeared on each edge of the lid, and gave the catalogue number of ELVIS 104. However, on the back of the box was a sticker which read 'ELVIS 104X' and the bar code. The 'X' denoted a special release - in this case the inclusion of the 10 inch LP.

The full track listing appeared on the back of the box, superimposed over a rural scene. Strangely, instead of using Album 1, or LP 1, the script read Vinyl One, Side One, for example, and the track numbers were featured thus: 01, 02, etc. The three logos, plus the production credits and copyright details, were situated in the bottom left hand corner; while details of Sanctuary Records Group Ltd. (who had absorbed Castle Music in 2000) appeared in the bottom right hand corner, just above the 'Made in England' legend.

There were two different label colours used: vinyl one, three and five featured a blue label, while vinyl two and four used a black label design. In each case though the information featured was the same - with the exception of vinyl one, vinyl two, etc., of course - side one showing '**Elvis Peace In The Valley The Complete Gospel Recordings**', the RCA, BMG and Castle Music logos to the left of the centre hole, 'ELVIS 104' to the right and just above the LC 6448 number, and various copyright information below. Side two of each record had small design detail and read 'Vinyl One - Side Two', for example. Etched into the run-out groove was the catalogue number (plus 1A or 1B) and the word 'Damont' - the name of the place where the set was mastered.

Strangely, only four of the five covers had a photo on the front (and in black and white, too). Vinyl one used the same cover shot as the original **His Hand In Mine** album (*LP 13*); vinyl two showed a shot from 14 November 1970 (at the L.A. Forum); vinyl three was a reverse image publicity pose from mid-1956; vinyl four featured no picture but showed the liner notes by Cheryl Thurber; while vinyl five showed a publicity shot of Elvis taken while he was in the army. Incidentally, the reference in the text to Elvis singing **(There'll be) Peace In The Valley (for me)** on the second Sullivan Show was, in fact, incorrect. Elvis sang this on his third and last show on 6 January 1957.

On the back of each album cover the tracks were listed, giving the timings, writers, recording dates and publishers. The numbering of each track was, in this instance, conventional: 1, 2, 3, etc. In the

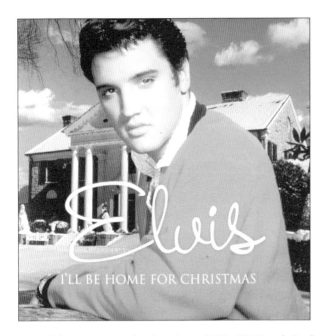

bottom left corner were the three logos (RCA, BMG and Castle Music), alongside the copyright details and the 'ELVIS 104' number.

As regards the 10 inch vinyl album, this featured a colour publicity shot (circa *Jailhouse Rock* in 1957) superimposed over a Christmas image of Graceland. The back cover showed a late fifties/early sixties shot, and another black and white shot from 14 November 1970 (Elvis's appearance at the L.A. Forum). Below these the tracks were listed, detailing timings, writers, publishers and recording dates. The label design of the 10 inch album was similar to that of the 12 inch albums, except that it was grey in colour.

This album though was not mastered at Damont, but by someone called 'Tim D' (his name was etched in the run-out groove). As with other specialist packages, it was possible to buy the set for around £40 or so, depending on where it was bought, although the general retail price was much higher.

Quite obviously, this set was a very limited edition (3,000 copies) as the inclusion of the 10 inch vinyl Christmas album and mid-December release date clearly showed. The plan then was to issue the 5 LP set (minus the 10 inch LP) again in mid-January 2001, this time bearing the 'ELVIS 104' number.

Almost inevitably with a package of this size there were some errors in writers' names

Vinyl one

The full title of the song *In My Father's House (are many mansions)* had never been used by RCA/BMG. Instead, the words in brackets are always omitted. We have amended the song index in line with this. The writer of *Mansion Over The Hilltop* was credited to Stanphill, instead of Stamphill. This error can be traced back to the album *His Hand In Mine* (*LP 13*).

Vinyl two

Elvis was shown as arranging and adapting *Amazing Grace* when it is known that the song was written by the Reverend John Newton.

Vinyl three

Elvis's name was added to those of Johnson, McFadden, Brooks on *Bosom Of Abraham*, an error repeated on vinyl four.

As with *In My Father's House (are many mansions)*, RCA have never used the full title *Put Your Hand In The Hand (of the man from Galilee)*. Again, we have amended the song index to reflect this.

Vinyl four

I Shall Not Be Moved is noted as 'Traditional', yet on the RCA CD *The Million Dollar Quartet* (74321 13840 2) the name Homer

Morris is mentioned.

On all previous appearances on both vinyl and CD, **On The Jericho Road** has been entitled **As We Travel Along The Jericho Road**. We can only assume that the title here was the correct one, and we have amended the song title index.

Vinyl five

I Asked The Lord is another of those songs which had been given a different title in the past. The song first appeared on **A Golden Celebration** (*LP 251*) when it was entitled **He's Only A Prayer Away**. When the CD version of **A Golden Celebration** was issued in 1998, the song had been re-titled **I Asked The Lord (He's only a prayer away)**. However, the correct title is **I Asked The Lord**. The writers of **Let Us Pray** - Weisman, Kaye - were shown in the wrong order.

On the 10 inch Christmas album, the writers of **I'll Be Home For Christmas (if only in my dreams)** and **Santa Bring My Baby Back (to me)** were shown in the wrong order, and the former title omitted the words in brackets. Someone called White was incorrectly credited along with Redner on **O Little Town Of Bethlehem**.

LP 333	Peace In The Valley The Complete Gospel Recordings
	RCA/Castle Music ELVIS 104

Vinyl One

Side 1

1. **His Hand In Mine** (Lister)
2. **I'm Gonna Walk Dem Golden Stairs** (Holt)
3. **In My Father's House** (Hanks)
4. **Milky White Way** (Arranged and adapted Presley)
5. **Known Only To Him** (Hamblen)
6. **I Believe In The Man In The Sky** (Howard)
7. **Joshua Fit The Battle** (Arranged and adapted Presley)
8. **He Knows Just What I Need** (Lister)
9. **Swing Down, Sweet Chariot** (Arranged and adapted Presley)

Side 2

1. **Mansion Over The Hilltop** (Stamphill)
2. **If We Never Meet Again** (Brumley)
3. **Working On The Building** (Hoyle, Bowles)
4. **Crying In The Chapel** (Glenn)
5. **How Great Thou Art** (Hine)
6. **In The Garden** (Miles)
7. **Somebody Bigger Than You And I** (Lange, Heath, Burke)
8. **Farther Along** (Arranged and adapted Presley)

Vinyl Two

Side 1

1. **Stand By Me** (Tindley)
2. **Without Him** (LeFevre)
3. **So High** (Arranged and adapted Presley)
4. **Where Could I Go But To The Lord** (Coats)
5. **By And By** (Arranged and adapted Presley)
6. **If The Lord Wasn't Walking By My Side** (Slaughter)
7. **Run On** (Arranged and adapted Presley)
8. **Where No One Stands Alone** (Lister)
9. **We Call On Him** (Karger, Wayne, Weisman)

Side 2

1. **You'll Never Walk Alone** (Rodgers, Hammerstein II)
2. **Who Am I?** (Goodman)
3. **Life** (Milete)
4. **Only Believe** (Rader)
5. **He Touched Me** (Gaither)
6. **I've Got Confidence** (Crouch)
7. **Amazing Grace** (Newton)

Vinyl Three

Side 1

1. **Seeing Is Believing** (West, Spreen)
2. **He Is My Everything** (Frazier)
3. **Bosom Of Abraham** (Johnson, McFadden, Brooks)
4. **An Evening Prayer** (Battersby, Gabriel)
5. **Lead Me, Guide Me** (Akers)
6. **There Is No God But God** (Kenny)
7. **A Thing Called Love** (Hubbard)
8. **I, John** (Johnson, McFadden, Brooks)
9. **Reach Out To Jesus** (Carmichael)

Side 2

1. **Miracle Of The Rosary** (Denson)
2. **Put Your Hand In The Hand** (MacLellan)
3. **I Got A Feelin' In My Body** (Linde)
4. **Help Me** (Gatlin)
5. **If That Isn't Love** (Rambo)
6. **Help Me** (Gatlin)
7. **Why Me Lord** (Kristofferson)

Vinyl Four

Side 1

1. **How Great Thou Art** (Hine)
2. **Farther Along** (Traditional)
3. **Oh Happy Day** (Hawkins)
4. **I, John** (Johnson, McFadden, Brooks)
5. **Bosom Of Abraham** (Johnson, McFadden, Brooks)
6. **You Better Run** (Traditional)
7. **Lead Me, Guide Me** (Akers)
8. **Turn Your Eyes Upon Jesus** (Lemmel, Clarke)
   Nearer My God To Thee (Adams, Mason)
9. **When The Saints Go Marching In** (Traditional)

Side 2

1. **Just A Little Talk With Jesus** (Derricks)
2. **Jesus Walked That Lonesome Valley** (Traditional)
3. **I Shall Not Be Moved** (Morris)
4. **(There'll Be) Peace In The Valley (for me)** (Dorsey)
5. **Down By The Riverside** (Traditional)
6. **Farther Along** (Traditional)
7. **Blessed Jesus (hold my hand)** (Traditional)
8. **On The Jericho Road** (Traditional)
9. **I Just Can't Make It By Myself** (Brewster)
10. **I Hear A Sweet Voice Calling** (Monroe)
11. **When The Saints Go Marching In** (Traditional)
12. **Softly And Tenderly** (Traditional)

Vinyl Five

Side 1

1. **(There'll be) Peace In The Valley (for me)** (Dorsey)
2. **It Is No Secret (what God can do)** (Hamblen)
3. **I Believe** (Drake, Graham, Shirl, Stillman)
4. **Take My Hand, Precious Lord,** (Dorsey)
5. **I Asked The Lord** (Lange, Duncan)
6. **He** (Richards, Mullen)
7. **Oh How I Love Jesus** (Traditional)
8. **Show Me Thy Ways, O Lord** (Shade)
9. **Hide Thou Me** (Lowry, Crosby)

Side 2

1. **Down By The Riverside**
   When The Saints Go Marching In (Arranged Giant, Baum, Kaye)
2. **Sing You Children** (Nelson, Burch)
3. **Swing Down, Sweet Chariot** (Arranged and adapted Presley)
4. **Let Us Pray** (Weisman, Kaye)
5. **Sometimes I Feel Like A Motherless Child** (Traditional)
   Where Could I Go But To The Lord (Coats)
   Up Above My Head (Brown)
   Saved (Leiber, Stoller)
6. **The Lord's Prayer** (Traditional)
7. **How Great Thou Art** (Hine)
8. **(There'll be) Peace In The Valley (for me)** (Dorsey)

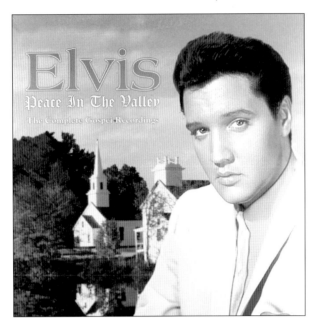

Released January 2001

The Lord's Prayer	16 May 1971
Bosom Of Abraham	31 March 1972
Lead Me, Guide Me	31 March 1972
I, John	31 March 1972

Errors in song titles and writing credits were the same as those found on the special edition version (**LP 332**).

With the exception of *"That's The Way It Is"* (**LP 328**), all of the previous Castle Music releases had followed the pattern whereby a special edition version was released after the regular version. (*"That's The Way It Is"* appeared as a regular release only.) For example, the regular issue of **Artist Of The Century** (**LP 323**) was accompanied by a limited edition blue vinyl set and followed, four months later, by a picture disc version (**LP 324**).

However, this was not the case with **Peace In The Valley The Complete Gospel Recordings** set, as the special edition version (**LP 332**) was released before the regular one. Presumably this was simply a question of timing. As the special edition version included a 10 inch album of Christmas songs, it was clearly essential that this product reached the shops in time to maximise sales. Nevertheless, the regular version was available by mid-January.

Outwardly, there were only minor differences to distinguish the special edition and regular versions. The sticker on the back which showed the catalogue number 'ELVIS 104X' (the 'X' denoting a special edition) had been removed on this set, revealing the regular bar code. And, unlike the special edition version, there was no sticker on the front of the box. In all other respects, the two sets were the same. Although the track listing of the five gospel albums was identical, we cannot class this as being a re-issue, as the omission of the 10 inch album meant that overall the two 'packages' were different.

Surprisingly, the release of **Peace In the Valley The Complete Gospel Recordings** highlighted the fact that a number of tracks had never appeared on vinyl previously, although they had, of course, been included on CD releases. In all, 12 performances were new to vinyl, although **Sometimes I Feel Like A Motherless Child** (a song featured as part of the gospel medley recorded for the NBC TV Special in 1968) did not feature Elvis's vocal. For those of you that are interested, the songs (and their recordings dates) were as follows:

You Better Run	31 March 1972
Turn Your Eyes Upon Jesus/Nearer My God To Thee	31 March 1972
I Asked The Lord	1959
He	1960
Oh How I Love Jesus	1966
Show Me Thy Ways, O Lord	1966
Hide Thou Me	1966
Sometimes I Feel Like A Motherless Child	21 June 1968

LP 334 — Elvis' Gold Records-Volume 4

RCA/Simply Vinyl
07863 67465 1 SVLP 342

Side 1

1. **Return To Sender** (Blackwell, Scott)
2. **Rock-A-Hula Baby** (Wise, Weisman, Fuller)
3. **Love Letters** (Young, Heyman)
4. **Bossa Nova Baby** (Leiber, Stoller)
5. **Witchcraft** (Bartholomew, King)
6. **Kissin' Cousins** (Wise, Starr)
7. **It Hurts Me** (Byers, Daniels)
8. **Viva Las Vegas** (Pomus, Shuman)
9. **What'd I Say** (Charles)

Side 2

1. **Please Don't Drag That String Around** (Blackwell, Scott)
2. **Indescribably Blue** (Glenn)
3. **(You're the) Devil In Disguise** (Giant, Baum, Kaye)
4. **Lonely Man** (Benjamin, Marcus)
5. **A Mess Of Blues** (Pomus, Shuman)
6. **Ask Me** (Modugno, Giant, Baum, Kaye)
7. **Ain't That Loving You Baby** (Otis, Hunter)
8. **Just Tell Her Jim Said Hello** (Leiber, Stoller)
9. **Crying In The Chapel** (Glenn)

Released July 2001

Having taken everyone by surprise at their vinyl release of **The 50 Greatest Hits** (**LP 331**) in November 2000 - an impressive triple LP set – Simply Vinyl returned to the continuing theme of issuing the Golden Records series in July 2001. Although the release of volume 4 had been talked about for a while, it had been subject to a delay in its release, though there was nothing untoward about this - it happens with most record companies.

As with all previous volumes issued by Simply Vinyl, this LP, while based on the original 1968 12 track release (*LP 34*), was the vinyl equivalent of BMG's upgraded CD version, bearing 18 tracks and issued in mid-July 1997.

Most of the additional tracks, with the exception of **Crying In The Chapel**, the last track, were all sequenced near the beginning of the album. **Crying In The Chapel** (*S 50*) was Elvis's last UK number one hit of the '60s. Its exclusion from the original album was probably because it had been added as a bonus track to the **How Great Thou Art** album (*LP 31*) in April 1967.

This revised release spanned an almost seven year time period, from **A Mess Of Blues** (*S 29*) in 1960, through to **Indescribably Blue** (*S 57*) in February 1967. Of course, the decision by BMG to include extra tracks created some anomolies, in that some of the tracks would have been more suited to volume 3 in the series. And, indeed, by the time the original LP was issued, the hits were far fewer in number and, in truth, some were relatively minor hits. Remember, **Ain't That Loving You Baby** (*S 47*) dated back to June 1958 when it was cut at Elvis's last pre-Army session in Nashville before he left for his army duties overseas. Of course, it wasn't issued until October 1964 when it was the A side of **Ask Me**, a track cut in Nashville in January 1964.

The table below illustrates the difficulties faced by the producers of both the original and the revised album. For example, **A Mess Of Blues** (*S 29*) was an odd inclusion for, in truth, it ought to have appeared on Volume 3 (its B side **The Girl Of My Best Friend** was included on the revised CD version in 1997). The fact that it wasn't included was probably because it was not an A side in the USA, but rather the B side of **It's Now Or Never**. Similarly, **Just Tell Her Jim Said Hello**, the original B side of **She's Not You** (*S 38*) had been included on **Elvis's Golden Records Vol. 3** (*LP 21*).

Release Number	Titles	Original Gold 4	Revised Gold 4	Original Gold 3	Revised Gold 3
S 29	A Mess Of Blues	Yes	Yes		
	The Girl Of My Best Friend	-	-	-	Yes
S 33	Surrender	-	-	-	Yes
	Lonely Man	Yes	Yes		
S 36	Rock-A-Hula Baby	-	Yes		
	Can't Help Falling In Love	-	-	-	Yes
S 38	She's Not You	-	-	Yes	Yes
	Just Tell Her Jim Said Hello	Yes	Yes		
S 39	Return To Sender	-	Yes		
	Where Do You Come From	-	-		
S 41	(You're the) Devil In Disguise	Yes	Yes		
	Please Don't Drag That String Around	Yes	Yes		
S 42	Bossa Nova Baby	-	Yes		
	Witchcraft	Yes	Yes		
S 44	Viva Las Vegas	-	Yes		
	What'd I Say	Yes	Yes		
S 45	Kissin' Cousins	-	Yes		
	It Hurts Me	Yes	Yes		
S 47	Ain't That Loving You Baby	Yes	Yes		
	Ask Me	Yes	Yes		
S 50	Crying In The Chapel	-	Yes		
	I Believe In The Man In The Sky	-	-		
S 54	Love Letters	Yes	Yes		
	Come What May	-	-		
S 57	Indescribably Blue	Yes	Yes		
	Fools Fall In Love	-	-		

As befitted the period, most tracks were in proper stereo, apart from **Ain't That Loving You Baby**, a mono recording from 1958, and the two tracks from **Viva Las Vegas**, neither of which appeared here in good stereo. There was separation on the tracks, but it sounded more like electronic stereo.

Oddly, the tracks were not sequenced in their original order, even taking into account the additional ones. Nor were they listed in order on the front cover. And as with all the other vinyl versions in this series, the main artwork on the front cover copied that of the CD. However, on the reverse side, the tracks were listed to the left of the mid-sixties' photo (they had been on the right on the CD version), just below the bar code and compilation credits. Underneath the tracks themselves were the two main logos - RCA and BMG - and a 1997 publication date.

Inside the album cover was an insert which featured a black and white photo of Elvis on one side (circa 1963/4) while on the other side all the tracks, timings, writers, publication and recording dates were given. Below these details were the compilation credits and the logos again. Colin Escott's sleeve notes were featured to the right of these details; while to the right again was a black and white picture from **Viva Las Vegas** and below this, photos of the original US covers for some of the singles included. Very strangely though, not only was there a picture of the **Fun In Acapulco** LP shown (for **Bossa Nova Baby** presumably), but there was an illustration for the single **Big Boss Man/ You Don't Know Me**, when neither track was included on the album! There were no covers shown for **Love Letters**, **Lonely Man** or **Just Tell Her Jim Said Hello**.

There were a couple of minor errors regarding the recording dates given. According to Ernst Jorgensen's book **A Life In Music**, **Return To Sender** was cut on 27 March 1962, not the 26th; **Witchcraft** was recorded on 26 May 1963, not the 27th; and **Kissin' Cousins** was shown as October 1963 when it ought to have been 30 September 1963. Clearly these dates had been refined by Jorgensen since the original CDs were issued in 1997.

The orange label LPs were pressed in Holland using 180gm vinyl. As with the other releases in the series, the label read Side 1 Stereo, gave the publication date as 1997, then the title, followed by a list of the tracks, though this time no timings were shown on the label. The small white RCA logo appeared to the left of the centre hole. Incidentally, the SVLP number was stamped into the run out groove on Side 1 and was shown as 342, and hand etched into Side 2, when originally it had been advertised as SVLP 341. As with all the Simply Vinyl LPs, this was the only place the Simply Vinyl catalogue number was shown.

As usual, the album cover was made of good quality card and was housed in the now customary thick plastic sleeve, complete with the Simply Vinyl logos on front and back. This time though there was no hologram on the back of the sleeve.

There were no writing credits printed on the label, only the song titles. However, full credits were to be found on the insert, and this contained the following errors. The old problem with the order of Young, Heyman, writers of **Love Letters**, re-occurred. Dave Bartholomew's name was mis-spelt Bartholemew, an error which had not been seen for many years.

Side **1** Stereo

0786367465 1A ℗1997 BMG Entertainment

ELVIS' GOLD RECORDS - VOLUME 4

1 RETURN TO SENDER
2 ROCK-A-HULA BABY
3 LOVE LETTERS

BIEM/GEMA
33 RPM
LC 00316

4 BOSSA NOVA BABY
5 WITCHCRAFT
6 KISSIN' COUSINS
7 IT HURTS ME
8 VIVA LAS VEGAS
9 WHAT'D I SAY

See insert for full credits

LP 335 — Live In Las Vegas

RCA/Castle Music ELVIS 108

Record One

Side A

1 **Blue Suede Shoes** (Perkins)
2 **I Got A Woman** (Charles)
3 **All Shook Up** (Blackwell, Presley)
4 **Elvis welcomes the audience**
5 **Love Me Tender** (Presley, Matson)
6 **Jailhouse Rock** (Leiber, Stoller)
   Don't Be Cruel (Blackwell, Presley)
7 **Heartbreak Hotel** (Axton, Durden, Presley)
8 **Hound Dog** (Leiber, Stoller)
9 **I Can't Stop Loving You** (Gibson)
10 **Johnny B. Goode** (Berry)
11 **Baby, What You Want Me To Do** (Reed)

Side B

1 **Runaway** (Crook, Shannon)
2 **Are You Lonesome Tonight?** (Turk, Handman)
3 **Yesterday** (Lennon, McCartney)
   Hey Jude (Lennon, McCartney)
4 **Introductions**
5 **In The Ghetto** (Davis)
6 **Suspicious Minds** (James)
7 **What'd I Say** (Charles)
8 **Can't Help Falling In Love** (Peretti, Creatore, Weiss)

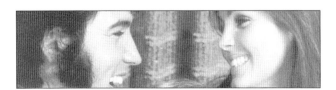

Record Two

Side A

1 **Elvis talks about his career**
2 **Heartbreak Hotel** (Axton, Durden, Presley)
3 **Long Tall Sally** (Johnson, Blackwell, Penniman)
4 **Blue Suede Shoes** (Perkins)
5 **Money Honey** (Stone)

Side B

1 **That's All Right** (Crudup)
2 **I Got A Woman** (Charles)
3 **Hound Dog** (Leiber, Stoller)
4 **Love Me Tender** (Presley, Matson)
5 **There Goes My Everything** (Frazier)
6 **Just Pretend** (Flett, Fletcher)
7 **I Just Can't Help Believin'** (Mann, Weil)

Record Three

Side A

1 **Something** (Harrison)
2 **Men With Broken Hearts** (Williams)
3 **Walk A Mile In My Shoes** (South)
4 **You've Lost That Lovin' Feelin'** (Spector, Mann, Weil)
5 **Polk Salad Annie** (White)
6 **One Night** (Bartholomew, King)
7 **Don't Be Cruel** (Blackwell, Presley)
8 **Love Me** (Leiber, Stoller)
9 **Instrumental vamp**
10 **Heartbreak Hotel** (Axton, Durden, Presley)

Side B

1 **Introductions**
2 **Bridge Over Troubled Water** (Simon)
3 **Suspicious Minds** (James)
4 **Can't Help Falling In Love** (Peretti, Creatore, Weiss)
5 **When The Snow Is On The Roses** (Last, Kusik, Snyder, Bader)
6 **See See Rider** (Broonzy)
7 **Release Me (and let me love again)** (Miller, Williams, Yount, Harris)
8 **Sweet Caroline** (Diamond)

Record Four

Side A

1 **The Wonder Of You** (Knight)
2 **Polk Salad Annie** (White)
3 **Proud Mary** (Fogerty)
4 **Walk A Mile In My Shoes** (South)
5 **In The Ghetto** (Davis)
6 **Let It Be Me (Je T'Appartiens)** (Curtis, Delanoe, Becaud)
7 **Don't Cry Daddy** (Davis)
8 **Kentucky Rain** (Rabbitt, Heard)
9 **Long Tall Sally** (Johnson, Blackwell, Penniman)
10 **I Can't Stop Loving You** (Gibson)

Side B

1 **Suspicious Minds** (James)
2 **Never Been To Spain** (Axton)
3 **You Gave Me A Mountain** (Robbins)
4 **It's Impossible** (Wayne, Manzanero)
5 **It's Over** (Rodgers)
6 **Hound Dog** (Leiber, Stoller)
7 **Little Sister** (Pomus, Shuman)
  Get Back (Lennon, McCartney)
8 **A Big Hunk O' Love** (Schroeder, Wyche)
9 **The Impossible Dream** (Leigh, Darion)
10 **An American Trilogy (The Quest)** (Arranged Newbury)

Record Five

Side A

1 **Promised Land** (Berry)
2 **It's Midnight** (Wheeler, Chesnut)
3 **If You Talk In Your Sleep** (West, Christopher)
4 **I'm Leavin'** (Jarrett, Charles)
5 **Why Me Lord** (Kristofferson)
6 **Help Me** (Gatlin)
7 **Softly, As I Leave You** (Calabrese, deVita, Shaper)
8 **My Baby Left Me** (Crudup)
9 **It's Now Or Never** (DiCapua, Schroeder, Gold)
10 **Hawaiian Wedding Song** (King, Hoffman, Manning)
11 **Trying To Get To You** (Singleton, McCoy)
12 **Green, Green Grass Of Home** (Putnam Jr.)

Side B

1 **You're The Reason I'm Living** (Darin)
2 **Big Boss Man** (Smith, Dixon)
3 **Burning Love** (Linde)
4 **My Boy** (Francois, Bourtayre, Martin, Coulter)
5 **And I Love You So** (McLean)
6 **Just Pretend** (Flett, Fletcher)
7 **How Great Thou Art** (Hine)
8 **America, The Beautiful** (Traditional. Arranged Presley)

Released August 2001

Originally, the UK CD set had been intended for release in July 2001 (indeed it was released on time in the USA) but a problem in the production of the packaging for the European release meant that its release date was delayed until August 2001. Therefore, unusually, this 5 LP limited edition version, courtesy of Sanctuary Music Group (using the Castle Music logo) in collaboration with BMG, was issued in the second week of August, virtually at the same time as the CD.

Over the previous couple of years, it had become obvious that there was still a demand for high quality vinyl releases, alongside CD versions of major releases. This meant that prestigious new releases, particularly boxed sets, were considered likely candidates for a vinyl equivalent. Certainly Roger Semon's role within Sanctuary Music, and his privileged position as a freelance producer for BMG, meant that we had seen this with the likes of the 5 LP version of *"That's The Way It Is"* (**LP 328**) in the summer of 2000, and the vinyl version of *Peace In The Valley The Complete Gospel Recordings* (**LP 332**) in December 2000. And, by all accounts, these limited edition sets had sold well – indeed it seems obvious to conclude that, had they not done so, then companies would not continue to release such luxurious and expensive items. Remember, in most cases, the CD set equivalents were cheaper to buy.

However, it was not just Castle Music exploiting this market niche. Remember too that Simply Vinyl was also issuing material on vinyl, though in the main it was drawn from back catalogue titles, with a few exceptions. For example, Simply Vinyl had negotiated with BMG for the rights to issue the vinyl version of *The 50 Greatest Hits* (**LP 331**) in late 2000.

However, to return to the *Live In Las Vegas* set, the philosophy behind this release generally was to try to present Elvis's Las Vegas appearances in a more positive light than they were normally perceived. And, just as producers Semon and Jorgensen had tried hard to re-present the seventies' studio material as positively as possible when it was released as part of the *Walk A Mile In My Shoes The Essential 70's Masters* set in 1995, it was felt that there was a need to have a companion set which reflected Elvis's extensive live work throughout the same era. In fact, as it turned out, the producers took the opportunity to widen the parameters in some respects. The set included Elvis's brief appearances in Las Vegas during his April/May dates in 1956 when he appeared at The New Frontier Hotel. It also embraced his return to live appearances in July 1969. And, just as the seventies' set was not definitive - in that certain songs were left off - this latest compilation of live material did not truly reflect all of the years he performed in Vegas. Instead it presented high spots: 1969, 1970, 1972, 1974 and 1975.

Of course, what needs to be remembered is that RCA did not record Elvis in Las Vegas during 1971 and after 1972. In fact, the material included from 1974 and 1975 was taken from soundboard recordings i.e. reference tapes recorded by the members of Elvis's staff manning the mixing desk, not RCA engineers, and almost certainly never intended for commercial release. Over the years, however, many such tapes found their way into the hands of bootleggers.

Nonetheless, the collector was well catered for on this set in that most of the material included was previously unreleased – i.e. unreleased performances. The main exceptions were the tracks from February 1970 and February 1972, as featured previously on the revised *On Stage* and *Burning Love* compilation CDs respectively, issued in the summer of 1999. Virtually everything else was an unreleased performance. Only two songs were entirely new to fans (officially, that is). An audience recording of *When The Snow Is On The Roses*, (from August 1970) - an unrehearsed and impromptu version of the song - sung in response to the fact that Ed Ames (who had had a hit with it) was in the audience at the time and also that Vernon, Elvis's father, liked the song. The other unreleased item was Bobby Darin's *You're The Reason I'm Living* from March 1975. It was clearly evident though that Elvis and the band had not rehearsed either song.

On the other hand, what many would regard as his peak years of this era – 1969/1970 – were both well represented on this set: there was the complete 24 August, 1969 dinner show, and the complete 11 August, 1970 show.

The packaging of this set was very eye-catching, using a live on stage shot from Elvis's 1970 season in Las Vegas on the front cover (the same one as featured on the CD set, of course). The box was black and the word Elvis was set in bold silver print, just above the **Live In Las Vegas** title. In the top right hand corner was a sticker on which the following was printed in white letters: 'Special 5-LP Vinyl Set LIMITED EDITION featuring many rare and unreleased performances DIGITALLY REMASTERED Also available on CD ELVIS 108'.

On the back of the box all of the tracks were listed; previously unreleased performances were asterisked. Unusually, the list of songs was slightly off-set from the vertical, and the bar code and production credits were positioned to the left of the list – as were the various logos (RCA, BMG and Castle Music) – while a small colour photo of Elvis sitting on a stool playing his guitar was set to the right. Around each edge of the box appeared the words 'Elvis Live In Las Vegas' and then further along the ELVIS 108 catalogue number followed by the three logos. Incidentally, the running order of the tracks varied slightly from that of the CD set.

Unlike previous boxed sets, there was no accompanying booklet. Instead, the five albums were housed in an outer sleeve, each of which featured photographs, the track listing, plus information about the writers, publishers, recording dates, and the various company logos on the back cover. And again, as on the outer box, previously unreleased performances were asterisked. On the front of each sleeve, set against a white background, the word Elvis was printed twice in bold print, and within each letter were images of him, though not necessarily from the relevant time period.

Inside each outer cover was a coloured inner cover with a cut-out revealing a picture of Elvis on the A side of the record label and production credits and company logos on the other. No tracks were listed on the record labels. The photos used on the labels were from the following years: Record One - December 1975; Record Two – July 1969; Record Three - July 1969; Record Four - August 1975; Record Five - January 1972. The extensive background essay by Colin Escott was printed on one side of the first album inner cover. The inner cover of each album was colour coded and matched the tint used on the photos featured on the front of the outer cover. The cover of Record One was tinted green; Record Two purple; Record Three mid-blue; Record Four orange, while Record Five was pink. The photos used on the back of the first album related to Elvis's appearances at The New Frontier in 1956, even though the album itself comprised material from a concert given on 24 August 1969. There were more of these photos used than had appeared in the booklet included with the CD set.

As regards the material included there was, naturally, some overlap with other releases – due of course to the kind of set it was – not to mention some inevitable duplication of tracks.

Record One

This comprised a full concert from 24 August 1969 (dinner show). Of the 17 music tracks, only one was previously issued: **Heartbreak Hotel** which had been included on **Collectors Gold** (**LP 315**) in 1991. This time though the mix was much better and the stereo image more distinct. This was the first time a complete show from 1969 had been released officially. Previous albums, such as **Elvis In Person At The International Hotel Las Vegas, Nevada** (**LP 316**) had simply been compilation sets, including songs from several different dates.

There was only one minor error: no comma in **Baby, What You Want Me To Do**.

Record Two

Side A featured the section entitled Elvis Talks About His Career, from 24 August 1969, which had been on the first disc of the CD set. This was followed by the four tracks originally recorded on 6 May 1956 at The New Frontier Hotel. On the CD set they had appeared on the fourth disc. Needless to say these tracks had been available for

many years, being first released on **Elvis Aron Presley** (*LP 126*) in 1980.

Side B began the full concert from 11 August 1970, which was continued on Record Three. All the tracks on Side B, Record Two, comprised previously unreleased versions. However, some of these performances had been included in **The Lost Performances** (1990) and **That's The Way It Is** (2001) special edition video/DVD versions.

The name Johnson was not shown as co-writer of **Long Tall Sally** and the names Penniman, Blackwell were usually shown the other way around. This error was repeated on Record Four.

Oddly, the writers of **Just Pretend** – Flett, Fletcher – were shown in the wrong order. Yet, they were listed correctly on Record Five. The writers of **I Just Can't Help Believin'** were also shown in the wrong order.

Record Three

Although Side A included some previously released items: **Something**, **Men With Broken Hearts** and **One Night** all of which been had featured on the **Walk A Mile In My Shoes The Essential 70's Masters** set in 1995 – they were now making their first appearance on vinyl. The 1970 concert concluded on Side B and, once again, these tracks were unreleased, including the audience recorded **When The Snow Is On The Roses** referred to earlier. Please note this was not from the same concert but was from the August 1970 season. The last three tracks on Side B took us back to February 1970, and comprised material found originally on the album **On Stage February 1970** (*LP 41*).

There were a number of song title and writing credit errors. The writers of **You've Lost That Lovin' Feelin'** were not in the correct order and the title was shown with a **'g'** at the end of **Lovin'** and **Feelin'**. **See See Rider** was shown as being 'Traditional', presumably to counter difficulties in identifying the actual writer. In the past the name Rainey had been used by RCA/BMG, although we have previously credited Big Bill Broonzy.

Release Me (and let me love again) was listed without the words in brackets. Also, the writers were listed in an unusual order and omitted the name Harris.

Record Four

The material for this album came from February 1970 and February 1972. And although all the tracks had been issued previously (mainly on CD only releases such as the 1995 boxed set **Walk A Mile In My Shoes The Essential 70's Masters**, **On Stage** and **Burning Love**, both issued 1999), some of them were making their debut on vinyl. Specifically, tracks 5, 7-10 side A, and tracks 1-3 and 5-8, side B.

Perhaps understandably, the words in brackets **(Je T'Appartiens)** were not shown after **Let It Be Me**. Similarly, **(The Quest)** was ommitted after **The Impossible Dream**.

Record Five

All the performances included here were previously unreleased and, with the exception of the last track on side A, all the material included was recorded at five dates during his August 1974 season. The last track, **Green, Green Grass Of Home** dated from March 1975. All tracks on Side B were also previously unreleased. Please note: 12 of the tracks on Record Five featured live versions of single releases which had appeared during his lifetime. And, as mentioned earlier, **You're The Reason I'm Living** (from March 1975), was one of the two previously unreleased songs on the whole set.

The name Calabrese was left out of **Softly, As I Leave You**, which was listed without the comma. DiCapua was not credited on **It's Now Or Never**, and on **My Boy** the name Lavot was added, while the others' names were shown in an unusual order. Finally, there was no comma shown in **America, The Beautiful**.

Incidentally, the dealer price of this boxed set was £29.99. Not surprisingly though, the retailers' prices varied considerably. The most competitive price seemed to be £39.95

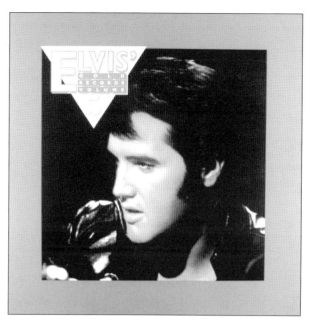

Released September 2001

The original Golden Record series started in October 1958 (*LP 7*) although, of course, at the time the first volume was not referred to as volume 1. Subsequently a further three volumes were issued (LPs *10, 21* and *34*) in 1960, 1964 and 1968, respectively. At that point it looked as though the series had run its natural course. However, in 1985, 17 years after volume 4 was issued, RCA in the UK released volume 5 (*LP 261*), though in recognition of there being fewer 'hits' in that period, the album contained only ten tracks. Indeed the US market had this release a year earlier, and the original plan was not to issue it in the UK, because Roger Semon felt that it did not represent good value for money. Incidentally, the first two volumes had included 14 tracks, while volumes 3 and 4 had comprised 12 tracks each.

LP 336 — Elvis' Gold Records-Volume 5

RCA/Simply Vinyl
07863 67466 1 SVLP 346

Side 1

1 **Suspicious Minds** (James)
2 **Kentucky Rain** (Rabbitt, Heard)
3 **In The Ghetto** (Davis)
4 **Clean Up Your Own Backyard** (Strange, Davis)
5 **Burning Love** (Linde)
6 **If You Talk In Your Sleep** (West, Christopher)
7 **For The Heart** (Linde)
8 **Moody Blue** (James)

Side 2

1 **Way Down** (Martine Jnr.)
2 **Big Boss Man** (Smith, Dixon)
3 **Guitar Man** (Hubbard))
4 **U.S. Male** (Hubbard)
5 **You Don't Have To Say You Love Me** (Pallavicini, Donaggio, Wickham, Napier-Bell)
6 **Edge Of Reality** (Giant, Baum, Kaye)
7 **Memories** (Strange, Davis)
8 **If I Can Dream** (Brown)

Not surprisingly, when Simply Vinyl started to issue the revised versions of the Golden Record series in vinyl format – based on the CD versions from 1997 – it seemed obvious that they would follow through and re-issue each of the five in the series. And so, two months after volume 4 was issued, volume 5 made its appearance. Of course, one obvious thing to note was that, having released a vinyl version of *The 50 Greatest Hits* (**LP 331**), there was, inevitably, a degree of duplication of tracks.

On this particular album, for instance, the following tracks had also been included on *The 50 Greatest Hits: Suspicious Minds, In The Ghetto, Burning Love, Moody Blue, Way Down, Guitar Man* and *If I Can Dream.*

The original track listing spanned the period from 1968 through to 1977 - a time of fewer 'hits' - although there were some strange exclusions from this period. The revised edition, featuring a slightly altered running order, and concluding with *If I Can Dream*, backtracked slightly and included material from 1967 also. Five of the additional tracks had appeared as singles in the UK, four of them as A sides: *Big Boss Man* (*S 61*) in November 1967; *Guitar Man* (*S 62*) in February 1968; *U.S. Male* (*S 63*) in May 1968; and *You Don't Have To Say You Love Me* (*S 75*) in January 1971. *Memories* was the B side of *If I Can Dream* (*S 67*), released in February 1969, while *Edge Of Reality*, although not issued as a single in the UK, was the B side of *If I Can Dream* (1968) in the US. UK fans had to wait until November 1970 to get this track, when it was issued on the budget album *Almost In Love* (*LP 44*). Nothing was included after *If You Talk In Your Sleep* (1974) until *Moody Blue* (1976). Unusually, the B side of *Moody Blue, For The Heart*, was also included.

As with all previous Simply Vinyl versions in this series, the artwork simply copied that of the 1997 CD releases. The front cover of this

261

album bore a 'live' shot from the sit-down portion of the 1968 NBC TV Special, whereas all earlier albums in the series had featured posed shots on the cover. The back cover used a very similar photograph to that featured on the front cover of the 1971 reissue of *Elvis' Golden Records* (*LP 50*) - itself a reverse image of the one used on the US picture cover single of *In The Ghetto*. To the right of Elvis's image was the catalogue number, bar code and compilation credits. Beneath these details was the track listing (no writers shown) and then the RCA and BMG logos. The copyright date was shown correctly as 1997. Oddly on the spine of the cover the title was shown as *Elvis Gold Records Volume 5* – note the lack of an apostrophe after Elvis's name.

As usual, the album bore a matt orange RCA label and kept the detail to a minimum. The mode, stereo, was shown and all the tracks were listed beneath the title. Again the copyright date was correctly given as 1997, and, as usual, there was no mention of Simply Vinyl at all anywhere on the album label or the cover. The only place it was mentioned was on the outer plastic sleeve and, as SVLP 346, between the run out grooves. Also inside the album cover was a 12 inch insert. On one side was a black and white photo from the NBC TV Special, while on the other were the track details (writers, timings, publishers, mechanical rights societies and recording dates). The same sleeve notes, by Colin Escott, as used on the CD version, featured to the right of the track listing. There was also a photo of Elvis from the *That's The Way It Is* era (summer 1970), beneath which were photographs of various US picture sleeve singles.

The LP, manufactured in 180gm vinyl, was housed in the thick plastic sleeve and had the usual sticker on the front cover, bearing the Simply Vinyl legend.

There were no song title or writing credit errors, though it is worth noting that both *Guitar Man* and *U.S. Male* credited Hubbard (as opposed to Reed), in keeping with BMG's revision of the credits for these songs.

many of which had long been deleted. They were, however, issued as Double Feature CDs, out of recognition of how short the running times some of the original soundtracks were. Some also included bonus material in the form of alternative takes.

This process started in March 1993. However, four major titles, *Loving You*, *King Creole*, *G.I. Blues* and *Blue Hawaii*, CD albums dating back to October 1987, were left as they were, but with the promise that sometime henceforward they too would be upgraded in terms of sound, content and presentation. The significance of this was that none of these albums had been remastered, and their sound quality was, by concensus, not very good. Incidentally, of the four, only *Blue Hawaii* had not undergone any changes from its original LP version. Remember, the first two (initially available in electronic stereo) had been reissued in mono, while *G.I. Blues* had been reissued in November 1990 to include *Tonight's All Right For Love*.

Finally, in April 1997, BMG issued the four film soundtracks mentioned on CD, plus a newly constructed album *Jailhouse Rock* (which also included the *Love Me Tender* soundtrack material) in a revised and upgraded form. At that time, of course, there was no vinyl equivalent of any of these titles.

However, in the autumn of 2001, the Castle Music label (part of the Sanctuary Music group) began releasing vinyl LP versions of the above-mentioned albums, comprising exactly the same track listings. This was a strangely ironic turn of events: whereby a company transferred a CD album to vinyl! Think of how often that had occurred in reverse order during the eighties and early nineties.

Anyway, Castle's programme started in September 2001 with *G.I. Blues* and *Blue Hawaii* (**LPs 337** and **338**). The attractive part of this was that not only were fans getting some material not previously available on vinyl, but Castle added an EP release (also featuring film material) with each LP as a bonus. It seemed obvious that the other three titles would follow soon – and they did, in early 2002. The dealer price on these albums was £10.99, which meant that most retailers charged at least £16 – still a reasonable price considering that each one included a bonus 7 inch EP.

Castle Music

During the early 1990s, BMG committed themselves to a complete revision of their Elvis catalogue, commencing with the CD *The King Of Rock 'N' Roll The Complete 50's Masters* (also on vinyl - **LP 318**) in July 1992. This was welcomed by fans and critically acclaimed also. Interestingly though, alongside the restoration programme of his studio work in the fifties and sixties, the company also undertook to restore to catalogue the film soundtrack albums from the sixties,

LP 337	G.I. Blues

RCA/Castle Music ELVIS 106

Side 1
1 **Tonight Is So Right For Love** (Wayne, Silver)
2 **What's She Really Like** (Wayne, Silver)
3 **Frankfort Special** (Wayne, Edwards)
4 **Wooden Heart** (Wise, Weisman, Twomey, Kaempfert)
5 **G.I. Blues** (Tepper, Bennett)
6 **Pocketful Of Rainbows** (Wise, Weisman)
7 **Shoppin' Around** (Tepper, Bennett, Schroeder)
8 **Big Boots** (Wayne, Edwards)
9 **Didja' Ever** (Wayne, Edwards)
10 **Blue Suede Shoes** (Perkins)

Side 2

1   **Doin' The Best I Can** (Pomus, Shuman)
2   **Tonight's All Right For Love** (Wayne, Silver, Lilly)
3   **Big Boots** (Wayne, Edwards)
4   **Shoppin' Around** (Tepper, Bennett, Schroeder)
5   **Frankfort Special** (Wayne, Edwards)
6   **Pocketful Of Rainbows** (Wise, Weisman)
7   **Didja' Ever** (Wayne, Edwards)
8   **Big Boots** (Wayne, Edwards)
9   **What's She Really Like** (Wayne, Silver)
10 **Doin' The Best I Can** (Pomus, Shuman)

Bonus EP *Live A Little, Love A Little*
EPA-1068

Side 1

1   **Almost In Love** (Bonfa, Starr)
2   **A Little Less Conversation** (Strange, Davis)

Side 2

1   **Wonderful World** (Fletcher, Flett)
2   **Edge Of Reality** (Giant, Baum, Kaye)

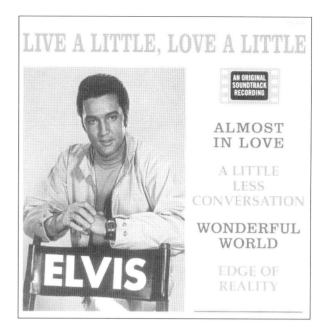

Released October 2001

The original album (*LP 12*), released in November 1960, was Elvis's first post army soundtrack album and, along with **Blue Hawaii**, became an enormous seller. Consequently, it remained on catalogue for many years – in various label formats - not actually being deleted until 1992.

Not surprisingly, it was one of the first film albums to be released as a CD and made its debut as such in October 1987, comprising its original 11 tracks. However, a couple of years later, in November 1990, the CD was modified slightly and became a 12 track release, including the song **Tonight's All Right For Love**, a song which when first recorded had run into all sorts of copyright difficulties in English speaking countries. Historically, this is why there were two versions of almost the same song.

By 1997 though, a remastered version was long overdue for, like **Blue Hawaii**, it had been overlooked in the early to mid-1990s when BMG set about reissuing all the film soundtrack albums as part of the double feature programme – in itself a move to restore to catalogue material/albums which had been unavailable to fans in any form for quite a long time. Nonetheless, at the time, Roger Semon was reported as saying that both this album and **Blue Hawaii** were in need of updating and that this would take place sometime henceforward. However, the pressure of other releases delayed this course of action for a few years.

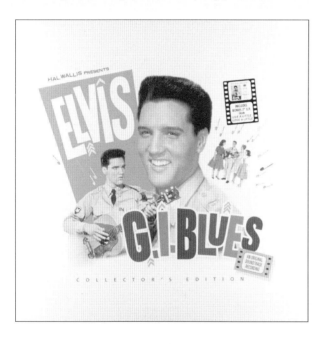

It did appear, finally, in 1997, when BMG reissued both albums in a remastered and repackaged form, and also included extra tracks. Unlike the soundtracks included in the Double Feature series, each album stood alone but, of course, no vinyl equivalent was available at that time. It was this revised version of the album on which Castle based its LP. However, although boasting extra tracks, not all of them were previously unissued on vinyl. Several had been released before: track 3, side 2, **Big Boots** (fast version) had first appeared on **Collectors Gold** (**LP 315**) in August 1991. **Pocketful Of Rainbows** (take 2), **What's She Really Like** (take 7), and **Doin' The Best I Can** (take 9) had first appeared on **The EP Collection Volume 2** (a UK only collection) in October 1982. However, **Frankfort Special** (fast version

263

– take 2) was an oddity. For although shown as previously issued, it was, in fact, a previously unreleased take. Perhaps the confusion arose because another take, also said to be take 2, had debuted on *Elvis - A Legendary Performer Volume 3* (*LP 106*) in January 1979. Clearly one of them had a wrongly assigned take number.

This meant that of the eight extra tracks only four were previously unreleased on vinyl: *Frankfort Special*, *Shoppin' Around* (take 13); *Didja' Ever* (take 1); and *Big Boots* (acoustic version). And while it made sense to 'round-up' these oddities and include them in one package, there was less of interest to the collector than on, say, *Blue Hawaii* (**LP 338**), which had a extra seven previously unissued performances.

The packaging was of a high quality, as we had come to expect, and the artwork was based on the Collector's Edition CD issued in 1997. In its twelve inch format, it looked very appealing. The label design of the LP used the same picture as was featured on the album front cover on side 1, along with the various copyright references (2001), and logos of RCA, BMG and Castle Music. Side 2 simply had a picture of Elvis. The album was housed in a colourful gloss inner sleeve (the labels were visible through the cut-outs), which in turn was enclosed in a predominantly white outer sleeve.

The front cover bore the legend 'Collector's Edition' which appeared in black print below the title. There was a rectangular box displaying a small picture of the EP cover and the legend 'Includes bonus 7" EP from *Live A Little, Love A Little'*.

However, because the EP was only available as part of this package (at this stage, at least) we have not assigned it a separate release number, nor has it been included in the EP section. The precedent for this was in *Sun Singles* (**S 182**) set which included a Sun EP – even though an Elvis one had never existed on this label format; this was a piece of artistic licence on the part of the producer, Roger Semon.

All of these tracks had appeared before on vinyl releases, though not on a discrete album. *A Little Less Conversation* and *Almost In Love* (*S 66*) had appeared back to back on a single release in November 1968; *Wonderful World* had first appeared on the album *Elvis Sings Flaming Star* (*LP 37*) in June 1969; while *Edge Of Reality* was included on the album *Almost In Love* (*LP 44*) in November 1970.

The actual label format was a copy of the RCA Victor logo from 1962, using a solid centre and displaying a Z/T tax code. This code actually related to records produced between April and November 1962, so clearly, in this instance, it was anachronistic. However, it meant the release was in keeping with the format of the two EP collections (1982) and, more recently, the newly released *The International EP Collection* (**EP 45**). The publishing date was shown as 2001, which related to the actual release itself and not the individual songs.

The album also included an eight page booklet which included some of the photographs from the CD booklet, along with 'behind the scene' information and credits.

LP 338 — Blue Hawaii

RCA/Castle Music ELVIS 107

Side 1

1. **Blue Hawaii** (Robin, Rainger)
2. **Almost Always True** (Wise, Weisman)
3. **Aloha-Oe** (Arranged and adapted Presley)
4. **No More** (Robertson, Blair)
5. **Can't Help Falling In Love** (Peretti, Creatore, Weiss)
6. **Rock-A-Hula Baby** (Wise, Weisman, Fuller)
7. **Moonlight Swim** (Dee, Weisman)
8. **Ku-U-I-Po** (Peretti, Creatore, Weiss)
9. **Ito Eats** (Tepper, Bennett)
10. **Slicin' Sand** (Tepper, Bennett)
11. **Hawaiian Sunset** (Tepper, Bennett)

Side 2

1. **Beach Boy Blues** (Tepper, Bennett)
2. **Island Of Love** (Tepper, Bennett)
3. **Hawaiian Wedding Song** (King, Hoffman, Manning)
4. **Steppin' Out Of Line** (Wise, Weisman, Fuller)
5. **Can't Help Falling In Love** (Peretti, Creatore, Weiss)
6. **Slicin' Sand** (Tepper, Bennett)
7. **No More** (Robertson, Blair)
8. **Rock-A-Hula Baby** (Wise, Weisman, Fuller)
9. **Beach Boy Blues** (Tepper, Bennett)
10. **Steppin' Out Of Line** (Wise, Weisman, Fuller)
11. **Blue Hawaii** (Robin, Rainger)

Bonus EP Stay Away, Joe
EX 2764

Side 1

1. **Stay Away, Joe** (Weisman, Wayne)
2. **Dominic** (Weisman, Wayne)
3. **All I Needed Was The Rain** (Weisman, Wayne)

Side 2

1. **Goin' Home** (Byers)
2. **Stay Away** (Tepper, Bennett)

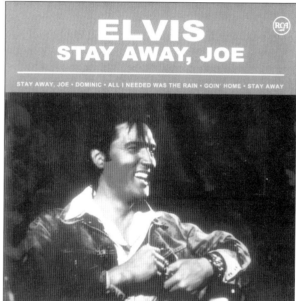

Released October 2001

The original version of this album (*LP 15*) was said to be Elvis's biggest seller in the 1960s. Indeed, from its original release date in December 1961, it remained on catalogue, in one form or another, until 1992. In fact, to digress slightly, well-respected authors and researchers have suggested that, such was the success of this album (and the film it represented), this put paid to any serious chance of Elvis pursuing a dramatic film career. Sadly, no film album after this rivalled its success in any regard and, as we are well aware, his film career petered out towards the end of the sixties also.

Blue Hawaii, along with three other major film soundtrack albums – *G.I. Blues*, *King Creole* and *Loving You* – had not been remastered and repackaged with the rest of the film soundtrack albums as part of the Double Feature CD series which commenced in 1993. It was not until April 1997 that revised editions of these CDs appeared, and each included some extra tracks.

Naturally, the vinyl version issued by Castle included the additional tracks also. They were as follows: track 4, side two, *Steppin' Out Of Line*, was a song cut from the original film and eventually released on the follow up album, *Pot Luck* (*LP 16*) in July 1962. However, the remainder of the tracks i.e. tracks 5 –11, side 2, were all previously unissued alternative takes, a couple of them movie versions. Of course, they had first been released on the CD version, but this was their debut on vinyl.

265

In addition to the **Blue Hawaii** soundtrack material, once again, Castle Music opted to include a bonus EP comprising the songs featured in the film **Stay Away, Joe**. Furthermore, there had never been an EP comprising this material in either the USA or the UK. With the exception of **Dominic** (said to be a song that Elvis had requested never to be released), which was making its debut on a vinyl release, the rest of the tracks had been issued on singles, or included on budget LPs. **Stay Away, Joe** first appeared on the album **Let's Be Friends** (*LP 40*) in May 1970; **Goin' Home** on the film soundtrack album **Speedway** (*LP 35*) in August 1968; **All I Needed Was The Rain** on the album **Elvis Sings Flaming Star** (*LP 37*), issued in June 1969; and **Stay Away** was the B side of **U.S. Male** (*S 63*) in May 1968. All of these tracks were first brought together on the Double Feature CD **Kissin' Cousins/Clambake/Stay Away, Joe**, released in June 1994.

Looking at the EP itself, it sported the black RCA Victor logo, was a solid centre and displayed the Z/T tax code which, if historically accurate, would have dated it to the period between April and November 1962. Of course, this was an anachronism, as the film itself was not made until 1968 (records from that time would have had the J/T code). However, using this tax code meant that the EP fitted in with those included in the original EP collections in 1982 and **The International EP Collection** (**EP 45**) issued in October 2001. Another oddity was the fact that the recording first published date was shown as 2001 – a clear reference to this release and not the actual songs, all of which had been issued from 1968 onwards on various releases. In the run-out grooves on both sides was etched 'Elvis 1077' – no doubt a reference to this being a 7 inch adjunct to 'Elvis 107'. The cover was gloss with a colour picture of Elvis from the film on the front cover and the tracks and writers listed on the back cover.

The packaging of the LP was based on the revised CD version (Collector's Edition) from 1997 and, in its 12 inch format, looked very appealing. The label design of the LP used the same picture as was featured on the album front cover on side 1, along with the various copyright references (2001), and logos of RCA, BMG and Castle Music. Side 2 simply had a picture of Elvis playing his guitar on the beach. The album was housed in a colourful inner sleeve (the labels were visible through the cut-outs), which in turn was enclosed in a predominantly white outer sleeve.

There was a small rectangular sticker displaying a small picture of the EP cover and the legend 'Includes bonus 7" EP from **Stay Away, Joe**'. The back cover showed three pictures from the film as if on a film reel, listed the 22 tracks (no writers given), and beneath the pictures the bar code, logos and copyright details were situated.

Included in the album sleeve was an eight page, full colour booklet. Its front cover was almost identical to that of the outer cover, minus the reference to the bonus EP, while the back cover showed the same three photos as shown on the album back cover but listed no tracks. Instead, to the right of the photos were the various credits. Page 1 listed all the tracks, their timings, writers, publishers, mechanical rights societies, recording dates and matrix numbers (although there were some numerical discrepancies between the standard versions and the outtakes, for some reason). Pages 2 – 4 showed colour stills from the movie, while page 5 printed the behind the scenes and soundtrack production notes.

Incidentally, nowhere on the either the LP or EP was there any reference to a recording mode. However, all tracks were in stereo.

The LP album and EP were pressed on 180gm vinyl, and, as with most vinyl product nowadays, was part of a restricted press run, said to be about 5,000. However, production was not without its problems, resulting in copies being returned to dealers. Both this LP and **G.I. Blues** were affected; the most obvious fault being a chipped edge in the record itself.

There were no song title or writers' names errors in the booklet, although the various credits, recording dates etc. for track 11, side 1, **Hawaiian Sunset**, were printed in a larger print that of the other tracks.

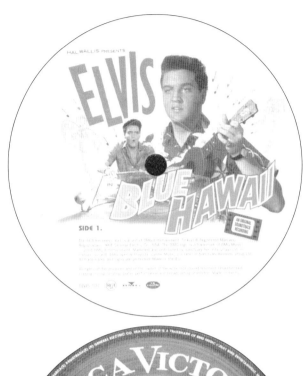

LP 339 | I'll Be Home For Christmas

RCA/Castle Music
ELVIS 109

Side 1

1 **Santa Claus Is Back In Town** (Leiber, Stoller)
2 **White Christmas** (Berlin)
3 **Here Comes Santa Claus (right down Santa Claus lane)** (Autry, Haldeman, Melka)
4 **I'll Be Home For Christmas (if only in my dreams)** (Kent, Gannon, Ram)

Side 2

1 **Blue Christmas** (Hayes, Johnson)
2 **Santa Bring My Baby Back (to me)** (Schroeder, DeMetrius)
3 **O Little Town Of Bethlehem** (Redner, Brooks)
4 **Silent Night** (Mohr, Gruber)

Released November 2001

Over the years there have been innumerable Elvis Christmas albums, starting with the original one from 1957 (*LP 5*). However, until late 2000, there had never been a 10 inch version. When Castle Music released the **Peace In The Valley The Complete Gospel Recordings** boxed set (**LP 332**) in December 2000, this 10 inch album was included as a bonus for a short period of time. However, it was not available separately, at least not until November 2001, when it was issued by Sanctuary Music Group (in conjunction with BMG Special Products), in response to 'unprecedented demand', or so the advertising sheet claimed.

And although the advertising sheet went on to assert that this was the first Elvis UK 10 inch vinyl album since 1957, this was not strictly true. That honour actually went to **The Louisiana Hayride/Little Rock, Arkansas** (**LP 322**), issued by Dave Travis's Stomper Time label in October 1997. Nonetheless, this latest 10 inch album revived what many thought was a redundant format. Previous to Stomper Time's album, only two other 10 inch Elvis albums had been issued in the UK: **Loving You** (*LP 3*) and **The Best Of Elvis** (*LP 4*) on the HMV label. Please note that, contrary to popular belief, the RCA 10 inch album predated the HMV one by two months.

In all major respects this new Christmas set was almost identical to its predecessor as included with the **Peace In The Valley The Complete Gospel Recordings** boxed set. The only discernible difference was the inclusion of the ELVIS 109 catalogue number on both the record label (situated beneath the words Side One and Side Two) and the back cover of the sleeve (in the bottom right hand corner just below the bar code). Of course, there had been no need for a separate bar code on the album included with **Peace In The Valley The Complete Gospel Recordings** boxed set. Indeed, it was obviously the same pressing as a close look at the run out grooves revealed. Also, the copyright date on both labels read 2000. The only other slight difference was that the inner bag on the latest release had no cut-out as the earlier one did.

These ten tracks dated from September 1957 and comprised what most fans would regard as his best Christmas collection. Not surprisingly, several songs had been issued on singles: **Santa Bring My Baby Back (to me)** and **Santa Claus Is Back In Town** had been issued in November 1957 (*S 16*); **Blue Christmas** (*S 48*) had been released as an A side in November 1964, coupled with **White Christmas**; and **Santa Claus Is Back In Town** (*S 124*) had also been an A side in November 1980.

The front cover artwork copied that of the **White Christmas** CD issued in late 2000. It was a posed publicity photo from 1957, circa the making of the film **Jailhouse Rock**, set against a winter scene at Graceland. The back cover had two black and white photos, one from early 1960; the other a live shot from the early '70s. Both had also appeared on the CD referred to above.

Buyers could expect to pay anything from £10.99 upwards for this album.

There were a few song title and writing credit errors. **I'll Be Home For Christmas (if only in my dreams)** omitted the words in brackets and the writers' names were shown in the wrong order. The names were reversed on **Santa Bring My Baby Back (to me)**, while **O Little Town Of Bethlehem** had the name White added to that of Redner, when in fact it should have included Brooks. This error seemed to originate on the **White Christmas** CD (07863 67959 2), released in 2000, as all other references credit Redner, Brooks.

RCA/Simply Vinyl
S125010

Side 1

1   **Heartbreak Hotel** (Axton, Durden, Presley)
2   **I Was The One** (Schroeder, DeMetrius, Blair, Peppers)
3   **Blue Suede Shoes** (Perkins)
4   **I'm Counting On You** (Robertson)
5   **I Got A Woman** (Charles)
6   **One-Sided Love Affair** (Campbell)
7   **I Love You Because** (Payne)
8   **Just Because** (B. & J. Shelton, Robin)
9   **Tutti Frutti** (LaBostrie, Penniman)

Side 2

1   **Trying To Get To You** (Singleton, McCoy)
2   **I'm Gonna Sit Right Down And Cry (over you)**
     (Thomas, Biggs)
3   **I'll Never Let You Go (little darlin')** (Wakely)
4   **Blue Moon** (Rodgers, Hart)
5   **Money Honey** (Stone)
6   **Shake, Rattle And Roll** (Calhoun)
7   **My Baby Left Me** (Crudup)
8   **Lawdy, Miss Clawdy** (Price)
9   **I Want You, I Need You, I Love You** (Mysels, Kosloff)

Released December 2001
Original Issue March 2000. RCA/Simply Vinyl 07863 67735 1
(SVLP 185) (LP 325)

From a collector's viewpoint it is sometimes difficult to understand the rationale behind certain releases. And this album, along with its companion *Elvis* (**LP 341**), released by Simply Vinyl in December 2001, is a case in point. From a purely commercial standpoint, the logic for any company, Simply Vinyl included, is straightforward: to make money. And there can be little argument with that for, if there is a perceived market and the company is prepared to take the risk, then they should reap the rewards. Presumably Simply Vinyl believed they could sell sufficient product to do just that. Yet (and this is where it becomes complicated), this was a re-issue of an album first released in March 2000, only this time the album had been produced on 125gm vinyl, not 180gm, and with reduced quality packaging; there was no outer plastic sleeve, for example. It would appear, therefore, that Simply Vinyl had either underestimated the demand for the deluxe original, or that they had recognised a weak point in the make-up of collectors – by definition they collect, and may well want to include additional copies of a given product in their collection. If Simply Vinyl were spurred on by the success of the 180gm version, then presumably the vinyl market was larger than was generally thought. Of course, had they estimated correctly, the press run would have been higher and, perhaps the price would have been lower, thus tempting more buyers.

Yet, it is not hard to see why there was a general air of cynicism amongst collectors. On the other hand, there were some benefits. Firstly, by issuing a reduced quality version there was a consequent reduction in price – to around £11, compared to £16 - which may have made it a more attractive proposition to some people. Secondly, by not issuing further copies of the 180gm version, original copies maintained their limited edition status.

Although the cover artwork was the same as the earlier Simply Vinyl album (**LP 325**), there were some notable differences. There was a new BMG catalogue number shown in the bar code –74321 89235 1 -which showed that the album had come under control of BMG's UK offices (the 74321 indicating UK, as opposed to the US code 07863). Not only that, but the album had been given a Simply Vinyl catalogue number – S125010 - the 125 indicating 125gm vinyl and, presumably, this was the tenth release in this series. Both catalogue numbers (the BMG one in the bar code) were shown on the back of the sleeve, but only the Simply Vinyl number was shown on the spine and on the record label. The spine, however, retained the RCA label name. This was something new, as all of the earlier Simply Vinyl releases had not shown their catalogue number on either the sleeve or label. Other than a revision to the publication and copyright dates (2001 instead of 2000), and the omission of the hologram on the back of the sleeve, all of the other sleeve details were the same.

As we have mentioned, there was no outer plastic wallet. Instead the album was shrink-wrapped and had a rectangular silver sticker applied to the front top right hand corner onto which was printed:

> 'Simply Vinyl
> Simply 125 Vinyl LP
> 125g Virgin Vinyl Pressing
> Classic Albums
> Heavy Quality Sleeves'

The pink and green colours on the front and general tone of the black and white print on the front and back cover appeared darker than the original Simply Vinyl release.

A disappointing feature was that the layout of the insert had been re-designed and now contained fewer photographs; and those that were included were the same as those on the back of the outer sleeve. And while the sleeve notes by Colin Escott were retained, it can only be assumed that the simplification was due to Simply Vinyl wanting to make this album 'different' from its predecessor, rather than wanting to reduce costs. Indeed, preparing revised artwork would have increased costs.

There were no circular cut-outs in the inner bag and the only changes to the label were the new catalogue number and revised publication date. The catalogue number was also etched around the run out grooves. The label colouring was a much darker orange and, unfortunately, retained the wholly inappropriate 'Stereo' tag.

The writing credit errors relating to *I Was The One* and *Just Because* were the same as on the original issue (**LP 325**).

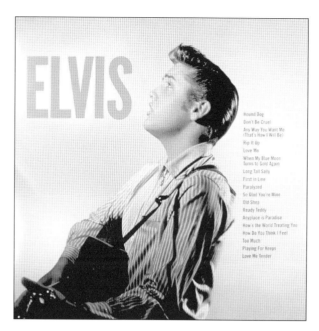

Released December 2001
Original Issue May 2000. RCA/Simply Vinyl 07863 67736 1
(SVLP 212) (LP 326)

LP 341 — Elvis

RCA/Simply Vinyl S125039

Side 1

1. **Hound Dog** (Leiber, Stoller)
2. **Don't Be Cruel** (Blackwell, Presley)
3. **Any Way You Want Me (that's how I will be)** (Schroeder, Owens)
4. **Rip It Up** (Blackwell, Marascalco)
5. **Love Me** (Leiber, Stoller)
6. **When My Blue Moon Turns To Gold Again** (Walker, Sullivan)
7. **Long Tall Sally** (Johnson, Blackwell, Penniman)
8. **First In Line** (Schroeder, Weisman)
9. **Paralyzed** (Blackwell, Presley)

Side 1

1. **So Glad You're Mine** (Crudup)
2. **Old Shep** (Foley, Arthur)
3. **Ready Teddy** (Blackwell, Marascalco)
4. **Anyplace Is Paradise** (Thomas)
5. **How's The World Treating You** (Atkins, Bryant)
6. **How Do You Think I Feel** (Walker, Pierce)
7. **Too Much** (Rosenburg, Weinman)
8. **Playin' For Keeps** (Kesler)
9. **Love Me Tender** (Presley, Matson)

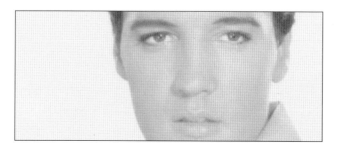

As with *Elvis Presley* (**LP 340**), this was a re-issue of the Simply Vinyl 180gm issue from May 2000 (**LP 326**), produced on 125gm vinyl. Obviously being a re-issue, the tracks were exactly the same as those featured on the original issue. Therefore, other than the obvious reduction in the quality of vinyl, the only differences between the two releases were confined to the catalogue number and packaging.

The album had been given a new catalogue number – S125039 – but, unlike the re-issue of *Elvis Presley*, the revised RCA catalogue number was also shown just below the bar code. However, on this occasion, the copyright date of the original release – 2000 – was retained, whereas this detail had been amended to read 2001 on *Elvis Presley*. On the spine, only the Simply Vinyl catalogue number was shown and (as with the original), there was no separation between the artist's name and album title, so that it read 'ELVIS PRESLEY ELVIS'. Another odd feature was the reference to the Mechanical Rights Societies BIEM/MCPS on the back of the sleeve (just below the bar code). On the label there was the usual reference to BIEM/GEMA, but there was no mention of MCPS.

Once again, the packaging had been simplified; no hologram appeared on the back of the sleeve, and instead of an outer plastic sleeve the album was shrink-wrapped, onto which a silver sticker had been applied. The sticker was identical to that found on the *Elvis Presley* re-issue.

Now, unlike the re-issue of the *Elvis Presley* (**LP 340**), no amendments had been made to the insert for this album. It featured exactly the same layout, text and photographs as the original issue.

Both the Simply Vinyl and RCA catalogue numbers were shown on the label, which retained the 2000 publishing date and 'Stereo' error. Again, the label was a different shade of orange from the original, although the layout was the same.

Another notable difference between this album and the re-issued *Elvis Presley* LP was that this album appeared not to have been remastered. At least, both the RCA and Simply Vinyl catalogue numbers etched between the run-out grooves referred to the original album, not this re-issue. This was not the case with the *Elvis Presley* re-issue which included the new Simply Vinyl catalogue number.

Not surprisingly, the errors found on the original issue (**LP 326**) were repeated here.

Side 1 Stereo
S125039 74321916491 A ℗©2000 BMG Entertainment

ELVIS PRESLEY
ELVIS

1 HOUND DOG 2.16
2 DON'T BE CRUEL 2.02
3 ANY WAY YOU WANT ME (THAT'S HOW I WILL BE) 2.13

BIEM/GEMA
33 RPM
LC 00316

4 RIP IT UP 1.53
5 LOVE ME 2.43
6 WHEN MY BLUE MOON TURNS TO GOLD AGAIN 2.21
7 LONG TALL SALLY 1.53
8 FIRST IN LINE 3.34
9 PARALYZED 2.23

See insert for full credits

LP 342 — *Loving You*

RCA/Castle Music ELVIS 110

Side 1

1 **Mean Woman Blues** (DeMetrius)
2 **(Let me be your) Teddy Bear** (Mann, Lowe)
3 **Loving You** (Leiber, Stoller)
4 **Got A Lot O' Livin' To Do!** (Schroeder, Weisman)
5 **Lonesome Cowboy** (Tepper, Bennett)
6 **Hot Dog** (Leiber, Stoller)
7 **Party** (Robinson)
8 **Blueberry Hill** (Lewis, Stock, Rose)
9 **True Love** (Porter)
10 **Don't Leave Me Now** (Schroeder, Weisman)

Side 2

1 **Have I Told You Lately That I Love You** (Weisman)
2 **I Need You So** (Hunter)
3 **Tell Me Why** (Turner)
4 **Is It So Strange** (Young)
5 **One Night Of Sin** (Bartholomew, King)
6 **When It Rains, It Really Pours** (Emerson)
7 **I Beg Of You** (McCoy, Owens)
8 **Party** (Robinson)
9 **Loving You** (Leiber, Stoller)
10 **Got A Lot O' Livin' To Do!** (Schroeder, Weisman)

Bonus EP *Wild In The Country*
ELVIS 1107

Side 1

1 **Wild In The Country** (Peretti, Creatore, Weiss)
2 **I Slipped, I Stumbled, I Fell** (Wise, Weisman)
3 **Lonely Man** (Benjamin, Marcus)

Side 2

1 **In My Way** (Wise, Weisman)
2 **Forget Me Never** (Wise, Weisman)
3 **I Slipped, I Stumbled, I Fell** (Wise, Weisman)

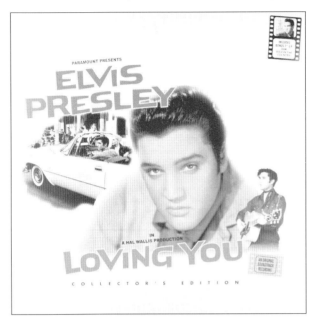

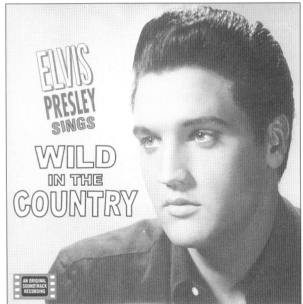

Released January 2002

As with many early Elvis albums in the UK, there was some confusion surrounding their release and, against this background, it seems sensible to look closely at the history of this particular album and how it developed over the years.

The first UK *Loving You* album (*LP 3*), issued in August 1957, was a 10 inch LP. It comprised eight tracks, although the movie only featured seven of them. The additional song was *True Love,* the Cole Porter song. Yet in many other parts of the world fans had a 12 inch album, which had featured 12 tracks. The additional tracks were *Blueberry Hill, Have I Told You Lately That I Love You, I Need You So,* plus an earlier version of *Don't Leave Me Now* (re-cut for the *Jailhouse Rock* soundtrack). Oddly, it was not until October 1977 that fans in the UK had the opportunity to buy a UK version of this 12 track album (*LP 98*).

In 1965 the original 10 inch LP was deleted. Then a strange thing happened: RCA in the UK chose to release an album entitled

270

Flaming Star And Summer Kisses (*LP 25*), a UK only release which featured the previously unreleased (in the UK) songs *Flaming Star* and *Summer Kisses, Winter Tears*, the songs from the UK 10 inch *Loving You* album, plus *It's Now Or Never* and *Are You Lonesome Tonight?*, two million selling singles from 1960 and 1961 respectively. It was an altogether strange mixture of material and, not surprisingly, it too was deleted, never to be re-issued, in the late 1960s. Thus, for a number of years, fans in the UK could not buy a UK copy of an album featuring the material from *Loving You*. Anyone wanting a copy had to rely on an imported version.

When, however, the album was released in 1977 the track listing comprised the eight original tracks but added the four extra songs from the same era, referred to above. This was the version of the LP that most countries had had for many years. Happily, the album remained on catalogue in one form or another from this point on until it was finally deleted in March 1992.

CD fans/collectors were, of course, able to obtain this album from October 1987 onwards, though not in very good sound quality (it had not been remastered). The best sounding versions of these songs appeared when the fifties' set (**LP 318**) was issued in July 1992. However, early in 1997, the original CD album was deleted, making way for a revised and upgraded CD version in April 1997 – comprising additional tracks and some unreleased performances. And it was this CD album on which the current vinyl release was based.

As with the following two releases, this album was originally scheduled for release in November 2001.

All the tracks on this set had been released previously. The only thing to note about them was that *One Night Of Sin* (note its modified title) - which had first appeared on the album *Elvis – A Legendary Performer Vol. 4* (*LP 204*) issued in November 1983 – was featured minus the short studio chat before the track, but did feature its correct ending which had been changed by Rick Rowe when it appeared on the album *Reconsider Baby* (*LP 271*) in May 1985. *I Beg Of You* – listed as an 'alternate mono master' – and *Loving You* (fast version, take 13) shown as 'uptempo version' - had first appeared on the '50s set (**LP 318**) in July 1992. As for the last three tracks on side two, although outtakes, they had been issued previously. *Party* (another 'alternate master') and *Got A Lot O' Livin' To Do!* (finale) had both made their debut on *Essential Elvis* (**LP 280**) in December 1986. The latter track had a slightly longer introduction on *Essential Elvis*, though otherwise was identical.

Strangely, a month or two before this album was issued on vinyl, BMG released a CD entitled *Silver Screen Stereo* as part of the Collector's Label. Included in the track listing was a recently found binaural version of *Loving You* (fast version – take 14).

Surprisingly, the principal artwork did not copy that of the 1997 CD version (itself a faithful representation of the original LP cover). Instead, the sleeve design (and those for *Jailhouse Rock* and *King Creole* – LPs 343 and 344 – released at the same time) was entirely new, and featured a montage of images on a white background. Obviously the concept was the same as that for the Collector's Edition *G.I. Blues* and *Blue Hawaii* CDs, already transferred successfully to vinyl by Castle (**LPs 337** and **338**). However, BMG had never intended to issue a Collector's Edition of these CD versions. Therefore, when Castle chose to bring out these albums on vinyl they generated their own original artwork for these releases. The overall effect was to bring a consistent and modern approach to the series of releases. As with the earlier Castle soundtrack LPs, there was a black and white rectangular sticker in the top right hand corner, in this case showing a picture of the *Wild In The Country* EP.

The high quality gloss inner sleeve featured several rarely seen 'on the set' photographs, and a circular cut-out on both sides allowed the picture labels to be viewed without having to remove the LP from its sleeve. The colour photograph of Elvis and Delores Hart on side 2 was exceptionally clear. Unfortunately, however, it was a photograph from the film *King Creole*, not *Loving You*.

An eight page booklet was again included. Although the behind the scenes information and credits were the same as the CD version, several photographs had been omitted in favour of some full page black and white shots from the film and backstage, along with some publicity stills.

As had become the 'norm' with the release of *G.I Blues* and *Blue Hawaii* (**LPs 337** and **338**), this LP also boasted a bonus six track EP featuring tracks from the film *Wild In The Country*. *Wild In The Country* (*S 34*) first appeared in August 1961 in the UK, backed with *I Feel So Bad*, while the original master of *I Slipped, I Stumbled, I Fell* was featured on the album *Something For Everybody* (*LP 14*) in October 1961. Of course, *In My Way* and *Forget Me Never* were not issued until November 1965 when they were included on the album *Elvis For Everyone* (*LP 26*).

The 'alternate master' of *I Slipped, I Stumbled, I Fell* and the solo version of *Lonely Man* had also appeared on vinyl before in 1991, when they were included on the album *Collectors Gold* (*LP 315*). *Lonely Man*, the standard version (not included here), had been the B side of *Surrender* (*S 33*) in May 1961.

Incidentally, this LP, along with *Jailhouse Rock* and *King Creole* (**LPs 343** and **344**), was pressed in France by MPO. The EPs, however, were pressed by Damont in the UK. 5,000 of each were manufactured.

Presumably to fit the three tracks onto each side of the 7 inch EP, the playing speed of the record was 33rpm, as opposed to the 'normal' 45rpm.

The only error was the incorrect spelling of the co-writer of *One Night Of Sin,* Dave Bartholomew. It was spelt Bartholemew.

LP 343 | Jailhouse Rock

RCA/Castle Music ELVIS 111

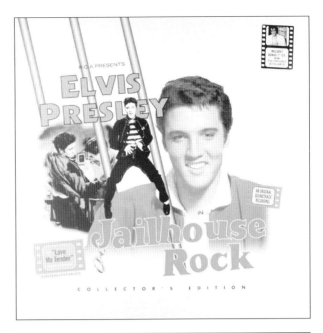

Side 1

1 **Jailhouse Rock** (Leiber, Stoller)
2 **Treat Me Nice** (Leiber, Stoller)
3 **I Want To Be Free** (Leiber, Stoller)
4 **Don't Leave Me Now** (Schroeder, Weisman)
5 **Young And Beautiful** (Silver, Schroeder)
6 **(You're so square) Baby I Don't Care** (Leiber, Stoller)
7 **Jailhouse Rock** (Leiber, Stoller)
8 **Treat Me Nice** (Leiber, Stoller)
9 **I Want To Be Free** (Leiber, Stoller)
10 **Young And Beautiful** (Silver, Schroeder)
11 **Don't Leave Me Now** (Schroeder, Weisman)

Side 2

1 **Love Me Tender** (Presley, Matson)
2 **Poor Boy** (Presley, Matson)
3 **Let Me** (Presley, Matson)
4 **We're Gonna Move** (Presley, Matson)
5 **Love Me Tender** (Presley, Matson)
6 **Let Me** (Presley, Matson)
7 **We're Gonna Move** (Presley, Matson)
8 **Poor Boy** (Presley, Matson)
9 **Love Me Tender** (Presley, Matson)

Bonus EP *The Trouble With Girls* ELVIS 1117

Side 1

1 **Clean Up Your Own Backyard** (Strange, Davis)
2 **Swing Down, Sweet Chariot** (Traditional. Arranged and adapted Presley)

Side 2

1 **Signs Of The Zodiac** (Kaye, Weisman)
2 **Almost** (Kaye, Weisman)
3 **The Whiffenpoof Song** (Galloway, Minnegerade, Pomeroy)
4 **Violet** (Duerker, Lohstroh)

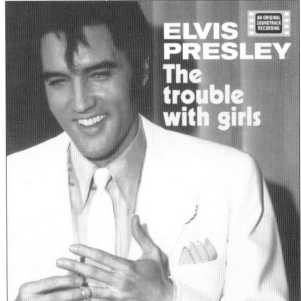

Released January 2002

When the film *Jailhouse Rock* was first released, most countries (certainly the USA and UK, at least) opted for an EP of the material included. After all, there were only six songs by Elvis in the film: the title track, *Young And Beautiful*, *I Want To Be Free*, *Don't Leave Me Now*, *Treat Me Nice*, and *(You're so square) Baby I Don't Care*. And, in fact, the film version of *Treat Me Nice* remained unreleased until 1986 when it was included on the *Essential Elvis* album (**LP 280**). The version of the song used as the B side of the single *Jailhouse Rock* (*S 18*) was not recorded until September 1957. Therefore, there was never really a need for an LP version of the soundtrack as, quite simply, there were not enough songs to warrant it. And, although there was an album entitled *Jailhouse Rock/Love In Las Vegas* (*LP 196*), issued in 1983, this was a means of bringing together the songs from two quite short film soundtracks.

Of course, the title track was a single release in the UK in January 1958 (*S 18*), coupled with the remade version of *Treat Me Nice*. A five track EP entitled *Jailhouse Rock* (*EP 5*) excluded *Treat Me Nice* but included the title song plus the four others. In subsequent years the title song was re-issued several times on singles.

However, in 1997, in keeping with BMG's undertaking to remaster all the film soundtrack material (a process started in 1993 with the emergence of the Double Feature film soundtrack collections - CD only releases), those soundtracks not included in the earlier programme were updated and upgraded i.e. the tracks were remastered and additional material was included. Thus, this vinyl LP was based closely on the CD album issued in March 1997. And, as the age-old problem of too few tracks still pertained, this time the soundtrack was coupled with the four songs from Elvis's first film, *Love Me Tender*.

Side 1 of the album comprised 11 tracks, all from *Jailhouse Rock*. Almost all of this material had been previously issued: tracks 1, 3, 4, 5, and 6 were the standard versions from the film, while track 2 was the single version of *Treat Me Nice* recorded in September 1957. Tracks 7–10 comprised the movie versions of the songs (including the earlier cut of *Treat Me Nice*), though track 11, *Don't Leave Me Now* (listed as an 'alternate master') was making its first appearance on vinyl. Until its release on CD in 1997 it too had been another unreleased performance. Of course, the movie version of the title track and *Treat Me Nice* had first appeared on *Essential Elvis* (**LP 280**) in December 1986, while the film versions of *I Want To Be Free* and *Young And Beautiful* had debuted on the '50s set (**LP 318**) in 1992.

Side 2, comprising 9 tracks, was devoted to the material from *Love Me Tender*. Tracks 1–4 were the regular versions from the film; track 5 was the end title version which had first appeared in 1986 on *Essential Elvis* (**LP 280**). However, tracks 6–8 featured material previously unissued on vinyl: *Let Me* (solo) – in reality Elvis's vocal track without the pre-recorded backing; plus stereo versions of *We're Gonna Move* (take 9 – the standard version), and *Poor Boy*. In the case of the latter song this was an edited version of the mono release, minus a verse and chorus. The final track was a stereo version of *Love Me Tender*, that had first been released on a US compilation entitled *Heart And Soul* in February 1995.

Interestingly, just a few months prior to this vinyl release appearing, BMG released a CD in the Collector's Label series entitled *Silver Screen Stereo* which included newly discovered binaural versions of *Jailhouse Rock* (take 5) and *Don't Leave Me Now* (takes 16, 17 & 18).

As with *Loving You* (**LP 342**), the artwork for this album was not the same as the 1997 CD version. Instead, Castle generated new artwork in the spirit of the Collector's Edition design first used by BMG on their *G.I. Blues* and *Blue Hawaii* CDs, and picked up by Castle for the vinyl issues in October 2001. The front cover again dispensed with the single head and shoulder shot design, as used on the CD cover – a publicity still photograph - and featured instead this image, along with a black and white photograph from the film's 'dance' sequence and a tinted picture of the fight scene. The inner sleeve featured two full-size black and white photographs, one from the *Love Me Tender* set featuring Elvis, Richard Egan, other cast members, and Scotty, Bill and D.J. Fontana. The other photograph was from *Jailhouse Rock* and showed Vince and Peggy packing copies of the *Treat Me Nice* single.

The eight page booklet included several full page black and white shots from *Jailhouse Rock* which were not included in the CD booklet.

In keeping with the vinyl versions of *G.I. Blues* and *Blue Hawaii* (**LPs 337** and **338**), issued in the autumn of 2001, this album also boasted a bonus EP comprising the six songs used in the MGM movie *The Trouble With Girls (and how to get into it)*. This brought all the material from this film together on vinyl for the first time. Remember, although there was no title track as such, the song *Clean Up Your Own Backyard* (*S 69*) had been an A side single release in August 1969. *Almost* had debuted on the album *Let's Be Friends* (*LP 40*) in May 1970, while *Swing Down, Sweet Chariot* had remained unreleased until November 1983 when it was included on the album *Elvis – A Legendary Performer Vol. 4* (*LP 204*). The remaining tracks: *Signs Of The Zodiac*, *The Whiffenpoof Song* and *Violet* had not been issued on vinyl before, but had been included as part of the CD release referred to earlier.

The EP itself was solid centred with a black RCA Victor label. The design matched that of EPs manufactured during 1962 (note the use of the Z/T tax code), even though the material was not recorded until 1969. Like those included with *Loving You* and *King Creole* it played at 33rpm.

LP 344 | *King Creole*

RCA/Castle Music ELVIS 112

Side 1

1. **King Creole** (Leiber, Stoller)
2. **As Long As I Have You** (Wise, Weisman)
3. **Hard Headed Woman** (DeMetrius)
4. **Trouble** (Leiber, Stoller)
5. **Dixieland Rock** (Schroeder, Frank)
6. **Don't Ask Me Why** (Wise, Weisman)
7. **Lover Doll** (Wayne, Silver)
8. **Crawfish** (Wise, Weisman)
9. **Young Dreams** (Kalmanoff, Schroeder)

Side 2

1. **Steadfast, Loyal And True** (Leiber, Stoller)
2. **New Orleans** (Tepper, Bennett)
3. **King Creole** (Leiber, Stoller)
4. **As Long As I Have You** (Wise, Weisman)
5. **Danny** (Wise, Weisman)
6. **Lover Doll** (Wayne, Silver)
7. **Steadfast, Loyal And True** (Leiber, Stoller)
8. **As Long As I Have You** (Wise, Weisman)
9. **King Creole** (Leiber, Stoller)

Bonus EP *Change Of Habit* ELVIS 1127

Side 1

1. **Change Of Habit** (Weisman, Kaye)
2. **Have A Happy** (Weisman, Kaye, Fuller)

Side 2

1. **Rubberneckin'** (Jones, Warren)
2. **Let Us Pray** (Weisman, Kaye)

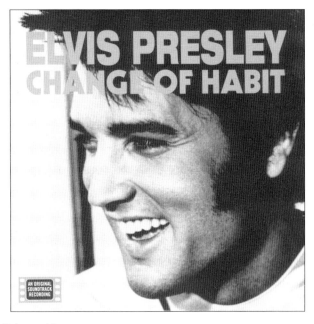

Released January 2002

Not only was the film ***King Creole*** generally regarded as one of Elvis's finest cinematic efforts, the soundtrack too was considered to be his best. So, not surprisingly, from the time of its release in October 1958 the original album (*LP 6*) remained on catalogue for many years and was later re-issued in various forms throughout the '70s and '80s.

However, when BMG began to restore original film albums to catalogue (as CD releases only) in the early 1990s, significantly, several of the major albums – ***Loving You***, ***G.I. Blues***, ***Blue Hawaii*** and, of course, ***King Creole*** - were by-passed. At the time though, Roger Semon did state that these albums would be upgraded sometime henceforward. In fairness, each of these albums had been transferred to CD in October 1987, though the sound quality was not very good, as they were mastered from poor sources. And, of course, at the time, there were still vinyl versions available to those who wanted them.

Finally, in 1997, BMG made good their promise to upgrade these various albums and did so in a very appealing way, not only by remastering the tracks but also, in some cases, by adding unreleased performances. At the time, of course, these were CD only releases and few, if any, would have imagined that just over four years later they would also surface as high quality vinyl albums too, albeit limited editions.

However, unlike the other LPs in this series, ***King Creole***, although a new collection on vinyl, did not actually include any performances which had not been available previously on vinyl. The track listing was, of course, exactly the same as the 1997 CD version, and, of the 18 tracks, there were only 12 songs featured – the 11 included on the original album, plus ***Danny***. This song had not been released until January 1979 when it appeared on ***Elvis – A Legendary Performer Volume 3*** (*LP 106*).

Backtracking slightly, in July 1990, BMG had released an album entitled ***Hits Like Never Before (Essential Elvis Vol. 3)*** (**LP 306**) that comprised some alternative takes from the ***King Creole*** film soundtrack, as well as outtakes from the June 1958 session in Nashville. Some of the film tracks reappeared on this new vinyl album, ***King Creole***.

The two takes of ***King Creole*** (3 and 18), and ***As Long As I Have You*** (4 and 8), plus ***Steadfast, Loyal And True*** had all been on ***Hits Like Never Before (Essential Elvis Vol. 3)*** (**LP 306**). So too was the undubbed ***Lover Doll*** which had first been available on ***King Creole Vol. 1*** (*EP 6*), issued in October 1958, and ***Danny***, referred to earlier. In effect, what this revised album attempted to do was bring all the available **King Creole** outtakes together with the masters. What a pity, then, that the instrumental version of the main title theme (track R, take 8) could not have been included for completeness. However, on the positive side, the sound quality on this album was appreciably better than that of **Hits Like Never Before (Essential Elvis Vol. 3)**, mainly because better source copies had been located, some of which had appeared on the fifties' set in 1992, of course.

Once again the sleeve had been re-designed from the 1997 CD version to be in keeping with the Collector's Edition **G.I. Blues** and **Blue Hawaii** CDs. In doing so, Castle had not only produced a contemporary design but had brought a rarely seen consistency to the five film soundtrack albums belatedly upgraded by BMG.

As with the other albums in the series, Castle had amended the main artwork and included several new photographs, on both the inner sleeve and in the booklet. Unfortunately, as the booklet re-printed the general background information about the film and soundtrack, it contained the same errors that were to be found in the CD booklet. The film ran for 116 minutes, not 106, and the single **Hard Headed Woman/Don't Ask Me Why** reached number 1 in the USA, and not number 2 as stated. It was also incorrect to say that this was Elvis's last 78rpm American single as **I Got Stung** was the last. On the other hand, a film caption error referring to Jan Shephard's character name (Mimi Fisher), instead of her real one, had been corrected.

The bonus EP material was from the film **Change Of Habit**. There had never been such an EP previously, so this was a welcome addition to the collection. And apart from **Rubberneckin'**, a song cut at a studio session in Memphis, early 1969, and released as the B side of **Don't Cry Daddy** (*S 71*) in February 1970, the three other tracks had not been available on a vinyl release for some years. In fact, when first issued, their release had been spread over a couple of years. **Change Of Habit** and **Have A Happy** had first appeared in May 1970 on the album **Let's Be Friends** (*LP 40*), while **Let Us Pray** had made its debut on **You'll Never Walk Alone** (*LP 48*) in March 1971.

As with the other four albums included in the series, the EP label featured an RCA Victor design (with a Z/T tax code). The solid centre EP played at 33rpm.

Incidentally, these EPs were pressed by Damont in the UK, while the LPs were pressed in France by MPO. 5,000 copies of each were made.

LP 345	Tickle Me

**RCA/Castle Music
ELVIS 113**

Side A

1. **(Such an) Easy Question)** (Blackwell, Scott)
2. **It Feels So Right** (Wise, Weisman)
3. **I Feel That I've Known You Forever** (Pomus, Jeffreys)
4. **Slowly But Surely** (Wayne, Weisman)
5. **Night Rider** (Pomus, Shuman)
6. **Put The Blame On Me** (Twomey, Wise, Blagman)
7. **Dirty, Dirty Feeling** (Leiber, Stoller)
8. **I'm Yours** (Robertson, Blair)
9. **(It's a) Long Lonely Highway** (Pomus, Shuman)
10. **Radio Spot**

Side B

1. **Slowly But Surely** (Wayne, Weisman)
2. **It Feel So Right** (Wise, Weisman)
3. **I'm Yours** (Robertson, Blair)
4. **(It's a) Long Lonely Highway** (Pomus, Shuman)
5. **I Feel That I've Known You Forever** (Pomus, Jeffreys)
6. **Night Rider** (Pomus, Shuman)
7. **Dirty, Dirty Feeling** (Leiber, Stoller)
8. **Put The Blame On Me** (Twomey, Wise, Blagman)
9. **(Such an) Easy Question** (Blackwell, Scott)
10. **Radio Spot**

Released June 2002

This album represented a departure from the other Elvis vinyl releases by Sanctuary Records Group. Specifically, the album was not based on a previously issued RCA 12 inch LP or CD release, as the majority of their other Elvis titles had been. Instead, it focused on a little known film from 1965, *Tickle Me*, a low budget effort, from which there had been no original LP soundtrack, but rather two extended play albums (*EPs 20* and *21*) – in the UK at least - issued in July and August 1965 respectively. It seems worth looking at this situation more closely.

Tickle Me was Elvis's 18th film. All previous films had generated original soundtrack recordings, even those like *Flaming Star* and *Wild In The Country*, which were made as dramatic, non-musical items, and included very few songs. However, *Tickle Me* was different, for not only were there no new recordings made – ostensibly to minimise the overall production costs – but Colonel Parker agreed to allow the financially ailing Allied Artists to use previously issued material for the soundtrack. In fact, all the material was taken from original recordings Elvis made in Nashville, during the early sixties. None had been used as singles at that point in time. Apparently Elvis had been presented with a list of 20 or more of his own recordings from which to make his selection. In the end, the nine tracks included here were used.

The material had been drawn from the following albums:

Elvis Is Back! (*LP 11*)	*It Feels So Right*
	Dirty, Dirty Feeling
Something For Everybody (*LP 14*)	*Night Rider*
	Put the Blame On Me
Pot Luck (*LP 16*)	*(Such an) Easy Question*
	I Feel That I've Known You Forever
	I'm Yours
Fun In Acapulco (*LP 20*)	*Slowly But Surely*
Kissin' Cousins (*LP 22*)	*(It's a) Long Lonely Highway*

The latter two songs had appeared on their respective film soundtrack LPs as bonus items, in 1963 and 1964 respectively.

As the film only contained nine songs, it would have proved problematical to produce a soundtrack LP. Not only would such a move have required the inclusion of 'bonus' tracks (at a time when few were readily available), but also all of the material had been used

previously. So, at a time when Elvis's film soundtrack albums were not selling as well as his earlier efforts, RCA opted for lower profile, but nonetheless commercially viable, EP releases. As we have said, two volumes, comprising five and four tracks respectively, were issued in the UK – uniquely, it seems. Only one *Tickle Me* EP was issued in America and this included the same songs as the first UK volume, but strangely, the running order was different.

Elsewhere in the world, other oddities occurred. In Spain, for example, a *Tickle Me* LP was issued containing the nine film songs and supplemented by a further four tracks: **She's Not You**, **Never Ending**, **Ain't That Loving You Baby** and **Just Tell Her Jim Said Hello**. Interestingly, an American bootleg LP entitled **Elvis Sings Songs From Tickle Me**, released in 1987, pre-empted the Castle LP as it featured alternative takes of the film songs, along with a couple of others from the **Spinout** soundtrack.

The mastering sources for this new album were as follows. In the main, the master takes were all taken from the CD **From Nashville To Memphis The Essential 60's Masters 1**, apart from **I'm Yours**, which was taken from the **Rare Elvis** CD (although this had also been a vinyl release – *LP 263* – in January 1985). As on the CD/LP version, the track appeared here in mono. It can only be assumed that a stereo master could not be located. All other music tracks were in stereo.

The alternative performances on side B were taken from a variety of sources. Tracks 1, 2 and 5 were culled from the Collector's Label CD (**It's a) Long Lonely Highway** (2000), as was the US single master of the same song, track 9, side A. (Incidentally, this had never been released as a single in the UK.) Track 6, side B, **Night Rider** (listed as alternate master), was take 3 of the version recorded in March 1962, whereas the original version (also take 3), as featured on the album **Pot Luck** (*LP 16*), had been cut in October 1961. The source used for the track on this new album was the BMG CD **Such A Night Essential Elvis Volume 6**, issued in the year 2000. Track 9, side B, **(Such an) Easy Question**, was taken from the same album. Finally, tracks 7 and 8, **Dirty, Dirty Feeling** and **Put The Blame On Me** were taken from the Collector's Label CD **Fame And Fortune**, issued in April 2002.

Both sides of the LP closed with what was described as a 'Radio Spot'. These originated in America and were, in effect, promotional pieces in the form of advertisements for the film, and were produced by a film company (Allied Artists, in this case) and sent to radio stations. The ones featured here were taken from an Allied Artists 7 inch 'single' of four different advertisements, which had been provided by Chris Giles from The Elvis Shop in London.

Chris also supplied the memorabilia, film stills and other pictures used for the booklet artwork. Indeed, there were so many rare and unusual items that the booklet was increased from the intended eight pages to twelve to accommodate them.

The total playing time for the album was fractionally over 41 minutes. This, however, included the radio spots featured at the end of each side of the album.

Breaking with the tradition of the other five Collector's Edition albums issued by Castle (Sanctuary), there was no bonus EP included with this release. However, the general front cover design (using a shot from the movie of Elvis playing his Gibson acoustic guitar – the same one that was featured on the 1965 album **Elvis For Everyone** - *LP 26*) was similar to that of the others in the series, in that images of Elvis were featured against a white background with the legend 'Collector's Edition' printed across the bottom part of the cover.

So too with the label design: side A included the front cover shot image along with a smaller and fainter image of the shot used on side B, below which was the Collector's Edition legend, followed by the various publishing credits and company logos – RCA, BMG and Castle. Side B showed a picture of Elvis with some of his co-stars from the film.

Incidentally, the publishing dates given for these songs in the booklet pertained to original US releases. This was a deliberate decision made by Sam Szczepanski, label manager at Sanctuary, who co-ordinated this release in the UK, as she felt it made more sense to credit their first publication date, wherever in the world that happened to be. Of course, for the purposes of our book, we record the first date the tracks appeared in the UK. Thus, the main difference between the dates shown and their correct UK publication concerned tracks 8 and 9 on side A, *I'm Yours* and *(It's a) Long Lonely Highway*, neither of which had been released in the UK until January 1977, when they were included on the album *Elvis In Demand* (*LP 90*). Fans in the US had been able to hear these versions as long ago as 1965 when they appeared on a single release.

And Finally ......

As we have mentioned frequently throughout the latter part of the text, it became obvious that vinyl releases were not going to die out as many had predicted. And just as it is a safe bet to say that there will be more releases from the likes of Castle Music, it is also true to say that the other non-BMG company, Simply Vinyl, fully intend to release yet more Presley product on vinyl.

Indeed, early in 2002 from conversations with management at Simply Vinyl, we were aware that they had been actively trying to obtain permission to release more Elvis albums. Ironically, several of the film titles they had expressed interest in - notably *Loving You*, *King Creole* and *Blue Hawaii* - had, unbeknown to them, been issued by Castle Music! When asked our view about what they ought to consider, our advice to them was to opt for albums such as *Elvis Is Back!*, *From Elvis In Memphis* and, perhaps, *On Stage*. And who knows, perhaps by the time you get to read this, these albums too might have been added to the ever-expanding catalogue.

Miscellaneous Releases

Introduction

We have reserved this section for those oddities which occur from time to time where releases do not conveniently fit into the normal release pattern of Elvis singles and LPs. Happily, the section is relatively small and, with one exception, is restricted to the non-singing voice of Elvis, as the records in question all contained interview material. Our reasons for not including these in the principal sections are various, but, in particular, we were concerned that their limited distribution and short-term availability favoured placing them in a category we established in *Elvis UK 1956-86*: to cover releases not generally available to the record buying public. However, far from being a precise science, this is obviously a difficult area and clearly open to some criticism and debate. Doubtless there are examples in the main section which could easily be similarly categorised but which, for one reason or another, have been included elsewhere. An additional factor – at least in the case of one particular record – was that we have been unable to confirm sufficient details about it to feel comfortable enough to 'upgrade' its status. In a number of cases, we have been unable to determine with any degree of accuracy their release dates, although we have been able to provide a general indication of when they first became available. However, this omission on our part does not suggest that there is anything untoward about its existence and, indeed, all of the records in this section are perfectly legitimate.

As we have said, the records mainly feature interview material, an area reasonably accessible to small labels, as it is largely uncontrolled and does not involve (usually) any kind of licencing arrangements.

The exception to the interview material releases came in the form of a single comprising *My Happiness* and *That's When Your Heartaches Begin*. Its inclusion in this section (rather than in the Singles' section itself) is because it was not available as a separate entity, as it could only be obtained with an 8 CD Sun Records Commemorative set, produced by Fab-U-Lus, a subsidiary of Sanctuary Records.

Ironically all of these records are now much sought after and are rarely seen in the secondhand marketplace.

Check List Of Miscellaneous Releases

Catalogue Number	Title	Release Date
Talkies EPPD 1	*The Voice Of Elvis Presley*	1986
Talkies ELVIS 1	*Elvis Aron Presley*	1987
No label EPPD 19	*Madison Square Garden Interview*	1986
Youngblood YBLT 1	*King Of Rock 'N' Roll*	1987
Youngblood YBP 1	*King Of Rock 'N' Roll*	1987
Fabulus FBUBX 0027	*My Happiness* *That's When Your Heartaches Begin*	May 2002

Talkies

Talkies were responsible for two Elvis singles, a 7 inch and a 12 inch version, both of which contained exactly the same material. Neither of these records received wide distribution and, in that sense, could be considered as not being generally available. In fact, both were distributed mainly through small wholesalers by a company called Backs which was based in Norwich. Consequently, availability was restricted to outlets which took small quantities, probably on a one-off basis. Having said that, copies of the 12 inch version did turn up in stores like HMV and Virgin, although it seemed probable that only one or two copies would have been available, and not necessarily at every branch. It was a case of individual stores choosing to stock certain items.

To illustrate further the size of the operation, it took up to a year before all copies were sold, indicating clearly the precarious nature of this kind of release and how important placing the product can be. Whilst this was undoubtedly a small business operation, that did not detract from the product itself. These were attractive and professional releases which are now much sought after.

Because of the limited distribution, many fans missed out on these releases, and we have to admit that it took us a very long time to locate the people responsible for their production. When we did, they proved most helpful, but were unable to recall just when the records were released! We have included as much detail as we can, therefore, but we have to admit that the precise dates the records became available eludes us. Neither record had a catalogue number, but a *Music Master* labels list notes 'Elvis 1' against the 7 inch pressing.

One fact we can be certain of though, no promotional copies or test pressings were made.

The Voice Of Elvis Presley

Talkies EPPD 1

Graceland, Memphis 7 March 1960

This was the first of the two Talkies records to appear which, according to the manufacturer, first emerged during 1983. If this was correct (and we do have some doubts about this) then details ought to have been included in **Elvis UK 1956-86**. As we have already said, we have been unable to date this record precisely, but the first actual reference we have located is an advert in issue 317 of **Elvis Monthly**, dated June 1986.

This 7 inch picture disc single featured a mid-sixties colour head shot of Elvis on the B side, with a black and white shot from 1970 on the A side. There was no printing on the B side, but the words 'The Voice of Elvis Presley' appeared across the top of the records and details of the content, 'The Gracelands Press Interview 1960', was shown just above, and to the right, of the centre hole. Note that an 's' was added to 'Graceland'. The only other print quoted the playing speed – 33 1/3 – and 'Side One'. As we have said, the single contained Elvis's 1960 press conference, recorded at Graceland shortly after Elvis had returned from Germany.

Although there was no catalogue number printed on the record, a matrix number, EPPD-1, was etched between the run-out grooves. Presumably this stood for 'Elvis Presley Picture Disc'. The single was sold in a clear plastic sleeve.

The single cost £3.90 and was manufactured by Lyntone, the company responsible for many of the flexi discs featuring Elvis. It is thought that only 2,000 copies were made. Incidentally, the Lyntone factory closed down on 31 December 1991, and work transferred to its sister factory Damont Audio, based in Hayes, Middlesex.

Elvis Aron Presley

Talkies ELVIS 1

Graceland, Memphis 7 March 1960

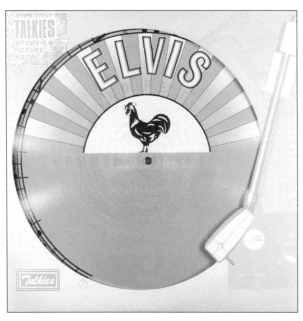

According to the person behind this release, this 12 inch interview picture disc first became available around March 1986. However, we think that it was more likely to have been during 1987, although, to be perfectly honest, the date given is a 'best guess'. What we do know is that in January and February 1988 copies had started to appear in both Virgin and HMV, priced around £5.

Talkies used a standard pink coloured sleeve which could be used for any of their output. The large central cut-out on the front enabled

identification of the contents, with a record player pick-up arm enhancing the effect. There was no catalogue number, which presumably meant that anyone ordering it had to refer to the artist only, nor was there any indication as to the speed of the record, which turned out to be 45 rpm. A catalogue number, ELVIS 1, was etched in the run-out grooves. The back of the sleeve listed other titles available in the 7 and 12 inch series. The record itself was inserted in a clear plastic sleeve and cost around £5. There was a note on the back of the sleeve indicating that each record contained a history of the artist, although this was not included in any copy we have seen of the Elvis single.

Only one side of the record featured a picture of Elvis (a blurred image from **Easy Come, Easy Go** on the A side) whilst the other side displayed a mock Sun Records label, claiming that this commemorative issue had been restricted to a limited edition of 10,000. This was interesting, for we were told that as few as 1,000 copies were actually produced making this, and the 7 inch version, quite rare.

The actual material was the same as the 7 inch version: the 1960 Graceland interview. Sadly the manufacturing process of picture discs did not enhance the sound quality of the recording. Nevertheless, the single has now become a collectors' item.

Madison Square Garden Interview

No label EPPD 19

Madison Square Garden, New York 9 June 1972

Without doubt this picture disc proved to be one of the most difficult records for us to establish any real background details on. And this was despite the fact that, for a short time prior to June 1986, copies were available in many of the large retailers, priced between £4.99 and £5.49, depending on where it was bought. It was sold in a clear plastic sleeve.

Most unusually, no catalogue number was printed on the disc (although etched between the run-out grooves was a 'catalogue' number, EPPD 19), and even more strange was the fact that there was absolutely no reference to who was responsible for its release. Indeed, there was not even a mention of a record label.

The likelihood was that it was probably made by the Lyntone/Damont group, as there were some similarities to their output, but we cannot be certain of this. All our enquiries drew a blank in that respect. The etched catalogue number, EPPD 19, was certainly similar in format and presentation to the Talkies 12 inch picture disc, also discussed in this section.

Both sides of the disc featured a different colour shot of Elvis taken during the **Aloha From Hawaii** concert in January 1973, and on the A side the words 'Elvis Interview Disc Limited Edition' appeared in blue print across the bottom of the record. Printed on the B side, again in blue print, was 'Elvis Recorded 1972 Before Gig At Madison Square Garden'.

As with many of these oddities, copies are now highly sought after and command high prices. It has been suggested that only 1,000 copies were produced, although we have not been able to confirm this.

Youngblood

The name Jan Olofsson may not be immediately familiar to you but, we have no doubt, a great deal of his work will be instantly recognisable. Many of you will recall the successful 1977 tribute **I Remember Elvis Presley**, recorded by Danny Mirror, which reached number four in the UK chart that year. Some of you will also be familiar with the song **In A Broken Dream** by Python Lee Jackson (featuring vocals by Rod Stewart), a 1972 UK number three hit. Both of these, and a whole host of others, were produced by Jan Olofsson. Jan had been a lifelong fan of Elvis and was so inspired that, in the late fifties, he sang and toured his native Sweden, under the name RockOla. Based in London during the sixties, Jan became a club owner, producer and photographer. In 1995, a superb collection of Jan's photographs, entitled **My Sixties**, was published by Taschen. The startling images of stars like the Stones and Hendrix, on and off stage, captured the spirit of the times and remains a fascinating reminder of that era.

Throughout his career there have been several Elvis 'connections'. For example, Jan produced an artist called Stu Stevens in RCA's studio B in Nashville (with Charley McCoy on harmonica). He represented Hoyt Axton (Mae's son) for many years and he saw, met, and photographed Elvis at Madison Square Garden in 1972.

The reason we mention all of the above is because Jan was responsible for another Elvis tribute, entitled **King Of Rock 'N' Roll**, which was sung by Johnny Roman and released on Jan's Youngblood label. Normally we would have not made any reference to a tribute record but, on this occasion, the record contains an Elvis interview (from 1955) which brings the record into our remit.

Johnny Roman (real name Ron Anderson) had worked with Jan for some time and had done reasonably well in Europe with his version of Buona Serra, although he remained virtually unknown in the UK. Three format versions – 7 inch, 12 inch and picture disc – were produced. The 7 inch single, YBL 1, comprised **King Of Rock 'N' Roll/I Love You** but it contained no Elvis material, although the front cover did feature a live shot of Elvis from 1956. A photograph on the back showed Johnny Roman holding the album **The First Live Recordings**, PG 89387, (LP 234).

King Of Rock 'N' Roll

YBLT 1 / YBP 1

Jacksonville, Florida with Mae Axton, 28 July 1955.

The 12 inch version, YBLT 1, contained the two songs above, plus Roman's reworking of **I Remember Elvis Presley**, and the interview

with Elvis by Mae Axton, recorded in July 1955. Although the interview had appeared in the UK once previously – it had been featured on a flexi-disc issued with the **Elvis Monthly Collector's Special** in November 1985 – the claim on the sleeve that it was rare seemed justified. The design on the front of the 12 inch version was identical to the 7 inch version, with additional references to the extra tracks. The Johnny Roman photograph on the back was replaced with a photograph of Elvis and Mae Axton which had been signed 'Best Wishes Mae Boren Axton'.

The 12 inch picture disc, YBP 1, had a modified design but retained the same photographs as the normal 12 inch version, although Mae Axton's autograph was missing, for some reason. It was released in a clear plastic sleeve.

The 7 and 12 inch versions were pressed by Adrenalin Records, based in Slough. 1,550 copies of each were produced in July 1987, while the picture disc was pressed by Orlake in August 1987 and had a run of 1,500 copies.

Not surprisingly, copies are hard to find and, thus, have become extremely collectable.

YBLT 1

YBP 1

281

My Happiness

Fab-U-Lus FBUBX 0027

My Happiness (Peterson, Begantine)
That's When Your Heartaches Begin (Raskin, Brown, Fisher)

Released May 2002

We have included details of this particular 7 inch release in the Miscellaneous Releases section because it was not available as a separate entity, and therefore not eligible for inclusion in the Singles' section. It came as part of an 8 CD boxed set of Sun material, comprising 198 tracks. The two Elvis recordings dated from 1953 and were taken from acetates cut before Elvis signed to the label in 1954. Both had been issued previously. In the wake of it being 'discovered' in the late eighties, *My Happiness* had been featured on the 1990 album *The Great Performances* (**LP 308**), while this version of *That's When Your Heartaches Begin* had first appeared on *The King Of Rock 'N' Roll The Complete 50's Masters* (**LP 318**) in 1992.

Those responsible for this collection of Sun material (Sanctuary Records Group) decided against featuring Elvis tracks on the CD set (possibly because of the cost involved in licensing them). They did, however, negotiate with Gary Hovey at Elvis Presley Enterprises, Shelby Singleton at Sun Entertainment Corporation, and BMG to use some unusual Elvis material on a single – though strictly as a bonus item to the set. Originally, some thought had been given to making it a 10 inch release (as the original acetate would have been), but problems of finding a suitable pressing facility, not to mention the impact on the packaging of the 8 CD set, effectively ruled this idea out.

Similarly, because these recordings were privately commissioned in 1953 the decision was also taken not to use the Sun label or, indeed, a Sun sleeve. Instead, the labels were white and the titles were printed in a typewritten form, as the originals would have been. Note that the placing of the title *My Happiness* was slightly off-centre - deliberately so. The logos – Fab-U-Lus and Sanctuary – appeared on the other side, along with the track details (writers and publishers) and the licensing arrangements. However, no mention was made of BMG at all. Although the Fab-U-Lus label had been formed in 2001 specifically to cater for the collectors market, the Sun CDs were only their second release. Incidentally, Damont in the UK manufactured the record, said to be part of a 5,000 press run.

Unusually, there was no catalogue number shown on the label, deliberately so, as it could not be bought separately from the CD package. The catalogue number FBUBX 0027 was allocated however, but only for internal administrative purposes, and comprised the CD catalogue number (FBUBX 002), with the additional digit 7 added in exactly the same way as had occurred with the bonus EPs issued with Castle's Collector's Edition LPs.

The full title of the CD set was *50 Golden Years. A Commemorative Collection – Classic And Rare Recordings From The Legendary Sun Label*. The concept for the set came from Sam Szczepanski, a label manager at Sanctuary, but was actually compiled by broadcaster, writer and producer Stuart Colman, who also produced the extensive booklet notes. Additional technical and photographic help came from Trevor Cajiao, editor of *Now Dig This*. Initially, the set was offered on the Internet at www.fab-u-lus.com but was intended for wider release in June 2002.

Finally, the writers of *My Happiness*, Peterson, Bergantine were shown the other way around, contrary to how they had appeared on *The Great Performances* (**LP 308**) and on the fifties' set (**LP 318**). *That's When Your Heartaches Begin* was credited to Fisher, Hill, Raskin - in keeping with the song's BMG appearances, although we regard the correct writers to be Raskin, Brown, Fisher.

282

Various Artist Compilation Albums

Introduction

This section is devoted to the various artist compilation albums that contain Elvis material, some of which may include only a single song, whilst some releases include complete albums of his work. Please note: this section is restricted to vinyl albums only and does not include any CD (or cassette) only releases which contained Elvis material. Of course, most of the albums included here were issued in all three formats.

Prior to 1985, the thought that an Elvis song would turn up on such releases was unthinkable, and it seems that RCA also held this view, for here was the world's major selling artist who sold records for RCA, not anyone else, and RCA seemed content to restrict any form of leasing arrangement in this context. Of course, some songs had been leased officially to other companies in the past, the most notable being the October 1974 release *Elvis's 40 Greatest* (*LP 73*) on Arcade and the Reader's Digest box set *Elvis Presley's Greatest Hits* (*LP 82*), released in July 1975, but these were complete collections and featured no other artists. Ironically, it was RCA themselves who started the use of Elvis tracks on albums containing material by other performers when they issued *A Century Of Sound*, RCA PL 42146 (**VA LP 1**), in May 1977, as a tribute to Edison, although this contained only RCA recording artists. The release of seven songs on *The Great Transatlantic Hits* (**VA LP 3**) produced by World Records, an EMI company, followed in 1978, with the first true RCA compilation coming in December 1983 with *A Country Christmas*, RCA NL 84809 (**VA LP 4**). Based on this release was the first 'other company' compilation on Starblend Records, *Christmas At The Country Store* (**VA LP 7**), details of which we included in *Elvis UK 1956-86*, although additional details are included in this section.

However, long before 1985, Elvis songs failed to achieve the same high standing in the market place as they had done previously and, as we have already commented many times elsewhere, no-one appeared to have the will or the interest to produce meaningful releases, forcing – or perhaps encouraging – RCA to look at leasing arrangements to supplement their income. And there was no question that the logic behind such a move was a tempting one from a purely financial viewpoint. For little effort on the company's part a steady income could be achieved with the added potential of further sales of their own product, should buyers of compilation albums find Elvis to their liking. We have no argument with the principle of making Elvis material available in this way, despite the obvious exploitation of the Elvis fan and collector who, if their collections were to remain complete, were 'forced' to buy products which they might not have previously considered. Many of the albums falling into this category were promoted on television, a sure way of adding to the cost of the record, and several were full-priced, making this an expensive area for little return for collectors. Our view is not unlike the record company, in that the inclusion of Elvis material may entice the purchaser into buying further Elvis records which, in turn, should have encouraged RCA into producing more albums themselves. Having said that, there was little evidence to support the argument, for many saw the saturation of various artist compilation records as being yet another cheapening of the image, a failure of RCA to properly look after Elvis's name by consigning many of his classic recordings to the scrap-heap, along with many other 'has-beens' from years gone by. Consequently many fans chose not to bother with a number of the albums featured in this section, a decision we readily acknowledge and understand. Nevertheless, others continued to expand their collections into this area.

Throughout the 1980s then, various artist compilations turned up with alarming regularity, sanctioned by RCA who continued to support this type of release until arguments between themselves and the Presley Estate began to be resolved, culminating with a decision to rescind some leasing arrangements during the late eighties/early nineties. The records themselves ranged from the acutely embarrassing to those which demonstrated quite clearly the potential to be derived from taking care and showing a little imagination with the finished article, resulting in product which could only be described as excellent. Whilst RCA opened a floodgate, they seemed to restrict the tracks that they allowed to reach other companies, with some tracks cropping up time and again on different releases. The bulk of the songs leased by RCA were hits which had reached number one in the charts, alongside a number of other top ten hits. The logic here presumably was that the inclusion of a well known track would encourage sales and, as the casual buyer formed a high proportion of the people who bought this type of material, then this seemed sensible.

Of course, to the Elvis fan there was nothing new, with two notable exceptions – Elvis's rendition of the Frank Sinatra song *Witchcraft*, included on the Sinatra LP *The Duets* (**VA LP 9**), and the alternative takes of *King Of The Whole Wide World* found on *The Last Temptation Of Elvis* (**VA LP 42**). In the main there was little incentive to buy, other than to maintain a collection. However, strangely, some less well known recordings found their way on to these releases, *Tomorrow Is A Long Time* and *I Forgot To Remember To Forget* being the most notable.

The year 1988 was by far the most notable for this type of release, with over twenty-five albums being released; but by 1990, the number of various artist releases had almost ceased, largely because of a change of mind on the part of BMG who, under pressure from the Estate, and from within the company itself, sought to restrict any form of leasing to other companies. Only Reader's Digest appeared to have survived this change of policy initially, although special high profile products have also appeared since. And indeed, by the early part of 1993, the increased popularity of the CD format had resulted in a rapid decline in the demand for vinyl anyway. Consequently, most of the major companies involved in the leasing of tracks to produce various artist compilations, including Reader's Digest, dropped the format altogether. The last vinyl compilation album to contain any Elvis material was *Lipstick On Your Collar* (**VA LP 50**), released in March 1993.

In collecting terms, most of these records had no great value and nor are they likely to have, for they sold in considerable numbers, often cheaply, when they were sold off after their initial run. Several managed to achieve a re-press, which resulted in variations appearing, unlike the majority of RCA's own product (we have noted in the text where variations occur). However, some were very difficult to locate, even when they were first released, and are likely to be sought after in years to come, but only the Elvis 'completest' is likely to be tempted in this way.

This section, then, contains a complete listing of various artist albums which have included Elvis material, and all have been allocated a release number for ease of reference and to show cumulative totals in exactly the same manner as the main releases. The first five compilation albums were covered in detail in *Elvis UK 1956-86*, but a brief summary is included again here. To further assist accessing each release, we have provided both chronological and alphabetical listings. In addition, we have listed separately each of the

Elvis songs included on these albums, along with the various artist compilation release number, in order to determine the appropriate record(s) and the number of occasions the song had been used.

A further refinement is that the title block for each album has been expanded to show the Elvis track(s) concerned (including writers' names), so that this section is more in line with that of singles and albums. However, track details by other artists are not shown.

UK Various Artist Compilation Albums Listed Chronologically

This section lists all of the various artist compilation albums to feature Elvis material and, in order to allow the number of such releases to be put into perspective, each release has been allocated a chronological numbering sequence.

This section should, therefore, enable you to determine, for each release, its release number, label and catalogue number and the date of release.

Release Number	Catalogue Number	Title	Release Date
VA LP 1	RCA PL 42146	*A Century Of Sound*	May 1977
VA LP 2	Harrods (PL 42146)	*A Century Of Sound*	? 1977
VA LP 3	World Records SW 9869	*The Great Transatlantic Hits*	? 1978
VA LP 4	RCA NL 84809	*A Country Christmas*	Dec 1983
VA LP 5	Reader's Digest GBIG-A-9-139	*Giants Of Country*	Mar 1985
VA LP 6	RCA PL 85463	*Rock & Roll: The Early Days*	Jul 1985
VA LP 7	Starblend NOEL 1	*Christmas At The Country Store*	Dec 1985
VA LP 8	Reader's Digest GRNR-A-9-149	*112 Rock 'N' Roll Greats*	Jan 1986
VA LP 9	Deja Vu DVLP 2051	*The Duets*	May 1986
VA LP 10	K-tel NE 1377	*Always*	Oct 1987
VA LP 11	EMI EMTV 44	*Unforgettable*	Feb 1988
VA LP 12	Connoisseur Collection YRNR LP69	*A Series – 25 Years of Rock 'N' Roll 1969*	Apr 1988
VA LP 13	Stylus SMR 855	*Sixties Mix 2*	Apr 1988
VA LP 14	Connoisseur Collection YRNR LP71	*A Series – 25 Years Of Rock 'N' Roll 1971*	May 1988
VA LP 15	Old Gold OG 1502	*Number Ones 50's Volume 2 – Pop*	May 1988
VA LP 16	Old Gold OG 1503	*Number Ones 60's Volume 1 – Pop*	May 1988
VA LP 17	Old Gold OG 1506	*Number Ones 60's Volume 3 – Ballads*	May 1988
VA LP 18	Old Gold OG 1507	*Number Ones 70's Volume 2 – Ballads*	May 1988
VA LP 19	RCA NL 90085	*Rock & Roll: The Early Days* (re-issue)	May 1988
VA LP 20	Trax TRX 501	*Best Of Country*	Jul 1988
VA LP 21	Trax TRX 504	*Big Country Classics Volume Three*	Jul 1988
VA LP 22	Trax TRX 505	*Big Country Classics Volume Four*	Jul 1988
VA LP 23	Connoisseur Collection VSOP LP112	*24 Most Requested Records From Radio 2*	Jul 1988
VA LP 24	Connoisseur Collection YRNR LP73	*A Series – 25 Years Of Rock 'N' Roll 1973*	Jul 1988
VA LP 25	Connoisseur Collection YRNR LP75	*A Series – 25 Years Of Rock 'N' Roll 1975*	Aug 1988
VA LP 26	Connoisseur Collection YRNR LP77	*A Series – 25 Years Of Rock 'N' Roll 1977*	Aug 1988
VA LP 27	Reader's Digest GLEG-A-190	*The Pop Legends*	Sep 1988
VA LP 28	Trax BOOMER 113	*Rollin' Seventies*	Sep 1988
VA LP 29	Trax BOOMER 116	*Mellow Seventies*	Sep 1988
VA LP 30	BBC REF 693	*Ones On 1. The Radio 1 21st Birthday Album*	Sep 1988
VA LP 31	Telstar STAR 2351	*The Heart 'N' Soul Of Rock 'N' Roll*	Oct 1988
VA LP 32	Filmtrax TRX 701	*Noel*	Oct 1988
VA LP 33	Connoisseur Collection TYNO LP 100	*30 Years Of 'Number Ones' Volume 1*	Nov 1988

VA LP 34 Connoisseur Collection TYNO LP 101	*30 Years Of 'Number Ones' Volume 2*	Nov 1988
VA LP 35 Telstar STAR 2337	*Morning Has Broken*	Nov 1988
VA LP 36 Telstar STAR 2352	*The Greatest Love II*	Nov 1988
VA LP 37 BBC REN 709	*Gloria Hunniford – At Your Request*	Jan 1989
VA LP 38 Trax TRX 508	*Big Country Classics The Fifties Vol. 7*	Feb 1989
VA LP 39 Start STDL 20	*The Songs Of Bob Dylan*	Mar 1989
VA LP 40 Reader's Digest GEASY-A-193	*Easy Listening Hits Of The 60's And 70's*	May 1989
VA LP 41 Old Gold OG 1512	*60's Number Ones – Volume 1*	Sep 1989
VA LP 42 Old Gold OG 1514	*70's Number Ones – Volume 2*	Sep 1989
VA LP 43 BBC REQ 739	*The Attack Of The Killer Bs*	Oct 1989
VA LP 44 NME LP 038/039	*The Last Temptation Of Elvis*	Feb 1990
VA LP 45 Reader's Digest GGSS-A-144	*Great Stars Sing Their Greatest Songs*	Feb 1990
VA LP 46 Reader's Digest GHSR-A-207	*The Heart And Soul Of Rock 'N' Roll*	Sep 1990
VA LP 47 Best ZL 74857	*Gazza And Friends – Let's Have A Party*	Nov 1990
VA LP 48 Reader's Digest GTOP-A-203	*40 Years Of Top Ten Hits*	Sep 1992
VA LP 49 Telstar STAR 2649	*Head Over Heels*	Feb 1993
VA LP 50 Polygram TV 516 086-1	*Lipstick On Your Collar*	Mar 1993

UK Various Artist Compilation Albums Listed Alphabetically

The Various Artist Compilation Albums section of this book shows all the details of those albums including Elvis material in chronological order, rather than alphabetically, to enable you to follow the developments and trends as they occurred. If, however, you do not know when a particular album was released, and you are unable to find it in the chronological section, then you can use this listing to determine its location in the chronological section, and turn to the page in question where the record is discussed in detail.

Where the same title has been used more than once on an album, the listings place the albums in a chronological sequence, but reference to the catalogue number will clearly distinguish between releases.

Title	Catalogue Number	Release Number
A Century Of Sound	RCA PL 42146	**VA LP 1**
A Century Of Sound	Harrods (PL 42146)	**VA LP 2**
A Country Christmas	RCA NL 84809	**VA LP 4**
A Series - 25 Years Of Rock 'N' Roll 1969	Connoisseur Collection YRNR LP69	**VA LP 12**
A Series - 25 Years Of Rock 'N' Roll 1971	Connoisseur Collection YRNR LP71	**VA LP 14**
A Series - 25 Years Of Rock 'N' Roll 1973	Connoisseur Collection YRNR LP73	**VA LP 24**
A Series - 25 Years Of Rock 'N' Roll 1975	Connoisseur Collection YRNR LP75	**VA LP 25**
A Series - 25 Years Of Rock 'N' Roll 1977	Connoisseur Collection YRNR LP77	**VA LP 26**
Always	K-tel NE 1377	**VA LP 10**
Best Of Country	Trax TRX 501	**VA LP 20**
Big Country Classics The Fifties Vol. 7	Trax TRX 508	**VA LP 38**
Big Country Classics Volume Three	Trax TRX 504	**VA LP 21**
Big Country Classics Volume Four	Trax TRX 505	**VA LP 22**
Christmas At The Country Store	Starblend NOEL 1	**VA LP 7**
Easy Listening Hits Of The 60's And 70's	Reader's Digest GEASY-A-193	**VA LP 40**

40 Years Of Top Ten Hits	Reader's Digest GTOP-A-203	VA LP 48
Gazza And Friends - Let's Have A Party	Best ZL 74857	VA LP 47
Giants Of Country	Reader's Digest GBIG-A-9-139	VA LP 5
Gloria Hunniford - At Your Request	BBC REN 709	VA LP 37
Great Stars Sing Their Greatest Songs	Reader's Digest GGSS-A-144	VA LP 45
Head Over Heels	Telstar STAR 2649	VA LP 49
Lipstick On Your Collar	Polygram TV 516 086-1	VA LP 50
Mellow Seventies	Trax BOOMER 116	VA LP 29
Morning Has Broken	Telstar STAR 2337	VA LP 35
Noel	Filmtrax TRX 701	VA LP 32
Number Ones 50's Volume 2 - Pop	Old Gold OG 1502	VA LP 15
Number Ones 60's Volume 1 - Pop	Old Gold OG 1503	VA LP 16
Number Ones 60's Volume 3 - Ballads	Old Gold OG 1506	VA LP 17
Number Ones 70's Volume 2 - Ballads	Old Gold OG 1507	VA LP 18
112 Rock 'N' Roll Greats	Reader's Digest GRNR-A-9-149	VA LP 8
Ones On 1. The Radio 1 21st Birthday Album	BBC REF 693	VA LP 30
Rock & Roll: The Early Days	RCA PL 85463	VA LP 6
Rock & Roll: The Early Days	RCA NL 90085	VA LP 19
Rollin' Seventies	Trax BOOMER 113	VA LP 28
60's Number Ones - Volume 1	Old Gold OG 1512	VA LP 41
70's Number Ones - Volume 2	Old Gold OG 1514	VA LP 42
Sixties Mix 2	Stylus SMR 855	VA LP 13
The Attack Of The Killer Bs	BBC REQ 739	VA LP 43

The Duets	Deja Vu DVLP 2051	VA LP 9
The Great Transatlantic Hits	World Records SW 9869	VA LP 3
The Greatest Love II	Telstar STAR 2352	VA LP 36
The Heart 'N' Soul Of Rock 'N' Roll	Telstar STAR 2351	VA LP 31
The Heart And Soul Of Rock 'N' Roll	Reader's Digest GHSR-A-144	VA LP 46
The Last Temptation Of Elvis	NME LP 038/039	VA LP 44
The Pop Legends	Reader's Digest GLEG-A-190	VA LP 27
The Songs Of Bob Dylan	Start STDL 20	VA LP 39
30 Years Of 'Number Ones' Volume 1	Connoisseur Collection TYNO LP 100	VA LP 33
30 Years Of 'Number Ones' Volume 2	Connoisseur Collection TYNO LP 101	VA LP 34
24 Most Requested Records From Radio 2	Connoisseur Collection VSOP LP112	VA LP 23
Unforgettable	EMI EMTV 44	VA LP 11

UK Various Artist Compilation Albums – The Songs

This section lists, in alphabetical order, all of the songs which were featured on the various artist albums issued in the UK from 1977 to date. In addition, the various artist compilation album release number(s) have been shown to make clear the total number of occasions each song has appeared.

A surprisingly large number of tracks were involved, considering the market at which the bulk of these albums were aimed, and an analysis of those featured is quite revealing.

In all, there were 63 different tracks, and of these, three deserve special mention. *Witchcraft* (the Frank Sinatra song, not the one normally associated with Elvis) made its first official appearance on a various artist album – *The Duets* (**VA LP 9**) in 1986. Ironically, the song, from Elvis's appearance on the Sinatra TV show in 1960, was not released by BMG until 1993, when it appeared on *From Nashville To Memphis The Essential 60's Masters 1* (**LP 319**).

More importantly, the three takes of *King Of The Whole Wide World* have only appeared on *The Last Temptation Of Elvis* (**VA LP 44**). In addition, a different edit (appallingly done) of the songs which comprised *The Elvis Medley* (counted as one 'track' in the total) could only be found on *Gazza And Friends - Let's Have A Party* (**VA LP 47**).

Thirty-nine of the songs had appeared only once to date, and included a mixture of extremely well known recordings, along with some less well known ones.

At this point we need to refer to the contribution made by Reader's Digest to the various artist album scene for, whilst it was true that several tracks had been heavily duplicated by the company, there was no doubt that the overall number of songs would have been reduced quite significantly had Reader's Digest not been involved in the leasing arrangements. According to our calculations, the 63 titles actually issued would have been reduced to 31. In other words, Reader's Digest contributed half of the total. Admittedly, one album, the *Giants Of Country* (**VA LP 5**) boxed set, with the 'bonus' album *Elvis Sings County Favourites* accounted for another thirteen songs which each made only one appearance. However, the other track on the album, *Are You Lonesome Tonight?*, was used on many occasions.

Not surprisingly, all of Elvis's seventeen UK number 1 hits were represented, in varying frequencies. For example, *Are You Lonesome Tonight?* appeared eight times, whereas **One Night** appeared only once. Many other top ten hits were included, and a few non-singles' tracks were also used.

A Complete Listing Of The Various Artist Compilation Albums

The first four releases were covered in detail in *Elvis UK 1956-86*, but for the benefit of new readers, we have included a brief synopsis of the records in question.

VA LP 1 | **A Century Of Sound**

RCA PL 42146

Are You Lonesome Tonight? (Turk, Handman)

Released May 1977

This was a limited edition of 5,000 boxed sets and issued as a celebration of the hundredth anniversary of Edison successfully recording and replaying sound. There were 32 tracks, including *Are You Lonesome Tonight?*

VA LP 2	A Century Of Sound
	Harrods (PL 42146)

Are You Lonesome Tonight? (Turk, Handman)

Released May 1977

Harrods produced their own box to market their special limited edition of *A Century Of Sound*. Only 1,000 sets were produced and this has become one of the most sought after UK releases.

VA LP 3	The Great Transatlantic Hits
	World Records SW 9869

Heartbreak Hotel (Axton, Durden, Presley)
Love Me Tender (Presley, Matson)
All Shook Up (Blackwell, Presley)
Jailhouse Rock (Leiber, Stoller)
It's Now Or Never (DiCapua, Schroeder, Gold)
Return To Sender (Blackwell, Scott)
Crying In The Chapel (Glenn)

Released ? 1978

This was a six record boxed set issued by World Records who were owned by EMI and operated on a mail-order basis, in much the same way as Reader's Digest. The set was produced in conjunction with RCA and was manufactured by them at their Washington, Tyne and Wear, pressing plant. In *Elvis UK 1956-86*, we omitted to show the catalogue number, an error which we are happy to correct. We should also point out that each individual album was given its own catalogue number, starting with SM 361 and running to SM 366. Seven Elvis tracks were included, not five, as we originally reported. In all, the collection featured 100 tracks.

VA LP 4 | A Country Christmas

RCA NL 84809

Silver Bells (Evans, Livingston)

Released December 1983

This was really the first time that RCA had issued an Elvis track on a various artist product that was widely distributed. To all intents and purposes, it was a normal German black label issue; indeed, it was one of the first such albums to be issued in the UK, having been mastered in February 1983.

Collectors may be interested to know that the album was re-pressed and that two variations in label design are known to exist. These follow the same pattern as the majority of Elvis's own albums, and reference to the label change details that are discussed in that section may be useful. The original pressing placed GEMA above BIEM, whilst the later ones (we think, in this case, 1987) reversed the order and placed the two in separate boxes.

Reader's Digest

In terms of Elvis records, most fans would have associated Reader's Digest with the seven album boxed set ***Elvis Presley's Greatest Hits***, GELV 6A (*LP 82*), issued in October 1975, the only occasion prior to 1985 that the company had issued any Elvis material in the UK. ***Elvis Presley's Greatest Hits*** was a huge success, well received by most fans, to the point where it had almost become an essential purchase. Confirmation of the album's appeal can be determined by its lifespan, which covered around fifteen years before it was 'replaced' by ***The Legend Lives On***, GELG-A-209 (**LP 310**), in November 1990.

Reader's Digest had a unique place in the Elvis market. Certainly no other company had produced two sets of the magnitude of ***Elvis Presley's Greatest Hits*** and ***The Legend Lives On***, supplemented with a lasting and ongoing licensing arrangement with RCA/BMG that enabled a number of other Elvis tracks to be included on Reader's Digest various artist compilation albums. Because of this, we thought it would be of interest to provide some relevant background of a general nature on Reader's Digest, as an introduction to the many compilation albums featuring Elvis material produced by the company since 1985, along with an overview of the procedural stages that were involved with the production of these items.

Reader's Digest was founded by DeWitt Wallace, an American, who formed the company in 1922. The idea for the venture came to Wallace when he was hospitalised after being wounded whilst fighting in World War I. During his convalescent stay in hospital he asked for magazines to relieve the inevitable boredom and found that, whatever the subject matter of the magazine, there were usually to be found some articles with bits and pieces that proved of interest.

This, then, formed the basis of an idea to collect unrelated articles together to produce a magazine of general interest. The problem was that no publisher was particularly excited by this concept, forcing Wallace to go ahead and publish the magazine himself. Since then, of course, Reader's Digest has gone from strength to strength, diversified into other areas, such as the music business, and established divisions in countries throughout the world (the UK division was formed in 1960).

Of course, the company changed over the years, and readers of daily newspapers will have noted frequent advertisements for Reader's Digest products – a relatively new departure – as the company was striving for a much higher profile, rather than relying mainly on an existing subscriber network.

Obviously we are primarily concerned with the company's record output, but there is no doubt that Reader's Digest have built a reputation for producing a wide variety of high quality product which is always attractively presented and which offers excellent value for money. As far as the records are concerned, behind the final product lies months of intensive research into the kind of material its customers want to buy, so, in a sense, Reader's Digest do not take the same risks as many record companies – they know their market and, in the main, stick to it. Their effort focuses on getting the right product together by careful selection of available material to meet their audience, with a clear emphasis on quality. It is known that the company's standards are high and their music division only uses the highest quality tapes provided by record companies – it is not unknown for tapes to be returned if they are not up to standard. At this point, however, we ought to say that many of the Elvis songs on Reader's Digest albums were issued prior to BMG's determination to use only original masters and, therefore, Reader's Digest used the best quality tapes available to them, which were sometimes better than the equivalent used by BMG. Mastering of Reader's Digest albums was carried out by their own engineer, Paddy Marchant, and various London studios were used for this purpose.

Albums were pressed in a variety of factories, as Reader's Digest were no different from most other organisations in that they were looking for the most competitive price for the work.

Reader's Digest have operations in other European countries (Reader's Digest call them territories), and each country may take another country's work, depending on the appeal of the product in question. A group like Abba, for example, would have a market in most European countries, but an album of Swiss yodelling songs would generate little interest in Spain! Therefore, when compiling various artist albums, selection of the tracks for inclusion had to be a meticulous process, carefully researched to ensure that the most popular artists or songs were chosen, thus broadening the albums' potential market and appeal. Of course, it could be argued that one disadvantage of this approach was that there was a danger of repetition, with some tracks being used over and over, but this was undoubtedly true of any form of 'greatest hits' package, as Elvis fans know only too well.

Broadly speaking, the procedure adopted by Reader's Digest was as follows: from the initial idea for an album there was a period of research into the market, the kind of material available, and so on. This was then followed by the process of track selection and negotiations with the appropriate record companies to license the tracks selected for inclusion. In this respect Reader's Digest was no different from any other company wishing to license recordings – they had no automatic right simply because they had issued a boxed set of Elvis material. In other words, each project was a separate entity and had to be processed accordingly. Indeed, there was a point when RCA said no and, like several other companies at that particular time, Reader's Digest was forced to look elsewhere for licensing deals. There was no question that Elvis was in demand by Reader's Digest and, because of his versatility and wide ranging, popular repertoire, many of his recordings would have fitted neatly into many Reader's Digest projects, such as their **Unforgettable Hits Of The 70's** and **The Number One Collection**, neither of which contained any Elvis material. But can you imagine an album of rock 'n' roll without Elvis?!

The initial licensing period was normally three years, which could be extended, providing the companies concerned could reach agreement. There was then a 'sell-off' period which allowed Reader's Digest to clear stocks, giving an overall lifespan of around five years for each compilation set.

The next phase of the process was most interesting. We mentioned earlier that Reader's Digest took few risks and were very careful to compile outstanding albums of high quality. Even so, Reader's Digest operated a refined sampling exercise which they referred to as a 'wet test' which, in a sense, was similar to the way that TV advertisements for a new product are launched in one TV region, in order to monitor the response and prior to going national. A 'wet test' was a sort of mail shot, whereby existing subscribers were sent details of the product, the intention being for Reader's Digest to attempt to establish how successful the product would be when it went on general sale. Later, newspaper and magazine advertisements served the same purpose. A quantity of records would be pressed up and the response of existing subscribers would dictate how many would be pressed for the 'bulk' run. In simple terms, then, the logic was this: if there was no response then the project might have been abandoned totally, but because of Reader's Digest's careful research this was virtually impossible – the project would never have been started! From the frequency and number of orders that the company received, they were able to forecast what the final demand would be, and pressing quantities could be determined fairly accurately, thus reducing the risk factor and costs. It has to be remembered that production costs were high for the kind of package that Reader's Digest specialise in, and clearly there was a need to ensure that costs were kept to a minimum. Similarly, it could be assumed that Reader's Digest needed to sell quite large numbers of product to re-coup costs – again the company had to get it right.

From the time the 'wet test' was instigated to the bulk run was normally about a year, but this could vary to some extent and often depended on other projects in the pipeline. Obviously the company would not want to issue two similar, or related, sets at the same time, so the bulk run for a particular project may have been delayed or advanced as appropriate.

However, not all Reader's Digest sets had a wet test, particularly when the actual response could be forecast accurately without the need for this phase. For example, Reader's Digest's Elvis set **The Legend Lives On** was not wet tested as it was thought unnecessary.

The principle of having a kind of trial run with the wet test confused the precise release date of these sets. And, we have to admit that until we realised and acknowledged the significance of the wet test, we too were confused. Consequently, the first of Reader's Digest's various artist compilation albums to include Elvis, **Giants Of Country** (**VA LP 5**), which was wet tested in March 1985 and went on general release in March 1986, should have been included in the previous volume, **Elvis UK 1956-86**. However, an unintended benefit of this error on our part is that all of the Reader's Digest's sets are included here in the one volume, which, having backtracked on other releases, now contains the bulk of the compilation albums with Elvis material.

A feature of many of the earlier Reader's Digest sets was the inclusion of a bonus album as part of their marketing policy. Indeed, the first two sets we discussed are of special interest, as the bonus albums comprised entirely Elvis songs, whereas later product incorporated Elvis into the main part of the work, with other 'themes' forming the bonus issue. Bonus albums are discussed more fully in the text for each set, where appropriate.

The first few Reader's Digest sets to include Elvis material were not available on compact disc, but we have made reference to the available formats for each release. Further evidence of the decline in vinyl sales could be seen by the way costs of this format rose in later years, and also changed price 'categories'. Using **The Pop Legends** (**VA LP 27**) as an example, in 1990 both LP and cassette formats cost £36.95 with the CD priced at £39.95. But, by 1992, costs had risen to £42.95 for the cassette format only, while LPs had joined CDs in the higher cost bracket at £47.95, reflecting the increased production costs of lower press runs

Reader's Digest used to produce promotional records in the form of flexi-discs sent to subscribers as a taster for a particular product – we covered the promotional flexi-disc for **Elvis Presley's Greatest Hits** and a more general Reader's Digest flexi disc in **Elvis UK 1956-86**. Now an outdated medium, flexi-discs could not truly reflect the quality of the final product, and Reader's Digest made the move to use CDs for promotional purposes. However, that does not mean that all releases had a promotional disc; this depended on the product in question. To the best of our knowledge, no promotional disc was produced for **The Legend Lives On**. Surprisingly, a flexi-disc comprising brief segments of several of the songs featured was issued in some territories, though not in the UK. It was, however, manufactured in the UK by Lyntone and had a catalogue number LYN 18708.

The catalogue numbering system used by Reader's Digest also deserves a mention. Each album was given a separate catalogue number – commencing with the prefix RDS (vinyl), RDC (cassette), and RDCD (compact disc) – followed by a five digit identifier. These numbers were allocated from the next available batch. So, if a set comprised eight albums, they would be sequentially numbered within the given range. In addition, each set was also 'catalogued' by a series of letters and digits which formed an overall reference for the set. These references took the following form:

Giants Of Country GBIG - A - 9 - 139

The block of letters – GBIG – (four in this case, but more are sometimes used) served two purposes. The initial letter denoted the audio format. G = vinyl records (the G originally stood for gramophone), C = cassette and L = compact disc. The second group of letters – BIG in this example, was a mnemonic – a fancy name given to a code used to jog the memory of those responsible for the set's compilation. In a way it was nothing more than an abbreviation of the set title, especially if it contained a simple word which could be used. If not, initial letters could be used. In this case no suitable word could be found in *Giants Of Country*, so 'Big' = 'Giant'! Other Reader's Digest sets were a little more obvious – *40 Years Of Top Ten Hits* was simplified to TOP; *Easy Listening Hits Of The 60's And 70's* to EASY. Some of the initial letters in *The Heart And Soul Of Rock 'N' Roll* give HSR. Therefore, rather than having to refer to the full title, these abbreviations were used.

The 'A' in the reference number was an indicator given to show that the set was as originally planned and released. A 'B' would be used if a modification had to be made to the original track listing.

The final three digits were simply an incremental reference number, generally showing the sequence of release. However, as we have already pointed out, releases could be advanced or delayed, and so the sequential number did not necessarily follow the actual release pattern.

As we have said, a more conventional catalogue numbering system was used by Reader's Digest on individual albums, such as those issued as a bonus to accompany boxed sets. *Elvis Sings Country Favourites*, the bonus LP for *Giants of Country*, was numbered RDS 10279; and, *Elvis Rocks! - 14 Golden Greats* which accompanied *112 Rock 'N' Roll Greats* (**VA LP 8**), RDS 10359. We have shown both the overall catalogue number and the one for the bonus LP in the title block for the releases in question.

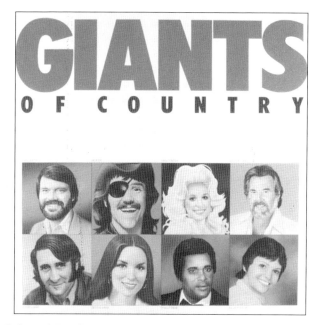

Released March 1985

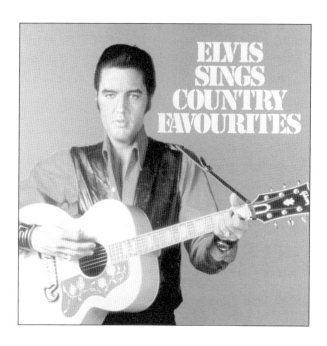

VA LP 5	**Giants Of Country**
	Reader's Digest GBIG-A-9-139
	Elvis Sings Country Favourites
	RDS 10279

Side 1

1 **Are You Lonesome Tonight?** (Turk, Handman)
2 **Release Me (and let me love again)** (Miller, Williams, Yount, Harris)
3 **I Can't Stop Loving You** (Gibson)
4 **Make The World Go Away** (Cochran)
5 **Your Cheatin' Heart** (Williams)
6 **Welcome To My World** (Winkler, Hathcock)
7 **I Really Don't Want To Know** (Barnes, Robertson)

Side 2

1 **Gentle On My Mind** (Hartford)
2 **Funny How Time Slips Away** (Nelson)
3 **I'm Movin' On** (Snow)
4 **Faded Love** (B. & J. Wills)
5 **I'm So Lonesome I Could Cry** (Williams)
6 **You Gave Me A Mountain** (Robbins)
7 **She Thinks I Still Care** (Lipscomb)

Elvis Sings Country Favourites was a bonus record issued free with the *Giants Of Country* boxed set and was the first Reader's Digest set to contain any Elvis material since the 1975 issue of *Elvis Presley's Greatest Hits*, GELV 6A (*LP 82*). As an added incentive to buy, Reader's Digest often provided a 'free' album to accompany their boxed sets – remember that *Elvis Presley's Greatest Hits* had included *Elvis In The Movies* as a bonus LP. These bonus albums had a separate identity and were not, therefore, actually part of the set, but were an addition to it. However, anyone who purchased *Giants Of Country* automatically received a copy of *Elvis Sings Country Favourites*.

Using Elvis on a bonus album to accompany a compilation of major country artists was in complete contrast to similar American projects where Elvis would be put on country albums and classed as a 'country' singer or, at least, a singer of country songs. American audiences had always associated him in this way, but in the UK Elvis is generally thought of as a 'rock 'n' roll' singer, and for this reason Reader's Digest thought it more appropriate to provide this bonus LP rather than include Elvis as a part of the main set.

Although **Giants Of Country** first became available in March 1985 – when it was 'wet tested' to existing subscribers – most fans had no idea that such an album was in existence. We confessed earlier that our original omission of the album from **Elvis UK 1956-86** was due to our understanding that the album did not become available until March 1986 – the date the album went on general release.

When collectors became aware of the Elvis involvement with the album it was much sought after and, as with **Elvis Rocks! 14 Golden Hits**, the bonus album supplied with the next Reader's Digest Elvis related product, **112 Rock 'N' Roll Greats** (**VA LP 8**), copies could be found in selected specialist stores and at record fairs attracting a price of £15 for each album. Many fans were happy to pay this amount, arguing that it made more economic sense than paying £37 for the complete set when the Elvis album was the sole reason for the purchase. It was an understandable move given these circumstances.

Ironically, late in 1989, Reader's Digest were selling off **Elvis Sings Country Favourites** as a separate album – priced at 99p! The album apparently had been re-pressed somewhere along the way for the label colour was white, not light blue, as the original copies were. Additionally, whilst the original label stated that the record was made in France, later copies gave no indication as to where the record was pressed.

Giants Of Country itself featured only eight artists:

>   Glen Campbell
>   Kenny Rogers
>   Don Williams
>   Crystal Gayle
>   Billie Jo Spears
>   Dolly Parton
>   Dr. Hook
>   Charley Pride

It was not, therefore, a multi-artist collection like most of the subsequent Reader's Digest releases. Most of the songs associated with these artists were to be found in the set, including most of their UK hits. The accompanying booklet provided well-written, detailed and informative background to each act, but there were no notes on Elvis.

In terms of content, the album was markedly different from the 'greatest hits' type material Reader's Digest later included on compilation albums, and the set was all the more refreshing for it. Indeed, thirteen of the fourteen Elvis tracks had never appeared on any other various artist album, and several had been little used by RCA/BMG. And, whilst Elvis had recorded many country songs, to date only one original concept album had ever been released by RCA – **I'm 10,000 Years Old – Elvis Country**, SF 8172 (*LP 49*), in 1971. Yet only two of the tracks found on **Elvis Sings Country Favourites** were taken from this album; the rest were from various sources and periods ranging from **Your Cheatin' Heart**, recorded in 1958, to **She Thinks I Still Care**, cut in 1976. Interesting then that the album included songs taken from the later period of Elvis's career, as these were not generally being issued by RCA, supposedly because of complications with the Presley Estate.

Because of the unusual nature of the compilation, it seems worth listing the source of the tracks on the album. The date given in brackets relates to the year the track was recorded.

Are You Lonesome Tonight? (1960). The standard studio recording.

Release Me (and let me love again) (1970). This was the remixed version as used on the **Welcome To My World** album, PL 12274 (*LP 92*).

I Can't Stop Loving You (1972). This version was taken from the afternoon show at Madison Square Garden which also first appeared on the **Welcome To My World** album.

Make The World Go Away (1970). From **I'm 10,000 Years Old – Elvis Country**, SF 8172 (*LP 49*).

Your Cheatin' Heart (1958). This was the standard studio recording.

Welcome To My World (1973). This was from the **Aloha From Hawaii** album, DPS 2040 (*LP 66*).

I Really Don't Want To Know (1970). From **I'm 10,000 Years Old – Elvis Country** (*LP 49*).

Gentle On My Mind (1969). This was the standard version as included in **From Elvis In Memphis**, RD/SF 8029 (*LP 38*).

Funny How Time Slips Away (1975). This was the live concert version from 1975 first featured on the **Elvis Aron Presley** eight album boxed set, CPL8 3699 (*LP 126*), released in August 1980.

I'm Movin' On (1969). As included in **From Elvis In Memphis** (*LP 38*).

Faded Love (1970). This was the overdubbed version as used on the **Guitar Man** LP, RCALP 5010 (*LP 146*), released in February 1981.

I'm So Lonesome I Could Cry and **You Gave Me A Mountain** (1973). Both were taken from the **Aloha From Hawaii** album (*LP 66*).

She Thinks I Still Care (1976). This version was taken from the **Moody Blue** album from August 1977, PL 12428 (*LP 93*).

Clues as to the source of these songs came from the publishing dates printed on the label, although these were far from accurate and cannot, therefore, be relied upon. **Are You Lonesome Tonight?** was not released in the UK until 1961, but the publishing date of 1960 referred to its US release. The two songs from **I'm 10,000 Years Old – Elvis Country**, **Make The World Go Away** and **I Really Don't Want To Know** were quoted as being first published in 1970 when, in fact, the album was not released until 1971 in both America and in the UK. **Funny How Time Slips Away**, the studio version, which also appeared on this album, was quoted as being first published in 1970, but this version dated from 1975, although it was not actually released until 1980. **I'm Movin' On** quoted 1975 when it should have read 1969, and, similarly, the overdubbed version of **Faded Love** should have read 1981.

Another unusual feature was that there was no printing whatsoever on the spine of the sleeve where, normally, details of the artist, album title and catalogue number would be found. The back of the sleeve showed a copyright date of 1984 and carried a note that two of the songs, **Your Cheatin' Heart** and **Funny How Time Slips Away** were electronically reprocessed for stereo. This was understandable for the former title (being a mono recording from 1958), but the reason for **Funny How Time Slips Away** being treated in this way was due to the fact that supposedly it was taken from a cassette source and featured on the eight album boxed set, **Elvis Aron Presley** (*LP 126*).

No compact disc format was ever produced for this set which survived for around four years before it was effectively replaced by other country collections, though without any Elvis contribution.

Note that **Are You Lonesome Tonight?** was included both here and on many of the later Reader's Digest compilations, including **The Pop Legends** (**VA LP 27**).

There was only one label error - **Welcome To My World** was co-written by Hathcock, not Hatchcock, as the label claimed.

Although a 'bonus' album for **Giants Of Country**, **Elvis Sings Country Favourites** comprised solely of Elvis tracks and was, therefore, an album in its own right. As several label variations exist for this album we have listed these below in the same format as the LP section.

Label Variations

BLUE LABEL

1   **1985 PRESSING:**
STEREO/ELECTRONIC STEREO
Made in France

WHITE LABEL

2   **1989? PRESSING:**
STEREO/ELECTRONIC STEREO
No country of manufacture

3   **1989? PRESSING:**
STEREO/ELECTRONIC STEREO
Made in England

We discussed the following album in more detail in ***Elvis UK 1956-86***.

VA LP 6   *Rock & Roll:*
The Early Days

RCA PL 85463

That's All Right (Crudup)

Released July 1985
Re-issued May 1988. RCA NL 90085 (VA LP 19)

Rock & Roll: The Early Days was issued to complement the video of the same name, and represented the first time that an Elvis track had been issued alongside other great names from the fifties. However, ***That's All Right*** was not included on the video compilation.

This was a full price album (PL) which featured an Elvis 50th anniversary sticker on the front of the sleeve. However, in May 1988, the album was given a new catalogue number, NL 90085, and re-issued as a mid-priced release. We have included full details of the release in this section (**VA LP 19**).

<table>
<tr><td>**VA LP 7**</td><td>**Christmas At The Country Store**</td></tr>
<tr><td></td><td>**Starblend NOEL 1**</td></tr>
</table>

Silver Bells (Evans, Livingston)

Released December 1985

We included brief details of this record in *Elvis UK 1956-86*, but through no fault of our own, this was printed on the wrong page and rather detracted from what we had intended. Actually in one sense the error was fortuitous, appearing as it did in the 'Rare Records' section, for this is a rare record. Why, you may ask? There are many reasons for this: firstly, it slipped by almost unnoticed. Secondly, sales were relatively poor – the Christmas compilation market is a difficult one at the best of times, but for a country compilation, almost impossible. Finally, and perhaps more significantly, this was the first record (excluding the special arrangements with EMI and Reader's Digest) to feature an Elvis track on a non-RCA album in the UK, making this record as important as it is rare. Having said that, RCA did have some involvement in this album.

Starblend Records, based in London, produced many records during the mid-eighties on their own label, and even more on their Country Store label which featured – no surprises here – well known country artists. This compilation featured artists like Tammy Wynette, Willie Nelson and Marty Robbins, but also included less familiar names. The album was produced in conjunction with RCA, CBS and EMI, and featured Elvis's *Silver Bells*, which had turned up on an RCA Christmas compilation, *A Country Christmas*, NL 84809 (**VA LP 4**), two years previously.

Interestingly, almost all of the tracks by RCA recording artists featured on *Christmas At The Country Store*, also appeared on the RCA album referred to above, which seemed to suggest that this leasing arrangement did not require too much effort on RCA's behalf. RCA also pressed the record in their German pressing plant and, therefore, the record displayed some, but not all, of the familiar trademarks, especially the bass clef around the spindle hole. The small picture of Elvis on the front cover was from the *Double Trouble* era.

The album was compiled by Chris and Tony Harding who owned Starblend.

Both the label and sleeve spelt Jay Livingston's name with an 'e' at the end.

<table>
<tr><td>**VA LP 8**</td><td>**112 Rock 'N' Roll Greats**</td></tr>
<tr><td></td><td>**Reader's Digest GRNR-A-9-149**</td></tr>
<tr><td></td><td>**Elvis Rocks! – 14 Golden Greats**</td></tr>
<tr><td></td><td>**RDS 10359**</td></tr>
</table>

Side 1
1 **Heartbreak Hotel** (Axton, Durden, Presley)
2 **Hound Dog** (Leiber, Stoller)
3 **All Shook Up** (Blackwell, Presley)
4 **(Let me be your) Teddy Bear** (Mann, Lowe)
5 **Jailhouse Rock** (Leiber, Stoller)
6 **King Creole** (Leiber, Stoller)
7 **I Got Stung** (Schroeder, Hill)

Side 2
1 **(Now and then there's) A Fool Such As I** (Trader)
2 **Stuck On You** (Schroeder, McFarland)
3 **(Marie's the name) His Latest Flame** (Pomus, Shuman)
4 **Good Luck Charm** (Schroeder, Gold)
5 **She's Not You** (Pomus, Leiber, Stoller)
6 **Return To Sender** (Blackwell, Scott)
7 **(You're the) Devil In Disguise** (Giant, Baum, Kaye)

Released January 1986

Elvis Rocks! - 14 Golden Greats was the bonus album produced to accompany *112 Rock 'N' Roll Greats*, an eight LP/four cassette package for which no CD format was produced.

Whenever the phrase 'rock 'n' roll' is used there is a tendency to consider that this automatically refers to the mid to late fifties' period. Yet, whilst this may well have been rock 'n' roll's golden age, there are many classic recordings made long after the end of the fifties that should not be dismissed, and many of these are featured on this set. Where rock 'n' roll stopped and 'pop' took over has long been a subjective argument which will not be resolved here. For many Elvis fans it was at the time when Elvis went into the army, or rather when he returned to recording in 1960 and failed to continue where he left off, with out-and-out rock 'n' roll tunes. But, did rock 'n' roll simply mellow, or just blend into a wider form? Whatever, it could be argued that the title of this Elvis album was misleading, in the sense that it covered the period from 1956-1963, and several of the tracks from side 2 probably leaned more towards the 'pop' category rather than straight rock 'n' roll.

Despite this, there could be no argument as to the pedigree of these recordings: quite simply they represented some of the finest recordings Elvis ever made, all instantly recognisable. What's more, between them they accounted for nine number one hits, while the remainder reached either number two or three in the charts. Although similar to other compilations issued by RCA themselves, this was an incredibly strong album, especially when considering the fact that it was intended as a bonus issue to a set costing around £37 when it was released.

There was no reference to the mode on either the label or sleeve, but all tracks on side 1 were in mono, while the six recordings from the sixties (tracks 2-7 on side 2) were all in stereo. The record was pressed in the UK.

On the front of the sleeve there was a black and white drawing of Elvis, with the words 'Elvis Rocks!' in bright red. On the back of the sleeve were four mid-fifties black and white live action shots of Elvis.

There were a number of label and sleeve errors, all of them relating to the tracks on side 2. Both label and sleeve omitted the words in brackets on *(Now and then there's) A Fool Such As I* and *(You're the) Devil In Disguise*. And the old error concerning the writers of *Stuck On You* reappeared again, with the claim that the song was written by Schroeder, Leslie, McFarland when Leslie McFarland was one person. The word 'of' was included in *(Marie's the name) His Latest Flame*, and Mort Shuman had his surname spelt Schuman on the sleeve – though it was correctly spelt on the label.

VA LP 9	The Duets
	Deja Vu DVLP 2051

Witchcraft (Coleman, Leigh)
Love Me Tender (Presley, Matson)

Released May 1986

Deja Vu was an Italian based company which issued a whole series of easy listening, blues and jazz albums which were widely distributed in the UK by a Manchester company. Deja Vu first started issuing material in October 1983, but were particularly prolific between the years 1985 and 1988, during which time this collection of duets between Frank Sinatra and other notable artists, including Nat King Cole and Doris Day, was released.

The duet with Elvis was taken from the TV soundtrack for the American TV company ABC's Frank Sinatra Timex Show recorded at the Fountainbleau Hotel in Miami on 26 March 1960, for which Elvis was the special guest. The recording was broadcast on 12 May 1960 on US TV. The 'duet' was actually Elvis singing part of one of

Sinatra's hits, **Witchcraft**, whilst Sinatra sang **Love Me Tender**, before both singers joined together on the latter song for the finale. In all honesty, neither song was complete, nor particularly inspiring, and the sound quality left much to be desired, but this record did represent the first time the recording had been released 'officially', although there were doubts at the time as to the legality of such a move. The recording had been heavily bootlegged in the past, the most significant being **TV Guide Presents Elvis**, one of the most sought after bootleg LPs at the time.

Whatever the truth was regarding the legitimacy of this release, the point was that for the majority of fans this was the only opportunity they had to hear this material until September 1993, when BMG issued their sixties' boxed set **From Nashville To Memphis The Essential 60's Masters 1** (**LP 319**), which included the recording. The Deja Vu album remained, therefore, the only available legitimate source for seven years, and one of the very few various artist albums to issue new material in such a way. Because of the unusual nature of the material, and for no other reason, we have listed both titles, despite the fact that Elvis sang only a few lines of **Love Me Tender**. Indeed, the whole thing lasted for less than two minutes.

Notably, this was the first of these various artist compilations to be issued in CD format in addition to the vinyl version. However, the CD version of **The Duets** (DVCD 2051) was not issued until July 1987, fourteen months after its initial appearance on vinyl. From this point onwards most, but not all, of these releases appeared in both formats. Those compilations which did not have a CD version are noted in the text.

Always On My Mind

One of the most frequently used songs on various artist compilation albums has been **Always On My Mind**, a song recorded in March 1972. We have made reference to different 'versions' of **Always On My Mind** previously but, in truth, these are not different versions (as in different takes) but radically different re-mixes which, because of the overall effect, radically alters the instrumental backing, creating the illusion of different recordings. The first genuine outtake (take 2) of the song appeared on a CD single in May 1997.

As different 'versions' are to be found on various artist compilations, we felt it necessary to be as clear as possible as to which 'version' (mix) was being used. To avoid confusion, we consider there to be three 'versions'/re-mixes.

1. The original single version from 1972 which is clearly distinguished by James Burton's electric guitar solo.

2. The **This Is Elvis** (*LP 150*) version, noticeable for the acoustic guitar and piano and lack of string section, was issued in 1981.

3. The **Always On My Mind** (*LP 272*) LP version on which the string arrangement is prominent and there was no electric lead guitar break, was first issued in 1985.

Only 'versions' one and three have been used on various artist compilation albums and the text for each album makes clear which one it is.

The writers of **Always On My Mind** have also created their own confusion! Our belief has always been that the song was written by Mark James, Wayne Carson and Johnny Christopher, although when the song was first released in the UK (on a single in December 1972 -*S 85*) – it was credited to Thompson, James, Christopher.

Indeed, over the years just about every permutation of these four surnames has been used and it was not until **This Is Elvis**, BL 84031(2) (*LP 226*), was released in May 1984 that the correct credits were shown. Unfortunately, subsequent issues, including the majority of various artist albums, have continued to show errors.

VA LP 10	Always
	K-tel NE 1377

Always On My Mind (James, Carson, Christopher)

Released October 1987

Elvis had been featured on K-tel albums four times previously: **Love Songs** (*LP 116*) in October 1979; **Inspirations** (*LP 139*) in November 1980; **The Ultimate Performance** (*LP 182*) in October 1981; and finally **Rock 'N Roll Rebel** (*LP 190*) in May 1982, but all of these releases had been Elvis-only material, not various artist compilations.

In fact, K-tel were extremely prolific producers of various artist compilation albums from the late seventies onwards and, for example, put out five other albums in addition to **Always** in the same month.

In common with the majority of K-tel albums, **Always** received extensive TV and radio promotion which centred around the 'title' track. Released in October 1987, **Always** was a full priced album, costing approximately £7.

Elvis's contribution, **Always On My Mind**, was destined to become one of the most used tracks of all in various artist compilations. This was the original single version of the song. Incidentally, the writers of the song were shown as James, Christopher, Thompson when they were normally shown as James, Carson, Christopher.

An interesting feature of the album was that, in addition to **Always On My Mind**, Elvis had recorded versions of a further five out of the total sixteen tracks – **Release Me (and let me love again)**, **Spanish Eyes**, **I Love You Because**, **And I Love You So** and **Green, Green Grass Of Home**.

Various Artist Releases – 1988

Up to this point the number of various artist albums had been minimal, totalling just ten releases in as many years. Discounting the first four, issued up to the end of 1983, the trickle from 1985 onwards was largely the responsibility of RCA themselves with the closely related Starblend release, **Christmas At The Country Store** (**VA LP 7**). A further two releases had been made by Reader's Digest who had issued a couple of Elvis-only 'bonus' albums to accompany their boxed sets. The Deja Vu **The Duets** (**VA LP 9**), was of dubious origin, leaving the K-tel **Always** (**VA LP 10**) album as the starting point for the rest to follow. And, in 1988, other companies did so with a vengeance, with 27 albums being released which included Elvis tracks.

VA LP 11	Unforgettable
	EMI EMTV 44

Always On My Mind (James, Carson, Christopher)

Released February 1988

During the early to mid-1980s, EMI were responsible for a series of TV promoted albums (as the catalogue number of this release confirmed), many of which were love song collections. This album was no exception, and, according to the advertisement, contained '18 of the finest love songs ever recorded'. Indeed, the album was sub-titled **18 Classic Songs Of Love**, and there was no doubt that this was the case with items like Nat 'King' Cole's **When I Fall In Love** and the title track, **Unforgettable**.

Once again the Elvis track was **Always On My Mind**, although this time it was not the original single version which K-tel had used on their **Always** (**VA LP 10**) album in October 1987 (the last various artist album prior to this release to feature an Elvis recording), but the 'stringed' version which had first appeared in 1985 on the RCA album **Always On My Mind** (*LP 272*).

Brief notes about the song accompanied the track listing, and these pointed out that Elvis's version of **Always On My Mind** reached number 9 in the charts during January 1973, while the Pet Shop Boys achieved a number 1 with the song in December 1987.

Interestingly, Elvis recorded versions of three other songs found on the album – **Love Letters**, **Fever**, and **You've Lost That Lovin' Feelin'**, although it was the original versions which were included here.

Unlike K-tel's **Always** album, the writers of **Always On My Mind** were correctly shown as James, Carson, Christopher.

Connoisseur Collection

The Connoisseur Collection Limited, based in London, quickly acquired a reputation for producing a large number of varied releases of a particularly high quality on LP, cassette and CD. Their repertoire ranged from classical recordings to heavy metal, and included some imaginative and spectacular compilation albums, worthy of serious consideration at a time when just about every company was seen to be producing such material in an apparent wave of nostalgia – directed towards the sixties, in particular.

Flagship releases for the company were their series of 25 years of Rock and Roll which seemed to have been prompted by the BBC series **The Rock and Roll Years**. The front of each album sleeve featured a headline page of the **Daily Mirror** newspaper from the appropriate year. The 1962 sleeve, for example, referred to the death of Marilyn Monroe, suggesting that she had committed suicide; whilst the 1964 sleeve carried front page headlines trying to convince us that by 1972 trains would be running under the English Channel. There were also extracts from the **New Musical Express**, again from the relevant year.

All in all this was an excellent series and, because it covered twenty five years, rather than just, say, the sixties, it enabled the producers to be a little more adventurous with their choice of material. This was particularly true of the Elvis tracks which appeared on five of the albums – 1969, 1971, 1973, 1975 and 1977 – for, alongside such various artist compilation favourites such as **Always On My Mind**, were tracks like **I Just Can't Help Believin'** and **Promised Land**, neither of which had appeared in this format before or since, for that matter.

Connoisseur Collection had planned to include an Elvis track on a further release in the series – the album covering 1980, which would have featured **It's Only Love**. The track was even listed in the catalogue, but as this was around the time when RCA were beginning to have second thoughts about leasing material to other companies, Connoisseur Collection failed to get permission for the song's inclusion. Consequently the song was substituted by a non-Elvis track and the 1980 album went ahead without any Elvis contribution.

Initially, the series was restricted to vinyl and cassette formats, though CDs were added later. The CDs covering the period 1962 to 1971 were released in September 1988, with the years 1972 to 1979 appearing in January 1989. CDs covering the later period – 1980 to 1981 – were released out of sequence in November 1988.

Connoisseur Collection were a small company that clearly put a great deal of effort into their work, with some clever concept and theme albums, some of which contained Elvis material. The **30 Years of No.1's**, another long series, carried several Elvis tracks from the 1960s, before leasing became a problem.

All Connoisseur Collection albums were reasonably priced at £6.49 for a double album, although if you had committed yourself to the two series mentioned above, then the overall outlay was considerable. Perhaps this also had an effect on Connoisseur Collection, who may well have overstretched themselves, because many of their albums turned up in large numbers at heavily reduced prices, presumably a sign that all was not well and stocks were being cleared.

VA LP 12	**A Series – 25 Years of Rock 'N' Roll 1969**
	Connoisseur Collection YRNR LP69

Suspicious Minds (James)

Released April 1988

This was the first release to feature an Elvis recording in the **25 Years Of Rock 'N' Roll** series put out by Connoisseur Collection, each containing 24 tracks selected to evoke the spirit of the year in question. Not all the tracks were big hits, a refreshing change in itself, but they did adequately show the tremendous range of material that made the charts in 1969.

Alongside Cream's **Badge** were tracks like The Fifth Dimension's **Aquarius/Let The Sun Shine In** and Jane Birkin/Serge Gainsbourg's **Je T'aime Moi Non Plus**. However, the quality track on the album was **Suspicious Minds**, and presumably Connoisseur Collection thought so too, as it was the first track on side 1.

This was the first time that **Suspicious Minds** had been used on a various artist album, and to date it has only appeared on one other compilation – **Easy Listening Hits Of The 60's And 70's** (**VA LP 40**) issued by Reader's Digest. However, in 1998 it did feature on **Heartbeat The Gold Collection** (RADCD 90), a Global TV release, released in conjunction with BMG. Of course, the latter was a CD only release; there was no vinyl available.

VA LP 13	**Sixties Mix 2**
	Stylus SMR 855

It's Now Or Never (DiCapua, Schroeder, Gold)
Return To Sender (Blackwell, Scott)

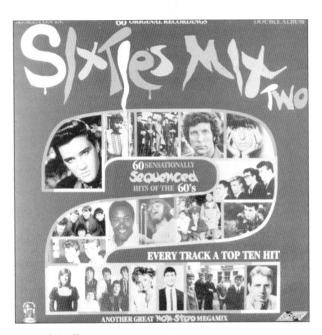

Released April 1988

As the title clearly suggested, this was the second release featuring sixty top ten hits from the sixties, but the first to include Elvis material. The record label showed the title of the album to be **Sixties Mix 2**, whereas the sleeve changed the **2** to **Two**. This double album, like its predecessor, was heavily promoted through TV advertising and did well because of it. The Disco Mix Club referred to on the back of the sleeve was managed by Tony Prince.

Two Elvis tracks were included: **It's Now Or Never** on side 1 and **Return To Sender** on side 3, but both were edited, or rather segued with other tracks to make a continuous recording. Normally Elvis fans disapproved of this treatment, arguing that Elvis's music should not be tampered with in such a way. The majority of fans, however, probably ignored the album. Whatever, the album was clearly designed for general appeal and, doubtless, many people would have found great pleasure in listening to this type of material. And if the Elvis tracks helped to enhance this, then perhaps we should not complain.

There was a black and white photograph of Elvis, circa **King Creole** (1958), on the front of the sleeve, the same early publicity still that had appeared on the front of **Personally Elvis**, AFESD 1032 (*LP 186*), but much smaller and in reverse image. Inside the gatefold sleeve the picture was used again, twice, to accompany the brief sleeve notes about the artists and tracks.

The album was issued in all three formats, and a video with selected tracks was also issued, but this did not include the Elvis selections.

The album cost £8.99, typical of prices at the time for TV advertised albums.

A promo single featuring **It's Now Or Never** and tracks by other artists was issued by Stylus to support this release.

A Series – 25 Years Of Rock 'N' Roll 1971

Connoisseur Collection YRNR LP71

I Just Can't Help Believin' (Mann, Weil)

Released May 1988

This was the second album in the **25 Years Of Rock 'N' Roll** series to feature an Elvis track, in this case **I Just Can't Help Believin'**, a song which entered the charts in December 1971, reaching a peak position of number six.

One of the reproduced **New Musical Express** front pages, dated 10 April 1971, featured on the inside of the gatefold sleeve, showed a picture of Elvis and Elton John with the headline 'Easter Suits', and a short story about men changing fashion trends. Reference to the LP chart of October 1971, also shown, revealed that Elvis's **C'mon Everybody** (LP 52) was in the charts at number 11.

It was quite unusual, even at this stage, to see a track like **I Just Can't Help Believin'** featured on this kind of compilation album, but a welcome change because of it. Indeed, this was the only occasion to date that the track had been used on this kind of release.

On both the label and sleeve the word **Believin'** was shown as **Believing**.

Old Gold

Old Gold had produced many 'hit' compilation albums before starting their number 1's series which covered three decades and many musical styles. This series was much less structured than the one put out later in the year by Connoisseur Collection, which contained material in a strict chronological sequence, concentrating on one year at a time.

Old Gold separated the series into the fifties, sixties and seventies, each with a further grouping so that there was some cohesion of

styles. This allowed albums featuring ballads, rock and roll, and pop to be issued for the period in question. All of the albums featured fourteen tracks, and it was good to see Old Gold giving the total running time on the sleeves, although this practice did highlight how short many of the songs were, particularly those from the earlier decade.

Elvis tracks were featured on four albums, two from the sixties and one each from the fifties and seventies, and all were released simultaneously on 23 May 1988. The sleeves featured the same basic design, but were coloured differently. However, towards the end of 1989, Old Gold were forced to modify the track listing of two these LPs by substituting a couple of tracks with two others. Both were re-issued, although the Elvis tracks were retained.

Old Gold's catalogue numbering system deserves a mention, as it differed from the practice adopted by most companies, with the actual number representing the audio format. LPs commenced with a 1, cassettes a 2, and CDs 3.

Number Ones 50's Volume 2 – Pop

Old Gold OG 1502

All Shook Up (Blackwell, Presley)
Jailhouse Rock (Leiber, Stoller)

Released May 1988

This was the second in Old Gold's series of number 1 hit singles. The first had also featured tracks from the fifties, but ballads, not rock 'n' roll songs, and significantly no Elvis tracks.

Trying to work out the actual title of this album is quite hard. We know that the series was entitled No. 1's, but Old Gold's catalogue referred to this album as **Vol.2 Rock 'N' Roll Number Ones Of The Fifties**, whilst the label had no reference to rock 'n' roll, describing the tracks as **Pop**. Later catalogues entitled the album **50's No. 1's Vol. 2 – Rock 'N' Roll**.

This album contained two Elvis tracks, both of which Old Gold had issued earlier on two of their single releases (**S 158** and **S 164**). They were **All Shook Up** and **Jailhouse Rock** which were later also to be found on volume 1 of Connoisseur Collection's **30 Years Of 'Number Ones'** (**VA LP 33**) series released in November 1988, showing the inevitable repetition that very quickly results with this kind of 'hits' package. These songs are now generally acknowledged as being the first and second of Elvis's UK number one hits, although some charts – such as the one produced by the music paper **Melody Maker** – had songs like **Party** reaching the number one spot.

The small picture of Elvis featured on the front of the sleeve was from 1958 (circa **King Creole**). The publishing date on the back cover for **Jailhouse Rock** was 1957 (the year it was recorded), although it was not published in the UK until January 1958.

VA LP 16	**Number Ones 60's Volume 1 – Pop**
	Old Gold OG 1503

Are You Lonesome Tonight? (Turk Handman)
Wooden Heart (Wise, Weisman, Twomey, Kaempfert)

Released May 1988

Elvis opened both sides of the album with the tracks **Are You Lonesome Tonight?** on side 1 and **Wooden Heart** on side 2. Although **Are You Lonesome Tonight?** had appeared several times before on various artist albums, **Wooden Heart** was making its debut on this kind of release.

Both of these songs had appeared together on an Old Gold single, OG 9702 (**S 157**), released in April 1987 and, like the single, both tracks were featured here in mono, even though they had been recorded in stereo and had appeared as such on countless other releases.

Two errors are worth pointing out: **Are You Lonesome Tonight?** appeared without the question mark on both label and sleeve, whilst it was claimed on the sleeve that the song's co-author was Ray Turk. The label used his correct Christian name, Roy.

In 1989, because the licencing arrangements with EMI had expired, Old Gold were forced to substitute two EMI recordings, the Shadows' **Apache** and Cliff Richard's **The Young Ones**, replacing them with **Nutrocker** and **My Old Man's A Dustman**. The LP was re-issued with a different catalogue number, OG 1512 (**VA LP 41**), and with a modified sleeve design.

VA LP 17	**Number Ones 60's Volume 3 – Ballads**
	Old Gold OG 1506

Crying In The Chapel (Glenn)
Can't Help Falling In Love (Peretti, Creatore, Weiss)

Released May 1988

This was the third volume of sixties' material, and the second to feature Elvis, who, once again, contributed two songs – **Crying In The Chapel**, which was in stereo, and **Can't Help Falling In Love** which, for some reason, remained in mono.

Crying In The Chapel, released for the second time on a various artist album, was the only track featured in the Number Ones series that had not appeared on any of Old Gold's singles, effectively increasing the number of songs leased by the company from BMG to 41.

A small, reverse image, photograph of Elvis (circa 1961) appeared on the front of the sleeve which was grey in colour, although much lighter than that of **Number Ones 50's Volume 2 – Pop**, OG 1502 (**VA LP 15**), released at the same time.

The Wonder Of You (Knight)

Released May 1988

This was the final Old Gold Number Ones album to feature Elvis, but, as with *Number Ones 60's Volume 1 – Pop* (**VA LP 16**), Old Gold re-issued this LP in September 1989, having substituted two of the tracks after their licencing arrangements had expired. *Mississippi*, by Pussycat, was replaced with *I Love To Love* by Tina Charles, and *Lucille*, by Kenny Rogers, was replaced with *Hold Me Close* by David Essex. The revised LP (**VA LP 42**) featured an amended sleeve design.

The picture of Elvis on the front of the sleeve was taken from the rehearsal sequence during the filming of *That's The Way It Is* in the summer of 1970.

The Wonder Of You featured here was, once again, in mono, as it had been on Old Gold's single, OG 9761 (**S 173**). Strangely, only one other track on the album was in mono – the instrumental *Eye Level*.

All three of the previous Old Gold Number One albums had featured two tracks which had fitted easily into the categories ascribed, 'Pop' and 'Ballads', covering both the fifties and sixties. Including a second track on this album of '70s ballads was, of course, not possible, as Elvis's only other number one of the period (also his last number one to date), *Way Down*, was not a ballad.

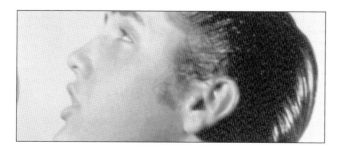

That's All Right (Crudup)

Released May 1988
Original Issue July 1985   RCA PL 85463 (VA LP 6)

Compilation albums usually had a fairly short shelf-life and often were to be found at reduced prices after an initial period of high volume sales. Most albums in this category share the common element of being one-off, in that they were issued, survived while sales lasted, and then disappeared without trace – only for the tracks to be re-compiled and circulated again. In particular, compilation albums of recent chart material have a very short lifespan and, while they are undoubtedly extremely popular, they are quickly replaced by albums comprising more up-to-date material.

This album, on the other hand, was a rarity amongst various artist compilation albums – a re-issue. Of course, *Rock & Roll: The Early Days* was a more serious album (in an historical sense) than those comprising contemporary chart material, and therefore had a timeless quality. Significantly, it was issued by BMG, and not a compilation specialist company who were leasing tracks from various sources.

The album was first released in July 1985 (**VA LP 6**) and it was covered in some detail in *Elvis UK 1956-86*, and in summary in this book. It was designed to complement a video of the same name issued by RCA/Columbia. The most significant aspect of this release was that an Elvis track, *That's All Right*, was included, for the first time, alongside tracks by some of the great rock 'n' roll acts of the fifties, such as Little Richard and Chuck Berry. The original issue was a full-priced, PL, album, whereas this re-issue was a mid-priced, NL, album, costing around £4 when it was issued. In a sense, therefore, it was no different from most RCA albums, being reduced in price from its original issue.

The front of the sleeve was identical to that of the original – a 'pinball' design featuring photographs of the main artists, including an artificially coloured live action shot of Elvis from the fifties. The back cover too featured the same design, but with a number of minor amendments – the price code change, distribution details and so on. A small round RCA logo replaced the computer style print logo. The shot of Elvis was a publicity photo from November 1955 when Elvis signed for RCA.

The label was almost the same with only minor amendments to the position of BIEM/GEMA. In other words it followed exactly the same pattern as all RCA albums of the period.

Trax

Trax Music Limited, a division of Filmtrax, a London based company, were responsible for a considerable number of albums in the late eighties, with releases involving two different compilation series and a Christmas album.

The first series involved country recordings, and was promoted under the heading **Big Country Classics**, whilst their **Baby Boomer** series was a collection of hit recordings covering the 1950s, '60s and '70s with each album having its own theme. They included releases involving 'pop', 'rocking', 'party time' and so on.

Quite clearly displayed on the back of all the record sleeves, was the fact that Trax albums were distributed by BMG Ltd. Actually, BMG did rather more than distribute the records, for an examination of the inner bag showed that this was identical to those produced by BMG, and the record itself bore many of the traditional German features such the bass clef around the spindle hole – confirmation that BMG manufactured many of these albums.

The **Big Country Classics** series was actually issued in two parts, with volumes 1 – 5 released in July 1988, and volumes 6 – 10 in February 1989, although Elvis was not featured on all of the albums. None of the releases actually showed the volume number on the label, referring only to **Big Country Classics**. Excluding the later volumes in the country series, all the records had the date of mastering engraved in the run out grooves and these show that the first country album, **Best Of Country** (**VA LP 20**), reached this stage in May 1988, whilst other albums in the series had June 1988. The **Baby Boomer** albums released later showed September 1988. A further Trax release, **Noel** (**VA LP 32**), was even more revealing, but we shall discuss this along with the actual album details later.

The **Baby Boomer** series sold for around £4 for each single album containing sixteen tracks, but only two featured an Elvis song. However, on the back of the sleeve were adverts for the other albums in the series, one of which, **Pop Seventies**, listed some of the artists featured on that particular record, a list headed by Elvis. Despite this, no Elvis track was included on the vinyl format. The reason for the confusion was that the CD version of the album contained two additional tracks, including Elvis's **Burning Love**, which had been used on another album in the series, **Rollin' Seventies** (**VA LP 28**).

All of the **Baby Boomer** series including Elvis tracks were first issued in September 1988, although other albums had been released earlier.

VA LP 20	Best Of Country
	Trax TRX 501

Always On My Mind (James, Carson, Christopher)

Released July 1988

This album was extensively advertised on TV and was a full priced album which, it has to be said, was expensive, retailing for over £8 at one time. However, like most TV promoted material, it seems that over-stocking, or rather an over estimation of demand, was the reason why copies could be picked up for less than £3, if one was prepared to wait.

One aspect of these country compilation albums produced by Trax that immediately captured people's attention was the beautifully photographed shots of American landscapes, in this case a striking rock formation rising above a desert scene.

This album contained sixteen tracks, as did all the others in the series. Many of the songs were familiar, but few were hits in the UK, and even some of the artists were less well known. Certainly artists like Charlie Rich, Tammy Wynette and Johnny Cash required no introduction, but Lee Greenwood and Donna Fargo were names which were relatively unknown in the UK. Even some of the songs were unfamiliar – Dolly Parton's **Two Doors Down** being a good example – all of which made the title somewhat questionable. The tracks featured on **Best Of Country** were not selections of the material found on the regular albums in the series, but were additional recordings.

302

In fairness, we do not profess to be experts in the field of country music, and so we will confine ourselves to saying that Elvis's contribution was *Always On My Mind*, now established as being a favourite track on various artist LPs, having been included on a couple of love song collections the year previous to this release. Here the song appeared again, this time on a country collection, but, as we have said, we are not experts in this field – was *Always On My Mind* a country song?

Once again, the version of *Always On My Mind* featured here was not the original single version of the song. It was the same as that found on the *Unforgettable* album, EMTV 44 (**VA LP 11**), which had first appeared on the album *Always On My Mind* (*LP 272*), complete with string arrangement. Despite the fact that this version dated from 1985, the label quoted 1972, the year the song was recorded. Writing credits were incorrectly attributed to Thompson, James, Christopher.

The back of the sleeve of this album, along with some short, uninformative sleeve notes, featured photographs of five releases in the *Big Country Classics* series, which *Best Of Country* was intended to promote. Interestingly, no licensing arrangements were shown on the back of the sleeve, unlike the other albums in the series.

VA LP 21 | **Big Country Classics Volume Three**

Trax TRX 504

Moody Blues (James)

Released July 1988

Of course it would have made more sense – to us at least – to have given *Best Of Country* the catalogue number 500, allowing the rest of the series to have a catalogue number in keeping with its allocated volume number. Had Trax done so, this album, volume 3, would have used, more logically, 503.

The sleeve notes offered more details regarding the series, explaining that the albums were 'dedicated to the seventies' and that all the songs were hits, not necessarily in the UK, but in America. Of course,

some of the featured tracks had been hits in the UK, Dolly Parton's *Jolene*, for example. And, while all of the artists were familiar names, the songs were not quite so well known or, as with the song *Chantilly Lace*, not normally associated with Jerry Lee Lewis.

The Elvis song included here was *Moody Blue*, which we really had never considered as a country song. Whatever, this was the only occasion to date that *Moody Blue* had appeared on one of these compilation albums, including those put out by Reader's Digest.

VA LP 22 | **Big Country Classics Volume Four**

Trax TRX 505

Way Down (Martine Jr.)

Released July 1988

This was the final release in the original batch of five Country Classics albums released by Trax to feature an Elvis recording. The song in question this time was his last UK number one, *Way Down*. But, wasn't it stretching the imagination to call *Way Down* a country song? Perhaps this was what was being referred to when the sleeve notes told us that 'Country music knows no boundaries...'. Country song or not, this was the first time that *Way Down* had appeared on a compilation album.

Many of the same artists cropped up again on this album, again singing a combination of well known and less familiar material.

The writer of the *Way Down* was identified as Martin Kennedy, whereas the first pressings of the UK single, PB 0998 (*S 116*), referred to L. Martin and J. Kennedy. The later pressings of the single and subsequent appearances on albums correctly credited Layng Martine Jnr., who was the sole writer of the song.

VA LP 23	**24 Most Requested Records From Radio 2**
	Connoisseur Collection VSOP LP112

VA LP 24	**A Series – 25 Years Of Rock 'N' Roll 1973**
	Connoisseur Collection YRNR LP73

It's Now Or Never (DiCapua, Schroeder, Gold)

Always On My Mind (James, Carson, Christopher)

Released July 1988

Released July 1988

There could be no doubt about it: this was a clever concept album. But whether or not this compilation of largely easy listening material actually comprised the most requested recordings received by Radio 2 wasn't important, and for that matter it is unlikely that anyone would know. Certainly we cannot argue with this, for these were popular songs that had received an enormous amount of airplay over the years. Perhaps it was fitting then that the Elvis track was *It's Now Or Never*, his best selling UK single, and, undoubtedly, the best selling single included on this collection – a fact which was not mentioned in the sleeve notes. In fairness though, Elvis did receive top billing on the front of the sleeve and *It's Now Or Never* did open side one.

Although the actual sleeve design seemed uninspired, this kind of collection showed a good deal of imagination and was a refreshing change from some of the more mundane love songs and country collections which had preceded it. The album, a double, contained 24 tracks and was priced at £5.49.

The spine of the album shortened the album's title to *Radio 2 Favourites*.

Connoisseur Collection tended to assess how well their vinyl albums were selling before they committed themselves to producing a version on CD. As no CD equivalent was issued for this particular collection, it seemed reasonable to assume that the vinyl sales' figures did not justify it.

Always On My Mind had become one of the most used tracks on compilation albums, having appeared on *Always*, *Unforgettable* and *Best Of Country* (**VA LPs 10, 11** and **20**) in the previous nine months, as well as an appearance on Old Gold. The sleeve correctly pointed out that the song actually first appeared in the charts in December 1972.

The writers of *Always On My Mind* were once again shown as Thompson, James, Christopher, thus perpetuating the errors found on RCA releases. The version of the song featured here was the one with the stringed arrangement, first found on the *Always On My Mind* (*LP 272*) album issued in 1985.

Promised Land (Berry)

Released August 1988

Elvis's **Promised Land** was featured on this collection of hits from 1975, and whilst many of the songs – and indeed the artists who recorded them – are still remembered, few of the songs were as memorable as Elvis's contribution.

Promised Land was another unusual selection for a compilation album, and was making its first and last appearance to date on this kind of release.

Way Down (Martine Jr.)

Released August 1988

This was the final album in the Connoisseur Collection Rock 'N' Roll series to feature an Elvis track, although they had intended to include **It's Only Love** on the 1980 album, but were prevented from doing so when RCA/BMG began to restrict their licensing arrangements.

It was inevitable that the 1977 album in the 25 Years Of Rock 'N' Roll series would feature the death of Elvis as one of the **Daily Mirror** lead headlines on the front of the sleeve. Just as inevitable was the inclusion of **Way Down**, Elvis's posthumous and final number 1 hit single to date.

The writer of **Way Down** was correctly identified as being Layng Martine, whereas the **Big Country Classics Volume Four** (**VA LP 22**) album, released a month earlier, credited L. Martin and J. Kennedy. This would seem to suggest that two different sources had passed the copyright details to Connoisseur Collection and Trax.

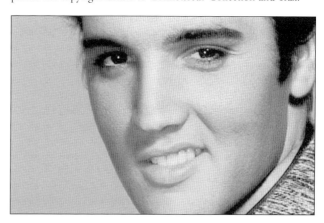

VA LP 27	The Pop Legends
	Reader's Digest GLEG-A-190 RDS 10571

Side 1

1. **Heartbreak Hotel** (Axton, Durden, Presley)
2. **All Shook Up** (Blackwell, Presley)
3. **Jailhouse Rock** (Leiber, Stoller)
4. **Hound Dog** (Leiber, Stoller)
5. **(Now and then there's) A Fool Such As I** (Trader)
6. **It's Now Or Never** (DiCapua, Schroeder, Gold)
7. **Are You Lonesome Tonight?** (Turk, Handman)

Side 2

1. **(Marie's the name) His Latest Flame**
(Pomus, Shuman)
2. **Wooden Heart** (Wise, Weisman, Twomey, Kaempfert)
3. **Can't Help Falling In Love** (Peretti, Creatore, Weiss)
4. **Good Luck Charm** (Schroeder, Gold)
5. **Return To Sender** (Blackwell, Scott)
6. **(You're the) Devil In Disguise** (Giant, Baum, Kaye)
7. **She's Not You** (Pomus, Leiber, Stoller)

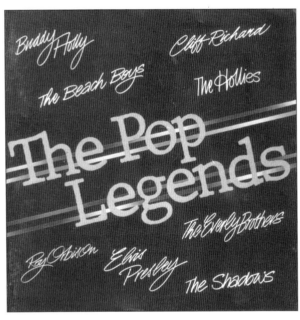

Released September 1988

The Pop Legends was one of the better concept albums issued by Reader's Digest, simply because it contained a broader selection of material in varying styles, rather than concentrating on one particular aspect. The idea of combining eight of the most well known names in popular music was a clever one – the brainchild of Martin Moritz, Reader's Digest's Repertoire Manager, who we know was particularly pleased with the final product.

There had been a gap of almost three years between the release of this album and the previous Reader's Digest set to include Elvis material – *112 Rock 'N' Roll Greats* (**VA LP 8**). The most notable feature of this album was that the Elvis tracks had been incorporated into the set itself, instead of being issued as a 'bonus' album as with the two earlier sets. Despite this, an entire album, comprising fourteen

tracks, was devoted to Elvis and, although there was nothing unusual in the material being presented, the collection was exceptionally strong. All but two of the tracks, *Heartbreak Hotel* and *Hound Dog*, were UK number one hits, but on the negative side, ten of these were duplicated from *112 Rock 'N' Roll Greats*. Indeed, only *It's Now Or Never*, *Wooden Heart* and *Can't Help Falling In Love* were making their Readers's Digest debut. This extreme example of repetition was almost inevitable, given the nature of Reader's Digest's marketplace, and should not be misconstrued as exploitation of Elvis collectors, as this kind of compilation was never directly aimed at them. Having said that, anyone who was collecting this type of material would appear to have a justifiable case for being dissatisfied. However, given the parameters with which Reader's Digest had to work – particularly the material which they were allowed to issue on licence – the album here was a good one.

The other artists featured were Buddy Holly, The Everly Brothers, Cliff Richard, The Shadows, Roy Orbison, The Hollies and The Beach Boys, with the set featuring many of their number ones hits and best known recordings. In all, the 116 tracks represented excellent value for money. In addition, an album entitled *Great Easy Listening Hits Of The 50's And 60's*, comprising a further fourteen songs – all top ten hits – came as a bonus to the set.

The Pop Legends was available in all three formats and was 'wet tested' in September 1988, with general release in September 1989.

The Elvis tracks covered the period 1956 to 1963, with nine of the fourteen tracks dating from the sixties. Interestingly, the songs did not follow a strictly chronological order.

The words in brackets were missing from two songs – *(Now and then there's) A Fool Such As I* and *(Marie's the name) His Latest Flame*, although they were featured in *(You're the) Devil In Disguise*. However, these were the only errors.

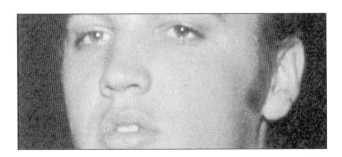

306

Burning Love (Linde)

Always On My Mind (James, Carson, Christopher)

Released September 1988

Released September 1988

This was the first of two albums issued by Trax on the Baby Boomer Classics series and both featured an Elvis recording. **Burning Love**, Elvis's 1972 recording, was the final track on the album, which featured on the front of the sleeve an impressive shot of a customised Honda motorbike, continuing the theme developed on sister albums **Rollin' Sixties** and **Rockin' Seventies**.

This vinyl album was the only occasion that Trax used **Burning Love**, but they did include it on the CD format of **Pop Seventies** as an extra track. This created some confusion at the time, as their advertisements, including the one on the back of this sleeve, listed Elvis's name as being one of the artists featured on the vinyl album.

Mellow Seventies contained Elvis's **Always On My Mind**, by now long established as the most used various artist compilation album track of the period. This was the fifth time the track had been used in such a way, although it was to be the last. The version of **Always On My Mind** featured here was the original single version of the song.

This was interesting in that Trax must have received two versions, as their earlier album **Best Of Country** (**VA LP 20**), featured the one with the stringed arrangement, which had first appeared on the RCA album **Always On My Mind** (*LP 272*). There was no obvious explanation for this other than a simple lack of overall control by BMG regarding which tapes were sent.

BBC

BBC Records, under the overall umbrella of BBC Enterprises, had been responsible for producing an enormous number of records over the years as a means of generating additional income for the corporation.

Up until September 1988 and the release of **Ones On 1. The Radio 1 21st Birthday Album** (**VA LP 30**) – a special compilation album celebrating 21 years of Top Of The Pops – no BBC album had contained an Elvis track. **Ones On 1. The Radio 1 21st Birthday Album** was a one-off, not a series, as many of the compilation albums released to date had been. However, the BBC did produce a series of albums in support of their annual Children In Need appeal, but only one of these contained an Elvis recording.

Ones On 1. The Radio 1 21st Birthday Album

BBC REF 693

The Heart 'N' Soul Of Rock 'N' Roll

Telstar STAR 2351

Way Down (Martine Jr.)

Love Me Tender (Presley, Matson)
All Shook Up (Blackwell, Presley)

Released September 1988

This double album was, as the title so clearly described, issued as a celebration of twenty one years of Radio 1, which first hit the airways on 30 September 1967.

The album contained thirty two tracks, which had been chosen to represent the spirit of the music covered by this extended period, and therefore involved a wide range of musical tastes and styles. Not every year was represented on the album – for example, there was no track from 1982.

Early copies of the album had a sticker on the front of the sleeve stating that there was a limited edition free souvenir single included. Later copies had no sticker, and, of course, no single. The single contained the opening minute or so from Radio 1's first day of broadcasting, along with snippets of chat and jingles from 1971.

The Elvis track, from 1977, was **Way Down**, his last number one hit in the UK to date.

Released October 1988

This TV advertised double album contained 45 songs and, unquestionably, contained some of the greatest songs from the rock and roll era, including Elvis's **Love Me Tender** and **All Shook Up**, both of which had appeared on various artist albums previously.

Released towards the end of October, the two albums were given their own title **The Heart 'N' Soul** and **Rock 'N' Roll**, with the Elvis tracks featuring on each. Every song included some brief background sleeve notes. Inside the gatefold sleeve were pictures of some of the artists, including one of Elvis – taken in early 1958, and previously featured on **Personally Elvis** (LP 186).

VA LP 32	Noel
	Filmtrax TRX 701

If Every Day Was Like Christmas (West)
Here Comes Santa Claus (right down Santa Claus lane)
(Autry, Haldeman, Melka)

Released October 1988

Whilst the back of the album sleeve carried the Trax logo, the label only referred to the parent company, Filmtrax. As we mentioned earlier, Trax was actually a part of Filmtrax, but it was unusual to see their name featured on a record label.

This Christmas offering was a double album, containing 37 tracks, and was an attractively presented collection of traditional songs and music. RCA/BMG artists formed the bulk of those featured, and BMG distributed the record, as well as pressing the product.

The sleeve showed a catalogue number TRXLP 701, whereas the label had TRX 701, with an additional digit for the two albums e.g. 1 and 2.

Elvis opened both side 2 and side 3 with *If Every Day Was Like Christmas* and *Here Comes Santa Claus (right down Santa Claus lane)* respectively, the latter listed minus the words in brackets. For both songs this was their first, and only, appearance on a various artist compilation album.

The origin of the record was quite mysterious, and observers will note that both sleeve and label quoted 1987 as the year when the record was both copyrighted and published. Indeed, a close examination of the engraving between the run-out grooves showed a mastering date of November 1987. Now, whether the anomalies regarding the catalogue number or label (Trax vs Filmtrax) had anything to do with this was unclear; whatever, the record was not released until October 1988.

VA LP 33	30 Years Of 'Number Ones' Volume 1
	Connoisseur Collection TYNO LP 100

All Shook Up (Blackwell, Presley)
Jailhouse Rock (Leiber, Stoller)

Released November 1988

This was the start of another long running Connoisseur Collection series, this time featuring a selection of UK number 1 records over a thirty year period from 1956, presented in chronological sequence. This format was quite unusual, a more typical approach being to present, say, number ones of the sixties or seventies, as Old Gold had done. This was typical of the kind of material that Connoisseur Collection came up with – a basic theme, but with a little bit of extra care and attention applied. Ironically, Old Gold had also used both *All Shook Up* and *Jailhouse Rock* on their *Number Ones 50's Volume 2 – Pop* (**VA LP 15**), released in May 1988.

A minor point, but one worth mentioning is the way in which the initial letters from the series' title had been used to form the catalogue number prefix. TYNO – Thirty Years Number Ones. A neat touch, we think.

However, the original sleeve design disappointing, giving an overall feeling of drabness, and did little to capture anyone's attention, despite the inclusion of an Elvis-like drawing on the front. We believe that Connoisseur Collection also had second thoughts about the sleeve design, for the sleeves for the earlier volumes were later substituted for a much more eye-catching design which continued to be used as the series progressed. Note that Elvis only appeared on volumes 1 and 2. Inside the gatefold sleeve were four photographs of artists included on the album, along with pictures of their original records, but these did not include Elvis.

The album covered the years 1956, 1957, and part of 1958, and included both of Elvis's first and second UK number 1 hits, *All Shook Up* and *Jailhouse Rock*, out of a total of 24 tracks.

VA LP 34	**30 Years Of 'Number Ones' Volume 2**

Connoisseur Collection TYNO LP 101

One Night (Bartholomew, King)
(Now and then there's) A Fool Such As I (Trader)
It's Now Or Never (DiCapua, Schroeder, Gold)

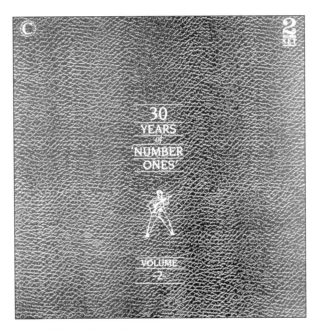

Released November 1988

This album, the second volume of *30 Years Of 'Number Ones'*, covered the remaining part of 1958 (not included on volume 1), 1959, 1960, and one song from 1961. Incidentally, the Shirley Bassey song, *As I Love You*, was a number 1 in 1959, not 1958 as the sleeve claimed.

This time three Elvis tracks were included: *One Night*, *(Now and then there's) A Fool Such As I* and *It's Now Or Never*, the three appearing in their rightful position as Elvis's third, fourth and fifth UK number 1 hits. As with the previous volume, no photograph of Elvis was used inside the gatefold sleeve.

All three songs were in mono, although *It's Now Or Never* had been recorded in stereo. This was probably because most of the other songs on the record were only available in mono. Both *(Now and then there's) A Fool Such As I* and *It's Now Or Never* had appeared previously on various artist compilations, but *One Night* was making its debut and only appearance to date.

The sleeve design was the same as volume 1 (**VA LP 33**), although it was blue instead of pink. It was changed at the same time as that of volume 1, becoming much more colourful and interesting.

Regrettably, this was the final record in Connoisseur Collection's series to feature an Elvis track, not because Elvis had no more number 1 hits, but because RCA had now become concerned about the principle of leasing tracks to other companies. Despite the fact that Connoisseur Collection wished to include further Elvis songs in the series, they were unable to do so.

VA LP 35	**Morning Has Broken**

Telstar STAR 2337

Crying In The Chapel (Glenn)

Released November 1988

Although the catalogue number was lower than the previous Telstar album to feature an Elvis track, *The Heart 'N' Soul Of Rock 'N' Roll*, STAR 2351 (**VA LP 31**), this record was released later to coincide with the Christmas market. Whilst not a Christmas record as such, it was billed as containing 20 religious favourites, many of which had become synonymous with the festive season, amongst them Belafonte's *Mary's Boy Child*.

The front of the sleeve had no reference to the fact that the album included Elvis's *Crying In The Chapel*, which was tucked away in the middle of side 1. Rather surprisingly, the label quoted a publishing date of 1960. And whilst the song was indeed recorded that year, it was 'held back' and not released until 1965, and, therefore, this should have been used as the date the song was first published.

There was no reference to the mode on either the label or sleeve, but *Crying In The Chapel* was presented here in mono form, even though a stereo version existed.

Following the Christmas 1988 season, the album turned up at reduced prices in many discount shops and, in 1992, when Telstar appear to have sold their entire warehouse stock to Woolworths, this album was amongst them.

VA LP 36	**The Greatest Love II**

Telstar STAR 2352

Can't Help Falling In Love (Peretti, Creatore, Weiss)

Released November 1988

This was the second in Telstar's **Greatest Love** series, but the first to contain an Elvis track. This was typical of the kind of TV advertised material which littered the screens at Christmas time. **The Greatest Love** series spawned several volumes and even a 3 record set **Best Of Greatest Love**, with tracks taken from the existing volumes, but no Elvis recording was included.

According to the TV advertisement, this record contained 30 of the greatest love songs of all time, and Elvis's **Can't Help Falling In Love** was a justifiable inclusion.

Inside the gatefold sleeve was a small picture of each of the artists featured, with the photograph of Elvis coming from the 1968 NBC TV Special.

In addition to black label versions, there are also some featuring white labels, suggesting that further pressings were done. Indeed, this album sold well enough to justify a 'special platinum edition' being made available in October 1989, with the original black sleeve being changed to silver.

The Wonder Of You (Knight)

Released January 1989

This album was one of a series of 'At Your Request' featuring various artists, each 'promoted' by a Radio Two personality, in this case Gloria Hunniford. Jimmy Young and Ken Bruce also contributed to the series but their 'selections' did not include an Elvis track.

The albums were produced in support of the BBC's annual Children In Need appeal, and a royalty from sales was donated to the fund. Each compilation supposedly featured a selection of Radio Two's listeners most requested tracks. Whether this was actually true we cannot say, but it is interesting to check and compare the tracks included on the Connoisseur Collection album **24 Most Requested Records From Radio 2**, VSOP LP112 (**VA LP 23**), released in July 1988, which, as the title suggested, ought to have covered similar ground. We cannot vouch for the other albums in the BBC series, but as far as this album was concerned, there was no duplication. This album featured **The Wonder Of You** (a live recording from 1970), whilst **It's Now Or Never** appeared on the Connoisseur Collection album.

This 16 track album cost about £6, but in view of the charity aspect, we would not criticise this. However, if a little more care had been taken to check the sleeve notes, it would have been revealed that Elvis's surname was misspelt 'Pressley'.

311

VA LP 38 | Big Country Classics The Fifties Vol. 7

Trax TRX 508

I Forgot To Remember To Forget (Kesler, Feathers)

Released February 1989

The second batch of Trax country albums, released seven months after the first, was different from the earlier volumes, in that the era covered was clearly identified on the front of the sleeve. Altogether, two albums comprised fifties' material and three concentrated on the sixties.

Elvis was featured on the second of the fifties' albums, with the opening track *I Forgot To Remember To Forget*, one of the earliest Elvis recordings to be included on a various artist compilation. This was the only occasion that the song had appeared on a various artist compilation.

If you own this album and one of the earlier Big Country Classics volumes it may be interesting to make some comparisons. This record was not pressed by BMG and this was quite evident, not only in the absence of the normal characteristics, but in the way the edges of the record were finished, which were very rough and unfinished here. However, the details on the spine of the sleeve were a great improvement over the earlier records in the series, having a much bolder print and spacing. Nonetheless, although being different, the series lacked continuity. The label colour was also different, being pale blue, whereas the earlier volumes used a yellow label.

VA LP 39 | The Songs Of Bob Dylan

Start STDL 20

Tomorrow Is A Long Time (Dylan)

Released March 1989

Start Records actually belonged to Old Gold who had widened their range in the late eighties to enable this kind of record to be released.

This was a neat concept album which featured some of the great recording artists – Jimi Hendrix, Eric Clapton amongst them – alongside some less well known names, all performing songs written by Bob Dylan. Clearly a great deal of effort had gone into the compilation of this work, which did rather well in terms of sales.

This high class collection of 32 songs included Elvis's 1966 recording of *Tomorrow Is A Long Time*, although there was little made of this in the sleeve notes which were spread over both sides of the gatefold sleeve. *Tomorrow Is A Long Time* was making its first and only appearance on a various artist LP.

VA LP 40 | Easy Listening Hits Of The 60's And 70's

Reader's Digest GEASY-A-193

Are You Lonesome Tonight? (Turk, Handman)
Love Letters (Young, Heyman)
Can't Help Falling In Love (Peretti, Creatore, Weiss)
Suspicious Minds (James)
You Don't Have To Say You Love Me (Pallavicini, Donaggio, Wickham, Napier-Bell)
Wooden Heart (Wise, Weisman, Twomey, Kaempfert)
The Wonder Of You (Knight)
Way Down (Martine Jr.)

Released May 1989

This album typified the kind of material that had formed the backbone of Reader's Digest's compilation albums over the years, with a variety of titles covering different decades and musical styles. Previous albums, without any Elvis involvement, had been **Superstars of the 70's And 80's** which, incidentally, came with **Great Easy Listening Chart Toppers** as a bonus LP, and **Golden Memories Of The 60's**. There was nothing wrong with this kind of approach, and nor was this album a light-weight throwaway set. Indeed, few people would quibble with the quality and depth of the 103 UK top 20 hits which included 53 million selling singles. Further evidence of the depth of material came with the inclusion of a bonus album of fourteen ABBA recordings.

Of course, this kind of material – especially in compilation form – did not appeal to everyone, and serious Elvis collectors, who faced the daunting prospect of spending over £40, found themselves in a dilemma. Whereas, up to this point, the three Reader's Digest sets to include Elvis material – **Giants Of Country** (**VA LP 5**), **112 Rock 'N' Roll Greats** (**VA LP 8**) and **The Pop Legends** (**VA LP 27**) – had each contained fourteen tracks which, importantly, were gathered together on a single album, **Easy Listening Hits Of The 60's And 70's** reduced the number of Elvis songs to eight, and spread them across several albums. There was, therefore, no prospect of picking up an Elvis album independently of the whole set, as there had been with the earlier releases. This set, then, finally deterred many collectors who had battled their way through the deluge of various artist compilation albums over the previous couple of years. Admittedly not every collector had embarked on this path; many had stopped at the first hurdle. However, this was not intended to be a criticism of Reader's Digest – far from it. The company were simply carrying out their normal business function of providing a fine selection of tracks for their particular market.

Whatever, the set did include eight Elvis tracks, three of which had appeared on their previous album, **The Pop Legends** (**VA LP 27**): **Are You Lonesome Tonight?**, **Can't Help Falling In Love** and **Wooden Heart**. On a more positive note, two songs, **Love Letters** and **You Don't Have To Say You Love Me**, were making their debut on a various artist release.

Each album in the set was individually titled so that, for both the '60s and '70s, there were, **Hall Of Fame**, **Golden Groups**, **Million Selling Gold** and **Great No.1's**.

The set first became available in May 1989 when it was 'wet tested', followed by general release in March 1990, slightly less than the normal twelve month gap. It was produced in all three formats, with cassettes costing £39.95 and LPs and CDs £44.95.

VA LP 41   **60's Number Ones Volume 1**

Old Gold OG 1512

Are You Lonesome Tonight? (Turk Handman)
Wooden Heart (Wise, Weisman, Twomey, Kaempfert)

Released September 1989

Old Gold had started their series of 'Number Ones' back in May 1988, when they issued four LPs featuring Elvis tracks. Two of these albums were subsequently re-released with a modified track listing, as some of the tracks Old Gold had licensed originally had been withdrawn by the company responsible, notably EMI. The original version had included **The Young Ones**, by Cliff Richard, and **Apache**, by The Shadows. These were replaced by **My Old Man's A Dustman** (Lonnie Donegan) and **Nutrocker** (B. Bumble And The Stingers).

This album had previously been entitled **Number Ones 60's Volume 1 – Pop** (**VA LP 16**), but this had been amended slightly, as had the sleeve, as it had originally included photographs of both Cliff and The Shadows.

Both Elvis tracks had been UK number ones in 1961.

VA LP 42   **70's Number Ones – Volume 2**

Old Gold OG 1514

The Wonder Of You (Knight)

Released September 1989

As with **60's Number Ones – Volume 1** (**VA LP 41**), in September 1989 Old Gold issued this LP with a modified track listing and new catalogue number when compared to the original May 1988 issue, **Number Ones 70's Volume 2 – Ballads** (**VA LP 18**).

Two of the tracks on the original version were substituted. **Mississippi**, by Pussycat, was replaced with **I Love To Love** by Tina Charles, and **Lucille**, by Kenny Rogers, was replaced with **Hold Me Close**, by David Essex. And, as the original sleeve featured a photograph of Kenny Rogers, new artwork was also needed.

The Elvis track included was a live recording from Las Vegas, and had originally appeared on the album **On Stage February 1970** (*LP 41*).

VA LP 43 — The Attack Of The Killer Bs

BBC REQ 739

The Girl Of My Best Friend (Ross, Bobrick)

Released October 1989

By the time this record was released, the flow of various artist compilation albums including an Elvis track had slowed considerably, as RCA's policy of restricting material began to take effect.

Clearly though, as this record demonstrated, the flow hadn't stopped altogether as **The Girl Of My Best Friend** was included here. And, as the song had not appeared previously on one of these albums, the choice of material appeared not to have been restricted in any way either.

For those who thought that the BBC was rather staid in its outlook, this record must have come as quite a shock featuring, as it did, a superbly lurid 1950s comic book style artwork, typical of many B feature movies from which the title was taken. All in all, this two album set of 32 B sides was a wonderful idea. Some classic recordings were included – Little Richard's **Ready Teddy**, Chuck Berry's **Let It Rock** and Them's **Gloria**, to name but a few. And these were B sides! The same comment goes for **The Girl Of My Best Friend**, a song so strong that even today many still consider it to have been the A side to **A Mess Of Blues** (*S 29*), its original UK coupling (in 1960). Indeed it was an A side release in 1976 (*S 97*).

The front of the sleeve bore a Radio 1 emblem and a free car sticker was included, promoting the fact that the station was available on FM stereo.

Licensing Deals – The Nineties

As we have mentioned elsewhere, the wheel regarding the licensing of Elvis product had just about come full circle. At one time (in fact up until the mid-seventies), all Elvis product was issued by RCA or through a special outlet – Camden releases through Pickwick, for example. Then, in the late seventies and eighties, there was a welter of material which appeared on non-RCA labels, a situation which was both messy and somewhat disrespectful to someone of Elvis's stature.

However, towards the end of the eighties, there was a concerted move by BMG (RCA) to curtail the number of licensing deals concerning Elvis. Old Gold, for instance, lost the rights to issue singles (remember they had issued twenty singles between 1986 and 1988). So, what was the thinking behind this clear shift of policy?

Basically, it was felt by the Committee responsible for planning and co-ordinating Elvis product, that the number of licensing deals was unmanageable and cheapened the value of the product, rather than enhancing it. Consequently, as previous licensing deals came to an end, few were renewed.

Notable exceptions to this rule were Reader's Digest (who had featured a major collection of Presley material in their catalogue since October 1975) and Time-Life, who issued a collection of early tracks. And the central reason why these licensing deals were permitted is easy to explain. BMG, quite rightly, had never perceived Reader's Digest and Time-Life as major rivals in the marketplace. Both organisations operated through mail-order systems, often reaching a quite distinct market from those who may have visited and bought from record shops. Quite simply, they were not competing for the same business and, thus, represented no threat to the sales of standard releases.

In brief, the process of licensing works thus. All requests to license any product, not just Elvis material, have to be made to the company concerned. In the case of Elvis tracks, all such requests are directed via BMG in New York. All requests would be viewed by the Legal Affairs Department, but then 'farmed out' to the various members of the Committee (whose composition changed from time to time) for their consideration. The criteria used for permitting the licencing of tracks is simple: if the project or proposed leasing is sound and creative and, moreover, does not conflict or compete with BMG product, then permission may be granted, in which case a Schedule E Clearance (the legal paperwork, authorising such a release) is issued. BMG though, retain full control of which tracks may be used – and which versions too. Therefore, although a company may request certain tracks, BMG may well deny this request but offer others in their place. Obviously, as we have seen all too clearly, certain tracks – **Always On My Mind**, for example – turned up with depressing frequency.

Licensing (or leasing) normally lasts for two or three years, after which it either expires, or is terminated by one of the companies involved. Although it is not possible to quote precise figures (for this is really the business of the two parties involved), there is a standard agreed rate for licensing tracks within the industry. Normally though, the company licensing the material will be expected to guarantee royalty payments in excess of 50,000 units – which means that they have to be confident of selling sufficient copies to at least cover their costs. Of course this may vary from release to release, as it is obvious Old Gold could not have guaranteed such high sales.

A list of all non-RCA releases issued prior to 1985 can be found in the introductory section under 'Licensing Deals'.

VA LP 44 — The Last Temptation Of Elvis

NME LP 038/039

King Of The Whole Wide World (Batchelor, Roberts)

Released February 1990

Quite a lot was written about this double album, little of it complimentary, and most of it heavily critical. It was first publicly referred to in October 1989 by Roy Carr, long associated with the **New Musical Express,** and later with **Vox** magazine. He was the fellow who wrote the original sleeve notes to **The Elvis Presley Sun Collection** album (*LP 80*), in 1975.

The original concept was a good one, and in aid of a very worthy cause: that is, to produce an album of Elvis songs, newly recorded by other artists, many of who were very famous (others less so), in support of the Nordoff-Robbins Music Therapy organisation, which tried to help handicapped children communicate via music. As with Carr's previous charitable venture, his all-star remake of The Beatles **Sgt. Pepper** – **Sgt. Pepper Knew My Father**, which spawned Wet Wet Wet's big hit **With A Little Help From My Friends**, (where all the proceeds went to Childline), the idea was to do a similar thing with an Elvis-related album. Apparently, while Carr was working on the sleeve notes to Paul McCartney's 'Russian' album, featuring old rock 'n' roll classics, the subject of the 'Elvis' album arose. McCartney volunteered a track immediately. His contribution was **It's Now Or Never**, a track he cut in 1987 for the **Choba B CCCP** album.

Entitled **The Last Temptation Of Elvis** (a parody on the film **The Last Temptation Of Christ**), Carr compiled a list of about 50 songs and proceeded to contact friends in the music industry, inviting them to contribute. Originally the plan had been for a 14 track single album, but the project was so well-received that it was oversubscribed (see track details for those involved), even to the point where some artists – David Cassidy, for example, – had to be turned down. Some would argue that it was a pity more subscribers were not similarly dealt with!

The supposed theme of the album was that it was to feature other artists' interpretations of some of Elvis's film songs, even though

some of the choices made, and the versions rendered, were rather bizarre. However, even this idea was not fully thought through, as three of the tracks: **It's Now Or Never**, **Guitar Man** and **Down In The Alley** were never featured in an Elvis film – thus giving a lie to the subtitle.

Carr also felt that Elvis ought to have a contribution on the album; so with the aid of BMG's Roger Semon, **King Of The Whole Wide World** (featuring two false starts and a complete take) was made available (though in mono). This was a previously unissued outtake and closed the album. In addition, and not mentioned anywhere in the sleeve notes or label, there were a few seconds of Elvis talking about rock 'n' roll.

All the artists and recording studio companies involved in the production of this album gave their services entirely free of charge, extensive details of which appeared on the back of the album cover, where the 26 artists appearing (including Elvis) were listed. The manufacturing companies did their work at cost price.

There was an extremely limited promo single featuring the McCartney and Springsteen tracks in two formats: a 10 inch 45 with picture labels in a plain white paper bag, and a 5 inch CD single. The LP and CD versions were pressed by Mayking in England.

By the end of January 1992, the project had raised in excess of £250,000, some of which was used to furbish a brand new Nordoff Robbins Music Therapy Centre in Camden, London, which was opened by the Duchess Of York, Sarah Ferguson.

The gatefold cover featured no photographs of Elvis, only drawings of some of the various artists included. Inside the gatefold there were actual photos of some of the artists involved, plus a list of their responses to some questions posed regarding Elvis. Perhaps it was this aspect of the project – leaving aside its dubious and patchy musical content – which caused so much offence, for much of what was written was fatuous, crass and puerile nonsense, quite unfunny, and totally out of faith with the project itself. However, the project did raise (and went on raising) money for a worthwhile cause. And obviously the fact that the album featured tracks by so many artists (unissued/not available elsewhere) guaranteed it a good sales' potential.

The white labels on each of the albums listed the artists' names in bold black type, followed by the song titles (but no writers' credits) in smaller print.

For your information the artists and songs were as follows:

Bruce Springsteen	*Viva Las Vegas*
Sydney Youngblood	*(Let me be your) Teddy Bear*
Tanita Tikaram	*Loving You*
Robert Plant	*Party*
The Pogues	*Got A Lot O' Livin' To Do!*
Holly Johnson	*Love Me Tender*
Paul McCartney	*It's Now Or Never*
Dion DiMucci	*Mean Woman Blues*
The Jesus and Mary Chain	*Guitar Man*
Cath Carroll & Steve Albini	*King Creole*
Aaron Neville	*Young And Beautiful*
Vivian Stanshall & the Big Boys	*(There's) No Room To Rhumba In A Sports Car*
The Primitives	*(You're so square) Baby I Don't Care*
Hall & Oates	*Can't Help Falling In Love*
The Reggae Philharmonic Orchestra	*Crawfish*
Ian McCulloch	*Return To Sender*
Fuzzbox	*Trouble*
The Hollow Men	*Thanks To The Rolling Sea*
The Blow Monkeys	*Follow That Dream*
Lemmy & The Upsetters with Mick Green	*Blue Suede Shoes*

Nanci Griffith & The Blue Moon Orchestra	
The Jeff Healey Band	*Wooden Heart*
The Cramps	*Down In The Alley*
Les Negressess Verts	*Jailhouse Rock*
Pop Will Eat Itself	*Marguerita*
Elvis Presley	*Rock-A-Hula Baby*
	King Of The Whole Wide World

VA LP 45

Great Stars Sing Their Greatest Songs

Reader's Digest GGSS-A-144

Are You Lonesome Tonight? (Turk, Handman)

Released February 1990

Great Stars Sing Their Greatest Songs, as the title suggested, featured a collection of songs identifiable with particular artists' singing, according to the advert in the Reader's Digest catalogue, 'their' songs. In total, the set contained 101 different artists, and amounted to four and a half hours playing time.

This was a clever concept for a compilation release, but must have provided those responsible with an enormous task of pulling the tracks together. There was no doubt about the pedigree of the material included, whatever your particular taste in music, and, indeed, many of the tracks will forever be associated with a particular artist. Who else could have sung *Over The Rainbow*, except Judy Garland? Can you think of another version of Slim Whitman's *Rose Marie*? Or Gene Pitney's *24 Hours From Tulsa*?

The songs themselves were divided into convenient categories, such as *1950's Hall Of Fame*, *Great British Greats*, *Golden Groups - Golden Memories* and *1960's Golden Hit Parade (1960-1964)* where Elvis's sole contribution, *Are You Lonesome Tonight?*, was located. Not everyone would agree, however, with the choice of *Are You Lonesome Tonight?* as being the song most associated with Elvis. The problem was that there were so many other candidates – *It's*

Now Or Never, his best selling single, springs to mind – with equal credentials and, doubtless, Reader's Digest could have justifiably included several different selections. However, it was felt that this song was the one that the general public most identified with Elvis, and the one best suited to fit in with the type of material included in the set. Of course, the fact that Reader's Digest already had the rights to *Are You Lonesome Tonight?*, made it relatively easy to include. After all, it had been featured by the company three times previously – on *Giants Of Country*, *The Pop Legends* and *Easy Listening Hits Of The 60's And 70's* (**VA LPs 5**, **27**, and **40**).

Great Stars Sing Their Greatest Songs was clearly a 'middle-of-the-road' collection of very popular material aimed, it has to be said, at the 50 plus age group. Elvis's recording of *Are You Lonesome Tonight?* (by no means the earliest recording featured) dated back to 1960 – 30 years prior to the release of this collection.

From a collector's viewpoint this set presented the ultimate financial nightmare! £40 for one Elvis track was a lot of money!

The set was available in all three formats, with cassettes costing around £40 and LPs and CDs £45. The initial release (wet test) was in February 1990, with the general release being in May 1991, slightly longer that the normal 'trial' period of twelve months.

VA LP 46

The Heart And Soul Of Rock 'N' Roll

Reader's Digest GHSR-A-207

Don't Be Cruel (Blackwell, Presley)
Love Me Tender (Presley, Matson)
Loving You (Leiber, Stoller)
A Big Hunk O' Love (Schroeder, Wyche)
Paralyzed (Blackwell, Presley)
Treat Me Nice (Leiber, Stoller)
Rock-A-Hula Baby (Wise, Weisman, Fuller)
Crying In The Chapel (Glenn)
Old Shep (Foley, Arthur)
Surrender (DeCurtis, Pomus, Shuman)

316

Released September 1990

The Heart And Soul Of Rock 'N' Roll was released at a time when various artist compilation albums bearing an Elvis track had been reduced to a trickle. The previous one, also by Reader's Digest, had been in February 1990. This was the second various artist compilation album to use the title *The Heart And Soul Of Rock 'N' Roll*, as Telstar had issued one in October 1988. Indeed, this album was in much the same vein, although there was more of it, a mixture – as the title implied – of soulful ballads mixed with rock 'n' roll songs.

Importantly for fans and collectors, a full complement of ten Elvis tracks were included, eight of which were making their various artist album debut. Only *Love Me Tender* and *Crying In The Chapel* had been featured previously.

In America, Reader's Digest had issued, in July 1990, a four CD set entitled *The Heart 'N' Soul Of Rock 'N' Roll*, which offered a bonus CD of twelve Elvis tracks, although no Elvis tracks were to be found on the main set. The bonus CD was called *Great Hits of 1956-57*. Interestingly, there was little correlation between the tracks used and those which appeared on the UK boxed set. In fact, only *Don't Be Cruel* was common to both issues.

The UK set was 'wet tested' in September 1990 and, effectively, had two general release dates – March and October 1991 – as the album was 'launched' twice. This was one of Reader's Digest better sets, featuring 112 tracks and sporting a glorious juke box cover picture – a great improvement over many of the previous title-only designs. Issued free with the set was a fourteen track collection of *Sixties Gold*.

The set was issued in all three formats, with the cassette version costing £42.95 and LPs/CDs, £47.95.

VA LP 47	**Gazza And Friends –** **Let's Have A Party**
Best ZL 74857	

The Elvis Presley Medley

Released November 1990

For those of you who are wondering, Paul Gascoigne (Gazza), a footballer from Tyneside, had gained enormous publicity when he had broken down and cried during the World Cup tournament of 1990. Media coverage (particularly by the tabloid press) then seemed to grow intensely, often focusing on everything but his football career. Presumably this was the principal reason why a footballer was allowed the privilege to have his own album. Incidentally, he also recorded a new version of *Fog On The Tyne* with the song's composers and original performers, Lindisfarne, also from Newcastle. Like the album itself, the single was a cynical attempt to cash in on what was a fad.

This album, produced to coincide with the Christmas market (when people buy records they normally would shy away from!), was a collection of chart hits chosen by Gascoigne, including *Fog On The Tyne* and assorted medleys. The reason we have to include it in this book – and for no other reason – is that it contained a medley of Elvis songs. Entitled *The Elvis Presley Medley*, it was not the version released on the singles RCAP 1028 (picture disc) (*S 137*) in January 1983 and RCA 476 (*S 145*) in January 1985, but a new edit, by Martin Kearney. This version, appallingly edited, featured much longer sections of the same songs giving a total running time of almost seven minutes, compared to less than four minutes on the 'official' RCA edit. The songs were: *Jailhouse Rock, (Let me be your) Teddy Bear, Hound Dog, Don't Be Cruel, Burning Love* and *Suspicious Minds*.

On the credit side though, part of the proceeds from the album went to the Nordoff-Robbins Music Therapy Centre, the same organisation which benefited from sales of the NME album *The Last Temptation Of Elvis* (**VA LP 44**). According to the sleeve, Best Records were licensed to BMG, whose logo appeared on both the label and sleeve, although the record was not pressed by BMG, for it bore none of the usual hallmarks of the company. The record was, in fact, made in England, whereas most BMG albums were pressed in Germany.

This record went unnoticed by many Elvis fans, unless they happened to be football fans as well, but the record, which cost around £7, did well over the Christmas 1990 period, although once the festivities were over, copies were sold off cheaply. By the end of 1991 all formats were deleted.

The use of Elvis material on albums such as this was considered in poor taste by many fans, and to find classic tracks like *Jailhouse Rock*, *Burning Love* and *Suspicious Minds* being subjected to such poor quality editing is beyond our comprehension, and so perhaps we should simply leave it to Mr Gascoigne to explain in an extract from his sleeve notes.

'… I am crying for joy because RCA have given special permission for the King, yes Elvis Presley to lend me (and you) his talents with a medley of his songs. Everyone who knows me knows that I think Elvis is the one and only, the biz, and it is my ambition to achieve in my footballing career what he achieved in the world of music.' We cried too, but not for joy.

VA LP 48	40 Years Of Top Ten Hits
	Reader's Digest GTOP-A-203

All Shook Up (Blackwell, Presley)
(Let me be your) Teddy Bear (Mann, Lowe)
Good Luck Charm (Schroeder, Gold)
It's Now Or Never (DiCapua, Schroeder, Gold)

Released September 1992

Exactly two years had passed since Reader's Digest issued an album set containing Elvis material – *The Heart And Soul Of Rock 'N' Roll* (**VA LP 46**) – and this issue came at a time when almost all other various artist compilations had ceased to include an Elvis track, as BMG tightened their leasing arrangements. As this was forty years after the first UK record chart to be published, this was a topical title and the set encompassed material from the very early years right up to the early nineties, reflecting all musical styles and tastes in popular music, and including 122 tracks with 71 number one hits. No easy

task. But, for those people intent on buying such a varied collection, this would be the one to go for. And, as we had come to expect from Reader's Digest, this was a quality product.

However, for Elvis fans and collectors there was little to interest them in terms of unusual items, for the four tracks featured were various artist compilation regulars, and all four had been used by Reader's Digest previously. Then again, given the context in which the tracks were being used – top ten hits – this should not have surprised anyone.

The 'wet test' date for the set was brought forward from November 1992 to September, suggesting that Reader's Digest clearly thought that this set would do well. And, even before it went to its bulk run in October 1993, it was advertised in the press early in 1993. Despite its cost – almost £50 for the eight albums (6 CDs) – it did, indeed, do very well for them in terms of sales.

The usual practice of sub-titling each album was again applied, the titles being:

1. *The Classic Number Ones 1952-1969*
2. *The Classic Number Ones 1970-1990*
3. *The Golden Groups*
4. *Magical Memories Of The 50s*
5. *Remembering The 60s*
6. *Best Of The Ballads*
7. *Great Stars – Golden Hits*
8. *The Top Ten Hall Of Fame*

An Elvis song was featured on four different albums, numbers 1, 4, 5 and 6.

VA LP 49	Head Over Heels
	Telstar STAR 2649

Hard Headed Woman (DeMetrius)
Love Me Tender (Presley, Matson)
Don't Be Cruel (Blackwell, Presley)

Released February 1993

Head Over Heels was the first various artist compilation album to be issued in the UK for quite some time, and was released to capitalise on the success of the Carlton TV series of the same name. Its release demonstrated that BMG had not abandoned leasing arrangements totally, and the high profile of this and, more significantly, the following album, *Lipstick On Your Collar*, offered far greater promotional opportunities than most of the compilation albums released earlier. *Head Over Heels* was released by Telstar, who had been responsible for other various artist compilations with an Elvis involvement, such as *Morning Has Broken* (**VA LP 35**), and *The Greatest Love II* (**VA LP 36**). The album featured 22 tracks, although two of them were not featured in the series. One of these, Kathy Kirby's *Secret Love*, was actually recorded in the sixties, not the fifties, although Doris Day had a number one hit with the song in 1954.

Although the album featured many classic performances, several of the selections had been included on similar collections over the years. Three Elvis tracks were included, with *Hard Headed Woman* being the lead track. This was the first time the song had been included on a various artist compilation and, while *Love Me Tender* was a regular, *Don't Be Cruel*, despite its popularity, was making only its second appearance. All three tracks were taken from BMG's boxed set *The King Of Rock 'N' Roll The Complete 50's Masters*, PL 90689(6) (**LP 318**), which was pictured on the back of the album sleeve – an unusual move for a various artist album issued by another company. Presumably BMG, who distributed the album, were happy to supply the tracks in return for the advert, amongst other considerations. A small photo of Elvis from 1956 was also included on the back of the sleeve.

When listing *Don't Be Cruel* on the back of the sleeve, *(to a heart that's true)* was added as a sub-title, erroneously, but this was not shown on the label. However, a publishing date of 1978 was given, which we can only assume referred to the song's appearance on a single in June of that year – PB 9265 (*S 118*), although why this should be the case remains unclear. Far worse though, was the unacceptable error of re-titling *Hard Headed Woman* as *Hard Hearted Woman* on the label (it was shown correctly on the sleeve). The writer – DeMetrius – was shown as Dimitrius.

Whether or not these errors were the responsibility of Telstar is something we cannot be sure about, but the use of the sub-title on *Don't Be Cruel* must have come from BMG who had been guilty of its use in the past. And, as the sub-title did not feature on *The King Of Rock 'N' Roll The Complete 50's Masters*, it would indicate that those responsible within BMG for leasing product were not keeping pace with the efforts and new standards of those in charge of new product.

Don't Be Cruel (Blackwell, Presley)

Released March 1993

Lipstick On Your Collar was the second various artist album based on a TV series to be issued in the space of two months. This album was the 'soundtrack' of Dennis Potter's Channel 4, '50s drama which featured the songs and music of the period. Supposedly set in 1956, the use of the title song *Lipstick On Your Collar* – ironically a recording from 1959 – was, like the drama itself, tongue-in-cheek. Most of the other tracks fell neatly into the required time frame.

Apart from the title track, *Don't Be Cruel* was the lead song, and both were featured in TV advertisements for the series. On all counts, this was a high profile series, which BMG were obviously happy to be associated with.

A total of 28 tracks were featured on the album which, like *Head Over Heels*, cost £8.99. Sales were extremely good, thanks no doubt to TV adverts which helped it achieve top ten album status. The tracks themselves were a mixture of familiar and less well-known recordings from the period, and there was little duplication with the previous album.

The picture of the TV series lead character showed him dressed in gold lame suit in typical Elvis pose. We also rather liked the picture of Winston Churchill in the background, as he seemed to be sporting his version of Elvis's gold suit also. Elvis headed the credits on the front of the sleeve.

The phrase *(to a heart that's true)* was again added to *Don't Be Cruel* on both label and sleeve. Notice also how, in the reference to BMG's Elvis boxed set, *50's* was, crucially, missing from *The King Of Rock 'N' Roll The Complete 50's Masters* (**LP 318**).

Various artist vinyl albums which featured Elvis tracks were produced over a 16 year period from 1977 to 1993. In all, exactly fifty compilations of this type were produced. Of course, the bulk of these were released over a two year period – 1988 and 1989 – when 33 were issued.

By early 1993, the last vinyl compilation had been released, and their demise could be attributed to two factors. Undoubtedly, the increased popularity of the CD format and, secondly, the licencing restrictions imposed by BMG as to who could issue product and exactly what they were allowed to have.

A decision taken during 1993 by Reader's Digest (the most reliable producer of various artist collections), to end vinyl production effectively completed this section (although the final two releases were prompted by TV programmes). By the end of 1993, Reader's Digest had virtually ceased to produce any vinyl product, concentrating instead on CD and cassette versions. Their decision to abandon vinyl was merely a reflection of market trends, but it did bring to an end a long and noteworthy series (dating back to 1985), of various artist collections containing Elvis tracks.

However the fact that Reader's Digest no longer produced vinyl had no bearing on their leasing arrangements with BMG: Elvis was still in demand by the company but, as we have already noted, BMG had imposed restrictions on such arrangements and were now guarding Elvis's legacy far more zealously than they had previously. Even so, Reader's Digest were able to lease five tracks for their ***Merry Christmas Everybody***, RDCD 601/5, 5 CD/cassette set which was 'wet tested' in October 1993.

The five songs chosen were:

If Every Day Was Like Christmas
Santa Bring My Baby Back (to me)
Here Comes Santa Claus (right down Santa Claus lane)
Silver Bells
It Won't Seem Like Christmas (without you)

Two of these, ***Santa Bring My Baby Back (to me)*** and ***It Won't Seem Like Christmas (without you)*** had not appeared previously on a various artist compilation album. However, as this book concentrates on vinyl releases, we have not included these tracks in the list of titles featured on various artist albums.

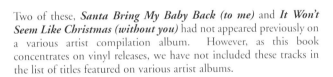

Promotional Records

The purpose of promotional records (promos) has, in one sense, always been the same: to promote i.e. bring to people's attention the fact that a particular record exists, and so encourage others to buy it, thus making profit for the company and artist concerned, if it was successful. At least that is the theory; in practice though, the reality was, and still is, to some extent, more complicated.

First of all, having explained why promotional records exist, you then must consider other matters, such as who they were intended for, and what forms they took. Of course, the physical appearance of promos changed considerably over the years, and in *Elvis UK 1956-86* we were fortunate enough to include details of these changes from the fairly basic white labels of HMV releases, the early single-sided Decca pressings, the more elaborate labels of later RCA labels, and on to the virtually standard orange label releases. The methods adopted to indicate the purpose of the records changed also, but words like Demonstration Sample and the use of a large 'A' to indicate the preferred side were commonplace. HMV used special sleeves for their promotional records and the whole process had a sense of urgency about it, and rightly so, for the whole purpose of the records was to get the right people to listen to them as quickly as possible in order to promote the titles and generate sales.

Who then were these people? In the fifties and sixties there were two main recipients: the music press and radio stations, or, to be more specific, disc jockeys. Both of these groups were very powerful - if they were not impressed by what they heard, then a record was probably doomed to certain failure. Even though there was relatively little exposure for mainstream pop music on national radio, it was essential to get a record played; and it was vital, therefore, that the elite top five or six national DJs were recruited. The music press too played a far greater role in this process than it does today; they were more influential and reached a much wider audience, although they seemed more sympathetic to the artists' cause. To supply this need, promotional records were made, though in relatively small quantities.

The process would work in the following way: a record company, having made a decision to release a certain record, would produce a separate batch, often pressed prior to the main bulk, sometimes featuring only the intended A side of a record, and often having only a white label or, as happened later, a different label configuration. These pre-release copies would be sent by companies or representatives to those who had been identified as being influential in either writing about a new release, or playing it on the radio. In both cases the company, anxious to have a positive response, hoped to whet the appetite of fans and the general public, and thus create a demand for a record prior to its release, with the sole objective of selling enough copies for a record to chart - and the higher the better. Done successfully, this marketing tactic could (and did) produce spectacular results. And fittingly, it was Elvis who holds the title as the first artist ever to enter the UK charts at number one. This was with the *Jailhouse Rock/Treat Me Nice* single RCA 1028, released in January 1958 (*S 18*). Of course, a most useful by-product of 'hyping' a record a couple of weeks before release meant that pre-release orders would mount up (and then be published, thus hyping the record even further), and the factories could be instructed as to what volume needed to be produced. In the case of the *Jailhouse Rock* single, advance orders amounted to a quarter of a million copies!

The process worked both ways as well, in the sense that writers working for the music press wanted to be the first to publicise a new release, just as disc jockeys were intent on being the first to play it, and this helped maintain their status and popularity with listeners.

In the fifties and sixties, comparatively few people held sufficient power to be able to fulfil the role demanded of them by record companies, but with the advent of more national radio stations, local radio, clubs and larger record stores, greater numbers of people became involved, and the influence of the few diminished and the power-base spread more widely.

However, at this stage promos were not held to be intrinsically special, collectable, different or valuable - that occurred much later on a wider scale - they were simply there to serve a particular function: to advertise a record prior to its public release. Now at what point these promos were judged to be collectable (presumably some far-sighted people always thought they were) is debateable. Certainly though, over the years, their notional importance in terms of collectability rose as their actual importance declined somewhat. So, even though record companies still chose to advertise products with a pre-release, they often did so with standard releases simply over-stamped or stickered, probably because it was cheaper to do so. And later, while promos for both past and present material are actively sought after by fans, the trend is to use the standard copies pulled out of the normal batch, though this does vary from artist to artist and company to company. And, as regards Elvis releases (the main focus of our attention, of course), promos are largely a thing of the past. Very special or unusual releases - the release of the original *Essential Elvis* (*LP 280*) in 1986, for example - warranted a promo, for it announced the birth of an important new series to the media and the industry generally.

Then, of course, there is the thorny issue of who promos actually reach. Some believe, quite cynically, that promos are a means by which certain individuals can profit by re-selling them to avid fans at costs far in excess of the value of the standard release. In this case, promos intended for in-store promotional use may never have reached their destination, bound instead to dealers or record fairs etc. This aspect of the industry is, as you might expect, not one which bears much scrutiny. Indeed, no-one wants to go public on the less-savoury side of this, and it is difficult to amass hard evidence of when, how and why certain things occur. What is clear though is that in the past (as now) promos have been mis-used and seen by some as almost a virtual licence to print money. But the biggest irony is that, along the way, the artist at the centre of all this squabbling might not actually benefit - particularly in the case where in-store promos never get played - often because they have been sold on. Some in the industry would doubtless argue that this was a justifiable perk.

However, the argument now advanced is that unless there are good reasons in terms of marketing to produce a promo then RCA/BMG often decline to do so. The thinking behind this is simple: record companies are now much more technologically advanced and ostensibly better organised in terms of release schedules. Moreover, in recent years, more prudence in terms of what is released, and how much it is likely to cost has been shown.

Basically companies have no wish to incur unnecessary expense. It is far easier to press copies of records/compact discs and simply send out advance copies to the intended parties. After all, it ought to be the audio material which is of the greatest importance: how it is packaged should be immaterial.

However major releases, such as boxed sets, have tended towards having a promotional package to promote them, simply because in terms of basic economics it made sense, to do so. For example, when BMG wanted to promote the fifties' set, the demand from the industry and journalists was so high that to have sent out complete sets as 'freebies' would have been prohibitive. Instead the company sent out cassette tape copies, but also had a CD promo that featured several tracks from the main set.

Thus, the trend has moved towards producing samplers for major releases, usually in compact disc form. The obvious merit of this is its cost effectiveness.

What is obvious from looking at the list below is that vinyl promotional items become somewhat of a rarity. Indeed, the last RCA inspired promotional album was *All Time Greatest Hits*, ETYA 001, in 1987. This pre-dates by several years the end of releases generally available in vinyl form.

Check List Of Promotional Records

Catalogue Number	Title	Date
RCA AREP 1	*Acuff-Rose Music Limited Presents Elvis*	1986
RCA ESSEL 1	*Essential Elvis*	1986
RCA ELPROMO 1 DJ	*Ain't That Loving You Baby*	1987
NME PRO 5	*I Dreampt I Was Elvis*	1987
RCA ETYA 001	*All Time Greatest Hits*	1987
Stylus SMR 855-7	*Sixties Mix Two*	1988
RCA TCB 001	*(Now and then there's) A Fool Such As I*	1990

Acuff-Rose Music Limited Presents Elvis

RCA AREP 1

Side 1
1 **There Goes My Everything** (Frazier)
2 **Your Cheatin' Heart** (Williams)
3 **Funny How Time Slips Away** (Nelson)
4 **I Can't Stop Loving You** (Gibson)
5 **She Wears My Ring** (B. & F. Bryant)
6 **I'm So Lonesome I Could Cry** (Williams)
7 **Miracle Of The Rosary** (Denson)

Side 2
1 **Release Me (and let me love again)** (Miller, Williams, Yount, Harris)
2 **Gentle On My Mind** (Hartford)
3 **Make The World Go Away** (Cochran)
4 **I Washed My Hands In Muddy Water** (Babcock)
5 **How's The World Treating You** (Atkins, Bryant)
6 **He Is My Everything** (Frazier)
7 **An American Trilogy** (Arr. Newbury)

Anything out of the ordinary in Elvis Presley record or CD releases has attracted a lot of fan interest. This vinyl LP, comprising 14 tracks Elvis recorded which were published by the American music industry Acuff-Rose company, was no exception.

Of course, the main difference here was that the album (in vinyl only) was not generally available to the record buying public. Instead the 1,000 copies produced at Grampian (having been mastered by Bob Jones at CTS on 18 November 1985), were used as promotional copies only, sent out to radio stations in support of Acuff-Rose's book (bearing the same title as the album), which contained the words and music to the 14 songs included on the album. The book itself cost £3.95 and it is claimed that, of the 1,000 copies of the record ordered, a total of 974 were distributed. The book artwork was the same as the album cover (see photograph) and was done by Acuff-Rose Opryland Music Ltd. themselves. The tapes for the tracks were supplied by RCA through Roger Semon's London office.

All of the tracks, spanning the years from 1956 to 1973, were published by Acuff-Rose Ltd. None were Elvis originals, in that they were his versions of other people's songs, obviously all of them country-flavoured.

Incidentally, as noted, the cutting date was November 1985. The inner bag had the printer's initials R.S. (Robert Stace) 12-85 stamped on it. The record label though, was all white with black script and stated a publishing and compilation date of 1986. According to RCA, the album was 'released' on 30 June 1986, and 'deleted' in January 1988. Above the centre hole was the clear legend: 'For Promotional Use Only - Not For Sale'. In the run-out groove on side 1 was 'Boppin' Bob' and 'Grampian', while side 2 was not personalised with Jones's signature, but had CTS Wembley. The discs were manufactured by the Grampian pressing plant, in Scotland.

With the exception of *Release Me (and let me love again)*, all the writers' names were given in full on both the label and album cover. The modes were given on the label, but not on the cover. The only two mono tracks were the pre-1960 recordings: *How's The World Treating You* (1956) and *Your Cheatin' Heart* (1958).

Now for each track the month and year of recording was given along with its release date. However, the release dates were somewhat confusing - they ought to have referred to UK release dates, but seemed to lean more towards American dates - though even then they were not always accurate. We see no point in listing them all but, as an example, will quote a couple. *There Goes My Everything* (correctly quoted as being released in December 1970 in the USA) was not issued in the UK until March 1971 (*S 76*); while *Your*

Cheatin' Heart was shown as being released in July 1965. It wasn't. It was issued in August 1965 in the USA and in November 1965 in the UK on the album *Elvis For Everyone!* (*LP 26*).

Needless to say this album was - and probably still - highly thought of and much sought after. Some of the copies sent out by Tony Peters (the co-ordinator from the Acuff-Rose side of things) had gold labels stuck to their covers bearing the name of the person it had been presented to. Not surprisingly, counterfeit copies of the album (pressed in Europe by all accounts) were in circulation, selling for large sums of money. They are recognisable for, among other things, not bearing Boppin' Bob's distinctive signature in the run-out groove.

As regards the material itself, it was nothing unusual or particularly collectable: simply a collection of Presley tracks published by Acuff-Rose. However, in turn, this promotional item was meant to stimulate interest in the media for the company's products. Jones had a couple of problems with some of the *I'm 10,000 Years Old - Elvis Country* tracks in that they were faded in and out with segments of *I Was Born About 10,000 Years Ago*. Consequently, as it was not at all appropriate to retain these pieces on this new compilation, he had to edit certain introductions and fade out other tracks early. For example *There Goes My Everything* was faded out; *Funny How Time Slips Away* had no instrumental introduction, while *I Washed My Hands In Muddy Water* also had a clipped introduction.

Essential Elvis

RCA ESSEL 1

Side 1

1   **Party** (Robinson) 1.09 {Alternative version}

2   **Loving You** (Leiber, Stoller) 1.42
     {Fast version - takes 20,21}

3   **Jailhouse Rock** (Leiber, Stoller) 1.56
     {Alternate version - take 5}

4   **Treat Me Nice** (Leiber, Stoller) 1.59
     {Alternate version - take 10}

5   **Got A Lot O' Living' To Do!** (Schroeder, Weisman) 1.22
     {Alternate version}

6   **Love Me Tender** (Presley, Matson) 1.12
     {Alternate 'End Title' version}

Side 2

1   **Jailhouse Rock** (Leiber, Stoller) 2.34
     {Alternate version with vocal overdub}

2   **Young And Beautiful** (Silver, Schroeder) 2.03
     {Alternate version - take 12}

3   **Loving You** (Leiber, Stoller) 1.37
     {Alternate fast version - take 1}

4   **Loving You** (Leiber, Stoller) 1.37
     {Alternate fast version - take 10}

5   **Mean Woman Blues** (DeMetrius) 2.33
     {Alternate film version}

6   **Loving You** (Leiber, Stoller) 1.37
     {Alternate slow version - take 1}

7   **Loving You** (Leiber, Stoller) 1.37
     {Alternate slow version - take 8}

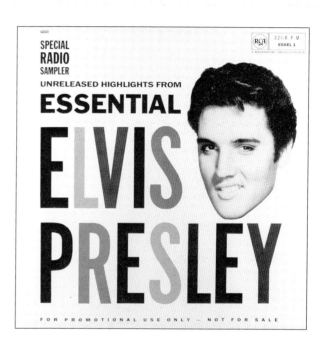

This release was significant for many reasons. Obviously it was highly collectable (as promos usually are), but its main virtue was that it was the first of its kind in the UK - that is, an LP to promote another LP! Of course, that is not to say none of the companies had produced promo LPs before, but what made this one different was that it was a thirteen track album comprising full, alternative versions of the songs. In other words, this LP had a distinct identity of its own, drawing its tracks from the standard LP and CD - which did differ slightly. To assist identification of which tracks were being used, we have added the following details to the track listing above: song timing and a description of the version itself, including take number. In the case of the final two tracks (two versions of *Loving You*), they were to be found only on the CD version of the regular album, and not on the vinyl format version (**LP 280**).

The front of the album cover carried the legend 'Special Radio Sampler Unreleased Highlights from Essential Elvis Presley For Promotional Use Only - Not For Sale'. In the top right hand side corner was the RCA logo and, underneath the playing speed, the catalogue number ESSEL 1. There was a small 'Mono' logo in the top left hand side corner. Along the spine of the cover and the top edging were the words 'RCA ESSEL 1 ELVIS PRESLEY ESSENTIAL ELVIS'.

The back cover had a 'Mono' logo top right above ESSEL 1. Down the left hand side were three black and white photographs. The top one was from *Love Me Tender* (and was used on the inner gatefold of the proper album), though it was slightly cropped at the bottom; the middle one was the famous 'down-on-my-knees' shot from

Loving You, during the end version of *Got A Lot O' Livin' To Do!* (also featured on the inner gatefold); and, finally, a shot from *Jailhouse Rock*, of Elvis singing the title song. The tracks were listed along with their timings and for most of them their take numbers. Mastering credits went to Boppin' Bob Jones, while project research was attributed to Ernst Mikael Jorgensen and Todd Slaughter. On this album though, unlike the standard release, Roger Semon was not credited as producer. The same statements regarding optimum sound quality which appeared on the standard album appeared here too.

The sleeve notes were unique to this promo, and read as follows:

> 'This promotional sampler album has been specially prepared for radio programming. It provides easy cue facilities to the unreleased gems on RCA's new commercial release *Essential Elvis*. This album contains original and alternate versions from Elvis' first three motion pictures. Studio chat and count in's (a must for Elvis fans) have been included in the commercial release (PL 89979) but edited from this sampler for song cue-ing purposes.

Essential Elvis has been originated by RCA UK and is the result of a full year of painstaking research. The priceless unreleased masters included on this sampler make it the most exciting single album release since his untimely death on 16th August 1977.'

Beneath this was the black RCA logo and the words 'FOR PROMOTIONAL USE ONLY - NOT FOR SALE'.

The label was white and had an RCA logo on it. Beneath it was 'Unreleased Highlights from *Essential Elvis*'; then underneath this 'FOR PROMOTIONAL USE ONLY - NOT FOR SALE'. The Mono legend was to the left of the centre-hole. And while the publishing dates were shown as 1957 (for the *Loving You* tracks), and 1956 for the end title version of *Love Me Tender*, they ought to have read 1986, the year they were officially published, not recorded. The same applied to the tracks on side B. Once again, all tracks were listed with their timings and, where appropriate, take numbers, but the label also included the writers' names - a detail not on the sleeve. Interestingly, track one on side B, *Jailhouse Rock*, was listed as 'Alternate version with vocal overdub' - and no take number was shown - on the cover, whereas on the label it read 'Alternate short version with vocal overdub (2.34)'. Now on the commercial release this track was shown on the album cover as 'unreleased with vocal overdub - take 6', which was the correct description we feel. It was actually the standard version, plus overdub, as used in the film. Perhaps the description 'short version' was intended for take 5 on side A which featured Scotty Moore playing a wrong note on the guitar break.

One of the most notable features between the promo and commercial release was that the former used the word 'Alternate' on the label and cover, while the latter preferred the term 'Unreleased Version', though this appeared only on the cover as the label made no reference at all. Take 1 of the slow version of *Loving You* and take 8 of the fast version of the same song were taken from the CD version of *Essential Elvis* (PD 89980), and not included on the vinyl album released commercially. Ironically, notes from the original track listing did include takes 4, 5 and 8 of *Loving You* (fast version), but this was later changed.

As regards *Mean Woman Blues*, the cover stated 'Alternate Film Version', whereas the label quoted 'Original Film Version' which we believe to be more accurate, as it was merely the studio version subjected to overdubs. On side B, *Young And Beautiful* was correctly listed as take 12, but the promo added the information on the album cover that the standard/original release of the song was a splice between takes 12 and 18. This was not quoted at all on the commercial release. Perhaps of particular interest to collectors was Joe Tunzi's revelation in *Elvis Sessions*, (1993), that the original version was, in fact, spliced from several takes, including 12, 18, 22 and 'a few sentences from 8, 11 and 19'.

Label copy details.

Predictably, *Got A Lot Of Livin' To Do!* omitted the exclamation mark, while oddly - and at variance with the commercial album - *Love Me Tender* was credited to Presley, Matson, correctly so.

This record was mastered by Bob Jones at CTS and his name was engraved in both run-out grooves. On side A, the words 'Ten Years On' were also etched in the run-out - pre-emptively if this was a reference to Elvis's death in 1977. The album was pressed by CBS.

Ain't That Loving You Baby

RCA   ELPROMO 1 DJ

Ain't That Loving You Baby (Otis, Hunter)
Bossa Nova Baby (Leiber, Stoller)

RCA issued this 12 inch promotional single to promote the ARON 1 single (*S 154*), containing the same tracks, released in March 1987. As the DJ catalogue number suffix suggested, this record was primarily intended for use in clubs, where the 12 inch format was more suitable than a 7 inch single. On this occasion, no 7 inch promotional single was produced.

The labels were white, and both carried a large red 'A', suggesting that both songs were to be considered of equal importance. However, they were identified as A and B sides under the catalogue number - ELPROMO 1A and 1B. Printed at the bottom of the label was 'For Promotional Use Only - Not For Resale', and both songs were given their correct publication dates - 1985 and 1963 respectively.

The record was the subject of a fairly large press run, large that is for a promotional issue of this kind, with, we believe, as many as 2,000 copies being produced. A high number were 'dumped' directly onto the collectors' market, where they commanded anything up to £15 at a time.

Bob Jones mastered the record and affectionately inscribed 'Roj The Poj' in between the run-out grooves on the A side, and, ever faithful, 'Cut It Loud 'E Sez!' on the B side.

The sleeve was made of thick black card with the RCA logo in white at the bottom of the front cover, and at the top on the back, with RCA's then address and country of manufacture at the bottom of the back only. The only other time that RCA had used this particular sleeve for an Elvis 12 inch release, was for the October 1980 release of *It's Only Love*, RCAT 4 (*S 123*).

Not surprisingly, the label featured the same error as the regular single, with **Ain't That Loving You Baby** appearing as **Ain't That Lovin' You Baby**.

I Dreamt I Was Elvis

NME   PRO 5

Good Rockin' Tonight (Brown)

According to the album sleeve this 12 inch LP was a 'radio-only promo for the NME cassette' of the same name, and was issued for DJ use only. In other words, this was a promotional item for a cassette issued by the music paper NME and, like the majority of promotional items, turned up for general sale to the public.

The album (and cassette) featured material recorded at Sun records by a variety of artists issued on Ace and Charly record labels, and was, therefore, a kind of sampler. Besides some well known names like Carl Perkins and Sonny Burgess, were others less familiar, but the one thing they had in common was that they all wanted to be the next Elvis - hence the title. In his short sleeve notes, Roy Carr suggested that these recordings were made by Sam Phillips in the hope that one of them would turn out to be exactly that!

This, then, was a collection of Sun label artists and was issued, according to the sleeve notes, to commemorate the tenth anniversary of Elvis's death. The promo first appeared in July 1987.

The artist these acts were trying to follow was featured on the lead track - **Good Rockin' Tonight** - but this version was not the Sun studio original and nor was it a complete song, although there was no suggestion of this. In fact, the album featured only 45 seconds or so (including the edited introduction) of the live version of the song from the Eagles Hall, Houston, Texas in March 1955 which had first appeared, officially, on the album *The First Year*, KING 1 (*LP 118*), in November 1979. The other five songs from this album appeared several times after this, including the Topline Records album *In The Beginning* (*LP 254*), issued at various times on vinyl and CD.

The sleeve, reminiscent of a bootleg, carried the words 'DJ Use only - Not For Sale' and on the back each copy was hand-numbered, showing that only 500 copies had been produced. The label was white with black print.

I DREAMT I WAS ELVIS

CHARLY RECORDS

NME PRO 5   33 RPM   SIDE ONE

℗ 1987 © 1987 NME

intro:
ELVIS PRESLEY – Good Rockin' Tonight
1 BILLY LEE RILEY – Red Hot
2 JACK EARLS – Let's Bop
3 RAY HARRIS – Where'd You Stay Last Night?
4 CARL PERKINS – Put Your Cat Clothes On
5 SONNY BURGESS – We Wanna Boogie
6 JERRY LEE LEWIS – Hillbilly Music
7 RUDY GRAYZELL – Judy
8 HAYDEN THOMPSON – Love My Baby
9 RAY SMITH – Break Up
10 GLEN HONEYCUTT – All Night Rock

This side ℗ 1987 Charly Holdings Inc © Charly Records Ltd

The Promo-Only Album of the NME Cassette,
I DREAMT I WAS ELVIS (029)

All Time Greatest Hits

RCA   ETYA 001

Side 1

1   **Blue Suede Shoes** (Perkins)

2   **Hound Dog** (Leiber, Stoller)

3   **All Shook Up** (Blackwell, Presley)

4   **Paralyzed** (Blackwell, Presley)

5   **Wear My Ring Around Your Neck** (Carroll, Moody)

6   **King Creole** (Leiber, Stoller)

7   **(Now and then there's) A Fool Such As I** (Trader)

8   **Stuck On You** (Schroeder, McFarland)

9   **(Marie's the name) His Latest Flame**
(Pomus, Shuman)

10 **Return To Sender** (Blackwell, Scott)

Side 2

1   **One Night** (Bartholomew, King)

2   **It's Now Or Never** (DiCapua, Schroeder, Gold)

3   **Are You Lonesome Tonight?** (Turk, Handman)

4   **Surrender** (DeCurtis, Pomus, Shuman)

5   **Can't Help Falling In Love** (Peretti, Creatore, Weiss)

6   **Crying In The Chapel** (Glenn)

7   **If I Can Dream** (Brown)

8   **The Wonder Of You** (Knight)

9   **I Just Can't Help Believin'** (Mann, Weil)

10 **Love Me Tender** (Presley, Matson)

As mentioned elsewhere in this book, *Presley - The All Time Greatest Hits (LP 287)* was the work of Roger Semon, then of BMG in the UK. The double album was a resounding success in all respects and, for a compilation album - not normally targeted at the real fans - it was inventive and a product of quality.

Released ten years after Elvis's death - hence the catalogue number ETYA 001 - 'Elvis Ten Years After' - this promo LP or, more correctly, in-store sampler album, was also a quality product. And, although none of the tracks comprised any alternative (unreleased) performances, this 20 track album was very desirable and greatly sought after - principally for its rarity value.

Its clearly intended market was record shops who, in turn, would be invited to play the release in order to promote the 45 track double album. However, as is often the case with promotional releases, there was some confusion as to how many reached their intended destination and, equally, how many found their way to second hand record dealers and record fairs where, not surprisingly, they commanded high prices. Now we are not in the business of being judgmental about this, but we were - and still are - struck by the irony of promotional items, specifically designed to promote an artist's product, not reaching where they should. And, although not scientific, our 'research' indicated that many major outlets in various parts of the country saw neither sight nor sign of this promo LP. There were, however, many available for sale! Perhaps the greatest irony is though that the official album sold phenomenally well despite this.

So, what did the promo album comprise? It included 20 tracks, taken from the 45 included on *Presley - The All Time Greatest Hits*, nine of which were pre-1958 recordings and the remaining tracks from the post 1960 era. As the track listing above shows, side one featured

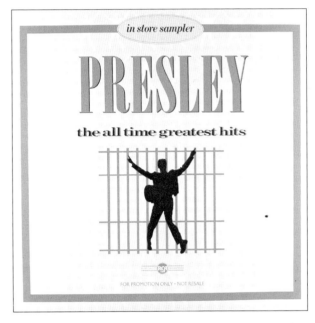

the up-tempo material, while side two focused on Elvis's slower material. This accounts for why *One Night* was out of sequence and opened side two, while *Love Me Tender*, a very slow, low key song, was programmed to finish off the set.

Label copy details.

326

The label was the new black RCA design. Notably the title was abbreviated to **All Time Greatest Hits** omitting *'Presley'* and *'The'* as shown on the cover. The recording modes were shown clearly, as were the UK publishing dates. We would not argue with the fact that the dates referred to their first UK appearance, even though in some cases they appeared on HMV first, and not RCA.

Below the title and artist's name was the legend 'Promotional Sampler Only', while the album cover (both front and back) stated 'In Store Sampler'. On the front cover were the words 'For Promotion Only. Not Resale'.

On the run-out groove of side one was the phrase 'Ten Years After', the catalogue number, and the word 'Bob' - Bob Jones. On side two, however, were the initials SW (signifying the pressing plant Spartan, in Wales) and CTS (the cutting studio). Ironically then, although the label said 'Made in England', the album was pressed in Wales. The album was cut by Jones on 4 August 1987 after he had cut the commercial albums.

The sleeve design used the same multi-image silhouette drawings which appeared on both the 7 and 12 inch **Love Me Tender** singles (**S 160** and **S 161**), which contained tracks from the album.

Included in the album cover was a poster, measuring approximately 600mm x 420mm, bearing a drawing of Elvis, along with a picture of **Presley - The All Time Greatest Hits** album. The brief script read 'There is only one King Forty Five all time greatest hits...'

'Sampler Taken From', and just above the centre hole 'Not For Resale Promotional Copy Only'. Each side contained four tracks, all of which were taken from side 1 of the actual album and, presumably to avoid further editing costs, the tracks were sequenced as on the album.

Each of the songs were segued so that **It's Now Or Never** was mixed into The Move's **Flowers In The Rain** (which preceded it), and Peter and Gordon's **A World Without Love** (which followed it).

Without doubt this is an extremely rare and collectable item.

Sixties Mix Two

Stylus   SMR 855-7

It's Now Or Never (DiCapua, Schroeder, Gold)

Stylus issued a 60 track double album of top ten hits in April 1988 which included both **It's Now Or Never** and **Return To Sender** (**VA LP 13**). This 7 inch single was issued to promote the album and, as far as we are aware, it was the only example of its kind.

Despite its unusual nature, the record itself was far from being attractive. It was issued in a plain white bag, not a picture sleeve, and had a white label with black print. Above the title were the words

(Now and then there's) A Fool Such As I

RCA   TCB 001

(Now and then there's) A Fool Such As I (Trader)
Danny (Wise, Weisman)

The May 1990 issue of **Elvis Monthly** announced details of the magazine's 30th anniversary convention, which was to be held on the 26 August 1990, and readers were informed that for every adult ticket purchased (£7.50), that this would include what was described as a 'valuable free gift' - a promotional RCA single. No further details were given regarding the tracks, but the advert did say that this was to be a specially pressed and limited edition issue.

Todd Slaughter had the original idea for the single, but it was Roger Semon who selected the tracks and made all the necessary arrangements for its release, including organising the mechanical rights.

The single was given to those attending the convention, and posted shortly afterwards to those fans who had purchased tickets but were unable to attend the convention itself. Years later, the single was widely available from various dealers, and by early 1999 copies were on sale in **Elvis Monthly** priced at £5.

The tracks featured, **(Now and then there's) A Fool Such As I** and **Danny**, were both taken from the album **Hits Like Never Before (Essential Elvis Vol. 3)**, PL 90486 (**LP 306**), released in July 1990 and, presumably, the single was justified on the grounds that it was a genuine promotional item. *(Now and then there's) A Fool Such As I* was an alternative take - take 3 - and this was the first time that *Danny* had appeared on a single release of any kind in the UK. As there was no regular single taken from the album for normal release this made TCB 001 all the more collectable.

The label design was unusual: white with black print with Elvis's name prominently displayed at the top of the label. Note also the use of TCB in the catalogue number. The record was pressed in the UK, and was issued in a plain black paper sleeve.

Song Index

For reference purposes we have included a master index of all of Elvis's songs released on vinyl in the UK from 1956 to date. Our intention is to provide a complete listing of songs and to itemise the number of times each song has appeared, and in what format. To achieve this it has been necessary to include details of material not covered in this book, but in the earlier *Elvis UK 1956-86*, making this index complete. By using a bolder print for each occasion that a song has appeared in the period covered by this book, referencing has been made easier. Where a record has been included in both books, and as we have added further details to correct omissions or to provide additional analysis, reference is made to this book only. Please note that this index covers songs released on vinyl, therefore if a title does not appear here, then the song in question has been released on CD only, not vinyl. Reference numbers for releases found in *Elvis UK 1956-86* are in italics, while those numbers in bold print relate to releases in this volume.

The index shows the release number for each of the following formats: singles (S), EPs (EP), LPs (LP) and various artist compilation LPs (VA LP). This refers to each appearance on a particular record, not to references made to a particular song in the actual text.

This index should therefore enable you to refer to each song, the format(s) on which it is to be found and, if required, determine total appearances, and so on.

There are several examples of records which feature different versions of the same song, the most notable example being the six album set *A Golden Celebration*, PL 85172 (6), released in October 1984, where songs like **Heartbreak Hotel, Hound Dog, Don't Be Cruel** and *I Want You, I Need You, I Love You* appear many times over. Instances like these count as separate appearances of a song and each occasion is noted. Therefore, **Heartbreak Hotel** is quoted as appearing a total of 6 times on *LP 251*. We have not, however, shown different takes of the same song as individual entries, and nor have we identified, either in the index or track listings, any songs which cannot be described as having been sung with the intention of being recorded and classed as a complete song. The kind of thing we have in mind here is where Elvis sings a couple of lines or hums parts of songs. The *Collectors Gold* (**LP 315**) three album set, PL 90574(3) release of August 1991 was littered with examples of this practice, particularly on the live album, with the most obvious illustration being Elvis's rendition of one line of *I Apologise* sung during a studio session. Whilst some consider this another Elvis song, we do not, although we have, of course, made reference to it in the actual text. We have, however, shown both **Surrender** and **Loving You** as they are listed on both the label and box.

We have made no distinction between studio, live, alternate takes or re-mixes in the index. These details are usually discussed in the text. In the introductory section we discussed in detail the song title errors that are all too often found on record labels and sleeves, and when discussing each release we have identified where errors occur. This index contains song titles which we believe to be accurate and we have made every effort to be precise and show the correct title. What we have strived to achieve is a consistency often lacking in record companies. To the best of our knowledge we have quoted the correct song title in full. For example *It Won't Seem Like Christmas (without you)* includes the words in brackets. And where brackets are used at the beginning of a title, these are included also, but the song is always listed under the first letter of the main heading, as this is how the song is generally known. Therefore *(Let me be your) Teddy Bear* can be found under the letter 'T', *(Now and then there's) A Fool Such As I* under 'A' and so on.

We should also point out that we have made a number of amendments to our original listing in *Elvis UK 1956-86*. The reasons behind this is that in recent years BMG have made considerable effort into issuing quality product, in all senses of the word, and the use of correct titles and writers' names is no exception. This has enabled us to review and, where necessary, amend the indexing. Where changes have been made we have said so in the text. This has had a major impact on some releases, notably some of the incorrect song titles and missing writers on *The Million Dollar Quartet* album, SUN 1006 (*LP 152*), have now been incorporated and these changes are outlined in detail in the notes accompanying the album *The Complete Million Dollar Quartet*, released by Charly in November 1987, SUN CDX 20 (**LP 291**).

It should be noted that when a 'Traditional' song, i.e. where there appears to be no known writer, was recorded by Elvis on another occasion, the details of the arrangement relate to the RCA recording, not that of the Million Dollar Quartet session. Of course, whilst all of the songs recorded at the session are included in the index, it has to be remembered that Elvis may not have participated in all of these. The inclusion of the songs is simply to help you locate them in the text.

In addition to showing what we believe is the correct song title, we have also included the writers in the same order as we believe they ought to appear on record labels and sleeves. Surnames are used throughout. Reference to the notes covering song title errors and errors in writers' names in the introductory section will hopefully prove of assistance to you.

We have divided the page numbers for each song title into categories relating to appearances on singles, EPs, LPs and on various artist releases, but we make no reference to promotional records or releases not intended for the general public. By grouping within parenthesis it is possible to determine how many times a song has appeared in each record format. For example:

It Won't Seem Like Christmas (without you)

S	*(120, 121)*	
EP	(-)	
LP	*(56, 117, 195, 252)*	**{311}**
VA LP	(-)	

In this case, *It Won't Seem Like Christmas (without you)*, has appeared on two singles; has never appeared on an EP and has made four appearances on LPs, the details of which were included in *Elvis UK 1956-86*; once on an LP in the period covered by this book (identified by the bold type); and has not been included on a release included in the various artists section. Remember, the numbers in italics refer to appearances of the song in *Elvis UK 1956-86*, whereas the numbers in bold pertain to references in this current book. This practice is also maintained in the text. In other words, if we make reference to the original *From Elvis In Memphis* (*LP 38*), then the reference number is in italics. However, if we are referring to the 1991 version of the album (**LP 313**), then this information would be in bold print.

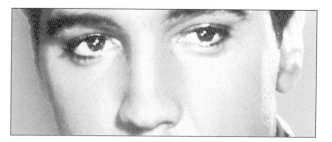

A

A Big Hunk O' Love (Schroeder, Wyche)
S   (27)
EP   (-)
LP   (10, 45, 50, 66, 73, 82, 105, 171, 181, 185,
          188, 194, 203, 216, 237, 253)
          {277, **285, 286, 287, 294, 307, 310, 318,
          323, 324, 329, 331, 335**}
VA LP   (-)   {**46**}

A Boy Like Me, A Girl Like You (Tepper, Bennett)
S   (-)
EP   (-)   {**45**}
LP   (18, 94, 158, 192, 220, 229)   {**278**}
VA LP   (-)

A Cane And A High Starched Collar (Tepper, Bennett)
S   (-)
EP   (41)
LP   (87)
VA LP   (-)

A Dog's Life (Wayne, Weisman)
S   (-)
EP   (-)   {**45**}
LP   (29, 126, 132, 215)
VA LP   (-)

(Now and then there's) A Fool Such As I (Trader)
S   (26, 103)   {**183**}
EP   (-)
LP   (10, 45, 50, 70, 73, 82, 105, 119, 126, 171,
          181, 183, 184, 189, 203, 216, 253, 258)
          {**285, 286, 287, 306, 307, 310, 318,
          323, 324, 328, 329, 331**}
VA LP   (-)   {**8, 27, 34**}

A House That Has Everything (Tepper, Bennett)
S   (-)
EP   (-)
LP   (33, 135, 223)
VA LP   (-)

A Little Bit Of Green (Arnold, Morrow, Martin)
S   (-)
EP   (-)
LP   (39, 231)   {**319**}
VA LP   (-)

A Little Less Conversation (Strange, Davis)
S   (66)   {**184, 184, 184**}
EP   (-)
LP   (44, 76, 85, 103, 138, 143, 264)
          {**337 Bonus EP**}
VA LP   (-)

A Mess Of Blues (Pomus, Shuman)
S   (29, 97)
EP   (-)
LP   (34, 45, 82, 173, 194, 205, 213, 246, 269)
          {**285, 289, 292, 300, 307, 310, 319,
          323, 324, 334**}
VA LP   (-)

A Thing Called Love (Hubbard)
S   (-)
EP   (-)
LP   (62, 139)   {**332, 333**}
VA LP   (-)

A Whistling Tune (Edwards, David)
S   (-)
EP   (16, 32)
LP   (52, 76, 85, 103)   {**315**}
VA LP   (-)

A World Of Our Own (Giant, Baum, Kaye)
S   (-)
EP   (-)
LP   (19, 128, 192, 220, 247)
VA LP   (-)

Adam And Evil (Wise, Starr)
S   (-)
EP   (-)
LP   (30, 133, 255)
VA LP   (-)

After Loving You (Miller, Lantz)
S   (-)
EP   (-)
LP   (38, 146)   {**284, 313, 319, 323, 324**}
VA LP   (-)

Ain't That Loving You Baby (Otis, Hunter)
S   (47)   {**147, 154, 155**}
EP   (-)
LP   (34, 45, 82, 151, 173, 205, 213, 269, 271)
          {**285, 289, 292, 297, 300, 306, 306, 310,
          318, 318, 334**}
VA LP   (-)

All I Needed Was The Rain (Weisman, Wayne)
S   (-)
EP   (-)
LP   (37, 110, 111)   {**338 Bonus EP**}
VA LP   (-)

All Shook Up (Blackwell, Presley)
S   (11, 23, 100)   {**158, 179, 183**}
EP   (40)
LP   (4, 7, 36, 39, 43, 45, 63, 73, 82, 104, 105, 126,
          126, 151, 153, 164, 170, 181, 183, 184, 194,
          216, 231, 232, 245, 258)
          {**277, 285, 286, 287, 297, 307, 310, 316,
          318, 320, 323, 324, 327, 328, 331, 335**}
VA LP   (-)   {**3, 8, 15, 27, 31, 33, 48**}

All That I Am (Tepper, Bennett)
S   (55)
EP   (-)
LP   (30, 82, 133, 192, 202, 220, 255)
VA LP   (-)

Almost (Kaye, Weisman)
S   (-)
EP   (-)
LP   (40)   {**343 Bonus EP**}
VA LP   (-)

Almost Always True (Wise, Weisman)
S   (-)
EP   (-)
LP   (15, 46, 166, 238)   {**338**}
VA LP   (-)

Almost In Love (Bonfa, Starr)
S   (66)
EP   (-)
LP   (44, 78, 85, 151, 199, 264)
          {**297, 337 Bonus EP**}
VA LP   (-)

Aloha-oe (Arranged and adapted Presley)
S (-)
EP (-)
LP (*15, 46, 166, 238*) {**285, 338**}
VA LP (-)

Always On My Mind (James, Carson, Christopher)
S (*85*) {**146, 147, 163, 166**}
EP (-)
LP (*67, 74, 82, 85, 103, 116, 137, 142, 150, 199, 226, 272*)
{**287, 308, 310, 317, 320, 323, 324, 331**}
VA LP (-) {**10, 11, 20, 24, 29**}

Am I Ready (Tepper, Bennett)
S (-)
EP (-)
LP (*30, 65, 133, 255*) {**315**}
VA LP (-)

Amazing Grace (Newton)
S (-)
EP (-)
LP (*62, 139*) {**332, 333**}
VA LP (-)

Amen (Pate, Mayfield)
S (-)
EP (-)
LP (*100, 126, 273*)
VA LP (-)

America, The Beautiful (Traditional. Arranged Presley)
S (*117*)
EP (-)
LP (*126, 258*) {**335**}
VA LP (-)

An American Trilogy (Arranged Newbury)
S (*83, 128*) {**152**}
EP (-)
LP (*63, 66, 72, 74, 82, 119, 126, 126, 150, 151, 182, 226, 237*)
{**287, 294, 297, 308, 310, 320, 323, 324, 331, 335**}
VA LP (-)

An Evening Prayer (Battersby, Gabriel)
S (-)
EP (-)
LP (*62, 101, 139*) {**332, 333**}
VA LP (-)

And I Love You So (McLean)
S (-)
EP (-)
LP (*79, 100, 273*) {**335**}
VA LP (-)

And Now Sweetheart You've Done Me Wrong
On BMG releases this song was entitled **Sweetheart You Done Me Wrong.** Appearances can be found under the latter title.

And The Grass Won't Pay No Mind (Diamond)
S (-)
EP (-)
LP (*39, 194, 231*) {**319**}
VA LP (-)

Angel (Tepper, Bennett)
S (-)
EP (*15, 31*)
LP (*52, 76, 85, 103, 185*)
VA LP (-)

Animal Instinct (Giant, Baum, Kaye)
S (-)
EP (-)
LP (*27, 130, 222*)
VA LP (-)

Any Day Now (Hilliard, Bacharach)
S (*68*)
EP (-)
LP (*38, 55*) {**284, 285, 313, 319**}
VA LP (-)

Any Way You Want Me (that's how I will be) (Schroeder, Owens)
S (*6*) {**162, 163**}
EP (-)
LP (*4, 7, 43, 45, 82, 113, 119, 170, 180, 232*)
{**310, 318, 321, 323, 324, 326, 327, 341**}
VA LP (-)

Anyone (could fall in love with you) (Benjamin, Marcus, DeJesus)
S (-)
EP (-)
LP (*22, 95, 159, 249*) {**279**}
VA LP (-)

Anyplace Is Paradise (Thomas)
S (-)
EP (*12*)
LP (*2, 17, 113, 169, 180, 211*)
{**318, 321, 323, 324, 326, 341**}
VA LP (-)

Anything That's Part Of You (Robertson)
S (*37, 110*) {**183**}
EP (-)
LP (*21, 45, 82, 116, 172, 192, 220, 256*)
{**285, 310, 319, 323, 324, 330**}
VA LP (-)

Are You Lonesome Tonight? (Turk, Handman)
S (*31, 80, 105, 133*) {**157, 163, 177, 178, 183**}
EP (-)
LP (*21, 25, 39, 45, 70, 73, 82, 100, 105, 116, 119, 126, 126, 150, 172, 182, 183, 185, 187, 189, 204, 219, 226, 231, 251, 256, 265, 270, 273, 274*)
{**277, 285, 286, 287, 307, 310, 315, 316, 317, 319, 320, 323, 324, 328, 330, 331, 335**}
VA LP (-) {**1, 2, 5, 16, 27, 40, 41, 45**}

Are You Sincere (Walker)
S (-)
EP (-)
LP (*69, 112*)
VA LP (-)

As Long As I Have You (Wise, Weisman)
S (-)
EP (*6, 29*)
LP (*6, 55, 58, 154, 212*)
{**306, 318, 318, 344, 344, 344**}
VA LP (-)

As We Travel Along On The Jericho Road (Traditional)
The correct title of this song is **On The Jericho Road**, and all apearances can be found under this title.

Ask Me (Modugno, Giant, Baum, Kaye)
S (*47*)
EP (-)
LP (*34, 55, 173, 192, 213, 220*)
{**285, 309, 315, 319, 334**}
VA LP (-)

B

(You're so square) Baby I Don't Care (Leiber, Stoller)
S   (138, 139)
EP   (5, 28)
LP   (55, 82, 125, 127, 190, 196, 200, 217,
          227, 242, 262)
          {280, 318, 323, 324, 343}
VA LP   (-)

Baby, If You'll Give Me All Your Love (Byers)
S   (-)
EP   (-)
LP   (32, 123, 134, 244)
VA LP   (-)

Baby Let's Play House (Gunter)
S   (9) {182}
EP   (-) {45}
LP   (9, 80, 108, 118, 127, 194, 198, 200, 201,
          227, 234, 242, 251, 251, 254, 254, 259)
          {283, 295, 302, 304, 318, 322, 323,
          324, 327}
VA LP   (-)

Baby, What You Want Me To Do (Reed)
S   (-) {178}
EP   (-)
LP   (36, 87, 104, 126, 153, 205, 245, 251,
          251, 269)
          {290, 292, 300, 315, 335}
VA LP   (-)

Barefoot Ballad (Fuller, Morris)
S   (-)
EP   (-)
LP   (22, 95, 159, 249) {279}
VA LP   (-)

Beach Boy Blues (Tepper, Bennett)
S   (-)
EP   (-)
LP   (15, 46, 166, 238) {338, 338}
VA LP   (-)

Beach Shack (Giant, Baum, Kaye)
S   (-)
EP   (-)
LP   (30, 133, 255)
VA LP   (-)

Because Of Love (Batchelor, Roberts)
S   (-)
EP   (-)
LP   (18, 94, 158, 229) {278}
VA LP   (-)

Beginner's Luck (Tepper, Bennett)
S   (-)
EP   (-)
LP   (28, 109, 111, 131, 241)
VA LP   (-)

Beyond The Bend (Weisman, Wise, Fuller)
S   (-)
EP   (-)
LP   (19, 128, 247) {315}
VA LP   (-)

Beyond The Reef (Pitman)
S   (122, 123)
EP   (-)
LP   (126, 265) {319}
VA LP   (-)

Big Boots (Wayne, Edwards)
S   (-)
EP   (33)
LP   (12, 155, 206) {315, 337, 337, 337}
VA LP   (-)

Big Boss Man (Smith, Dixon)
S   (61)
EP   (-)
LP   (33, 36, 64, 86, 89, 104, 121, 122, 135,
          137, 142, 153, 194, 205, 223, 245, 269)
          {290, 292, 300, 310, 319, 319, 323, 324,
          335, 336}
VA LP   (-)

Big Love Big Heartache (Fuller, Morris, Hendrix)
S   (-)
EP   (-)
LP   (23, 96, 161, 240)
VA LP   (-)

Bitter They are, Harder They Fall (Gatlin)
S   (-)
EP   (-)
LP   (88, 266, 272)
VA LP   (-)

Black Bottom Stomp (Morton)
This was entitled **Jerry's Boogie** on *LP 291*.
S   (-)
EP   (-)
LP   (-) {291}
VA LP   (-)

Black Star (Wayne, Edwards)
S   (-)
EP   (-)
LP   (-) {315}
VA LP   (-)

Blessed Jesus (hold my hand) (Traditional)
S   (-)
EP   (-)
LP   (152) {291, 332, 333}
VA LP   (-)

Blue Christmas (Hayes, Johnson)
S   (48, 132)
EP   (8)
LP   (5, 36, 42, 81, 87, 104, 126, 140, 153,
          218, 245, 251, 275)
          {310, 312, 318, 332, 339}
VA LP   (-)

Blue Eyes Crying In The Rain (Rose)
S   (-)
EP   (-)
LP   (88, 266)
VA LP   (-)

Blue Hawaii (Robin, Rainger)
S   (-)
EP   (-)
LP   (15, 46, 87, 123, 166, 189, 191, 238, 258, 268)
          {285, 288, 294, 299, 338, 338}
VA LP   (-)

Blue Moon (Rodgers, Hart)
  S   (5, 94) {**150**}
  EP   (34)
  LP   (4, 9, 80, 82, 108, 201, 202, 267)
           {**283, 285, 295, 304, 310, 318, 318,
           325, 340**}
  VA LP   (-)

Blue Moon Of Kentucky (Monroe)
  S   (-) {**182**}
  EP   (3, 40)
  LP   (9, 80, 108, 118, 119, 127, 183, 184, 190,
           194, 198, 201, 242, 251, 254, 254, 259)
           {**283, 283, 295, 302, 304, 318, 318, 322**}
  VA LP   (-)

Blue River (Evans, Tobias)
  S   (52)
  EP   (-)
  LP   (32, 134, 244) {**309, 319**}
  VA LP   (-)

Blue Suede Shoes (Perkins)
  S   (2, 24, 145)
  EP   (23)
  LP   (1, 8, 12, 39, 60, 66, 73, 82, 87, 102, 105,
           119, 126, 150, 151, 155, 164, 175, 179, 181,
           182, 194, 206, 216, 226, 231, 236, 237, 251,
           251, 251, 251, 251, 262, 265, 267)
           {**276, 277, 285, 287, 294, 297, 302, 303, 307,
           308, 310, 315, 316, 318, 318, 321, 322, 323,
           324, 325, 327, 328, 331, 335, 335, 337, 340**}
  VA LP   (-)

Blueberry Hill (Lewis, Stock, Rose)
  S   (-)
  EP   (4, 36)
  LP   (72, 82, 98, 160, 210)
           {**285, 298, 298, 318, 342**}
  VA LP   (-)

Bosom Of Abraham (Johnson, McFadden, Brooks)
  S   (-)
  EP   (-)
  LP   (62, 139) {**332, 332, 333, 333**}
  VA LP   (-)

Bossa Nova Baby (Leiber, Stoller)
  S   (42) {**154, 155, 161**}
  EP   (-)
  LP   (20, 45, 82, 83, 97, 124, 125, 157, 191,
           217, 246, 257, 268)
           {**285, 286, 288, 299, 310, 334**}
  VA LP   (-)

Bridge Over Troubled Water (Simon)
  S   (127)
  EP   (-)
  LP   (47, 82, 167, 224) {**328, 328, 335**}
  VA LP   (-)

Bringing It Back (Gordon)
  S   (-)
  EP   (-)
  LP   (79)
  VA LP   (-)

Britches (Wayne, Edwards)
  S   (-)
  EP   (41)
  LP   (106, 107)
  VA LP   (-)

Brown Eyed Handsome Man (Berry)
  S   (-)
  EP   (-)
  LP   (-) {**291, 291, 291**}
  VA LP   (-)

Burning Love (Linde)
  S   (84, 137, 145) {**166, 180**}
  EP   (-)
  LP   (65, 66, 74, 78, 82, 85, 120, 122, 126,
           138, 143, 151, 182, 185, 196, 199, 237, 261)
           {**285, 286, 287, 294, 297, 310, 323, 324,
           331, 335, 336**}
  VA LP   (-) {**28**}

By And By (Arranged and adapted Presley)
  S   (-)
  EP   (-)
  LP   (31, 53, 174, 235) {**332, 333**}
  VA LP   (-)

C

Can't Help Falling In Love (Peretti, Creatore, Weiss)
  S   (36, 109) {**170, 183**}
  EP   (-)
  LP   (15, 36, 39, 45, 46, 63, 66, 70, 72, 73, 82,
           100, 104, 105, 116, 126, 126, 153, 166,
           182, 187, 189, 197, 219, 231, 237, 238,
           245, 265, 270, 273, 274)
           {**277, 285, 286, 287, 294, 310, 316, 317, 320,
           323, 324, 328, 330, 331, 335, 335, 338, 338**}
  VA LP   (-) {**17, 27, 36, 40**}

Carny Town (Wise, Starr)
  S   (-)
  EP   (-)
  LP   (23, 96, 161, 240)
  VA LP   (-)

Catchin' On Fast (Giant, Baum, Kaye)
  S   (-)
  EP   (-)
  LP   (22, 95, 159, 249) {**279**}
  VA LP   (-)

Change Of Habit (Weisman, Kaye)
  S   (-)
  EP   (-)
  LP   (40, 109, 111) {**344 Bonus EP**}
  VA LP   (-)

Charro (Strange, Davis)
  S   (-)
  EP   (-)
  LP   (44, 121, 122, 191, 197, 268) {**288, 299**}
  VA LP   (-)

Chesay (Karger, Wayne, Weisman)
  S   (-)
  EP   (-)
  LP   (28, 131, 241)
  VA LP   (-)

Cindy, Cindy (Kaye, Weisman, Fuller)
  S   (-)
  EP   (-)
  LP   (51, 149, 250) {**328**}
  VA LP   (-)

City By Night (Giant, Baum, Kaye)
S   (-)
EP   (-)
LP   (*32, 134, 244*)
VA LP   (-)

Clambake (Wayne, Weisman)
S   (-)
EP   (-)
LP   (*33, 83, 124, 135, 223*)
VA LP   (-)

Clean Up Your Own Backyard (Strange, Davis)
S   (*69*)
EP   (-)
LP   (*44, 109, 111, 138, 143, 146, 261*)
         {**336, 343 Bonus EP**}
VA LP   (-)

C'mon Everybody (Byers)
S   (-)
EP   (*17, 42*)
LP   (*52, 76, 85, 103, 137, 142, 196*) {**276**}
VA LP   (-)

Come Along (Hess)
S   (-)
EP   (-)
LP   (*28, 109, 111, 131, 138, 143, 241*)
VA LP   (-)

Come What May (Tableporter)
S   (*54*)
EP   (-)
LP   (*183, 263*) {**315, 319**}
VA LP   (-)

Confidence (Tepper, Bennett)
S   (-)
EP   (-)
LP   (*33, 64, 86, 89, 135, 137, 142, 223*)
VA LP   (-)

Cotton Candy Land (Batchelor, Roberts)
S   (-)
EP   (-)
LP   (*19, 128, 247*)
VA LP   (-)

Cottonfields (Ledbetter)
S   (-)
EP   (-)
LP   (-) {**328**}
VALP   (-)

Could I Fall In Love (Starr)
S   (-)
EP   (-)
LP   (*32, 134, 244*)
VA LP   (-)

Crawfish (Wise, Weisman)
S   (-)
EP   (*7, 37*)
LP   (*6, 55, 58, 154, 212*) {**306, 318, 344**}
VA LP   (-)

Crazy Arms (Mooney, Seals)
S   (-)
EP   (-)
LP   (*152*) {**291, 291**}
VA LP   (-)

Cross My Heart And Hope To Die (Wayne, Weisman)
S   (-)
EP   (-)
LP   (*24, 129, 248*)
VA LP   (-)

Crying In The Chapel (Glenn)
S   (*50, 114*) {**183**}
EP   (-)
LP   (*31, 45, 53, 73, 82, 105, 106, 107, 119,
         139, 151, 163, 174, 183, 187, 219, 235,
         258, 274*)
         {**277, 285, 286, 287, 297, 310, 331,
         332, 333, 334**}
VA LP   (-) {**3, 17, 35, 46**}

D

Danny (Wise, Weisman)
S   (-)
EP   (-)
LP   (*106, 107*) {**306, 318, 344**}
VA LP   (-)

Danny Boy (Weatherly)
S   (-)
EP   (-)
LP   (*88, 251, 266*)
VA LP   (-)

Dark Moon (Miller)
S   (-) {**147**}
EP   (-)
LP   (*251*)
VA LP   (-)

Datin' (Wise, Starr)
S   (-)
EP   (-)
LP   (*29, 126, 132, 215, 265*)
VA LP   (-)

(You're the) Devil In Disguise (Giant, Baum, Kaye)
S   (*41, 113*) {**183**}
EP   (-)
LP   (*34, 45, 73, 82, 105, 151, 173, 187, 188,
         193, 213, 219, 221*)
         {**277, 285, 286, 287, 297, 309, 310, 319,
         320, 323, 324, 331, 334**}
VA LP   (-) {**8, 27**}

Didja' Ever (Wayne, Edwards)
S   (-)
EP   (-)
LP   (*12, 155, 206*) {**337, 337**}
VA LP   (-)

Dirty, Dirty Feeling (Leiber, Stoller)
S   (-)
EP   (*20*)
LP   (*11, 125, 168, 217, 230*) {**319, 345, 345**}
VA LP   (-)

Dixieland Rock (Schroeder, Frank)
S   (*22*)
EP   (*7, 37*)
LP   (*6, 55, 58, 154, 190, 212*) {**285, 318, 344**}
VA LP   (-)

Do Not Disturb (Giant, Baum, Kaye)
S   (52)
EP   (-)
LP   (24, 90, 129, 176, 248)
VA LP (-)

Do The Clam (Wayne, Weisman, Fuller)
S   (49)
EP   (-)
LP   (24, 82, 83, 124, 129, 141, 246, 248)
          {285, 310}
VA LP (-)

Do The Vega (Giant, Baum, Kaye)
S   (-)
EP   (-)
LP   (37, 110, 111, 196)
VA LP (-)

Do You Know Who I Am (Russell)
S   (-)
EP   (-)
LP   (39, 194, 231) {319}
VA LP (-)

Doin' The Best I Can (Pomus, Shuman)
S   (-)
EP   (43)
LP   (12, 155, 192, 206, 220, 264) {337, 337}
VA LP (-)

Dominic (Weisman, Wayne)
S   (-)
EP   (-)
LP   (-) {338 Bonus EP}
VA LP (-)

Doncha' Think It's Time (Otis, Dixon)
S   (20)
EP   (-)
LP   (10, 50, 55, 171, 203, 253, 263)
          {285, 306, 310, 318, 329}
VA LP (-)

Don't (Leiber, Stoller)
S   (19) {169}
EP   (11, 38)
LP   (10, 45, 50, 73, 82, 105, 125, 163, 171,
          181, 200, 203, 216, 217, 227, 253, 274)
          {277, 285, 286, 287, 307, 310, 317, 318,
          323, 324, 329, 331}
VA LP (-)

Don't Ask Me Why (Wise, Weisman)
S   (21)
EP   (37)
LP   (6, 55, 58, 154, 212) {318, 344}
VA LP (-)

Don't Be Cruel (Blackwell, Presley)
S   (4, 78, 118, 137, 145) {156, 179}
EP   (25)
LP   (4, 7, 43, 45, 63, 70, 82, 100, 102, 126,
          126, 150, 151, 170, 179, 183, 184, 196,
          200, 226, 232, 251, 251, 251, 251, 251,
          258, 273)
          {285, 286, 291, 291, 297, 307, 308, 310,
          315, 318, 320, 321, 323, 324, 326, 327,
          331, 335, 335, 341}
VA LP (-) {46, 49, 50}

Don't Cry Daddy (Davis)
S   (71)
EP   (-)
LP   (45, 73, 82, 105, 185, 187, 189, 219, 263,
          272, 274)
          {284, 286, 287, 319, 323, 324, 328, 331, 335}
VA LP (-)

Don't Forbid Me (Singleton)
S   (-)
EP   (-)
LP   (152) {291}
VA LP (-)

Don't Leave Me Now (Schroeder, Weisman)
S   (-)
EP   (4, 5, 28, 36)
LP   (98, 160, 196, 196, 210)
          {280, 318, 318, 335, 342, 343, 343}
VA LP (-)

Don't Think Twice, It's All Right (Dylan)
S   (-)
EP   (-)
LP   (68, 114)
VA LP (-)

Double Trouble (Pomus, Shuman)
S   (-)
EP   (-)
LP   (32, 82, 83, 124, 134, 191, 244, 268)
          {288, 299}
VA LP (-)

Down By The Riverside (Arranged Giant, Baum, Kaye)
S   (-)
EP   (-)
LP   (28, 64, 86, 89, 131, 152, 241)
          {291, 332, 332, 333, 333}
VA LP (-)

Down In The Alley (Jesse Stone and The Clovers)
S   (-)
EP   (-)
LP   (30, 133, 255, 271)
          {319, 319, 323, 324}
VA LP (-)

Drums Of The Islands (Polynesian Cultural Centre, Tepper, Bennett)
S   (-)
EP   (-)
LP   (29, 132, 215)
VA LP (-)

E

Early Mornin' Rain (Lightfoot)
S   (-)
EP   (-)
LP   (61, 100, 123, 263, 273)
VA LP (-)

Earth Angel (will you be mine) (Belvin)
S   (-)
EP   (-)
LP   (251)
VA LP (-)

Earth Boy (Tepper, Bennett)
S (-)
EP (-)
LP (*18, 94, 158, 229*) {**278**}
VA LP (-)

Easy Come, Easy Go (Wayne, Weisman)
S (-)
EP (*22*)
LP (*52, 76, 85, 103, 121, 122, 137, 142, 197*)
VA LP (-)

(Such an) Easy Question (Blackwell, Scott)
S (-)
EP (*21*)
LP (*16, 148, 233*) {**285, 310, 319, 345, 345**}
VA LP (-)

Echoes Of Love (Roberts, McMains)
S (-)
EP (-)
LP (*22, 95, 159, 192, 220, 249*)
{**279, 285, 309, 319**}
VA LP (-)

Edge Of Reality (Giant, Baum, Kaye)
S (-)
EP (-)
LP (*44, 109, 111*) {**336, 337 Bonus EP**}
VA LP (-)

El Toro (Giant, Baum, Kaye)
S (-)
EP (-)
LP (*20, 97, 157, 257*)
VA LP (-)

End Of The Road (Lewis)
S (-)
EP (-)
LP (-) {**291**}
VA LP (-)

Everybody Come Aboard (Giant, Baum, Kaye)
S (-)
EP (-)
LP (*28, 131, 241*)
VA LP (-)

F

Faded Love (B. & J. Wills)
S (*125*)
EP (-)
LP (*49, 146, 162, 239*)
VA LP (-) {**5**}

Fairy Tale (A. & B. Pointer)
S (-)
EP (-)
LP (*79, 100, 273*)
VA LP (-)

Fame And Fortune (Wise, Weisman)
S (*28*)
EP (-)
LP (*21, 55, 106, 107, 172, 183, 256, 270*)
{**285, 308, 310, 319, 330**}
VA LP (-)

Farther Along (Arranged and adapted Presley)
S (-)
EP (-)
LP (*31, 53, 152, 174, 235*)
{**291, 328, 332, 332, 332, 333, 333, 333**}
VA LP (-)

Fever (Davenport, Cooley)
S (-)
EP (-)
LP (*11, 66, 73, 82, 105, 168, 187, 188, 219, 230, 237, 270*) {**277, 285, 294, 319**}
VA LP (-)

Find Out What's Happening (Crutchfield)
S (-)
EP (-)
LP (*69, 114*)
VA LP (-)

Finders Keepers, Losers Weepers (D. & O. Jones)
S (-)
EP (-)
LP (*26, 59, 144, 193, 221, 225*) {**309, 319**}
VA LP (-)

First In Line (Schroeder, Weisman)
S (-)
EP (*19*) {**45**}
LP (*2, 17, 113, 169, 180, 211*) {**318, 326, 341**}
VA LP (-)

Five Sleepy Heads (Tepper, Bennett)
S (-)
EP (-)
LP (*35, 136, 228*)
VA LP (-)

Flaming Star (Wayne, Edwards)
S (-)
EP (*41*)
LP (*25, 37, 82, 110, 111, 120, 122, 138, 143, 191, 268*)
{**288, 299, 310**}
VA LP (-)

Flip, Flop And Fly (Turner, Calhoun)
S (*144*)
EP (-)
LP (*72, 150, 200, 226, 251, 265*) {**308**}
VA LP (-)

Follow That Dream (Wise, Weisman)
S (-)
EP (*15, 31*)
LP (*52, 76, 85, 103, 120, 122, 126, 191, 197, 246, 268*) {**288, 299, 310, 330**}
VA LP (-)

Fool (Sigman, Last)
S (*87*)
EP (-)
LP (*68, 126, 194, 207, 209*) {**310**}
VA LP (-)

Fool, Fool, Fool (Nugetre)
S (-)
EP (-)
LP (-) {**318**}
VA LP (-)

Fools Fall In Love (Leiber, Stoller)
S (*57*)
EP (-)
LP (*57, 84, 86, 120, 122, 125, 138, 143, 163, 199, 217*) {**319**}
VA LP (-)

Fools Rush In (where angels fear to tread) (Mercer, Bloom)
S   (-)
EP   (-)
LP   (61)
VA LP   (-)

(That's what you get) For Lovin' Me (Lightfoot)
S   (-)
EP   (-)
LP   (68)
VA LP   (-)

For Ol' Times Sake (White)
S   (88)
EP   (-)
LP   (69)
VA LP   (-)

For The Good Times (Kristofferson)
S   (-)
EP   (-)
LP   (63, 92, 177)
VA LP   (-)

For The Heart (Linde)
S   (96)
EP   (-)
LP   (88, 114, 261, 266) {**323, 324, 336**}
VA LP   (-)

For The Millionth And Last Time (Tepper, Bennett)
S   (-)
EP   (-)
LP   (26, 59, 144, 192, 220, 225) {**319**}
VA LP   (-)

Forget Me Never (Wise, Weisman)
S   (-)
EP   (-)
LP   (26, 59, 67, 85, 103, 144, 225)
         {**342 Bonus EP**}
VA LP   (-)

Fort Lauderdale Chamber Of Commerce (Tepper, Bennett)
S   (-)
EP   (-)
LP   (24, 129, 248)
VA LP   (-)

Fountain Of Love (Giant, Lewis)
S   (-)
EP   (-)
LP   (16, 148, 233) {**319**}
VA LP   (-)

Frankfort Special (Wayne, Edwards)
S   (-)
EP   (33)
LP   (12, 106, 107, 155, 206) {**337, 337**}
VA LP   (-)

Frankie And Johnny (Gottlieb, Karger, Weisman)
S   (53)
EP   (-)
LP   (28, 64, 82, 86, 89, 121, 122, 131, 137,
         142, 191, 197, 202, 241, 268)
         {**288, 299, 310**}
VA LP   (-)

From A Jack To A King (Miller)
S   (133)
EP   (-)
LP   (39, 231) {**319**}
VA LP   (-)

Fun In Acapulco (Weisman, Wayne)
S   (-)
EP   (-)
LP   (20, 83, 97, 124, 157, 191, 257, 268)
         {**288, 299**}
VA LP   (-)

Funny How Time Slips Away (Nelson)
S   (-)
EP   (-)
LP   (49, 63, 126, 162, 239) {**315**}
VA LP   (-) {**5**}

G

Gentle On My Mind (Hartford)
S   (-)
EP   (-)
LP   (38, 92, 177) {**284, 285, 313, 319**}
VA LP   (-) {**5**}

Gently (Wizell, Lisbona)
S   (-)
EP   (-)
LP   (14, 165, 243) {**315, 319**}
VA LP   (-)

Get Back (Lennon, McCartney)
S   (-)
EP   (-)
LP   (126) {**328, 328, 335**}
VA LP   (-)

G.I. Blues (Tepper, Bennett)
S   (-)
EP   (43)
LP   (12, 141, 150, 155, 191, 197, 206, 226, 264, 268)
         {**288, 299, 315, 337**}
VA LP   (-)

Girl Happy (Pomus, Meade)
S   (-)
EP   (-)
LP   (24, 83, 124, 129, 191, 248, 268)
         {**288, 299, 315**}
VA LP   (-)

Girl Next Door Went A'Walking (Rice, Wayne)
S   (-)
EP   (-)
LP   (11, 168, 230) {**319**}
VA LP   (-)

Girl Of Mine (Mason, Reed)
S   (-)
EP   (-)
LP   (69, 112)
VA LP   (-)

Girls! Girls! Girls! (Leiber, Stoller)
S   (-)
EP   (-) {**45**}
LP   (18, 83, 94, 124, 125, 141, 158, 191, 197,
         217, 229, 268) {**278, 288, 299**}
VA LP   (-)

337

Give Me The Right (Wise, Blagman)
S   (-)
EP   (-)
LP   (*14, 165, 205, 243, 269, 270*)
           {**289, 292, 300, 315, 319**}
VA LP   (-)

Go East, Young Man (Giant, Baum, Kaye)
S   (-)
EP   (-)
LP   (*27, 130, 222*)
VA LP   (-)

Goin' Home (Byers)
S   (-)
EP   (-)
LP   (*35, 136, 228*) {**315, 338 Bonus EP**}
VA LP   (-)

Golden Coins (Giant, Baum, Kaye)
S   (-)
EP   (-)
LP   (*27, 130, 222*)
VA LP   (-)

Gonna Get Back Home Somehow (Pomus, Shuman)
S   (-)
EP   (-)
LP   (*16, 148, 233*) {**319**}
VA LP   (-)

Good Luck Charm (Schroeder, Gold)
S   (*37, 110*) {**183**}
EP   (*44*)
LP   (*21, 45, 73, 82, 105, 151, 172, 187, 188, 219, 256, 264*)
           {**277, 285, 286, 287, 297, 310, 317, 319, 320, 323, 324, 330, 331**}
VA LP   (-) {**8, 27, 48**}

Good Rockin' Tonight (Brown)
S   (*131*) {**182**}
EP   (*3, 11, 38*)
LP   (*9, 80, 82, 108, 118, 119, 127, 190, 194, 198, 201, 202, 242, 254, 254, 259*)
           {**283, 295, 302, 304, 318, 323, 324**}
VA LP   (-)

Good Time Charlie's Got The Blues (O'Keefe)
S   (-)
EP   (-)
LP   (*71*)
VA LP   (-)

Got A Lot O' Livin' To Do! (Schroeder, Weisman)
S   (*14*) {**149**}
EP   (*27*)
LP   (*3, 25, 55, 73, 82, 90, 98, 105, 151, 160, 176, 181, 188, 210, 216*)
           {**277, 280, 280, 285, 297, 308, 310, 318, 323, 324, 329, 342, 342**}
VA LP   (-)

Got My Mojo Working (Waters)
S   (-)
EP   (-)
LP   (*51, 149, 250*)
VA LP   (-)

Green, Green Grass Of Home (Putnam Jr.)
S   (*95, 142*)
EP   (-)
LP   (*79, 114, 207, 209*) {**335**}
VA LP   (-)

Guadalajara (Guizar)
S   (-)
EP   (-)
LP   (*20, 65, 76, 85, 97, 103, 106, 107, 157, 257*)
VA LP   (-)

Guitar Man (Hubbard)
S   (*62, 125*)
EP   (-)
LP   (*33, 36, 36, 36, 64, 73, 82, 86, 89, 104, 104, 104, 105, 135, 146, 151, 153, 153, 153, 164, 183, 187, 219, 223, 245, 245, 245*)
           {**276, 277, 285, 297, 310, 319, 323, 324, 331, 336**}
VA LP   (-)

H

Happy Ending (Wayne, Weisman)
S   (-)
EP   (-)
LP   (*19, 123, 128, 247*)
VA LP   (-)

Harbour Lights (Kennedy, Williams)
S   (*130*) {**182**}
EP   (-)
LP   (*87, 201, 251*) {**283, 295, 318**}
VA LP   (-)

Hard Headed Woman (DeMetrius)
S   (*21*) {**168**}
EP   (*11, 38*)
LP   (*6, 45, 58, 73, 82, 105, 141, 154, 181, 189, 190, 212, 216*)
           {**277, 285, 286, 287, 307, 310, 318, 323, 324, 329, 331, 344**}
VA LP   (-) {**49**}

Hard Knocks (Byers)
S   (-)
EP   (-)
LP   (*23, 96, 161, 240*)
VA LP   (-)

Hard Luck (Wayne, Weisman)
S   (-)
EP   (-)
LP   (*28, 109, 111, 131, 138, 143, 194, 241*)
VA LP   (-)

Harem Holiday (Andreoli, Poncia)
S   (-)
EP   (-)
LP   (*27, 130, 222*)
VA LP   (-)

Have A Happy (Weisman, Kaye, Fuller)
S   (-)
EP   (-)
LP   (*40, 109, 111*) {**344 Bonus EP**}
VA LP   (-)

Have I Told You Lately That I Love You (Weisman)
S   (-)
EP   (4, 36)
LP   (90, 98, 141, 160, 163, 176, 199, 210)
         {**298, 298, 298, 318, 342**}
VA LP   (-)

Hawaiian Sunset (Tepper, Bennett)
S   (-)
EP   (-)
LP   (15, 46, 166, 238) {**338**}
VA LP   (-)

Hawaiian Wedding Song (King, Hoffman, Manning)
S   (-)
EP   (-)
LP   (15, 46, 100, 123, 166, 199, 238, 263,
         273, 274) {**335, 338**}
VA LP   (-)

He (Richards, Mullen)
S   (-)
EP   (-)
LP   (-) {**332, 333**}
VA LP   (-)

He Is My Everything (Frazier)
S   (-)
EP   (-)
LP   (62, 101, 139) {**332, 333**}
VA LP   (-)

He Knows Just What I Need (Lister)
S   (-)
EP   (-)
LP   (13, 54, 156, 214) {**332, 333**}
VA LP   (-)

He Touched Me (Gaither)
S   (-)
EP   (-)
LP   (62, 139, 195, 252) {**332, 333**}
VA LP   (-)

Heartbreak Hotel (Axton, Durden, Presley)
S   (1, 23, 78, 100) {**158, 181, 181**}
EP   (24)
LP   (4, 7, 36, 43, 45, 63, 70, 73, 82, 102, 104,
         105, 119, 126, 126, 150, 151, 153, 164, 170,
         179, 181, 183, 184, 200, 216, 226, 232, 245,
         251, 251, 251, 251, 251, 251, 265)
         {**277, 285, 286, 287, 297, 302, 307, 308,
         310, 315, 318, 318, 320, 321, 321, 322, 323,
         324, 325, 327, 328, 331, 335, 335, 335, 340**}
VA LP   (-) {**3, 8, 27**}

Heart Of Rome (Stephens, Blaikley, Howard)
S   (79)
EP   (-)
LP   (51, 149, 250)
VA LP   (-)

He'll Have To Go (J. & A. Allison)
S   (-)
EP   (-)
LP   (93, 178, 260) {**296**}
VA LP   (-)

Help Me (Gatlin)
S   (90)
EP   (-)
LP   (72, 75) {**332, 332, 333, 333, 335**}
VA LP   (-)

Help Me Make It Through The Night (Kristofferson)
S   (-)
EP   (-)
LP   (61, 92, 177, 194)
VA LP   (-)

Here Comes Santa Claus (right down Santa Claus lane)
(Autry, Haldeman, Melka)
S   (-)
EP   (-)
LP   (5, 42, 81, 140, 218, 275)
         {**312, 318, 332, 339**}
VA LP   (-) {**32**}

He's Only A Prayer Away (Duncan, Lange)
On the LP *A Golden Celebration* (LP 251), this was how
the title was shown. However, when the CD version was
issued in February 1998, the song had been re-titled *I Asked
The Lord (He's only a prayer away)*. Later, the song was
listed without the words in brackets. Appearances are
shown under *I Asked The Lord (He's only a prayer away)*.

He's Your Uncle Not Your Dad (Wayne, Weisman)
S   (-)
EP   (-)
LP   (35, 136, 228)
VA LP   (-)

Hey, Hey, Hey (Byers)
S   (-)
EP   (-)
LP   (33, 135, 223)
VA LP   (-)

Hey Jude (Lennon, McCartney)
S   (-)
EP   (-)
LP   (61) {**319, 335**}
VA LP   (-)

Hey Little Girl (Byers)
S   (-)
EP   (-)
LP   (27, 130, 222)
VA LP   (-)

Hi Heel Sneakers (Higgenbotham)
S   (62)
EP   (-)
LP   (90, 126, 151, 176, 263, 271)
         {**276, 297, 319**}
VA LP   (-)

Hide Thou Me (Lowry, Crosby)
S   (-)
EP   (-)
LP   (-) {**332, 333**}
VA LP   (-)

His Hand In Mine (Lister)
S   (-)
EP   (-) {**45**}
LP   (13, 54, 156, 195, 214, 252) {**332, 333**}
VA LP   (-)

(Marie's the name) His Latest Flame (Pomus, Shuman)
S   (35, 108) {**151, 183**}
EP   (44)
LP   (21, 55, 73, 82, 105, 150, 151, 164, 172,
         183, 187, 193, 219, 221, 226, 256, 264)
         {**285, 286, 287, 297, 310, 319, 319, 320,
         323, 324, 330, 331**}
VA LP   (-) {**8, 27**}

Holly Leaves And Christmas Trees (West, Spreen)
S (-)
EP (-)
LP (*56, 117, 195, 252*) {**311**}
VA LP (-)

Home Is Where The Heart Is (Edwards, David)
S (-)
EP (*16, 32*)
LP (*57, 84, 86, 138, 143, 197*)
VA LP (-)

Hot Dog (Leiber, Stoller)
S (-)
EP (-)
LP (*3, 25, 55, 98, 125, 160, 210, 217*)
{**280, 318, 342**}
VA LP (-)

Hound Dog (Leiber, Stoller)
S (*4, 24, 78, 118, 137, 145*) {**156**}
EP (**25**)
LP (*4, 7, 36, 39, 43, 45, 63, 66, 72, 73, 82,
100, 102, 104, 105, 106, 107, 125, 126,
126, 150, 151, 153, 164, 170, 179, 181,
183, 184, 196, 200, 216, 217, 226, 231,
232, 234, 237, 245, 251, 251, 251, 251,
251, 251, 251, 262, 265, 273*)
{**277, 285, 286, 287, 297, 302, 307, 310,
316, 318, 320, 321, 322, 323, 324, 326,
327, 328, 331, 335, 335, 335, 341**}
VA LP (-) {**8, 27**}

House Of Sand (Giant, Baum, Kaye)
S (-)
EP (-) {**45**}
LP (*29, 132, 215*)
VA LP (-)

How Can You Lose What You Never Had (Weisman, Wayne)
S (-)
EP (-)
LP (*33, 135, 223*) {**315**}
VA LP (-)

How Do You Think I Feel (Walker, Pierce)
S (*17*)
EP (*19*) {**45**}
LP (*2, 17, 113, 169, 180, 211*) {**318, 326, 341**}
VA LP (-)

How Great Thou Art (Hine)
S (-)
EP (-)
LP (*31, 53, 72, 87, 100, 101, 119, 126, 139,
174, 235, 273*)
{**332, 332, 332, 333, 333, 333, 335**}
VA LP (-)

How The Web Was Woven (Westlake, Most)
S (*81*)
EP (-)
LP (*47, 167, 224*) {**328**}
VA LP (-)

How Would You Like To Be (Raleigh, Barkan)
S (*56*)
EP (-)
LP (*19, 64, 86, 89, 128, 247*)
VA LP (-)

How's The World Treating You (Atkins, Bryant)
S (-)
EP (*19*) {**45**}
LP (*2, 17, 113, 169, 180, 211*) {**318, 326, 341**}
VA LP (-)

Hurt (Craine, Jacobs)
S (*96*)
EP (-)
LP (*88, 100, 207, 209, 266, 272, 273*) {**310**}
VA LP (-)

I

I Asked The Lord (Lange, Duncan)
S (-)
EP (-)
LP (*251*) {**332, 333**}
VA LP (-)

I Beg Of You (McCoy, Owens)
S (*19*) {**175, 176**}
EP (*38*)
LP (*10, 45, 50, 171, 183, 184, 203, 253*)
{**285, 286, 298, 298, 298, 310, 318, 318,
329, 342**}
VA LP (-)

I Believe (Drake, Graham, Shirl, Stillman)
S (*124*)
EP (*2, 35*) {**45**}
LP (*5, 48, 86, 89, 137, 140, 142, 218, 275*)
{**312, 318, 332, 333**}
VA LP (-)

I Believe In The Man In The Sky (Howard)
S (*50, 114*) {**183**}
EP (-)
LP (*13, 54, 55, 139, 156, 214*) {**332, 333**}
VA LP (-)

I Can Help (Swan)
S (*140, 141*)
EP (-)
LP (*79, 114, 207, 209*)
VA LP (-)

I Can't Stop Loving You (Gibson)
S (-)
EP (-)
LP (*39, 63, 66, 72, 92, 177, 182, 231, 237*)
{**316, 319, 328, 328, 335, 335**}
VA LP (-) {**5**}

I Don't Care If The Sun Don't Shine (David)
S (*5*) {**150, 182**}
EP (-)
LP (*4, 9, 80, 108, 119, 190, 194, 201, 246, 251*)
{**283, 283, 295, 304, 310, 318**}
VA LP (-)

I Don't Wanna Be Tied (Giant, Baum, Kaye)
S (-)
EP (-) {**45**}
LP (*18, 94, 158, 229*) {**278**}
VA LP (-)

I Don't Want To (Torre, Spielman)
S   (-)
EP   (-)
LP   (*18, 94, 158, 192, 220, 229*) {**278**}
VA LP   (-)

I Feel So Bad (Willis)
S   (*34*) {**159**}
EP   (-)
LP   (*21, 45, 82, 172, 205, 246, 256, 269, 271*)
{**285, 286, 290, 292, 300, 310, 319, 330**}
VA LP   (-)

I Feel That I've Known You Forever (Pomus, Jeffreys)
S   (-)
EP   (*20*)
LP   (*16, 148, 192, 220, 233*) {**319, 345, 345**}
VA LP   (-)

I Forgot To Remember To Forget (Kesler, Feathers)
S   (*8*) {**182**}
EP   (*24*)
LP   (*7, 43, 80, 108, 127, 151, 170, 201, 242*)
{**283, 295, 297, 318**}
VA LP   (-) {**38**}

I Got A Feelin' In My Body (Linde)
S   (-)
EP   (-)
LP   (*71, 114*) {**332, 333**}
VA LP   (-)

I Got A Woman (Charles)
S   (-)
EP   (*23*) {**45**}
LP   (*1, 9, 60, 72, 100, 102, 118, 126, 126,
126, 175, 179, 190, 198, 236, 251, 251,
251, 254, 254, 259, 262, 267, 273*)
{**285, 302, 302, 304, 315, 318, 321, 322,
325, 328, 335, 335, 340**}
VA LP   (-)

I Got Lucky (Wise, Weisman, Fuller)
S   (-)
EP   (*16, 32*)
LP   (*57, 84, 86, 138, 143, 197*)
VA LP   (-)

I Got Stung (Schroeder, Hill)
S   (*25, 102*) {**183**}
EP   (-) {**45**}
LP   (*10, 45, 50, 73, 82, 105, 164, 171, 181,
183, 184, 194, 202, 203, 216, 253*)
{**277, 285, 286, 306, 306, 307, 310, 318, 329**}
VA LP   (-) {**8**}

I Gotta Know (Evans, Williams)
S   (*31, 105*) {**183**}
EP   (-)
LP   (*21, 45, 82, 172, 183, 193, 221, 256*)
{**285, 310, 319, 330**}
VA LP   (-)

I Hear A Sweet Voice Calling (Monroe)
S   (-)
EP   (-)
LP   (*152*) {**291, 332, 333**}
VA LP   (-)

I, John (Johnson, McFadden, Brooks)
S   (-)
EP   (-)
LP   (*62*) {**332, 332, 333, 333**}
VA LP   (-)

I Just Can't Help Believin' (Mann, Weil)
S   (*81, 127*)
EP   (-)
LP   (*47, 74, 82, 116, 151, 167, 224, 258*)
{**285, 287, 297, 310, 317, 320, 323, 324,
328, 331, 335**}
VA LP   (-) {**14**}

I Just Can't Make It By Myself (Brewster)
S   (-)
EP   (-)
LP   (*152*) {**291, 332, 333**}
VA LP   (-)

I Love Only One Girl (Tepper, Bennett)
S   (-)
EP   (-)
LP   (*32, 65, 76, 85, 103, 134, 199, 244*)
VA LP   (-)

I Love You Because (Payne)
S   (-)
EP   (*34, 34*)
LP   (*7, 43, 70, 80, 80, 82, 108, 108, 170, 201,
201, 267*)
{**283, 283, 283, 283, 283, 295, 295, 318,
325, 340**}
VA LP   (-)

I Met Her Today (Robertson, Blair)
S   (-)
EP   (-)
LP   (*26, 59, 67, 85, 103, 144, 192, 220, 225*)
{**315, 319**}
VA LP   (-)

I Miss You (Sumner)
S   (-)
EP   (-)
LP   (*69, 272*)
VA LP   (-)

I Need Somebody To Lean On (Pomus, Shuman)
S   (-)
EP   (*17, 42*)
LP   (*57, 84, 86, 196, 270*)
VA LP   (-)

I Need You So (Hunter)
S   (-)
EP   (*4, 36*)
LP   (*98, 160, 210*) {**318, 342**}
VA LP   (-)

I Need Your Love Tonight (Wayne, Reichner)
S   (*26, 103*) {**179, 183**}
EP   (-)
LP   (*10, 50, 55, 73, 82, 105, 126, 150, 163,
171, 181, 183, 184, 203, 216, 226, 253*)
{**286, 306, 306, 307, 310, 318, 329**}
VA LP   (-)

I Really Don't Want To Know (Barnes, Robertson)
S   (*76*)
EP   (-)
LP   (*49, 55, 92, 100, 162, 177, 239, 273*)
VA LP   (-) {**5**}

I Shall Not Be Moved (Morris)
S   (-)
EP   (-)
LP   (*152*) {**291, 332, 333**}
VA LP   (-)M

I Slipped, I Stumbled, I Fell (Wise, Weisman)
S (-)
EP (-)
LP (*14, 67, 85, 103, 137, 142, 164, 165, 199, 243*) **{315, 342 Bonus EP, 342 Bonus EP}**
VA LP (-)

I Think I'm Gonna Like It Here (Robertson, Blair)
S (-)
EP (-)
LP (*20, 97, 157, 257*)
VA LP (-)

I Want To Be Free (Leiber, Stoller)
S (-)
EP (*5, 28*)
LP (*55, 125, 127, 196, 205, 217, 242, 269*) **{280, 289, 292, 300, 318, 318, 343, 343}**
VA LP (-)

I Want You, I Need You, I Love You (Mysels, Kosloff)
S (*3*)
EP (*25*)
LP (*7, 43, 45, 82, 87, 102, 116, 151, 170, 179, 232, 246, 251, 251, 251*) **{285, 286, 297, 307, 310, 318, 318, 321, 325, 327, 340}**
VA LP (-)

I Want You With Me (Harris)
S (-)
EP (-)
LP (*14, 165, 193, 205, 221, 243, 269*) **{290, 292, 300, 315, 319}**
VA LP (-)

I Was Born About Ten Thousand Years Ago (Arranged Presley)
S (-)
EP (-)
LP (*61*)
VA LP (-)

I Was The One (Schroeder, DeMetrius, Blair, Peppers)
S (*1*) **{181, 181}**
EP (*24*)
LP (*8, 45, 82, 102, 179, 200, 227, 251, 251, 251, 270*) **{302, 303, 318, 321, 322, 325, 327, 328, 340}**
VA LP (-)

I Washed My Hands In Muddy Water (Babcock)
S (-)
EP (-)
LP (*49, 162, 239*) **{328}**
VA LP (-)

I Will Be Home Again (Benjamin, Leveen, Singer)
S (-)
EP (-)
LP (*11, 168, 230*) **{319}**
VA LP (-)

I Will Be True (Hunter)
S (-)
EP (-)
LP (*68, 126*)
VA LP (-)

If Every Day Was Like Christmas (West)
S (*56, 132, 141*)
EP (-)
LP (*42, 81, 195, 252*) **{319}**
VA LP (-) **{32}**

If I Can Dream (Brown)
S (*67*) **{160, 161, 173}**
EP (-)
LP (*36, 45, 82, 87, 101, 104, 153, 245, 261*) **{287, 308, 310, 323, 324, 331, 336}**
VA LP (-)

If I Get Home On Christmas Day (McCaulay)
S (-)
EP (-)
LP (*56, 117, 195, 252*) **{311}**
VA LP (-)

If I Were You (Nelson)
S (-)
EP (-)
LP (*51, 149, 251*)
VA LP (-)

If I'm A Fool (for loving you) (Kesler)
S (-)
EP (-)
LP (*40, 78, 85, 199*) **{319}**
VA LP (-)

If That Isn't Love (Rambo)
S (-)
EP (-)
LP (*71*) **{332, 333}**
VA LP (-)

If The Lord Wasn't Walking By My Side (Slaughter)
S (-)
EP (-)
LP (*31, 53, 174, 235*) **{332, 333}**
VA LP (-)

If We Never Meet Again (Brumley)
S (-)
EP (-)
LP (*13, 54, 156, 195, 214, 252*) **{332, 333}**
VA LP (-)

If You Don't Come Back (Leiber, Stoller)
S (-)
EP (-)
LP (*69*)
VA LP (-)

If You Love Me (let me know) (Rostill)
S (-)
EP (-)
LP (*93, 100, 126, 178, 260, 273*) **{296}**
VA LP (-)

If You Talk In Your Sleep (West, Christopher)
S (*90*)
EP (-)
LP (*75, 207, 209, 261*) **{335, 336}**
VA LP (-)

If You Think I Don't Need You (West, Cooper)
S (-)
EP (*17, 42*)
LP (*57, 84, 86, 121, 122, 138, 143, 196*)
VA LP (-)

I'll Be Back (Wayne, Weisman)
S (-)
EP (-)
LP (*30, 133, 193, 221, 255*)
VA LP (-)

I'll Be Home For Christmas (if only in my dreams)
(Kent, Gannon, Ram)
S   (-)
EP   (8)
LP   (5, 42, 81, 140, 218, 275) {**312, 318, 332, 339**}
VA LP   (-)

I'll Be Home On Christmas Day (Jarrett)
S   (-)
EP   (-)
LP   (56, 117, 195, 252) {**311**}
VA LP   (-)

I'll Be There (if ever you want me) (Darin)
S   (-)
EP   (-)
LP   (40, 76, 85, 103, 120, 122, 137, 142) {**319**}
VA LP   (-)

I'll Hold You In My Heart (till I can hold you in my arms)
(Arnold, Horton, Dilbeck)
S   (-)
EP   (-)
LP   (38) {**284, 313, 319, 323, 324**}
VA LP   (-)

I'll Never Fall In Love Again (Currie, Donegan)
S   (-)
EP   (-)
LP   (88, 112, 266)
VA LP   (-)

I'll Never Know (Karger, Wayne, Weisman)
S   (135, 135)
EP   (-)
LP   (51, 149, 250) {**328**}
VA LP   (-)

I'll Never Let You Go (little darlin') (Wakely)
S   (-)
EP   (-)
LP   (7, 43, 80, 108, 170, 201, 251, 267) {**283, 283, 295, 318, 325, 340**}
VA LP   (-)

I'll Remember You (Lee)
S   (-)
EP   (-)
LP   (30, 66, 126, 133, 204, 237, 255) {**294, 319**}
VA LP   (-)

I'll Take Love (Fuller, Barkan)
S   (-)
EP   (22)
LP   (52, 78, 85, 199)
VA LP   (-)

I'll Take You Home Again Kathleen (Westendorf)
S   (-)
EP   (-)
LP   (68, 126)
VA LP   (-)

I'm Beginning To Forget You (Phelps)
S   (-)
EP   (-)
LP   (204)
VA LP   (-)

I'm Comin' Home (Rich)
S   (-) {**155**}
EP   (-)
LP   (14, 165, 193, 221, 243) {**319**}
VA LP   (-)

I'm Counting On You (Robertson)
S   (-)
EP   (-)
LP   (1, 8, 60, 102, 175, 179, 236, 267) {**303, 318, 325, 340**}
VA LP   (-)

I'm Falling In Love Tonight (Robertson)
S   (-)
EP   (-)
LP   (19, 126, 128, 247, 265)
VA LP   (-)

I'm Gonna Bid My Blues Goodbye (Snow)
S   (-)
EP   (-)
LP   (-) {**291**}
VA LP   (-)

I'm Gonna Sit Right Down And Cry (over you) (Thomas, Biggs)
S   (-)
EP   (-) {**45**}
LP   (1, 9, 60, 82, 102, 175, 179, 194, 236, 267) {**304, 318, 325, 340**}
VA LP   (-)

I'm Gonna Walk Dem Golden Stairs (Holt)
S   (-)
EP   (-) {**45**}
LP   (13, 54, 139, 156, 214) {**332, 333**}
VA LP   (-)

I'm Leavin' (Jarrett, Charles)
S   (79)
EP   (-)
LP   (74, 82, 126, 151, 194) {**297, 310, 323, 324, 335**}
VA LP   (-)

I'm Left, You're Right, She's Gone (Kesler, Taylor)
S   (17, 94) {**182**}
EP   (-)
LP   (1, 8, 60, 80, 82, 108, 151, 175, 190, 201, 236, 246, 251) {**283, 283, 283, 283, 283, 283, 283, 283, 295, 297, 303, 310, 318, 318**}
VA LP   (-)

I'm Movin' On (Snow)
S   (-)
EP   (-)
LP   (38, 146) {**284, 313, 319**}
VA LP   (-) {**5**}

I'm Not The Marrying Kind (David, Edwards)
S   (-)
EP   (15, 31)
LP   (52)
VA LP   (-)

I'm So Lonesome I Could Cry (Williams)
S   (-)
EP   (-)
LP   (66, 92, 177, 237) {**294**}
VA LP   (-) {**5**}

I'm With A Crowd But So Alone (Tubb, Story)
S   (-)
EP   (-)
LP   (152) {**291**}
VA LP   (-)

I'm Yours (Robertson, Blair)
S   (-)
EP   (*21*)
LP   (*16, 148, 192, 220, 233, 258, 263*) {**319, 319**}
VA LP (-)

In My Father's House (Hanks)
S   (-)
EP   (-)
LP   (*13, 54, 139, 156, 214*) {**332, 333**}
VA LP (-)

In My Way (Wise, Weisman)
S   (-)
EP   (-)
LP   (*26, 59, 67, 85, 103, 144, 225*) {**342 Bonus EP**}
VA LP (-)

In The Garden (Miles)
S   (-)
EP   (-)
LP   (*31, 53, 174, 235*) {**332, 333**}
VA LP (-)

In The Ghetto (Davis)
S   (*68*) {**148**}
EP   (-)
LP   (*38, 39, 45, 73, 82, 105, 106, 107, 126, 151, 182, 183, 187, 188, 202, 219, 231, 261, 274*) {**277, 284, 285, 286, 287, 297, 310, 313, 316, 319, 319, 320, 323, 324, 328, 331, 335, 335, 336**}
VA LP (-)

In Your Arms (Schroeder, Gold)
S   (-)
EP   (-)
LP   (*14, 165, 243*) {**319**}
VA LP (-)

Indescribably Blue (Glenn)
S   (*57*)
EP   (-)
LP   (*34, 151, 173, 192, 213, 220*) {**285, 297, 319, 334**}
VA LP (-)

Inherit The Wind (Rabbitt)
S   (-)
EP   (-)
LP   (*39, 231*) {**284, 315, 319**}
VA LP (-)

Is It So Strange (Young)
S   (-)
EP   (*12*)
LP   (*9, 67, 85, 103, 127, 242*) {**291, 298, 298, 304, 318, 342**}
VA LP (-)

Island Of Love (Tepper, Bennett)
S   (-)
EP   (-)
LP   (*15, 46, 166, 238*) {**338**}
VA LP (-)

It Ain't No Big Thing (but it's growing) (Merritt, Joy, Hall)
S   (-)
EP   (-)
LP   (*51, 149, 250*)
VA LP (-)

It Feels So Right (Wise, Weisman)
S   (-)
EP   (*14, 21, 30*)
LP   (*11, 82, 168, 194, 205, 230, 269, 270*) {**290, 292, 300, 319, 345, 345**}
VA LP (-)

It Hurts Me (Byers, Daniels)
S   (*45*)
EP   (-)
LP   (*34, 55, 90, 106, 107, 173, 176, 192, 213, 220*) {**285, 309, 319, 323, 324, 334**}
VA LP (-)

It Is No Secret (what God can do) (Hamblen)
S   (-)
EP   (*2, 35*) {**45**}
LP   (*5, 48, 86, 89, 139, 140, 218, 275*) {**298, 312, 318, 332, 333**}
VA LP (-)

It Keeps Right On A-Hurtin' (Tillotson)
S   (-)
EP   (-)
LP   (*38*) {**284, 313, 319**}
VA LP (-)

It Won't Be Long (Wayne, Weisman)
S   (-)
EP   (-)
LP   (*32, 134, 244*)
VA LP (-)

It Won't Seem Like Christmas (without you) (Balthrop)
S   (*120, 121*)
EP   (-)
LP   (*56, 117, 195, 252*) {**311**}
VA LP (-)

Ito Eats (Tepper, Bennett)
S   (-)
EP   (-)
LP   (*15, 46, 166, 238*) {**338**}
VA LP (-)

It's A Matter Of Time (Westlake)
S   (*84*)
EP   (-)
LP   (*65, 78, 85, 121, 122, 138, 143*)
VA LP (-)

It's A Sin (Rose, Turner)
S   (-)
EP   (-)
LP   (*14, 165, 243*) {**319**}
VA LP (-)

It's A Wonderful World (Tepper, Bennett)
S   (-)
EP   (-)
LP   (*23, 82, 96, 161, 240*)
VA LP ( )

It's Carnival Time (Weisman, Wayne)
S   (-)
EP   (-)
LP   (*23, 96, 161, 240*)
VA LP (-)

It's Easy For You (Webber, Rice)
S   (*143, 144*)
EP   (-)
LP   (*93, 178, 260*) {**296**}
VA LP (-)

It's Impossible (Wayne, Manzanero)
S   *(-)*
EP   *(-)*
LP   *(68)* {**335**}
VA LP   *(-)*

It's Midnight (Wheeler, Chesnut)
S   *(92)*
EP   *(-)*
LP   *(75, 112, 272)* {**335**}
VA LP   *(-)*

It's Now Or Never (DiCapua, Schroeder, Gold)
S   *(30, 104)* {**165, 183**}
EP   *(-)*
LP   *(21, 25, 45, 73, 82, 87, 100, 105, 116, 126, 163, 172, 183, 187, 219, 256, 273, 274)* {**277, 285, 286, 287, 307, 310, 317, 319, 319, 320, 323, 324, 328, 330, 331, 335**}
VA LP   *(-)* {**3, 13, 23, 27, 34, 48**}

It's Only Love (James, Tyrell)
S   *(122, 123)*
EP   *(-)*
LP   *(90, 126, 176, 185, 263, 274)* {**287**}
VA LP   *(-)*

It's Over (Rodgers)
S   *(-)*
EP   *(-)*
LP   *(66, 237)* {**294, 335**}
VA LP   *(-)*

It's Still Here (Hunter)
S   *(-)*
EP   *(-)*
LP   *(68, 126)*
VA LP   *(-)*

It's Your Baby, You Rock It (Milete, Fowler)
S   *(-)*
EP   *(-)*
LP   *(49, 162, 239)*
VA LP   *(-)*

I've Got A Thing About You Baby (White)
S   *(89)*
EP   *(-)*
LP   *(71, 150, 226)*
VA LP   *(-)*

I've Got Confidence (Crouch)
S   *(-)*
EP   *(-)*
LP   *(62)* {**332, 333**}
VA LP   *(-)*

I've Got To Find My Baby (Byers)
S   *(-)*
EP   *(-)*
LP   *(24, 129, 248)*
VA LP   *(-)*

I've Lost You (Howard, Blaikley)
S   *(74)*
EP   *(-)*
LP   *(47, 55, 74, 82, 151, 167, 224, 272)* {**285, 297, 323, 324, 328**}
VA LP   *(-)*

J

Jailhouse Rock (Leiber, Stoller)
S   *(18, 80, 101, 136, 137, 145)* {**164, 179, 183**}
EP   *(5, 28)*
LP   *(10, 36, 45, 50, 72, 73, 82, 87, 100, 104, 105, 125, 126, 150, 151, 153, 164, 171, 181, 183, 184, 190, 191, 196, 196, 216, 217, 226, 232, 245, 262, 268, 273)* {**276, 277, 280, 280, 285, 286, 287, 288, 297, 299, 307, 308, 310, 315, 318, 320, 323, 324, 327, 331, 335, 343, 343**}
VA LP   *(-)* {**3, 8, 15, 27, 33**}

Jesus Walked That Lonesome Valley (Traditional)
S   *(-)*
EP   *(-)*
LP   *(152)* {**291, 332, 333**}
VA LP   *(-)*

Johnny B. Goode (Berry)
S   *(-)*
EP   *(-)*
LP   *(39, 66, 100, 126, 182, 231, 237, 273)* {**316, 328, 335**}
VA LP   *(-)*

Joshua Fit The Battle (Arranged and Adapted Presley)
S   *(-)*
EP   *(-)* {**45**}
LP   *(13, 54, 156, 214)* {**332, 333**}
VA LP   *(-)*

Judy (Redell)
S   *(60)*
EP   *(44)*
LP   *(14, 165, 183, 193, 221, 243, 264)* {**319**}
VA LP   *(-)*

Just A Little Bit (Thornton, Brown, Bass, Washington)
S   *(-)*
EP   *(-)*
LP   *(69)*
VA LP   *(-)*

Just A Little Talk With Jesus (Derricks)
S   *(-)*
EP   *(-)*
LP   *(152)* {**291, 332, 333**}
VA LP   *(-)*

Just Because (B. & J. Shelton, Robin)
S   *(-)*
EP   *(3, 23)* {**45**}
LP   *(9, 80, 108, 151, 201, 267)* {**283, 295, 297, 304, 318, 325, 340**}
VA LP   *(-)*

Just Call Me Lonesome (Griffin)
S   *(-)*
EP   *(-)*
LP   *(33, 135, 146, 223)* {**319**}
VA LP   *(-)*

Just For Old Times's Sake (Tepper, Bennett)
S   *(-)*
EP   *(-)*
LP   *(16, 148, 233)* {**319**}
VA LP   *(-)*

Just Pretend (Flett, Fletcher)
  S   (-)
  EP   (-)
  LP   *(47, 116, 167, 224)* {**328, 328, 335, 335**}
  VA LP (-)

Just Tell Her Jim Said Hello (Leiber, Stoller)
  S   *(38, 111)* {**183**}
  EP   (-)
  LP   *(34, 55, 82, 125, 173, 183, 213, 217)*
      {**310, 315, 319, 334**}
  VA LP (-)

K

Keeper Of The Key (Howard, Devine, Guynes, Stewart)
  S   (-)
  EP   (-)
  LP   *(152)* {**291**}
  VA LP (-)

Kentucky Rain (Rabbitt, Heard)
  S   *(72)*
  EP   (-)
  LP   *(45, 74, 82, 116, 126, 151, 185, 261)*
      {**284, 297, 319, 319, 335, 336**}
  VA LP (-)

King Creole (Leiber, Stoller)
  S   *(22)* {**168**}
  EP   *(6, 29)*
  LP   *(6, 55, 58, 73, 82, 105, 125, 154, 164,*
      181, 183, 184, 190, 191, 212, 216, 217,
      253, 268) {**277, 285, 287, 288, 299, 306,**
      306, 308, 310, 318, 318, 329, 331, 344,
      344, 344}
  VA LP (-) {**8**}

King Of The Whole Wide World (Batchelor, Roberts)
  S   (-)
  EP   *(16, 32)*
  LP   *(52)* {**285, 310, 330**}
  VA LP (-) {**44**}

Kiss Me Quick (Pomus, Shuman)
  S   *(43)*
  EP   (-)
  LP   *(16, 82, 148, 233, 258)* {**285, 310, 319**}
  VA LP (-)

Kissin' Cousins (Wise, Starr)
  S   *(45)*
  EP   (-)
  LP   *(22, 45, 82, 95, 159, 191, 249, 268)*
      {**279, 285, 288, 299, 310, 334**}
  VA LP (-)

Kissin' Cousins (No. 2) (Giant, Baum, Kaye)
  S   (-)
  EP   (-)
  LP   *(22, 95, 159, 249)* {**279**}
  VA LP (-)

Kismet (Tepper, Bennett)
  S   (-)
  EP   (-)
  LP   *(27, 130, 222)*
  VA LP (-)

Known Only To Him (Hamblen)
  S   (-)
  EP   (-)
  LP   *(13, 54, 101, 139, 156, 214)* {**332, 333**}
  VA LP (-)

Ku-U-I-Po (Peretti, Creatore, Weiss)
  S   (-)
  EP   (-)
  LP   *(15, 46, 123, 166, 238, 263)* {**338**}
  VA LP (-)

L

Lawdy, Miss Clawdy (Price)
  S   *(15)*
  EP   *(34)* {**45**}
  LP   *(1, 8, 36, 60, 72, 82, 102, 104, 119, 126,*
      151, 153, 175, 179, 190, 236, 245, 251, 262)
      {**276, 297, 303, 310, 318, 318, 321, 323,**
      324, 325, 331, 340}
  VA LP (-)

Lead Me, Guide Me (Akers)
  S   (-)
  EP   (-)
  LP   *(62, 139)* {**332, 332, 333, 333**}
  VA LP (-)

Let It Be Me (Je T'Appartiens) (Curtis, Delanoe, Becaud)
  S   (-)
  EP   (-)
  LP   *(41, 90, 106, 107, 176)* {**314, 335**}
  VA LP (-)

Let Me (Presley, Matson)
  S   (-)
  EP   *(1, 26)* {**45**}
  LP   *(9, 55, 113, 180)* {**280, 304, 318, 343, 343**}
  VA LP (-)

Let Me Be There (Rostill)
  S   (-)
  EP   (-)
  LP   *(72, 93, 126, 178, 260)* {**296**}
  VA LP (-)

Let Us Pray (Weisman, Kaye)
  S   (-)
  EP   (-)
  LP   *(48, 86, 89)* {**332, 333, 344 Bonus EP**}
  VA LP (-)

Let Yourself Go (Byers)
  S   *(64)*
  EP   (-)
  LP   *(35, 106, 107, 136, 228)*
  VA LP (-)

Let's Be Friends (Arnold, Morrow, Martin)
  S   (-)
  EP   (-)
  LP   *(40, 78, 85, 138, 143)*
  VA LP (-)

Let's Forget About The Stars (Owens)
  S   (-)
  EP   (-)
  LP   *(40, 78, 85)*
  VA LP (-)

Life (Milete)
S   (-)
EP   (-)
LP   (51, 149, 250, 264) {**332, 333**}
VA LP   (-)

Like A Baby (Stone)
S   (-)
EP   (14, 30)
LP   (11, 168, 194, 205, 230, 269)
         {**289, 292, 300, 315, 319, 323, 324**}
VA LP   (-)

Little Cabin On The Hill (Monroe, Flatt)
S   (-)
EP   (-)
LP   (49, 152, 162, 239) {**291**}
VA LP   (-)

Little Darlin' (Williams)
S   (-)
EP   (-)
LP   (93, 126, 178, 260) {**296**}
VA LP   (-)

Little Egypt (Leiber, Stoller)
S   (-)
EP   (-)
LP   (23, 36, 83, 96, 104, 124, 125, 153, 161,
         217, 240, 245) {**285**}
VA LP   (-)

Little Sister (Pomus, Shuman)
S   (35, 108) {**183**}
EP   (44)
LP   (21, 45, 100, 126, 172, 193, 200, 205,
         221, 227, 256, 264, 269, 273)
         {**285, 286, 290, 292, 300, 310, 319, 323,
         324, 328, 328, 330, 335**}
VA LP   (-)

Lonely Man (Benjamin, Marcus)
S   (33, 107) {**183**}
EP   (-)
LP   (34, 55, 173, 213)
         {**285, 310, 315, 334, 342 Bonus EP**}
VA LP   (-)

Lonesome Cowboy (Tepper, Bennett)
S   (-)
EP   (-)
LP   (3, 25, 55, 82, 98, 160, 210)
         {**280, 318, 342**}
VA LP   (-)

Long Black Limousine (Stovall, George)
S   (-)
EP   (-)
LP   (38) {**284, 313, 319**}
VA LP   (-)

Long Legged Girl (with the short dress on) (McFarland, Scott)
S   (59)
EP   (-)
LP   (32, 44, 64, 76, 82, 85, 86, 89, 103, 134,
         138, 143, 151, 244) {**297**}
VA LP   (-)

Long Live Rock And Roll (Colyer)
S   (-)
EP   (-)
LP   (126)
VA LP   (-)

(It's a) Long Lonely Highway (Pomus, Shuman)
S   (98)
EP   (21)
LP   (22, 90, 95, 159, 176, 193, 221, 249, 264)
         {**279, 285, 309, 319, 345, 345**}
VA LP   (-)

Long Tall Sally (Johnson, Blackwell, Penniman)
S   (-)
EP   (19) {**45**}
LP   (2, 17, 66, 72, 82, 113, 119, 126, 169,
         180, 211, 237, 251, 262, 265)
         {**276, 285, 302, 318, 318, 322, 326, 335,
         335, 341**}
VA LP   (-)

Look Out, Broadway (Wise, Starr)
S   (-)
EP   (-)
LP   (28, 131, 241)
VA LP   (-)

Love Coming Down (Chesnut)
S   (-)
EP   (-)
LP   (88, 266)
VA LP   (-)

Love Letters (Young, Heyman)
S   (54)
EP   (-)
LP   (34, 51, 82, 116, 149, 151, 173, 202, 213,
         250, 270)
         {**285, 287, 297, 310, 315, 317, 319, 328,
         331, 334**}
VA LP   (-) {**40**}

Love Me (Leiber, Stoller)
S   (7)
EP   (18) {**45**}
LP   (2, 7, 17, 43, 55, 63, 66, 70, 72, 100, 113,
         125, 126, 126, 169, 170, 180, 182, 211,
         217, 232, 237, 251, 251, 273)
         {**286, 294, 310, 318, 321, 323, 324, 326,
         327, 328, 335, 341**}
VA LP   (-)

Love Me, Love The Life I Lead (Macaulay, Greenaway)
S   (-)
EP   (-)
LP   (68)
VA LP   (-)

Love Me Tender (Presley, Matson)
S   (6) {**153, 160, 161**}
EP   (1, 10, 26) {**45**}
LP   (7, 36, 43, 45, 63, 70, 73, 82, 104, 105,
         113, 116, 126, 150, 151, 153, 163, 170,
         180, 181, 216, 226, 232, 245, 251, 251,
         251, 251)
         {**277, 280, 280, 285, 286, 287, 297, 307,
         310, 315, 317, 318, 319, 320, 323, 324, 326,
         327, 328, 331, 335, 335, 341, 343, 343, 343**}
VA LP   (-) {**3, 9, 31, 46, 49**}

Love Me Tonight (Robertson)
S   (-)
EP   (-)
LP   (20, 97, 157, 192, 220, 257) {**309, 315, 319**}
VA LP   (-)

Lover Doll (Wayne, Silver)
S   (-)
EP   (6, 10, 29)
LP   (6, 55, 58, 154, 212, 263)
         {285, 306, 318, 344, 344}
VA LP   (-)

Love Song Of The Year (Christian)
S   (-)
EP   (-)
LP   (75)
VA LP   (-)

Loving Arms (Jans)
S   (91, 126)
EP   (-)
LP   (71, 146)
VA LP   (-)

Loving You (Leiber, Stoller)
S   (12) {167}
EP   (27) {45}
LP   (3, 10, 25, 45, 82, 98, 116, 125, 160, 171,
         210, 217, 232)
         {280, 280, 280, 285, 310, 315, 317, 318,
         318, 318, 327, 331, 342, 342}
VA LP   (-) {46}

M

Make Me Know It (Blackwell)
S   (30, 104) {183}
EP   (14, 30)
LP   (11, 168, 193, 194, 221, 230) {285, 319}
VA LP   (-)

Make The World Go Away (Cochran)
S   (-)
EP   (-)
LP   (49, 92, 162, 177, 239) {328}
VA LP   (-) {5}

Mama (O'Curran, Brooks)
S   (-)
EP   (-)
LP   (40, 120, 122, 246)
VA LP   (-)

Mama Don't Dance (Loggins, Messina)
S   (-)
EP   (-)
LP   (72)
VA LP   (-)

Mama Liked The Roses (Christopher)
S   (73, 115) {183}
EP   (-)
LP   (42, 81) {284, 319}
VA LP   (-)

Mansion Over The Hilltop (Stamphill)
S   (-)
EP   (-)
LP   (13, 54, 139, 156, 214) {332, 333}
VA LP   (-)

Marguerita (Robertson)
S   (-)
EP   (-)
LP   (20, 97, 157, 257)
VA LP   (-)

Mary In The Morning (Cymbol, Rashkow)
S   (-)
EP   (-)
LP   (47, 167, 224) {328, 328}
VA LP   (-)

Maybellene (Berry)
S   (-)
EP   (-)
LP   (234, 254) {302, 318, 322}
VA LP   (-)

Mean Woman Blues (DeMetrius)
S   (-) {175, 176, 176}
EP   (-)
LP   (3, 25, 55, 82, 98, 150, 160, 205, 210,
         226, 269)
         {280, 285, 289, 292, 298, 300, 318, 329, 342}
VA LP   (-)

Memories (Strange, Davis)
S   (67)
EP   (-)
LP   (36, 104, 116, 150, 151, 153, 183, 226, 245)
         {297, 308, 315, 336}
VA LP   (-)

Memphis, Tennessee (Berry)
S   (-)
EP   (-)
LP   (26, 59, 144, 193, 221, 225)
         {285, 309, 315, 319, 319, 323, 324}
VA LP   (-)

Men With Broken Hearts (Williams)
S   (-)
EP   (-)
LP   (-) {335}
VA LP   (-)

Merry Christmas Baby (Baxter, Moore)
S   (120, 121)
EP   (-)
LP   (56, 117, 150, 195, 205, 226, 252, 269, 271)
         {290, 292, 300, 311, 323, 324}
VA LP   (-)

Mexico (Tepper, Bennett)
S   (-)
EP   (-)
LP   (20, 97, 157, 257) {285}
VA LP   (-)

Milkcow Blues Boogie (Arnold)
S   (-) {182}
EP   (3)
LP   (9, 80, 82, 108, 127, 201, 242)
         {283, 295, 304, 318}
VA LP   (-)

Milky White Way (Arranged and adapted Presley)
S   (-)
EP   (-)
LP   (13, 54, 156, 214) {332, 333}
VA LP   (-)

Mine (Tepper, Bennett)
S   (-)
EP   (-)
LP   (35, 136, 192, 220, 228) {**319**}
VA LP   (-)

Miracle Of The Rosary (Denson)
S   (-)
EP   (-)
LP   (61, 101) {**332, 333**}
VA LP   (-)

Mirage (Giant, Baum, Kaye)
S   (-)
EP   (-)
LP   (27, 130, 222)
VA LP   (-)

Mona Lisa (Livingston, Evans)
S   (-)
EP   (-)
LP   (204)
VA LP   (-)

Money Honey (Stone)
S   ( )
EP   (24) {**45**}
LP   (1, 8, 60, 82, 102, 126, 175, 179, 194,
         236, 251, 262, 265, 267)
         {**285, 302, 303, 310, 318, 318, 321, 322, 325,
         335, 340**}
VA LP   (-)

Moody Blue (James)
S   (99, 134) {**172, 183**}
EP   (-)
LP   (93, 150, 178, 207, 209, 226, 260, 261, 274)
         {**287, 296, 310, 320, 331, 336**}
VA LP   (-) {**21**}

Moonlight Swim (Dee, Weisman)
S   (-)
EP   (-)
LP   (15, 46, 166, 238) {**338**}
VA LP   (-)

Mr. Songman (Sumner)
S   (93)
EP   (-)
LP   (75)
VA LP   (-)

My Babe (Dixon)
S   (-)
EP   (-)
LP   (39, 126, 231) {**316**}
VA LP   (-)

My Baby Left Me (Crudup)
S   (3)
EP   (25)
LP   (8, 55, 72, 73, 82, 102, 105, 150, 151, 164,
         179, 181, 190, 194, 200, 216, 226, 227, 271)
         {**277, 285, 297, 303, 310, 318, 321, 323,
         324, 325, 327, 335, 340**}
VA LP   (-)

My Boy (Francois, Bourtayre, Martin, Coulter)
S   (91) {**171**}
EP   (-)
LP   (71, 112, 207, 209, 272, 274) {**287, 310, 335**}
VA LP   (-)

My Desert Serenade (Gelber)
S   (-)
EP   (-)
LP   (27, 130, 222)
VA LP   (-)

My Happiness (Peterson, Bergantine)
S   (-)
EP   (-)
LP   (-) {**308, 318**}
VA LP   (-)
Misc   (-) {**6**}

My Heart Cries For You (Faith, Sigman)
S   (144)
EP   (-)
LP   (251)
VA LP   (-)

My Little Friend (Milete)
S   (72)
EP   (-)
LP   (44, 78, 85) {**319**}
VA LP   (-)

My Way (Thibault, Francois, Revaux, Anka)
S   (117) {**171**}
EP   (-)
LP   (66, 100, 126, 150, 151, 226, 231, 213, 214)
         {**285, 294, 297, 310**}
VA LP   (-)

My Wish Came True (Hunter)
S   (27)
EP   (-)
LP   (10, 50, 55, 171, 203, 253) {**310, 318, 329**}
VA LP   (-)

Mystery Train (Parker, Phillips)
S   (7, 8, 131) {**182**}
EP   (-)
LP   (1, 8, 39, 60, 80, 108, 119, 126, 175, 183,
         184, 190, 194, 201, 202, 231, 236)
         {**283, 295, 303, 310, 315, 316, 318, 323,
         324, 327, 328, 331**}
VA LP   (-)

N

Nearer My God To Thee (Adams, Mason)
S   (-)
EP   (-)
LP   (-) {**332, 333**}
VA LP   (-)

Never Again (Wheeler, Chesnut)
S   (-)
EP   (-)
LP   (88, 112, 266)
VA LP   (-)

Never Been To Spain (Axton)
S   (-)
EP   (-)
LP   (63, 182) {**335**}
VA LP   (-)

Never Ending (Kaye, Springer)
S   (46)
EP   (-)
LP   (32, 134, 244) {**309, 319**}
VA LP   (-)

Never Say Yes (Pomus, Shuman)
S   (-)
EP   (-)
LP   (30, 133, 255)
VA LP   (-)

New Orleans (Tepper, Bennett)
S   (-)
EP   (6, 29)
LP   (6, 55, 58, 154, 212) {**318, 344**}
VA LP   (-)

Night Life (Giant, Baum, Kaye)
S   (-)
EP   (-)
LP   (37, 110, 111, 196)
VA LP   (-)

Night Rider (Pomus, Shuman)
S   (-)
EP   (20)
LP   (16, 148, 233) {**285, 315, 319, 345, 345**}
VA LP   (-)

No More (Robertson, Blair)
S   (-)
EP   (-)
LP   (15, 46, 65, 78, 85, 123, 166, 238, 263)
         {**285, 338, 338**}
VA LP   (-)

(There's) No Room To Rhumba In A Sports Car (Wise, Manning)
S   (-)
EP   (-)
LP   (20, 97, 157, 257)
VA LP   (-)

Nothingville (Strange, Davis)
S   (-)
EP   (-)
LP   (36, 104, 153, 245)
VA LP   (-)

O

O Come, All Ye Faithful (Traditional. Arranged Presley)
S   (-)
EP   (-)
LP   (56, 117, 195, 252) {**311**}
VA LP   (-)

O Little Town Of Bethlehem (Redner, Brooks)
S   (-)
EP   (-)
LP   (5, 42, 81, 140, 218, 275) {**312, 318, 332, 339**}
VA LP   (-)

Oh Happy Day (Hawkins)
S   (-)
EP   (-)
LP   (-) {**328, 332, 333**}
VA LP   (-)

Oh How I Love Jesus (Traditional)
S   (-)
EP   (-)
LP   (-) {**332, 333**}
VA LP   (-)

Old MacDonald (Starr)
S   (-)
EP   (-)
LP   (32, 64, 86, 89, 134, 244)
VA LP   (-)

Old Shep (Foley, Arthur)
S   (119)
EP   (12)
LP   (2, 17, 67, 73, 82, 85, 103, 105, 113, 119,
         120, 122, 138, 143, 169, 180, 181, 188,
         202, 211, 216) {**310, 318, 318, 326, 341**}
VA LP   (-) {**46**}

On A Snowy Christmas Night (Gelber)
S   (-)
EP   (-)
LP   (56, 117, 195, 252) {**311**}
VA LP   (-)

On The Jericho Road
S   (-)
EP   (-)
LP   (152) {**291, 332, 333**}
VA LP   (-)

Once Is Enough (Tepper, Bennett)
S   (-)
EP   (-)
LP   (22, 95, 141, 159, 249) {**279**}
VA LP   (-)

One Boy, Two Little Girls (Giant, Baum, Kaye)
S   (-)
EP   (-)
LP   (22, 95, 159, 249) {**279**}
VA LP   (-)

One Broken Heart For Sale (Blackwell, Scott)
S   (40)
EP   (-)
LP   (19, 45, 82, 123, 128, 163, 193, 197, 221, 247)
         {**310, 315**}
VA LP   (-)

One Night (Bartholomew, King)
S   (25, 102) {**183**}
EP   (13, 39) {**45**}
LP   (10, 36, 50, 55, 73, 82, 104, 105, 126,
         153, 171, 181, 183, 184, 188, 190, 203,
         204, 205, 216, 245, 251, 253, 269)
         {**277, 285, 286, 287, 289, 292, 300, 307,
         310, 318, 323, 324, 328, 329, 331, 335**}
VA LP   (-) {**34**}

One Night Of Sin (Bartholomew, King)
S   (-)
EP   (-)
LP   (271) {**318, 342**}
VA LP   (-)

One-Sided Love Affair (Campbell)
S   (139)
EP   (-) {**45**}
LP   (1, 9, 60, 102, 175, 179, 236, 267)
         {**304, 318, 321, 325, 340**}
VA LP   (-)

One Track Heart (Giant, Baum, Kaye)
S   (-)
EP   (-)
LP   (23, 96, 161, 240)
VA LP   (-)

Only Believe (Rader)
S   (-)
EP   (-)
LP   (51, 149, 250) {332, 333}
VA LP   (-)

Only The Strong Survive (Gamble, Huff, Butler)
S   (-)
EP   (-)
LP   (38, 207, 209) {284, 313, 319, 323, 324}
VA LP   (-)

Out Of Sight, Out Of Mind (Hunter, Otis)
S   (-)
EP   (-)
LP   (-) {291}
VA LP   (-)

P

Padre (Larue, Webster, Romans)
S   (-)
EP   (-)
LP   (68, 101, 139)
VA LP   (-)

Paradise, Hawaiian Style (Giant, Baum, Kaye)
S   (-)
EP   (-)
LP   (29, 83, 124, 132, 215)
VA LP   (-)

Paralyzed (Blackwell, Presley)
S   (13, 119) {167}
EP   (12, 18)
LP   (2, 17, 55, 82, 113, 151, 169, 180, 190,
           194, 200, 211, 227, 253)
           {287, 291, 297, 310, 318, 321, 326, 329, 341}
VA LP   (-) {46}

Party (Robinson)
S   (14) {149, 176}
EP   (27) {45}
LP   (3, 25, 73, 82, 98, 105, 151, 160, 181,
           188, 190, 210, 216, 253, 258)
           {280, 280, 287, 297, 307, 310, 318, 329, 331,
           342, 342}
VA LP   (-)

Patch It Up (Rabbitt, Bourke)
S   (75)
EP   (-)
LP   (47, 55, 82, 167, 224, 263) {328}
VA LP   (-)

(There'll be) Peace In The Valley (for me) (Dorsey)
S   (-)
EP   (2, 35)
LP   (5, 48, 70, 82, 86, 89, 121, 122, 139, 140,
           152, 218, 251, 275)
           {291, 298, 298, 310, 312, 318, 329, 332,
           332, 332, 333, 333, 333}
VA LP   (-)

Peter Gunn Theme (Instrumental) (Mancini)
S   (-)
EP   (-)
LP   (-) {328}
VALP   (-)

Petunia, The Gardener's Daughter (Tepper, Bennett)
S   (-)
EP   (-)
LP   (28, 109, 111, 131, 241)
VA LP   (-)

Pieces Of My Life (Seals)
S   (-)
EP   (-)
LP   (79, 272)
VA LP   (-)

Plantation Rock (Giant, Baum, Kaye, Fuller)
S   (-)
EP   (-)
LP   (204)
VA LP   (-)

Playin' For Keeps (Kesler)
S   (10)
EP   (-)
LP   (4, 8, 45, 82, 113, 180, 183, 184, 270)
           {303, 310, 318, 326, 329, 341}
VA LP   (-)

Please Don't Drag That String Around (Blackwell, Scott)
S   (41, 113) {183}
EP   (-)
LP   (34, 55, 90, 173, 176, 193, 213, 221)
           {285, 309, 319, 334}
VA LP   (-)

Please Don't Stop Loving Me (Byers)
S   (53)
EP   (-)
LP   (28, 109, 111, 131, 138, 143, 199, 241)
VA LP   (-)

Pledging My Love (Robey, Washington)
S   (116) {183}
EP   (-)
LP   (93, 178, 260) {296}
VA LP   (-)

Pocketful Of Rainbows (Wise, Weisman)
S   (-)
EP   (43)
LP   (12, 155, 206, 264) {315, 337, 337}
VA LP   (-)

Poison Ivy League (Giant, Baum, Kaye)
S   (-)
EP   (-)
LP   (23, 96, 161, 240)
VA LP   (-)

Polk Salad Annie (White)
S   (86)
EP   (-)
LP   (41, 63, 126, 182)
           {314, 323, 324, 328, 335, 335}
VA LP   (-)

Poor Boy (Presley, Matson)
S   (-)
EP   (1, 26) {45}
LP   (8, 55, 113, 180, 190, 202)
           {280, 303, 310, 318, 343, 343}
VA LP   (-)

Power Of My Love (Giant, Baum, Kaye)
S   (-)
EP   (-)
LP   *(38)* {**284, 313, 319**}
VA LP   (-)

Promised Land (Berry)
S   *(92)*
EP   (-)
LP   *(75, 150, 207, 209, 226)*
       {**310, 323, 324, 335**}
VA LP   (-) {**25**}

Proud Mary (Fogerty)
S   (-)
EP   (-)
LP   *(41, 63, 82)* {**314, 335**}
VA LP   (-)

Puppet On A String (Tepper, Bennett)
S   *(51)*
EP   (-)
LP   *(24, 55, 90, 129, 176, 248)*
VA LP   (-)

Put The Blame On Me (Twomey, Wise, Blagman)
S   (-)
EP   *(20)*
LP   *(14, 165, 243)* {**319, 345, 345**}
VA LP   (-)

Put Your Hand In The Hand (Maclellan)
S   (-)
EP   (-)
LP   *(61)* {**332, 333**}
VA LP   (-)

Q

Queenie Wahine's Papaya (Giant, Baum, Kaye)
S   (-)
EP   (-)
LP   *(29, 132, 215)*
VA LP   (-)

R

Rags To Riches (Adler, Ross)
S   *(77)*
EP   (-)
LP   *(74, 82, 126, 194)* {**328**}
VA LP   (-)

Raised On Rock (James)
S   *(88)*
EP   (-)
LP   *(69, 207, 209)*
VA LP   (-)

Reach Out To Jesus (Carmichael)
S   (-)
EP   (-)
LP   *(62, 195, 252)* {**332, 333**}
VA LP   (-)

Ready Teddy (Blackwell, Marascalco)
S   (-)
EP   (-)
LP   *(2, 17, 82, 113, 169, 180, 190, 200, 211,*
       227, 251, 251, 262)
       {**276, 308, 318, 321, 326, 341**}
VA LP   (-)

Reconsider Baby (Fulson)
S   (-) {**177, 178**}
EP   (-)
LP   *(11, 126, 168, 194, 204, 205, 230, 269, 271)*
       {**289, 292, 300, 315, 318, 319, 323, 324**}
VA LP   (-)

Relax (Tepper, Bennett)
S   (-)
EP   (-)
LP   *(19, 123, 128, 247)*
VA LP   (-)

Release Me (and let me love again)
(Miller, Williams, Yount, Harris)
S   *(142)*
EP   (-)
LP   *(41, 92, 177, 194)* {**314, 335**}
VA LP   (-) {**5**}

Return To Sender (Blackwell, Scott)
S   *(39, 112)* {**183**}
EP   (-) {**45**}
LP   *(18, 45, 73, 82, 83, 94, 105, 124, 141,*
       158, 187, 188, 193, 219, 221, 229)
       {**277, 278, 285, 286, 287, 308, 310, 320,**
       323, 324, 331, 334}
VA LP   (-) {**3, 8, 13, 27**}

Riding The Rainbow (Wise, Weisman)
S   (-)
EP   *(16, 32)*
LP   *(57, 84, 86)*
VA LP   (-)

Rip It Up (Blackwell, Marascalco)
S   *(9)*
EP   *(18)*
LP   *(2, 17, 55, 82, 113, 119, 169, 180, 190,*
       194, 200, 211, 227, 262)
       {**276, 291, 310, 318, 321, 326, 341**}
VA LP   (-)

Rock-A-Hula Baby (Wise, Weisman, Fuller)
S   *(36, 109)* {**155, 170, 183**}
EP   (-)
LP   *(15, 45, 46, 73, 82, 83, 105, 124, 151,*
       166, 187, 189, 191, 197, 219, 238, 268)
       {**277, 285, 288, 297, 299, 310, 334, 338, 338**}
VA LP   (-) {**46**}

Roustabout (Giant, Baum, Kaye)
S   (-)
EP   (-)
LP   *(23, 83, 96, 124, 141, 161, 191, 197, 240, 268)*
       {**288, 299, 315**}
VA LP   (-)

Rubberneckin' (Jones, Warren)
S   *(71)*
EP   (-)
LP   *(44, 109, 111, 121, 122, 138, 143, 197)*
       {**284, 315, 319, 344 Bonus EP**}
VA LP   (-)

Runaway (Crook, Shannon)
S   (-) {**178**}
EP   (-)
LP   (*41*) {**314, 315, 335**}
VA LP   (-)

Run On (Arranged and adapted Presley)
S   (-)
EP   (-)
LP   (*31, 53, 174, 235*)
         {**323, 324, 332, 333**}
VA LP   (-)

Sand Castles (Goldberg, Hess)
S   (-)
EP   (-)
LP   (*29, 132, 215*)
VA LP   (-)

Santa Bring My Baby Back (to me) (Schroeder, DeMetrius)
S   (*16*)
EP   (*8*)
LP   (*5, 42, 81, 140, 218, 253, 275*)
         {**310, 312, 318, 329, 332, 339**}
VA LP   (-)

Santa Claus Is Back In Town (Leiber, Stoller)
S   (*16*)
EP   (*8*)
LP   (*5, 42, 81, 125, 140, 205, 217, 218, 269, 275*)
         {**290, 292, 300, 312, 318, 323, 324, 328,
         329, 332, 339**}
VA LP   (-)

Santa Lucia (DiCapua)
S   (-)
EP   (-)
LP   (*26, 59, 65, 76, 85, 103, 138, 143, 144,
         196, 225*) {**285**}
VA LP   (-)

Saved (Leiber, Stoller)
S   (-)
EP   (-)
LP   (*36, 104, 125, 153, 217, 245*) {**332, 333**}
VA LP   (-)

Scratch My Back (then I'll scratch yours) (Giant, Baum, Kaye)
S   (-)
EP   (-) {**45**}
LP   (*29, 132, 215*)
VA LP   (-)

See See Rider (Broonzy)
S   (*86*)
EP   (-)
LP   (*41, 66, 72, 100, 126, 182, 237, 273*)
         {**294, 314, 335**}
VA LP   (-)

Seeing Is Believing (West, Spreen)
S   (-)
EP   (-)
LP   (*62*) {**332, 333**}
VA LP   (-)

Sentimental Me (Cassin, Morehead)
S   (-)
EP   (-)
LP   (*14, 67, 85, 103, 137, 142, 165, 243*)
         {**319**}
VA LP   (-)

Separate Ways (West, Mainegra)
S   (*85*)
EP   (-)
LP   (*67, 85, 103, 119, 121, 122, 137, 142, 272*)
VA LP   (-)

Shake A Hand (Morris)
S   (-)
EP   (-)
LP   (*79*)
VA LP   (-)

Shake, Rattle And Roll (Calhoun)
S   (*144*)
EP   (*34*) {**45**}
LP   (*1, 8, 60, 82, 102, 119, 150, 175, 179,
         190, 200, 226, 236, 251, 262, 265*)
         {**276, 303, 308, 318, 318, 318, 321, 325, 340**}
VA LP   (-)

Shake That Tambourine (Giant, Baum, Kaye)
S   (-)
EP   (-)
LP   (*27, 130, 222*)
VA LP   (-)

She Thinks I Still Care (Lipscomb)
S   (*99*)
EP   (-)
LP   (*93, 112, 146, 178, 260*) {**296, 310**}
VA LP   (-) {**5**}

She Wears My Ring (B. & F. Bryant)
S   (-)
EP   (-)
LP   (*71, 114*)
VA LP   (-)

She's A Machine (Byers)
S   (-)
EP   (-)
LP   (*37, 110, 111*)
VA LP   (-)

She's Not You (Pomus, Leiber, Stoller)
S   (*38, 111*) {**183**}
EP   (-)
LP   (*21, 45, 73, 82, 105, 116, 151, 163, 172,
         183, 187, 219, 256*)
         {**285, 286, 287, 297, 310, 317, 319,
         323, 324, 330, 331**}
VA LP   (-) {**8, 27**}

Shoppin' Around (Tepper, Bennett, Schroeder)
S   (-)
EP   (*33*)
LP   (*12, 126, 155, 193, 206, 221, 265*)
         {**337, 337**}
VA LP   (-)

Shout It Out (Giant, Baum, Kaye)
S   (-)
EP   (-)
LP   (*28, 109, 111, 131, 241*)
VA LP   (-)

Show Me Thy Ways, O Lord (Shade)
S   (-)
EP   (-)
LP   (-) {**332, 333**}
VA LP   (-)

Signs Of The Zodiac (Kaye, Weisman)
S   (-)
EP   (-)
LP   (-) {**343 Bonus EP**}
VA LP   (-)

Silent Night (Mohr, Gruber)
S   (-)
EP   (-) {**45**}
LP   (*5, 42, 81, 140, 195, 218, 252, 275*)
           {**312, 318, 332, 339**}
VA LP   (-)

Silver Bells (Evans, Livingston)
S   (-)
EP   (-)
LP   (*56, 117*) {**311**}
VA LP   (-) {**4, 7**}

Sing You Children (Nelson, Burch)
S   (-)
EP   (*22*)
LP   (*48, 86, 89*) {**332, 333**}
VA LP   (-)

Singing Tree (Owens, Solberg)
S   (-)
EP   (-)
LP   (*33, 135, 223*) {**319**}
VA LP   (-)

Slicin' Sand (Tepper, Bennett)
S   (-)
EP   (-)
LP   (*15, 46, 166, 238*) {**338, 338**}
VA LP   (-)

Slowly But Surely (Wayne, Weisman)
S   (-)
EP   (*20*)
LP   (*20, 97, 141, 157, 257*) {**309, 319, 345, 345**}
VA LP   (-)

Smokey Mountain Boy (Rosenblatt, Millrose)
S   (-)
EP   (-)
LP   (*22, 95, 159, 249*) {**279**}
VA LP   (-)

Smorgasbord (Tepper, Bennett)
S   (-)
EP   (-)
LP   (*30, 133, 255*)
VA LP   (-)

Snowbird (MacLellan)
S   (-)
EP   (-)
LP   (*49, 162, 239*)
VA LP   (-)

So Close, Yet So Far (Byers)
S   (-)
EP   (-)
LP   (*27, 123, 130, 222*) {**315**}
VA LP   (-)

So Glad You're Mine (Crudup)
S   (-)
EP   (-)
LP   (*2, 17, 102, 169, 179, 194, 205, 211, 269, 271*)
           {**290, 292, 300, 318, 321, 326, 341**}
VA LP   (-)

So High (Arranged and adapted Presley)
S   (-)
EP   (-)
LP   (*31, 53, 174, 235*) {**332, 333**}
VA LP   (-)

Softly And Tenderly (Traditional)
S   (-)
EP   (-)
LP   (-) {**291, 332, 333**}
VA LP   (-)

Softly, As I Leave You (Calabrese, deVita, Shaper)
S   (-)
EP   (-)
LP   (*126*) {**335**}
VA LP   (-)

Soldier Boy (Jones, Williams Jnr.)
S   (-)
EP   (-)
LP   (*11, 82, 168, 230, 251*) {**319**}
VA LP   (-)

Solitaire (Sedaka, Cody)
S   (*142*)
EP   (-)
LP   (*88, 112, 266, 272*)
VA LP   (-)

Somebody Bigger Than You And I (Lange, Heath, Burke)
S   (-)
EP   (-)
LP   (*31, 53, 101, 139, 174, 235*) {**332, 333**}
VA LP   (-)

Something (Harrison)
S   (-)
EP   (-)
LP   (*66, 237*) {**294, 328, 335**}
VA LP   (-)

Something Blue (Evans, Byron)
S   (*43*)
EP   (-)
LP   (*16, 148, 192, 220, 233*) {**319**}
VA LP   (-)

Sometimes I Feel Like A Motherless Child (Traditional)
S   (-)
EP   (-)
LP   (-) {**332, 333**}
VA LP   (-)

Song Of The Shrimp (Tepper, Bennett)
S   (-)
EP   (-)
LP   (*18, 94, 158, 229*) {**278**}
VA LP   (-)

Sound Advice (Giant, Baum, Kaye)
S   (-)
EP   (*31*)
LP   (*26, 59, 144, 225*)
VA LP   (-)

Spanish Eyes (Kaemphert, Singleton, Snyder)
S   (-)
EP   (-)
LP   *(71, 112)*
VA LP   (-)

Speedway (Glazer, Schlaks)
S   (-)
EP   (-)
LP   *(35, 136, 228)*
VA LP   (-)

Spinout (Wayne, Weisman, Fuller)
S   *(55)*
EP   (-)
LP   *(30, 133, 191, 255, 268)* {**288, 299**}
VA LP   (-)

Spring Fever (Giant, Baum, Kaye)
S   (-)
EP   (-)
LP   *(24, 129, 248)*
VA LP   (-)

Stand By Me (Tindley)
S   (-)
EP   (-)
LP   *(31, 53, 174, 235)* {**332, 333**}
VA LP   (-)

Starting Today (Robertson)
S   (-)
EP   (-)
LP   *(14, 165, 192, 220, 243)* {**319**}
VA LP   (-)

Startin' Tonight (Rosenblatt, Millrose)
S   (-)
EP   (-)
LP   *(24, 129, 248)*
VA LP   (-)

Stay Away (Tepper, Bennett)
S   *(63)*
EP   (-)
LP   (-) {**338 Bonus EP**}
VA LP   (-)

Stay Away, Joe (Weisman, Wayne)
S   (-)
EP   (-)
LP   *(40, 44)* {**338 Bonus EP**}
VA LP   (-)

Steadfast, Loyal And True (Leiber, Stoller)
S   *(80)*
EP   *(37)*
LP   *(6, 58, 125, 141, 154, 212, 217)* {**306, 318, 344, 344**}
VA LP   (-)

Steamroller Blues (Taylor)
S   *(87)*
EP   (-)
LP   *(66, 185, 194, 237)* {**294**}
VA LP   (-)

Steppin' Out Of Line (Wise, Weisman, Fuller)
S   (-)
EP   (-)
LP   *(16, 148, 233)* {**338, 338**}
VA LP   (-)

Stop, Look And Listen (Byers)
S   (-)
EP   (-)
LP   *(30, 133, 255)* {**315**}
VA LP   (-)

Stop Where You Are (Giant, Baum, Kaye)
S   (-)
EP   (-) {**45**}
LP   *(29, 132, 215)*
VA LP   (-)

Stranger In My Own Home Town (Mayfield)
S   (-)
EP   (-)
LP   *(39, 231, 271)* {**284, 319, 323, 324**}
VA LP   (-)

Stranger In The Crowd (Scott)
S   (-)
EP   (-)
LP   *(47, 167, 224)* {**328, 328**}
VA LP   (-)

Stuck On You (Schroeder, McFarland)
S   *(28)* {**162, 163**}
EP   (-)
LP   *(21, 45, 73, 82, 105, 163, 172, 181, 205, 216, 256, 269)* {**277, 285, 286, 287, 290, 292, 300, 307, 310, 319, 323, 324, 330, 331**}
VA LP   (-) {**8**}

Such A Night (Chase)
S   *(46)*
EP   *(14, 30)*
LP   *(11, 82, 87, 126, 168, 183, 193, 205, 221, 230, 246, 269)* {**285, 289, 292, 300, 310, 319, 323, 324, 328**}
VA LP   (-)

Summer Kisses, Winter Tears (Wise, Weisman, Lloyd)
S   (-)
EP   *(41)*
LP   *(25, 90, 144, 176, 225)* {**315**}
VA LP   (-)

Summertime Is Past And Gone (Monroe)
S   (-)
EP   (-)
LP   *(152)* {**291**}
VA LP   (-)

Suppose (Dee, Goehring)
S   (-)
EP   (-)
LP   *(35, 136, 228, 251)* {**319**}
VA LP   (-)

Surrender (DeCurtis, Pomus, Shuman)
S   *(33, 107)* {**165, 183**}
EP   (-)
LP   *(21, 45, 73, 82, 105, 106, 107, 116, 172, 187, 189, 219, 256, 258)* {**277, 285, 286, 287, 310, 315, 319, 319, 323, 324, 330, 331**}
VA LP   (-) {**46**}

Susan When She Tried (Reid)
S   (-)
EP   (-)
LP   *(79)*
VA LP   (-)

Suspicion (Pomus, Shuman)
S   *(98, 129)*
EP   *(-)*
LP   *(16, 90, 148, 176, 183, 233, 258, 274)*
     {285, 287, 317, 319, 331}
VA LP   *(-)*

Suspicious Minds (James)
S   *(70, 128, 137, 145)* **{148}**
EP   *(-)*
LP   *(39, 45, 63, 66, 73, 82, 105, 116, 126, 150, 151, 182, 185, 187, 188, 196, 219, 226, 231, 237, 261, 274)*
     {277, 284, 285, 286, 287, 294, 297, 310, 316, 317, 319, 319, 320, 323, 324, 328, 331 335, 335, 335, 336}
VA LP   *(-)* **{12, 40}**

Sweet Angeline (Arnold, Morrow, Martin)
S   *(-)*
EP   *(-)*
LP   *(69, 207, 209)*
VA LP   *(-)*

Sweet Caroline (Diamond)
S   *(-)*
EP   *(-)*
LP   *(41, 119, 126, 265)* **{314, 328, 335}**
VA LP   *(-)*

Sweetheart You Done Me Wrong (Monroe, Flatt)
S   *(-)*
EP   *(-)*
LP   *(152)* **{291}**
VA LP   *(-)*

Swing Down, Sweet Chariot (Arranged and adapted Presley)

S   *(-)*
EP   *(-)* **{45}**
LP   *(13, 48, 54, 86, 89, 126, 156, 204, 214)*
     {332, 332, 333, 333, 343 Bonus EP}
VA LP   *(-)*

Sylvia (Stephens, Reed)
S   *(-)*
EP   *(-)*
LP   *(61)* **{328}**
VA LP   *(-)*

T

Take Good Care Of Her (Warren, Kent)
S   *(89)*
EP   *(-)*
LP   *(71, 112, 207, 209)*
VA LP   *(-)*

Take Me To The Fair (Tepper, Bennett)
S   *(-)*
EP   *(-)*
LP   *(19, 128, 247)*
VA LP   *(-)*

Take My Hand, Precious Lord (Dorsey)
S   *(-)*
EP   *(2, 35)*
LP   *(5, 48, 86, 89, 140, 218, 275)*
     {312, 318, 332, 333}
VA LP   *(-)*

Talk About The Good Times (Reed)
S   *(-)*
EP   *(-)*
LP   *(71)*
VA LP   *(-)*

(Let me be your) Teddy Bear (Mann, Lowe)
S   *(12, 80, 137, 145)* **{153}**
EP   *(11, 27)* **{45}**
LP   *(3, 10, 25, 45, 50, 63, 73, 82, 98, 100, 105, 126, 150, 151, 160, 163, 171, 181, 196, 210, 216, 226, 232, 273)*
     {276, 277, 280, 285, 286, 287, 297, 307, 308, 310, 318, 320, 323, 324, 327, 331, 342}
VA LP   *(-)* **{8, 48}**

Tell Me Why (Turner)
S   *(51)*
EP   *(36)*
LP   *(55, 82, 270)* **{318, 342}**
VA LP   *(-)*

Tender Feeling (Giant, Baum, Kaye)
S   *(-)*
EP   *(-)*
LP   *(22, 65, 95, 120, 122, 138, 143, 159, 199, 249)*
     {279}
VA LP   *(-)*

Thanks To The Rolling Sea (Batchelor, Roberts)
S   *(-)*
EP   *(-)*
LP   *(18, 94, 126, 158, 229, 265)* **{278}**
VA LP   *(-)*

That's All Right (Crudup)
S   *(130, 144)* **{182, 182}**
EP   *(13, 39)*
LP   *(1, 8, 60, 63, 70, 80, 100, 108, 118, 119, 126, 150, 175, 194, 198, 201, 204, 226, 234, 236, 251, 251, 254, 254, 259, 273)*
     {283, 283, 295, 302, 303, 308, 310, 318, 322, 322, 323, 324, 327, 328, 328, 331, 335}
VA LP   *(-)* **{6, 19}**

That's My Desire (Loveday, Dresa)
S   *(-)*
EP   *(-)*
LP   *(-)* **{291}**
VA LP   *(-)*

That's Someone You Never Forget (West, Presley)
S   *(59)*
EP   *(-)*
LP   *(16, 148, 233)* **{319, 319, 323, 324}**
VA LP   *(-)*

That's When Your Heartaches Begin (Raskin, Brown, Fisher)
S   *(11)* **{183}**
EP   *(40)*
LP   *(7, 43, 45, 82, 151, 170, 232)*
     {291, 297, 298, 310, 318, 318, 327}
VA LP   *(-)*
Misc   *(-)* **{6}**

The Bullfighter Was A Lady (Tepper, Bennett)
S   *(-)*
EP   *(-)*
LP   *(20, 97, 157, 257)*
VA LP   *(-)*

The Eyes Of Texas (Sinclair)
S   *(-)*
EP   *(-)*
LP   *(37, 110, 111, 196)*
VA LP   *(-)*

The Fair's Moving On (Fletcher, Flett)
S   *(69)*
EP   *(-)*
LP   *(39, 231)* **{284, 319}**
VA LP   *(-)*

The First Noel (Traditional. Arranged Presley)
S   *(-)*
EP   *(-)*
LP   *(56, 117)* **{311}**
VA LP   *(-)*

The First Time Ever I Saw Your Face (MacColl)
S   *(83)*
EP   *(-)*
LP   *(90, 126, 176, 263)*
VA LP   *(-)*

The Fool (Ford)
S   *(-)*
EP   *(-)*
LP   *(49, 162, 239, 251)*
VA LP   *(-)*

The Girl I Never Loved (Starr)
S   *(-)*
EP   *(-)*
LP   *(33, 135, 223)*
VA LP   *(-)*

The Girl Of My Best Friend (Ross, Bobrick)
S   *(29, 97, 129)* **{151}**
EP   *(-)*
LP   *(11, 82, 141, 168, 183, 189, 199, 230, 258, 274)* **{285, 287, 310, 317, 319, 320, 323, 324, 330, 331}**
VA LP   *(-)* **{43}**

The Impossible Dream (The Quest) (Leigh, Darion)
S   *(-)*
EP   *(-)*
LP   *(63, 101, 139, 182)* **{335}**
VA LP   *(-)*

The Lady Loves Me (Tepper, Bennett)
S   *(140, 141)*
EP   *(-)*
LP   *(204)*
VA LP   *(-)*

The Last Farewell (Whittaker, Webster)
S   *(143, 144)*
EP   *(-)*
LP   *(88, 266)*
VA LP   *(-)*

The Lord's Prayer (Traditional)
S   *(-)*
EP   *(-)*
LP   *(-)* **{332, 333}**
VA LP   *(-)*

The Love Machine (Nelson, Burch, Taylor)
S   *(58)*
EP   *(-)*
LP   *(57, 84, 86)*
VA LP   *(-)*

The Meanest Girl In Town (Byers)
S   *(-)*
EP   *(-)*
LP   *(24, 129, 248)*
VA LP   *(-)*

The Next Step Is Love (Evans, Parnes)
S   *(74)*
EP   *(-)*
LP   *(47, 55, 82, 151, 167, 224)* **{297, 328, 328}**
VA LP   *(-)*

The Sound Of Your Cry (Giant, Baum, Kaye)
S   *(135, 135)*
EP   *(-)*
LP   *(90, 176, 185, 263)*
VA LP   *(-)*

The Twelfth Of Never (Livingstone, Webster)
S   *(-)* **{180}**
EP   *(-)*
LP   *(-)*
VA LP   *(-)*

The Walls Have Ears (Tepper, Bennett)
S   *(-)*
EP   *(-)* **{45}**
LP   *(18, 94, 158, 229)* **{278}**
VA LP   *(-)*

The Whiffenpoof Song (Galloway, Minnegerade, Pomeroy)
S   *(-)*
EP   *(-)*
LP   *(-)* **{343 Bonus EP}**
VA LP   *(-)*

The Wonder Of You (Knight)
S   *(73, 115)* **{173, 183}**
EP   *(-)*
LP   *(41, 55, 74, 82, 116, 119, 126, 151, 258, 274)* **{285, 286, 287, 297, 310, 314, 317, 320, 323, 324, 328, 331, 335}**
VA LP   *(-)* **{18, 37, 40, 42}**

The Wonderful World Of Christmas (Tobias, Frisch)
S   *(-)*
EP   *(-)*
LP   *(56, 117, 195, 252)* **{311}**
VA LP   *(-)*

There Ain't Nothing Like A Song (Byers, Johnston)
S   *(-)*
EP   *(-)*
LP   *(35, 136, 228)*
VA LP   *(-)*

There Goes My Everything (Frazier)
S   *(76)*
EP   *(-)*
LP   *(49, 55, 73, 74, 82, 105, 114, 162, 163, 187, 219, 239, 274)* **{277, 285, 317, 328, 335}**
VA LP   *(-)*

There Is No God But God (Kenny)
S   *(-)*
EP   *(-)*
LP   *(62)* **{332, 333}**
VA LP   *(-)*

There Is So Much World To See (Tepper, Weisman)
S   *(-)*
EP   *(-)*
LP   *(32, 134, 244)*
VA LP   *(-)*

There's A Brand New Day On The Horizon (Byers)
S   (-)
EP   (-)
LP   (23, 96, 161, 240)
VA LP   (-)

There's A Honky Tonk Angel (who will take me back in)
(Seals, Rice)
S   (-)
EP   (-)
LP   (75, 114)
VA LP   (-)

There's Always Me (Robertson)
S   (60)
EP   (-)
LP   (14, 73, 105, 151, 165, 187, 189, 192,
         219, 220, 243) {**297, 315, 319**}
VA LP   (-)

There's Gold In The Mountains (Giant, Baum, Kaye)
S   (-)
EP   (-)
LP   (22, 95, 159, 249) {**279**}
VA LP   (-)

There's No Place Like Home (Traditional)
S   (-)
EP   (-)
LP   (-) {**291**}
VA LP   (-)

They Remind Me Too Much Of You (Robertson)
S   (40)
EP   (-)
LP   (19, 55, 64, 86, 89, 126, 128, 191, 247, 268)
         {**288, 299, 310**}
VA LP   (-)

Thinking About You (Baty)
S   (95)
EP   (-)
LP   (75, 114)
VA LP   (-)

This Is Living (Wise, Weisman)
S   (-)
EP   (16, 32)
LP   (52)
VA LP   (-)

This Is My Heaven (Giant, Baum, Kaye)
S   (-)
EP   (-)
LP   (29, 132, 215)
VA LP   (-)

This Is Our Dance (Reed, Stephens)
S   (-)
EP   (-)
LP   (51, 149, 250)
VA LP   (-)

This Is The Story (Arnold, Morrow, Martin)
S   (-)
EP   (-)
LP   (39, 231) {**315, 319**}
VA LP   (-)

This Time (Moman)
S   (-)
EP   (-)
LP   (-) {**319**}
VA LP   (-)

Three Corn Patches (Leiber, Stoller)
S   (-)
EP   (-)
LP   (69)
VA LP   (-)

Thrill Of Your Love (Kesler)
S   (-)
EP   (-)
LP   (11, 168, 230) {**319**}
VA LP   (-)

Tiger Man (Lewis, Burns)
S   (-)
EP   (-)
LP   (37, 39, 110, 111, 126, 231, 251)
         {**315, 316, 323, 324, 328**}
VA LP   (-)

Today, Tomorrow And Forever (Giant, Baum, Kaye)
S   (-)
EP   (17, 42)
LP   (52, 78, 85, 138, 143, 196)
VA LP   (-)

Tomorrow Is A Long Time (Dylan)
S   (-)
EP   (-)
LP   (30, 90, 133, 176, 255, 270)
         {**319, 323, 324**}
VA LP   (-) {**39**}

Tomorrow Never Comes (Tubb, Bond)
S   (-)
EP   (-)
LP   (49, 162, 239)
VA LP   (-)

Tomorrow Night (Coslow, Grosz)
S   (-) {**146, 147, 182**}
EP   (-)
LP   (26, 59, 144, 205, 225, 269, 271)
         {**283, 290, 292, 300, 318**}
VA LP   (-)

Tonight's All Right For Love (Wayne, Silver, Lilly)
S   (-)
EP   (33)
LP   (70, 126, 206, 265) {**337**}
VA LP   (-)

Tonight Is So Right For Love (Wayne, Silver)
S   (32, 106) {**183**}
EP   (-)
LP   (12, 65, 76, 85, 103, 155, 199) {**337**}
VA LP   (-)

Too Much (Rosenberg, Weinman)
S   (10)
EP   (40)
LP   (4, 7, 43, 45, 82, 113, 170, 180, 202, 232, 251)
         {**285, 286, 287, 307, 310, 318, 321, 326,
         327, 331, 341**}
VA LP   (-)

Too Much Monkey Business (Berry)
S   (-)
EP   (-)
LP   (37, 110, 111, 138, 143, 146, 150, 226)
         {**291, 319**}
VA LP   (-)

Treat Me Nice (Leiber, Stoller)
S   (18, 101, 136) {**164, 183**}
EP   (13, 28)
LP   (10, 45, 50, 125, 171, 183, 184, 196, 217, 232)
         {**280, 285, 308, 310, 318, 323, 324, 327, 343, 343**}
VA LP   (-) {**46**}

T-R-O-U-B-L-E (Chesnut)
S   (93)
EP   (-)
LP   (79, 126, 207, 209) {**310**}
VA LP   (-)

Trouble (Leiber, Stoller)
S   (-)
EP   (7, 37)
LP   (6, 36, 36, 55, 58, 104, 104, 125, 153, 153, 154, 205, 212, 217, 245, 245, 269)
         {**289, 292, 300, 308, 310, 318, 323, 324, 331, 344**}
VA LP   (-)

True Love (Porter)
S   (138)
EP   (10) {**45**}
LP   (3, 25, 98, 160, 210) {**318, 342**}
VA LP   (-)

True Love Travels On A Gravel Road (Owens, Frazier)
S   (-)
EP   (-)
LP   (38) {**284, 313, 319**}
VA LP   (-)

Trying To Get To You (Singleton, McCoy)
S   (15) {**182**}
EP   (-) {**45**}
LP   (1, 8, 60, 70, 72, 80, 82, 100, 108, 126, 175, 201, 205, 236, 251, 267, 269, 273)
         {**283, 289, 292, 295, 300, 303, 310, 318, 323, 324, 325, 335, 340**}
VA LP   (-)

Turn Your Eyes Upon Jesus (Lemmel, Clarke)
S   (-)
EP   (-)
LP   (-) {**332, 333**}
VA LP   (-)

Tutti Frutti (LaBostrie, Penniman)
S   (2, 139)
EP   (23)
LP   (4, 9, 82, 102, 179, 251, 251, 262, 267)
         {**285, 304, 318, 321, 325, 340**}
VA LP   (-)

Tweedle Dee (Scott)
S   (-)
EP   (-)
LP   (234, 254) {**302, 318, 322**}
VA LP   (-)

Twenty Days And Twenty Nights (Weisman, Westlake)
S   (-)
EP   (-)
LP   (47, 167, 224) {**328, 328**}
VA LP   (-)

Unchained Melody (North, Zaret)
S   (-)
EP   (-)
LP   (93, 126, 178, 260, 272) {**296, 308**}
VA LP   (-)

Until It's Time For You To Go (Sainte-Marie)
S   (82) {**152**}
EP   (-)
LP   (61, 74, 82, 116, 151) {**297, 310, 317**}
VA LP   (-)

Up Above My Head (Brown)
S   (-)
EP   (-)
LP   (36, 104, 153, 245) {**332, 333**}
VA LP   (-)

U.S. Male (Hubbard)
S   (63)
EP   (-)
LP   (44, 78, 82, 85, 121, 122, 138, 143, 151, 188, 193, 221) {**297, 310, 319, 336**}
VA LP   (-)

Vino, Dinero Y Amor (Tepper, Bennett)
S   (-)
EP   (-)
LP   (20, 97, 157, 257)
VA LP   (-)

Violet (Duerker, Lohstroh)
S   (-)
EP   (-)
LP   (-) {**343 Bonus EP**}
VA LP   (-)

Viva Las Vegas (Pomus, Shuman)
S   (44)
EP   (42)
LP   (45, 82, 90, 150, 176, 191, 196, 226, 246, 264, 268)
         {**285, 288, 299, 310, 331, 334**}
VA LP   (-)

Walk A Mile In My Shoes (South)
S   (-) {**180**}
EP   (-)
LP   (41) {**314, 328, 335, 335**}
VA LP   (-)

Walk That Lonesome Valley
On BMG releases this song was entitled **Jesus Walked That Lonesome Valley**. Appearances can be found under the latter title.

359

Way Down (Martine Jnr.)
S   *(116, 134)* {**172, 183**}
EP   (-)
LP   *(93, 114, 178, 207, 209, 260, 261)*
         {**287, 296, 310, 331, 336**}
VA LP   (-) {**22, 26, 30, 40**}

We Call On Him (Karger, Wayne, Weisman)
S   *(65)*
EP   (-)
LP   *(48, 86, 89)* {**332, 333**}
VA LP   (-)

We Can Make The Morning (Ramsey)
S   *(82)*
EP   (-)
LP   *(61)*
VA LP   (-)

Wear My Ring Around Your Neck (Carroll, Moody)
S   *(20)* {**169**}
EP   *(13, 39)*
LP   *(10, 45, 50, 82, 171, 183, 184, 200, 203,*
         227, 246, 253)
         {**285, 286, 287, 306, 306, 307, 310, 318,**
         323, 324, 329, 331}
VA LP   (-)

Wearin' That Loved On Look (Frazier, Owens)
S   (-)
EP   (-)
LP   *(38)* {**284, 313, 319**}
VA LP   (-)

Welcome To My World (Winkler, Hathcock)
S   (-)
EP   (-)
LP   *(66, 92, 126, 177, 237)* {**294**}
VA LP   (-) {**5**}

We'll Be Together (O'Curran, Brooks)
S   (-)
EP   (-)
LP   *(18, 65, 78, 85, 94, 158, 229)* {**278**}
VA LP   (-)

We're Coming In Loaded (Blackwell, Scott)
S   (-)
EP   (-) {**45**}
LP   *(18, 94, 158, 229)* {**278**}
VA LP   (-)

We're Gonna Move (Presley, Matson)
S   (-)
EP   *(1, 26)* {**45**}
LP   *(9, 55, 113, 127, 180, 242)*
         {**280, 304, 318, 318, 343, 343**}
VA LP   (-)

Western Union (Tepper, Bennett)
S   (-)
EP   (-)
LP   *(35, 136, 193, 221, 228)* {**309, 319**}
VA LP   ( )

What A Wonderful Life (Wayne, Livingston)
S   (-)
EP   *(15, 31)*
LP   *(57, 84, 86, 138, 143, 197)* {**315**}
VA LP   (-)

What Every Woman Lives For (Pomus, Shuman)
S   (-)
EP   (-)
LP   *(28, 109, 111, 131, 241)*
VA LP   (-)

What Now My Love (Delanoe, Becaud, Sigman)
S   (-)
EP   (-)
LP   *(66, 237)* {**294**}
VA LP   (-)

What Now, What Next, Where To (Robertson, Blair)
S   (-)
EP   (-)
LP   *(32, 67, 85, 103, 134, 244)* {**309, 319**}
VA LP   (-)

What'd I Say (Charles)
S   *(44)*
EP   *(42)*
LP   *(34, 100, 173, 185, 196, 205, 213, 264,*
         269, 273)
         {**276, 285, 290, 292, 300, 310, 315, 319,**
         334, 335}
VA LP   (-)

What's She Really Like (Wayne, Silver)
S   (-)
EP   *(43)*
LP   *(12, 155, 206, 264)* {**337, 337**}
VA LP   (-)

Wheels On My Heels (Tepper, Bennett)
S   (-)
EP   (-)
LP   *(23, 96, 161, 240)*
VA LP   (-)

When God Dips His Love In My Heart (Traditional)
S   (-)
EP   (-)
LP   (-) {**291**}
VA LP   (-)

When I'm Over You (Milete)
S   (-)
EP   (-)
LP   *(51, 149, 250)* {**328**}
VA LP   (-)

When It Rains, It Really Pours (Emerson)
S   (-)
EP   *(36)*
LP   *(26, 59, 144, 204, 205, 225, 251, 269, 271)*
         {**283, 289, 292, 300, 318, 318, 342**}
VA LP   (-)

When My Blue Moon Turns To Gold Again (Walker, Sullivan)
S   *(13)*
EP   *(18)*
LP   *(2, 17, 55, 113, 169, 180, 211, 251)*
         {**310, 318, 326, 341**}
VA LP   (-)

When The Saints Go Marching In (Traditional/Arranged Giant, Baum, Kaye)
S   (-)
EP   (-)
LP   *(28, 64, 86, 89, 131, 241)*
         {**291, 332, 332, 332, 333, 333, 333**}
VA LP   (-)

When The Snow Is On The Roses (Last, Kusik, Snyder, Bader)
S   (-)
EP   (-)
LP   (-) {**335**}
VA LP   (-)

Where Could I Go But To The Lord (Coats)
S   (-)
EP   (-)
LP   *(31, 36, 53, 104, 139, 153, 174, 235, 245)* **{332, 332, 333, 333}**
VA LP (-)

Where Did They Go, Lord (Frazier, Owens)
S   *(77)*
EP   (-)
LP   *(101)*
VA LP (-)

Where Do I Go From Here (Williams)
S   (-)
EP   (-)
LP   *(68)*
VA LP (-)

Where Do You Come From (Batchelor, Roberts)
S   *(39, 112)* **{183}**
EP   (-)
LP   *(18, 45, 94, 158, 229)* **{278}**
VA LP (-)

Where No One Stands Alone (Lister)
S   (-)
EP   (-)
LP   *(31, 53, 174, 195, 235, 252)* **{332, 333}**
VA LP (-)

White Christmas (Berlin)
S   *(48)*
EP   (-) **{45}**
LP   *(5, 42, 81, 140, 218, 275)* **{312, 318, 332, 339}**
VA LP (-)

Who Am I? (Goodman)
S   (-)
EP   (-)
LP   *(48, 86, 89, 101)* **{284, 319, 332, 333}**
VA LP (-)

Who Are You? (who am I?) (Wayne, Weisman)
S   (-)
EP   (-)
LP   *(35, 136, 228)*
VA LP (-)

Who Needs Money (Starr)
S   (-)
EP   (-)
LP   *(33, 135, 223)*
VA LP (-)

Whole Lotta Shakin' Goin' On (Williams, David)
S   (-)
EP   (-)
LP   *(49, 66, 72, 141, 162, 164, 237, 239)*
VA LP (-)

Why Me Lord (Kristofferson)
S   (-)
EP   (-)
LP   *(72, 126)* **{332, 333, 335}**
VA LP (-)

Wild In The Country (Peretti, Creatore, Weiss)
S   *(34)* **{159}**
EP   (-)
LP   *(26, 55, 59, 73, 82, 105, 126, 151, 187, 189, 191, 219, 268)* **{277, 285, 288, 297, 299, 310, 330, 342 Bonus EP}**
VA LP (-)

Winter Wonderland (Smith, Bernard)
S   (-)
EP   (-)
LP   *(56, 117)* **{311}**
VA LP (-)

Wisdom Of The Ages (Giant, Baum, Kaye)
S   (-)
EP   (-)
LP   *(27, 130, 222)*
VA LP (-)

Witchcraft (Bartholomew, King)
S   *(42)*
EP   (-)
LP   *(34, 55, 173, 193, 213, 221)* **{285, 309, 310, 315, 319, 334}**
VA LP (-)

Witchcraft (Coleman, Leigh) (the Frank Sinatra song)
S   (-)
EP   (-)
LP   (-) **{319}**
VA LP (-) **{9}**

Without Him (LeFevre)
S   (-)
EP   (-)
LP   *(31, 53, 174, 235)* **{332, 333}**
VA LP (-)

Without Love (there is nothing) (Small)
S   (-)
EP   (-)
LP   *(39, 231)* **{284, 319}**
VA LP (-)

Wolf Call (Giant, Baum, Kaye)
S   (-)
EP   (-)
LP   *(24, 129, 248)*
VA LP (-)

Woman Without Love (Chesnut)
S   (-)
EP   (-)
LP   *(79)*
VA LP (-)

Wonderful World (Fletcher, Flett)
S   (-)
EP   (-)
LP   *(37, 110, 111, 138, 143)* **{337 Bonus EP}**
VA LP (-)

Wooden Heart (Wise, Weisman, Twomey, Kaempfert)
S   *(32, 106)* **{157, 183}**
EP   (-)
LP   *(12, 45, 73, 82, 105, 116, 155, 187, 189, 204, 206, 219, 274)* **{277, 285, 287, 307, 310, 317, 320, 330, 331, 337}**
VA LP (-) **{16, 27, 40, 41}**

Words (B., R., & M. Gibb)
S   (-)
EP   (-)
LP   *(39, 182, 231)* **{316, 328}**
VA LP (-)

Working On The Building (Hoyle, Bowles)
S   (-)
EP   (-)
LP   *(13, 54, 156, 214)* **{332, 333}**
VA LP (-) **{40}**

Write To Me From Naples (Alstone, Kennedy)
S   (-)
EP   (-)
LP   (251)
VA LP   (-)

Y

Yellow Rose Of Texas (Arranged Wise, Starr)
S   (-)
EP   (-)
LP   (37, 110, 111, 120, 122, 138, 143, 196)
VA LP   (-)

Yesterday (Lennon, McCartney)
S   (-)
EP   (-)
LP   (41, 126) {**314, 328, 335**}
VA LP   (-)

Yoga Is As Yoga Does (Nelson, Burch)
S   (-)
EP   (22)
LP   (57, 84, 86)
VA LP   (-)

You Asked Me To (Jennings, Shaver)
S   (126)
EP   (-)
LP   (75, 146)
VA LP   (-)

You Belong To My Heart (Gilbert, Lara)
S   (-)
EP   (-)
LP   (-) {**291**}
VA LP   (-)

You Better Run (Traditional)
S   (-)
EP   (-)
LP   (-) {**332, 333**}
VA LP   (-)

You Can't Say No In Acapulco (Feller, Fuller, Morris)
S   (-)
EP   (-)
LP   (20, 97, 157, 257)
VA LP   (-)

You Don't Have To Say You Love Me
(Pallavicini, Donaggio, Wickham, Napier-Bell)
S   (75)
EP   (-)
LP   (47, 55, 63, 74, 82, 116, 167, 182, 224)
         {**285, 310, 317, 323, 324, 328, 328, 336**}
VA LP   (-) {**40**}

You Don't Know Me (Walker, Arnold)
S   (61)
EP   (-)
LP   (33, 64, 86, 89, 135, 137, 142, 192, 220, 223)
         {**319**}
VA LP   (-)

You Gave Me A Mountain (Robbins)
S   (-)
EP   (-)
LP   (66, 100, 126, 237, 272, 273) {**294, 335**}
VA LP   (-) {**5**}

You Gotta Stop (Giant, Baum, Kaye)
S   (58)
EP   (-)
LP   (57, 84, 86, 151) {**297**}
VA LP   (-)

You'll Be Gone (West, Presley, Hodge)
S   (49)
EP   (-)
LP   (24, 129, 248) {**319**}
VA LP   (-)

You'll Never Walk Alone (Rodgers, Hammerstein II)
S   (65)
EP   (-)
LP   (48, 86, 89, 120, 122, 151, 185, 202)
         {**297, 310, 332, 333**}
VA LP   (-)

You'll Think Of Me (Shuman)
S   (70)
EP   (-)
LP   (39, 55, 231, 264) {**284, 319**}
VA LP   (-)

Young And Beautiful (Silver, Schroeder)
S   (-)
EP   (5, 10, 28)
LP   (55, 127, 196, 200, 227, 242, 270)
         {**280, 318, 318, 343, 343**}
VA LP   (-)

Young Dreams (Kalmanoff, Schroeder)
S   (-)
EP   (7, 37)
LP   (6, 55, 58, 154, 212) {**318, 344**}
VA LP   (-)

Your Cheatin' Heart (Williams)
S   (-)
EP   (39)
LP   (26, 59, 82, 92, 144, 177, 200, 225, 264)
         {**285, 306, 306, 318**}
VA LP   (-) {**5**}

Your Love's Been A Long Time Coming (Bourke)
S   (-)
EP   (-)
LP   (75, 112)
VA LP   (-)

Your Time Hasn't Come Yet Baby (Hirschhorn, Kashka)
S   (64)
EP   (-)
LP   (35, 136, 151, 228) {**297**}
VA LP   (-)

You're A Heartbreaker (Sallee)
S   (94) {**182**}
EP   (-) {**45**}
LP   (7, 8, 43, 80, 108, 170, 201)
         {**283, 295, 303, 318**}
VA LP   (-)

You're The Boss (Leiber, Stoller)
S   (-)
EP   (-)
LP   (-) {**315**}
VA LP   (-)

You're The Only Star In My Blue Heaven (Autry)

       S   (-)
       EP   (-)
       LP   (-) {**291**}
       VA LP   (-)

You're The Reason I'm Leaving (Darin)

       S   (-)
       EP   (-)
       LP   (-) {**335**}
       VA LP   (-)

You've Lost That Lovin' Feelin' (Spector, Mann, Weil)

       S   (-)
       EP   (-)
       LP   (*47, 63, 82, 126, 167, 224*) {**328, 328, 335**}
       VA LP   (-)

Interview Index

As with the song index, we have provided a master list of all interviews (and spoken material) released on vinyl in the UK from 1956 to date. In doing so, we have provided a complete listing and itemised the number of times each interview has appeared, and on what format. All of the details from *Elvis UK 1956-86* have been included, making this index complete, we believe. By using a bolder print for each occasion that an interview has appeared in the period covered by this book, referencing has been made easier. Please note that this index covers interviews released on vinyl, therefore if an interview does not appear here, then the interview in question has been released on CD only, not vinyl. Reference numbers for releases found in *Elvis UK 1956-86* are in italics, while those numbers in bold print relate to releases in this volume.

The index shows the release numbers for the following formats: singles (S), LPs (LP), Other Releases, Miscellaneous Releases and Flexi-discs. This refers to each appearance on a particular record, not to references made in the text.

This index should therefore enable you to refer to each interview, the format(s) on which it is to be found and, if required, determine total appearances, and so on.

In the past, the actual recording date of many interviews (and spoken pieces) have often been reported inaccurately, and many discrepancies have appeared where one source quotes one date, and another a different one. The same situation applies to locations and the person carrying out the interview. Over the last few years, new details have come to light and we have been able to incorporate these in this listing, making it as complete, and accurate, as possible. Therefore, a number of amendments have been made to our original listing in *Elvis UK 1956-86*. Although every attempt has been made to date these interviews accurately, in several instances this has proven very difficult, despite referring to several major texts and cross-referencing the information. Indeed, perhaps quoting the precise dates is not that important in the overall scheme of things, although if we can be accurate then clearly that is better. The precise recording location of some interviews is not known.

What has to be made clear is that sometimes interviews have been edited or re-arranged. However, unless the changes have been significant, then we do not make reference to them.

One final point. We should not forget that in the early years - probably until late 1956 - Elvis was interviewed countless times, and not all have been released, of course. Thereafter, as the index will reveal, the number of significant interviews was very small.

1955

28 July 1955	**Jacksonville, Florida,** with Mae Axton
	LP {**305**}
	Flexi-disc (*10*)
	Miscellaneous releases {**4, 5**}

31 August 1955	**WMPS, Memphis,** with Bob Neal
	S {**174**}
	LP (*145, 186, 208, 254*) {**282, 293, 301, 305**}
	Other releases (*11*)

1956

24 March 1956	**Warwick Hotel, New York,** with Robert Carlton Brown
	S {**174**}
	LP (*145, 186, 208*) {**282, 293**}

| 9 April 1956 | **Wichita Falls, Texas,** with Jay Thompson |
| | LP (*87, 99*) {**301, 305**} |

15 April 1956	**San Antonio, Texas,** with Charlie Walker
	S {**174**}
	LP (*99, 145, 186, 208*) {**282, 293**}
	Other releases (*12*)

| 14 May 1956 | **LaCrosse, Wisconsin** |
| | LP {**302, 305**} |

| 16 May 1956 | **Little Rock, Arkansas,** with Ray Green |
| | LP {**302, 305**} |

16 June 1956	**KLAC TV, Memphis,** with Wink Martindale
	LP {**305**}
	Flexi-disc (*10*)

| 1 July 1956 | Hy Gardner |
| | LP (*150, 226*) |

9 July 1956	**WNOE Radio, New Orleans, Louisiana**
	LP {**305**}
	Other releases (*10*)
	Flexi-disc (*9*)

10 July 1956	**New Orleans, Louisiana,** with Jim Stewart
	LP {**301, 305**}
	Other releases (*10*)

| 5 August 1956 | Excerpt from an interview by Ray and Norma Pellow, **Tampa, Florida** |
| | LP (*204*) |

| 6 August 1956 | Excerpts from *TV Guide*, **Lakeland, Florida,** with Paul Wilder |
| | LP (*106, 107*) {*251*} |

| 7 August 1956 | **St. Petersburg, Florida,** with Bob Hoffer |
| | LP (*118, 198, 259*) {**301, 305**} |

22 or 29 August 1956	*The Truth About Me*
	LP {**305**}
	Other releases (1)
	Flexi-disc (8)

1956 (continued)

26 September 1956
Tupelo, Mississippi, with Jack Christal
An Audio Self Portrait
Promo only

14 October 1956
County Coliseum, San Antonio, Texas, with Al Hickock
LP (*145,186*) {**282**}
Other releases (*12*)

1957

31 August 1957
Vancouver, Canada, with Red Robinson. Press conference.
LP (*91*) {**281**}
Other releases (*6*)

2 September 1957
Portland, Oregan
Other releases (*10*)

1958

24 March 1958
Army swearing in
LP (*150, 226*)

22 September 1958
Brooklyn, New York
(departure for Germany)
EP (*9*)
LP (*45, 70, 150, 226, 263*)
+ unreleased portions LP {**318**}

1959

19 June 1959
Interview en route to Paris
Flexi-disc (*7*)

1960

8 January 1960
AFN (Germany), with Dick Clark
Other releases (*11*)
Flexi-disc (*4*)

7 March 1960
Graceland, Memphis, Tennessee
LP (*150, 226*)
Other releases (*8, 13*)
Miscellaneous releases {**1, 2**}

1961

25 February 1961
Memphis, Tennessee
LP (*115, 147*) {**301**}

25 March 1961
Pearl Harbour, Hawaii,
Presentation of awards
LP (*87*)

1962

Summer 1962
Hollywood, California, with Lloyd Shearer
LP (*126*)

1964

26 April 1964
Message to Elvis's British fans
Flexi-disc (*8*)

1965

18 August 1965
Honolulu, Hawaii, with Tom Moffett and Peter Noone (on the set of ***Paradise, Hawaiian Style***)
LP (*145, 186*) {**282, 293**}
Flexi-disc (*6*)

1970

27 February 1970
Houston, Texas
LP {**301**}
Other releases (14)

1971

16 January 1971
JC Awards, **Memphis, Tennessee**
LP (*150, 226*)

1972

9 June 1972
Madison Square Garden, New York
LP (*150, 226*) {**301**}
Other releases {**14**}
Miscellaneous releases {**3**}
Flexi-disc (5)

Rarities

As in our original work, *Elvis UK 1956-86,* generally we have made no attempt to place financial values on anything included in the text, believing this not only beyond our remit, but also outside of our expertise. Furthermore though, price guides are just that: guides. And giving an item a notional value is affected by a host of factors, hence our reluctance to enter into this at all. However, what we do feel confident about is offering some advice as to what, in our opinion, was hard to obtain and, by extension, variations or versions of records which are worth trying to find. Naturally this information will go some way towards helping you decide on how collectable (and valuable) an item is. Ultimately though, you must decide what an item is worth, and whether or not you are prepared to accept the asking price. A word of caution though. Remember: an item is only worth what someone is prepared to pay for it.

Now in this section we are dealing with records generally available to the public, not promotional items, which are dealt with separately. And, perhaps, it is ironic to note that some of the items listed have no intrinsic worth, apart from the fact that at the time of their release they were generally ignored or not known about by collectors. Subsequently though, because there were few made or, alternatively, because of limited availability, then they have become collectable.

First then, perhaps, we need to define our terms of reference here. When we talk about something being rare it clearly implies that it is difficult to obtain, for one reason or another, though one major factor here might be how widely, or not, something was distributed. A further crucial factor is usually to do with how many copies of something were made. And here, it must be stressed, a rare item might well comprise previously issued material. Rarely (pardon the pun) does it mean that the release comprises out-of-the ordinary material - but its rarity value derives from how hard-to-obtain it has become. Going back to the late sixties, for instance, the rare items then were the six singles re-pressed on the orange RCA label (bearing their original catalogue number) and, to a lesser extent, the EPs and LPs re-pressed on orange labels. And here the rarity element comes directly from two factors: a) how relatively few were manufactured; and, b) how short a time scale they were available before being deleted.

Ironically, none of the songs included in the above releases were hard to obtain items, but in those formats, they were.

Another factor to take into account is the general decline in vinyl sales over the years. Thus, as collectors turned their attention to CDs, for instance, some low-key vinyl releases with a limited press run (and hardly ever would it be subject to a re-pressing) would appear - frequently unannounced - and then just as quickly disappear without trace. If the collector happened to be unaware of this then, in a sense, the opportunity would have been lost. And if you are not convinced, consider again a few items from the sixties and seventies which command what some would regard as overly-inflated prices, simply because they sold poorly for whatever reason. For example, the single *There's Always Me* (S 60); *Take Good Care Of Her,* the UK pressing, (S 89); and, of course, the album *Raised On Rock/For Ol' Times Sake,* UK pressing, (LP 69). In the latter case, this album was, by general consensus, regarded as a poor one. But a UK pressing is still highly sought after.

While there may be some critically acclaimed vinyl releases in the 'rarities' category, in the main many of those we regard as being rare - using the limited number and/or distribution factor - were, paradoxically, often quite cheap to buy initially, and were often produced by relatively unknown labels.

Singles

All of the singles from 1986 onwards were produced in far fewer numbers than most of their predecessors, and, with one or two exceptions, were probably bought by fans and collectors, rather than the general public. Therefore, it is unusual for any of these to emerge in any great quantities on the second-hand market. Some are rarely seen, although, in itself, this cannot be the only factor in determining whether a particular item is rare. The question of whether or not a record is desirable must also be considered. The singles produced by Old Gold are typical of this situation.

Old Gold released 20 Elvis singles between October 1986 and January 1988, and as few as 2,000 copies were manufactured for some of the titles. 2,000 copies is a relatively small number when compared to press runs in the '60s and '70s, and would suggest that there must be some difficulty in obtaining copies, because there are so few of them. Yet, some collectors disregard Old Gold product because they were not issued by RCA/BMG. When copies do turn up, they fail to attract more than £2-£3, little more than the price they cost when they were first issued.

Of course, collectors on the look-out for an Old Gold single with a picture sleeve have found it very difficult to locate a copy, presumably because they were bought by collectors initially and retained in their collections. Old Gold issued picture sleeves when sales of a particular title achieved a certain level and, in the case of the Old Gold single *An American Trilogy* (S 152), three different picture sleeves were made (two different designs), and all are difficult to locate.

Pride of place in singles' terms undoubtedly goes to copies of the Old Gold single *Love Me Tender* (S 153) which has a catalogue number OG 9611, instead of the intended OG 9626.

All RCA singles from this period were issued in picture sleeves, and while none are particularly rare, copies do not turn up regularly on the second-hand market. The 12 inch versions are the most difficult to locate. Throughout this period, few RCA singles were re-pressed following initial production. However, one single that was re-pressed was *The Twelfth Of Never* (S 180) and, as this created a variation in that a cream coloured label was used (instead of the silver label found on the original copies), this is probably one to look out for.

The four black and white picture disc singles issued by Baktabak in April 1988 (S 174) are also difficult to locate and, as their distribution was limited, many fans were not even aware of their existence. Consequently, these singles have become desirable and expensive.

Finally, the existence of a variation of the BMG single *Heartbreak Hotel* (S 181), featuring a better quality card sleeve and minor label differences came as a complete surprise.

LPs

In many ways the rarity of LPs is similar to that of singles. Most BMG albums had a single press run, and relatively few were re-pressed. And those that were re-pressed were done in sufficient quantities so that there was little difficulty in obtaining copies. The albums that are now more difficult to obtain were those produced by small independent labels. Many of these appeared to have little financial value or appeal to collectors at the time. Several albums in this category were generally ignored by collectors because they were re-issues of earlier albums.

The final three Camden LPs - *The Rock Hits* (LP 276), *Girls! Girls! Girls!* (LP 278), and *Kissin' Cousins* (LP 279) - were examples of unexceptional compilations and albums which had been re-issued several times. As such, they appear to have little real value and, when they turn up on the secondhand market, they sell for small sums. Yet, **Girls! Girls! Girls!** is unique in that one track (**Earth Bo**y), from side 1 of the original album, was moved to side two to make the playing time of both sides more even.

All of the following non-BMG LPs can be considered as being difficult to obtain because of their small press runs, and consequently, we believe, their rarity value is increased.

> **The Elvis Tapes** (**LP 281**)
>
> **Confidential.... Elvis** (**LP 282**)
>
> **In Hollywood** (**LP 288**)
>
> **Mess O' Blues - Volume 1** (LP 289)
>
> **Mess O' Blues - Volume 2** (**LP 290**)
>
> **The Complete Million Dollar Quartet** (**LP 291**)
>
> **Mess O' Blues - Volumes 1 & 2** (**LP 292**)
>
> **20 Golden Greats** (**LP 299**)
>
> **Mess O' Blues - 24 Classic Tracks** (**LP 300**)
>
> **The Voice Of The King** (**LP 301**)
>
> **Elvis Live** (**LP 302**)
>
> **The Fifties Interviews** (**LP 305**)
>
> **The Rock 'N' Roll Era Elvis Presley: 1956-1961** (**LP 307**)
>
> **The Legend Lives On** (**LP 310**)
>
> **The Louisiana Hayride/Little Rock, Arkansas** (**LP 322**)

One album produced for sale in selected HMV stores deserves special mention. **The Elvis Presley Sun Collection** (**LP 295**), was the regular BMG record housed in a unique box. Only 3,500 copies were made (although a CD version was also available) and copies are now extremely difficult to locate.

The two boxed collections produced by RCA/BMG - **Elvis Forever - 96 Hits Of The King** (**LP 285**), and **Special Edition** (**LP 297**) - were
generally ignored by collectors (even if they knew of their existence), and both sets are rarely seen. The same situation occurred with some of the last re-issues BMG made of earlier vinyl releases, in particular the two Christmas albums, **Elvis Sings The Wonderful World Of Christmas** (**LP 311**) and **Elvis' Christmas Album** (**LP 312**), both of which were issued at the end of 1990.

If one of the factors which determines rarity value is the number of items pressed, then surely the blue vinyl version of **Artist Of The Century** (**LP 323**) must qualify, as only 500 copies were made for sale in selected HMV stores at the end of 1999.

Various Artist LPs

Perhaps an unusual inclusion here has to be a reference to the Various Artist LPs which featured an Elvis track. Although the general contents of these albums may have held little interest for Elvis collectors, what has become obvious is that they are very hard to find - simply because their appeal (indeed their intended audience) was very broad. Consequently, many collectors may not have seen or been aware of these releases. And this applies even to TV advertised collections. Quite simply, they usually had a very limited shelf-life and so finding copies can prove very difficult. In our view, this makes such items collectable. This may seem quite an irony when normally they featured only one Elvis track.

Future Releases

What became obvious to us as we reasearched this book was that, despite all predictions and industry trends, vinyl releases were still held in great affection by many collectors; and so it came as no real surprise that the medium never completely died out. Yes, major companies focused on CD releases in the main, but from time to time would release special edition vinyl collections. Of course, they earned companies valuable revenue and ultimately, that is what companies want.

Thus, as this book concludes, far from reporting on the death of vinyl as a medium (as we ourselves thought we would be doing in the mid-1990s), it is obvious that it will continue indefinitely - as long as it sells. And while the likes of BMG may or may not produce Elvis material again on vinyl, what seems certain is that other companies will do so, albeit on a modest scale.

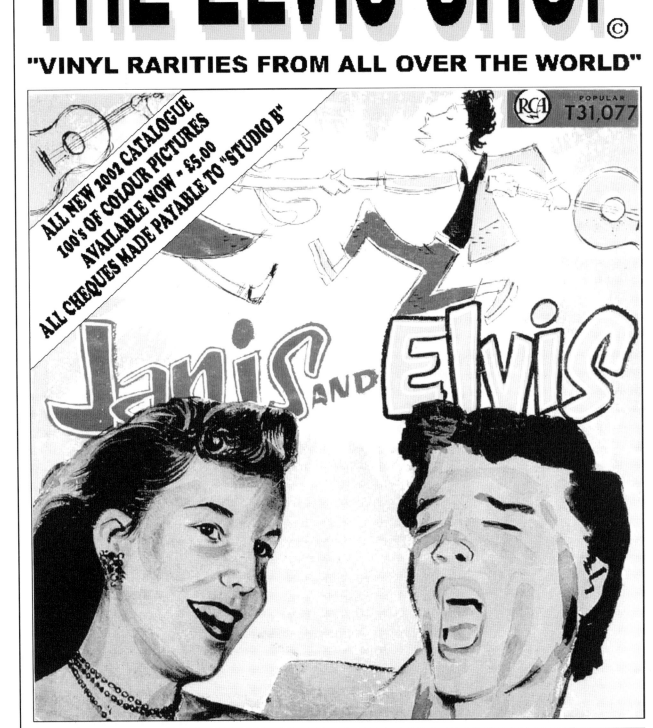

WELCOME! JOIN THE WORLD'S MOST RESPECTED FAN CLUB TODAY!

Now is the time to Join the World's most respected Fan Club

The official Elvis Presley Fan Club of Great Britain was established back in 1957, and as we enter our 6th decade, isn't about time you became a member? All members receive six full colour magazines each year, a membership card, plus details throughout the year of our various activities, from local social events through to national & international conventions. We also host holidays here in the UK, and in Europe

Plus, let's not forget our tours to the United States which not only include Memphis & Elvis Presley's Graceland but can include visits to Florida, Los Angeles, Arizona, Las Vegas, New York, and as with our Tour 2000 - Hawaii.

Being a fan club member you can be part of an internationally respected organisation which has become the largest Elvis Presley Fan Club anywhere in the world.

We have a pen-pal section, and social calendar which will give you the opportunity to meet Elvis fans not only here in the UK, but from the four corners of the world, and Elvis fans are the nicest people - you had better believe it.

And we attract new members from all age groups, be it seven or seventy. Remember, you are never alone by being A fan!

The official Elvis Presley Fan Club is regularly featured on BBC, ITV, Sky, and CNN, plus are activities appear on television throughout the world. Our charitable activities too are legendary.

Join today. Send £12.00 for a full 12 months subscription to

**ELVIS PRESLEY FAN CLUB,
PO Box 4,
LIECESTER, LE3 5HY**
Make cheques and postal orders payable to "E.P.F.C.", or you can quote your Visa/Mastercard credit card number add expiry date.

TELEPHONE: 0116 253 7271
FAX: 0116 253 1875

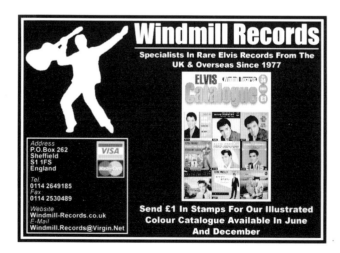

A Little Less Conversation

We were aware of BMG's plans for this single long before its actual release and, conscious that there were high expectations in terms of chart success, we delayed (and not for the first time!) final preparations for **Elvis UK2**. By this time, the type setting had been completed, and to put the script for this single in its correct position at the end of the Singles Section would have meant changing all subsequent page numbering. Whilst we have updated the Song Index, updates to chronological and alphabetical listings have not been made, and nor have we been able to amend references to **Way Down** being Elvis's 'last number one'. We hope you understand why this has been necessary.

S 184	RCA	74321 94357 1

A Little Less Conversation {S} (Strange, Davis)
12 inch extended remix
Radio edit remmix
NBC TV Special version

Released June 2002

This record was not a re-release, as some thought, because it was an entirely different version from the 7 inch single (S 66) issued in November 1968. At that time, the original single release did not even reach the charts in the UK. The song had been taken from the soundtrack of **Live A little, Love A Little**, by concensus an offbeat, though somewhat nondescript film from 1968. An alternative version of the song (said to be take 10, although some reference sources quote take 15) appeared on the budget album **Almost In Love** (LP 44) issued in November 1970.

The release of this 12 inch single in June 2002 was significant for a number of reasons. First of all it was the first of its kind since **Are You Lonesome Tonight?** (S 178) in January 1991, but more than that, at the point of its release on 10 June, it was predicted to top the UK charts by the end of its first week on sale. And, of course, it did so, becoming the first Elvis record to hit the number one spot in the UK since August 1977 when **Way Down** (S 116) topped the charts in the wake of Elvis's death. In truth, many, if not most, fans never believed they would live to see this phenomenon. This gave Elvis his 18th number record in the UK, thus setting an all time record for any artist. Previously to this, both Elvis and The Beatles had shared honours for having the same number of chart toppers in the UK. However, the background to this new release warrants some explanation.

This latest version of the song was not based on the original single release, rather the version recorded on 23 June 1968 for the NBC TV Special. Strangely though, the main backing track was from the session which produced the 1968 single version in March 1968, but Elvis had overdubbed a new vocal track while filming the now fabled '68 TV Special in June of that year. However, at the time, not only was the track not used, but also very few people knew of its existence. Indeed, it only secured a release in 1998 when BMG issued the double CD set **Memories The '68 Comeback Special**. The track had a running time of 1.43 and faded out very quickly.

This version of the song was actually featured in the film **Ocean's 11** (a remake of the '60s film) in the early part of 2002. And although the precise chronology is not known in detail, apparently the song was heard by the advertising agency working for Nike who decided to approach Adam Bradley of BMG UK with a view to featuring it in their $90m World Cup promotional adverts on television. BMG agreed (as did Gary Povey of the Presley Estate) and in turn an approach was made to Dutch DJ Tom Holkenbourg (JXL), to remix and edit the track. He did so, overdubbing additional instrumentation liberally. Adam Bradley of BMG in the UK picks up the story.

'There's a very interesting story about finding the right version, which Nike wanted on the ad and really is best of the 3 versions I've since discovered. We had folk woken up in the States, jumping on planes etc. as we had to turn the whole music to ad within a week, and that was the week between the Brits and Grammy's!! Not easy to reach the right folk, so we we're literally taking calculated risks so not to miss this incredible opportunity. To make matters worse the original remixer (to remain nameless), phoned me at 10pm the evening before the big presentation that he couldn't finish the job (I'm driving with the creative director from the ad agency!!) - as his father was critically ill. Coupled with that, when the master arrived from Pittsburgh there were two takes on the master, not the required one. A little further investigation with our Hamburg studio and Elvis recording specialist revealed that this take we were after, never existed on a master and only ever on acetate - it was the track used in the movie, **Live A Little, Love A Little**.

So, I'm confronted with a looming deadline, no remixer and the track only on CD, i.e. not separated vocal so very difficult to work with. Fortunately I was introduced to JXL by the creative director, after that call from the original remixer who had to bail out. (I'm driving with the creative director, having just come back from the studio thinking all's well). And I called JXL immediately, about 11.30pm his time (Amsterdam based). I explained the whole situation and we agreed a deal on the phone - the ad agency knew him already and had worked with him previously. He had the visual and track on CD. Basically JXL worked through the entire night and separated the vocal with precise skill and rebuilt the backing track. We won the business.

As for the single, well JXL had more time and brought in a backing vocalist, hammond organ and much skill and love for the project - he went to Spain to work on it, so not to be interrupted!! As they say the rest is history...'

Of course, this was the first time the Elvis Presley Estate and RCA had allowed a third party to remix an Elvis track in this way, so apart from making number one, this record made a piece of history in other ways, too! Elvis shared billing with Holkenbourg (the label read 'Elvis Vs JXL'). Incidentally, Holkenbourg normally used the name 'Junkie XL', but agreed to modify it, reportedly because of objections by the Estate. The clear intention was to make this an international release, including the U.S. However, the first territory to feature it on radio was the UK and the reaction was overwhelmingly positive. Unusually, the track - issued as a promo CD - was played extensively on radio prior to its release, as well as featuring heavily in adverts on commercial television. Not surprisingly then, following its release on 10 June, it entered the charts at number one, beating the likes of Kylie Minogue who was, herself, enjoying renewed popularity and chart success. According to BMG in London, the release (in CD, 12 inch vinyl and cassette formats) had sold 500,000 copies in the first week of its release. Very unusually there was no image of Elvis anywhere on the sleeve or label.

The release comprised 3 tracks: the radio edit remix running for about 3.30; a twelve inch extended remix lasting 6.07; and, finally, the '68 TV Special version running for 1.39. Not surprisingly, the planned release of a number ones album planned for the autumn of 2002, was expected to include this extra track. Ironically, having done such a magnificent job of restoring the Elvis catalogue over the previous decade, neither Roger Semon nor Ernst Jorgensen had anything directly to do with the release of this single!

At the time of writing, no one knew for sure what the long-term implications of the success of this single would be. Nonetheless, despite the welcome publicity afforded to Elvis generally (it had now become fashionable to like him again, it seemed), perhaps it is safe to say that a number of fans felt ambivalent about such a release; some even adopted a very hostile stance to it. Whatever though, there was no doubt that its chart success was due to a number of factors, not least of which was that it captured the imagination of a wide range of buyers, way beyond the usual Elvis fandom. Moreover, for those of a cynical mind, it also illustrated in a stark way the power of media hype and 'talking up' a release. Needless to say the saturation cover on a diverse range of radio stations, plus the television commercials, simply confirmed the inevitability of it being a big hit. And not just in the UK either, as the single became a worldwide hit on a major scale, including hitting number one in the USA. Long before the single had relinquished the number one position in the UK, work had commenced on a follow-up and a number of tracks were being discussed for possible release.

Finally, as the single notched up its fourth week at number one in the UK, BMG took the unusual step of deleting the record. Reportedly this was done to clear the way for a new release by Gareth Gates, which the company hoped would also make the number one position.